Esquire
The Best of Forty Years

Esquire

The Best of Forty Years

compiled by

The Editors of Esquire

DAVID McKAY COMPANY, INC.
New York

All pieces in this volume first appeared in *Esquire* magazine. In some cases, subsequent publication rights were reassigned to certain authors, their agents or publishers. We are grateful to the following for permission to reprint material:

On the Blue Water
 (Copyright 1936 by Ernest Hemingway) is reprinted by permission of Charles Scribner's Sons from *By-Line Ernest Hemingway*.

The Snows of Kilimanjaro
 (Copyright 1936 by Ernest Hemingway) is reprinted by permission of Charles Scribner's Sons from *The Short Stories of Ernest Hemingway*.

The Death of James Dean
 Reprinted by permission of Elizabeth H. Dos Passos, co-executor of the Estate of John Dos Passos.

New York
 Copyright © 1960 by Gay Talese.

Moving Out
 Copyright © 1960 by John Cheever.

The Fully Automated Foreign Policy
 From *The McLandress Dimension* by John Kenneth Galbraith. Copyright © 1963 by John Kenneth Galbraith. Reprinted by permission of Houghton Mifflin Company.

Kennedy Without Tears
 Reprinted by permission of William Morrow & Company, Inc. Copyright © 1964 by Tom Wicker.

When Demirgian Comes Marching Home Again (Hurrah? Hurrah?)
 This essay appears in *The Man-Eating Machine* by John Sack as "Varoujan" (and in different form). Copyright © 1973 by John Sack. It is reprinted by permission of the author.

The Hollow Men
 Abridgement of "The Hollow Men" in *You Can't Go Home Again* by Thomas Wolfe. Copyright © 1940 by Maxwell Perkins as Executor; renewed, 1968 by Paul Gitlin. Reprinted by permission of Harper & Row, Inc.

The Last American Hero Is Junior Johnson, Yes!
 This essay appears in *The Kandy-Kolored Tangerine-Flake Streamline Baby* as "The Last American Hero." Copyright © 1965 by Thomas K. Wolfe, Jr. It is reprinted with the permission of Farrar, Straus & Giroux, Inc.

The Trial of Arthur Miller
 Copyright © 1957 by John Steinbeck.

The Happy Jack Fish Hatchery Papers
 Reprinted by permission of the authors.

The Golden Age/Time Past
 Copyright © 1958 by Ralph Ellison. Reprinted from *Shadow and Act*, by Ralph Ellison, by permission of Random House, Inc.

What Makes Sammy Jr. Run
 Copyright © 1964 by Thomas B. Morgan.

A Perfect Analysis Given By a Parrot
 Copyright © 1958 by Tennessee Williams.

The Eighty-Yard Run
 Copyright 1940 and renewed 1968 by Irwin Shaw. Reprinted from *Selected Short Stories of Irwin Shaw*, by permission of Random House, Inc.

The Little Mysteries of Pomp and Circumstance
 From *The Time Element and Other Stories* by John O'Hara. Copyright © 1972 by United States Trust Company of New York, as executor of and trustee under the will of John O'Hara. Reprinted by permission of Random House, Inc.

When Greek Meets Greek
 From *21 Stories* by Graham Greene. Copyright 1941, Copyright © renewed 1969 by Graham Greene. Reprinted by permission of The Viking Press, Inc. This story originally appeared in Esquire under the title *Her Uncle vs. His Father*.

The Growing Stone
 From *Exile and the Kingdom* by Albert Camus, translated by Justin O'Brien. Copyright © 1957, 1958 by Alfred A. Knopf, Inc. Reprinted by permission of the publisher.

The Potato Elf
 First published in English in Esquire magazine in 1939, © 1939 by Esquire, Inc. This volume presents a new translation which appears in *A Russian Beauty and Other Stories* by Vladimir Nabokov. Copyright © 1973 by McGraw-Hill International.

Breakfast at Tiffany's
 Copyright © 1958 by Truman Capote. Reprinted from *Breakfast at Tiffany's* by Truman Capote, and from *Selected Writings of Truman Capote*, by permission of Random House, Inc.

ISBN: 0-679-50470-2 (CLOTH): 0-679-30264-6 (PAPER)
LIBRARY OF CONGRESS CATALOG CARD NUMBER: 74-76961
MANUFACTURED IN THE UNITED STATES OF AMERICA

Contents

Esquire
The Best of Forty Years

TIME ZONES

Esquire turned forty in October of 1973, the occasion for this celebration. Born in elegance during the Depression, Esquire endured a world war and survived the fits and starts and night terrors of the nuclear age. Then through a decade of silence, the Fifties, and through a decade of noise, the Sixties, it managed always to make itself heard. It has spoken for forty years with its own voice, one compounded with the voices of many, each speaking, with whatever claim on permanence, out of the concerns of a particular time. It is fitting, therefore, that this anniversary celebration should begin with four personal reflections on generations past. F. Scott Fitzgerald and Gary Wills, writing on the Twenties and the Sixties, are the prelude and the finale; one defines the Lost Generation, while the other describes the unnameable horde that passed by only yesterday. Novelists John Steinbeck and William Styron account for the middle period in evocations of the Thirties and Forties. The rest of this book fills in the gaps. The first life of an Esquire article lasts a month only, a heartbeat in a forty-year experience. Now a generous selection of the best of these writings is all together in one place, re-creating the experience itself: four decades of life, through which, behold! we have come. Now, at the end of *this* celebration, other decades begin, bringing, no doubt, better times and worse; but let this book summon up the past that brought us to where the future starts.

F. Scott Fitzgerald:

My Generation

The Twenties: The most beautiful thing in the world
was a football captain killed in battle

In 1918 the present writer stole an engine, together
with its trustful engineer, and drove two hundred
miles in it to keep from being A.W.O.L. He can
still be tried for the offense, so the details must
remain undisclosed. It is set down here only to bear
witness to the fact that in those days we were red-
blooded—*Children! Don't bring those parachutes
into the house!* All right, we'll drop that approach
altogether.

We who are now between forty and forty-five were
born mostly at home in gaslight or in the country by
oil lamps. Mewling and burping unscientifically in our
nurses' arms we were unaware of being the Great
Inheritors—unaware that, as we took over the remnants of the crumbled Spanish Empire, the robe of
primacy was being wrapped around our little shoulders. About ten million of us were born with the
Empire, and in our first Buster Brown collars we were
treated to a new kind of circus parade, a Wild West
Show on water—the Fleet was being sent on a trip
to show the world. At the turn of the previous century
—in 1800—it had likewise been bracing to be an
American, but that was from ignorance, for beyond
our own shore we were a small potato indeed. This
time, though, there was no doubt of it—when even
our nursery books showed the last sinking turrets of
Cervera's fleet we were incorrigibly a great nation.

We were the great believers. Edmund Wilson has
remarked that the force of the disillusion in *A Farewell to Arms* derives from Hemingway's original hope
and belief. Without that he could not have written of
the war: "... finally only the names of places had
dignity. . . . Abstract words such as glory, honor,
courage or hallow were obscene beside the concrete
names of villages, the numbers of roads, the names of
rivers, the numbers of regiments and the dates."
Hemingway felt that way in 1918. In 1899 when he
was born there was faith and hope such as few modern
nations have known.

It is important just when a generation first sees the
light—and by a generation I mean that reaction
against the fathers which seems to occur about three
times in a century. It is distinguished by a set of ideas,
inherited in moderated form from the madmen and

*It was when Fitzgerald's daughter Scottie wrote a piece on her
generation for* Mademoiselle *that Scott was moved to do a comparable
essay, which remained unpublished until it appeared in our thirty-
fifth anniversary issue.*

the outlaws of the generation before; if it is a real
generation it has its own leaders and spokesmen, and
it draws into its orbit those born just before it and
just after, whose ideas are less clear-cut and defiant. A
strongly individual generation sprouts most readily
from a time of stress and emergency—tensity, communicated from parent to child, seems to leave a
pattern on the heart. The generation which reached
maturity around 1800 was born spiritually at Valley
Forge. Its milk was the illiterate letters, the verbal
messages, the casualty reports written during the
desperate seven-year retreat from Massachusetts to
the Carolinas—and the return back to the Virginia
town; its toys were the flintlock in the corner, the
epaulets of a Hessian grenadier; its first legend the
print of Washington on the schoolroom wall. It grew
up to be the hard-boiled generation of Andrew Jackson
and Daniel Webster, Fulton and Eli Whitney, Lewis
and Clark. Its few authors, Washington Irving and
James Fenimore Cooper, struggled to give America a
past, a breathing record of those who had known its
forests and fields and towns, a special service for its
dead.

They were tougher and rougher than their fathers;
they were adrift in a land more remote from the mainstream and all their doubt clothed them in desperation. They revived the duel, long moribund in
England. They had a mess on their hands—Washington had died with more apprehension for the republic
than he had felt at the lowest ebb of the revolution,
and the forces of the time gave life a restless stamp.
In retrospect the men seem all of one piece. When the
last of them, old General Winfield Scott, watched a
new tragedy begin at Bull Run there could have been
few men alive to whom he could speak the language
of his broken heart.

In haste let me add that my generation is very much
alive. One of us recently married Hedy Lamarr!

II

We were born to power and intense nationalism. We
did not have to stand up in a movie house and recite
a child's pledge to the flag to be aware of it. We were
told, individually and as a unit, that we were a race
that could potentially lick ten others of any genus.

This is not a nostalgic article for it has a point to make —but we began life in post-Fauntleroy suits (often a sailor's uniform as a taunt to Spain). Jingo was the lingo—we saw plays named *Paul Revere* and *Secret Service* and raced toy boats called the *Columbia* and the *Reliance* after the cup defenders. We carved our own swords whistling, *Way Down in Colon Town,* where we would presently engage in battle with lesser breeds. We sang *Tease Me, Coax Me, Kiss Me Good Night, Dear Love,* and *If You Talk in Your Sleep Don't Mention My Name* (which, due to the malice of some false friends, was Fitzboomski all through the Russo-Japanese war). We made "buckboards" out of velocipede wheels and didn't get a page in *Life* about it, and we printed our own photographs in fading brown and blue. The mechanical age was coming fast but many of the things we played with we made ourselves.

That America passed away somewhere between 1910 and 1920; and the fact gives my generation its uniqueness—we are at once prewar and postwar. We were well-grown in the tense Spring of 1917, but for the most part not married and settled. The peace found us almost intact—less than five percent of my college class were killed in the war, and the colleges had a high average compared to the country as a whole. Men of our age in Europe simply do not exist. I have looked for them often, but they are twenty-five years dead.

So we inherited two worlds—the one of hope to which we had been bred; the one of disillusion which we had discovered early for ourselves. And that first world was growing as remote as another country, however close in time. My father wrote the old-fashioned "s" in his youthful letters and as a boy during the Civil War was an integral part of the Confederate spy system between Washington and Richmond. In moments of supreme exasperation he said, "Confound it!" I live without madness in a world of scientific miracles where curses or Promethean cries are bolder— and more ineffectual. I do not "accept" that world, as for instance my daughter does. But I function in it with familiarity, and to a growing extent my generation is beginning to run it.

III

What are these men who, about the time of their majority, found themselves singing, "We're in the army now." Their first discovery of 1919 was that nobody cared. Cut out the war talk—every so often life was doomed to be a cockeyed and disorderly business. Forget quickly.

All right then. Hank McGraw, who had been a major in France, came back to Princeton and captained a winning football team—I never saw him play without wondering what he thought about it all. Tommy Hitchcock, who had escaped from Germany by jumping from a train, went up to Harvard—perhaps to find out why. The best musician I ever knew was so confused that he walked out to put shirts on girls in the Society Islands! Men of fifty had the gall to

tell us that when their cellars were exhausted they would drink no more—but they had fixed it so *we* could start with rotgut right now. Most of us took a drink by that time but honestly it wasn't our invention—though both moonshine and heavy necking, which had spread up from the Deep South and out of Chicago as early as 1915, were put upon our bill.

The truth was that we found the youth younger than ourselves, the sheiks and the flappers, rather disturbing. We had settled down to work. George Gershwin was picking out tunes between other people's auditions in Tin Pan Alley and Ernest Hemingway was reporting the massacres in Smyrna. Ben Hecht and Charlie MacArthur were watching the Chicago underworld in bud. Dempsey, scarred in reverse by the war, was becoming the brave of his day, while Tunney bided his time. Donald Peattie was coming into his inheritance of the woods and what he found there. George Antheil's music and Paul Nelson's suspended house were a little way off, but Vincent Youmans already had charmed his audience with "O me, O my, O you." Merian Cooper would fly a little longer as a soldier of fortune before settling down to make *Chang* and *Grass.* Denny Holden wasn't through with war either—in his plane last summer perished a gallant and lively jack-of-many-trades whose life was a hundred stories.

The late Tom Wolfe left the Norfolk shipyards and went to college for more education. His end was so tragic that I am glad I knew him in carefree and fortunate times. He had that flair for the extravagant and fantastic which has been an American characteristic from Irving and Poe to Dashiell Hammett. He was six feet eight inches tall and I was with him one night on Lake Geneva when he found to his amazement that not only could he reach the street wires over his head but that when he pulled them he caused a blackout of Montreux. To the inquiring mind this is something of a discovery, not a thing that happens every day. I had a hard time getting Tom away from there quickly. Windows opened, voices called, there were running footsteps, and still Tom played at his blackout with the casualness of a conductor ringing up fares. We drove over the French border that night.

Wolfe was a grievous loss. With Hemingway, Dos Passos, Wilder and Faulkner he was one of a group of talents for fiction such as rarely appear in a single hatching. Each of these authors created a world quite his own and lived in it convincingly. Decimated Europe had nothing to set beside the work of these young men.

The poets of my time set a more precarious course, or so I believe, for the novel had become elastic enough to say almost anything. But some of the critics, Wilson, Mumford, Seldes among others, have had powerful influence upon the taste and interests of the past two decades. The playwrights, Sherwood and Behrman, Barry and Stallings, Hecht and MacArthur, have been so successful that they are now their own angels—contemplating a production, they call for the private sucker list, and find their own names at the top. And that art which stockholders, producers and public have kept in its perennial infancy owes a great debt to those two directors, Frank Capra and King Vidor, who have fought themselves free of producers' control.

All in all it was a husky generation. Match me Tommy Hitchcock or Bill Tilden for sheer power of survival as champions. Outside of a few Eastern cities there was a vacant lot in every block and I played humbly on the same teams with future Minnesota linemen, a national golf medalist, Dudley Mudge, and a national amateur champion, Harrison Johnston.

Later, pursued from hideout to hideout by the truant officers, I came in early contact with a few incipient men of letters. I was at prep school in New Jersey with Pulitzer Prizeman Herbert Agar and novelists Cyril Hume and Edward Hope Coffey. Hope and I were destined to follow a similar pattern —to write librettos at Princeton, "drool" for the college comic and, later, college novels. But I remember him best when he was center and I was quarterback on the second team at school. We were both fifteen— and awful. There were a couple of one-hundred-eighty-pound tackles (one of them now headmaster for his sins) who liked to practice taking me out, and Hope gave me no protection—no protection at all —and I would have paid well for protection. We were the laziest and lowest-ranking boys in school.

In college I was luckier. I knew the future presidents of many banks and oil companies, the Governor of Tennessee, and among the intellectuals encountered John Peale Bishop, warbird Elliott Springs, Judge John Biggs and Hamilton Fish Armstrong. Of course I had no idea who they were, and neither did they, or I could have started an autographed tablecloth. Things were stirring: Richard Cleveland, Henry Strater and David Bruce led a revolt against the "social system." Spence and Pumpelly and Charlie Taft did the same at Yale.

Next on my list I find Al Capone, born in 1899— but he saw the light in Naples. Anyhow, it's a good place to stop.

IV

Those I have mentioned are only a platoon in an army of five million. Are they representative of my generation—of those who have one foot planted before the war and one after it? They are at any rate the articulate and my claim is that they have not been "sheltered"—when any moppet assures me that we "lived in an ivory tower," my blood boils and I weep into my paraldehyde. *The Jungle* and *The Octopus* were on our shelves before John Steinbeck ate the grape of wrath. In 1920 the present writer recommended the immediate machine-gunning of all men in a position to marry. The revolution wasn't just around the corner—it was under my hat. But it is a fact that the capacity of this generation to believe has run very thin. The war, the peace, the boom, the Depression, the shadow of the new war scarcely correspond to the idea of manifest destiny. Many men of my age are inclined to paraphrase Sir Edward Grey of 1914—"The lamps are going out all over the world; we shall not see them lit again in our time."

It should be said that Steinbeck and Dr. Hutchins, Peter Arno and the late Irving Thalberg, Caldwell and O'Hara, Saroyan and Odets, Colonel Lindbergh and District Attorney Dewey were all too young to play on our team. Their experiences, achievements, and certainties are not of our world. We are closer in time to the hulk in a veterans' hospital—for these younger men did not dance the Grizzly Bear and the Bunny Hug when one was risking ostracism, or march a thousand miles to *Beautiful Katie*. But they swim, one and all, in our orbit; as the painter Picasso says: "You do something *first* and then somebody comes along and does it pretty." *Easy with that space gun! You oughtn't to point things!* By and large I grant them a grace we do not have, and for all we know the Messiah may be among them. But we are something else again.

Well—many are dead, and some I have quarreled with and don't see anymore. But I have never cared for any men as much as for these who felt the first springs when I did, and saw death ahead, and were reprieved—and who now walk the long stormy summer. It is a generation staunch by inheritance, sophisticated by fact—and rather deeply wise. More than that what I feel about them is summed up in a line of Willa Cather's: "We possess together the precious, the incommunicable past."

John Steinbeck:

A Primer on the Thirties

For those who have forgotten what it was like . . .
For those too young to know . . .

Sure I remember the Nineteen Thirties, the terrible, troubled, triumphant, surging Thirties. I can't think of any decade in history when so much happened in so many directions. Violent changes took place. Our country was modeled, our lives remolded, our Government rebuilt, forced to functions, duties and responsibilities it never had before and can never relinquish. The most rabid, hysterical Roosevelt-hater would not dare to suggest removing the reforms, the safeguards and the new concept that the Government is responsible for all its citizens.

Looking back, the decade seems to have been as carefully designed as a play. It had beginning, middle and end, even a prologue—1929 gave contrast and tragic stature to the ensuing ten years.

I remember '29 very well. We had it made (I didn't but most people did). I remember the drugged and happy faces of people who built paper fortunes on stocks they couldn't possibly have paid for. "I made ten grand in ten minutes today. Let's see—that's eighty thousand for the week."

In our little town bank presidents and track workers rushed to pay phones to call brokers. Everyone was a broker, more or less. At lunch hour, store clerks and stenographers munched sandwiches while they watched the stock boards and calculated their pyramiding fortunes. Their eyes had the look you see around the roulette table.

I saw it sharply because I was on the outside, writing books no one would buy. I didn't have even the margin to start my fortune. I saw the wild spending, the champagne and caviar through windows, smelled the heady perfumes on fur-draped ladies when they came warm and shining out of the theatres.

Then the bottom dropped out, and I could see that clearly too because I had been practicing for the Depression a long time. I wasn't involved with loss.

I remember how the Big Boys, the men in the know, were interviewed and re-interviewed. Some of them bought space to reassure the crumbling millionaires: "It's just a natural setback." "Don't be afraid—buy—keep buying." Meanwhile the Big Boys sold and the market fell on its face.

Then came panic, and panic changed to dull shock.

John Steinbeck contributed fiction to the earliest issues of Esquire; some of it ranks among his most important work in the short story. This examination of his generation appeared in our June, 1960, issue.

When the market fell, the factories, mines, and steelworks closed and then no one could buy anything, not even food. People walked about looking as if they'd been slugged. The papers told of ruined men jumping from buildings. When they landed on the pavement, they were really ruined. The uncle of one of my friends was a very rich millionaire. From seven millions he dropped to two millions in a few weeks, but two millions cash. He complained that he didn't know how he was going to eat, cut himself down to one egg for breakfast. His cheeks grew gaunt and his eyes feverish. Finally he shot himself. He figured he would starve to death on two millions. That's how values were.

Then people remembered their little bank balances, the only certainties in a treacherous world. They rushed to draw the money out. There were fights and riots and lines of policemen. Some banks failed; rumors began to fly. Then frightened and angry people stormed the banks until the doors clanged shut.

I felt sorry for Mr. Hoover in the White House. He drew on his encyclopedic arsenal of obsolescence. His gift for ineptness with words amounted to genius. His suggestion that the unemployed sell apples became the "Let them eat cake" of the Thirties. His campaign slogans—"Prosperity is just around the corner; a chicken in every pot"—sounded satiric to the shuffling recruits on the breadlines. Visiting the Virgin Islands, recently purchased from Denmark, he called them the garbage dump of the Caribbean. The islanders still remember that.

Brigades of Bonus Marchers converged on Washington. Congress had voted the bonus money, but for later. Some of these men might have been hustlers and perhaps there were a few Communists among them, but most were ex-soldiers who had served the nation, frightened men with hungry families. The ragged hordes blocked traffic, clung like swarming bees to the steps of the Capitol. They needed their money now. They built a shacktown on the edge of Washington. Many had brought their wives and children. Contemporary reports mention the orderliness and discipline of these soldiers of misfortune.

What happened in the seats of power? It looked then and it still looks as though the Government got scared. The White House, roped off and surrounded by troops, was taken to indicate that the President was afraid of his own people. The rumor spread that Mr. Hoover had stocked his Santa Cruz Mountain estate with

food for three years. It doesn't matter whether or not it was true. People believed it. And there must have been fear in the Administration because only the frightened fall back on force. The Army got called out to disperse the hungry and tattered ex-Army.

Four companies of infantry, four troops of cavalry, a machine-gun squadron and two tanks drove the petitioners from the streets of Washington, moved under a cloud of tear gas on the scrap-and-kindling shantytown and burned that pitiful citadel of misery. It is interesting that the commandant was General Douglas MacArthur. Of course he was under orders. They cleared the ragamuffins out.

I speak of this phase at length because it was symptomatic of many of the positions of leadership. Business leaders panicked, banks panicked. Workers demanded that factories stay open when their products were unsalable. People on all levels began hoarding nonperishable food as though for an invasion. Voices shrill with terror continued to tell the people that what was happening couldn't happen. The unfortunate Mr. Hoover was quoted as having said Prohibition was a noble experiment. He didn't say that; he said noble in intent.

The noble intention had created inner governments by gangster, little states which fought wars, committed murders, bought officials, issued patronage and sold liquor. Not only was this new aristocracy supported by any citizen who had the high price for a bottle of bad liquor, but successful gangsters were better known, even more respected, than any other Americans save movie stars. Their lives, loves, felonies and funerals were fully reported and hungrily read. Important citizens courted their acquaintance and favor. They seemed the only people in the land who weren't confused or afraid.

Then Mr. Hoover, running for reelection with a weary momentum, came up with another beauty. He said grass would grow in the streets if Roosevelt were elected. He should have looked. Grass was already growing in the streets. Farmers dumped milk, burned crops to keep prices from collapsing. Armed neighbors guarded homes against mortgage-foreclosing sheriffs. Grass was growing not only in the streets but between the rusting tracks of factory railroad sidings.

There wasn't much doubt of the election's outcome. In Dizzy Dean's immortal words, Franklin D. Roosevelt slud home.

I guess Mr. Roosevelt was called more names and accused of more crimes than any man in history, but no one ever thought or said he was afraid. Furthermore, he spread his fearlessness about among the whole people. Much later, when business picked up and business leaders howled with rage against Government control and Mr. Roosevelt, they seemed to forget that they had laid their heads in his lap and wept, begged him to take over, to tell them what to do and how to do it, that they had marched and shouted and fought for the Blue Eagle, that symbol of Government control—but they had.

There are whole libraries of books about the Thirties —millions of feet of films, still and moving. It is a completely recorded and documented period. But to those of us who lived through the period and perhaps were formed by it, the Thirties are a library of personal memories. My own recollections will not be exactly like others, but perhaps they will set you thinking and raise up your memories.

The Depression was no financial shock to me. I didn't have any money to lose, but in common with millions I did dislike hunger and cold. I had two assets. My father owned a tiny three-room cottage in Pacific Grove in California, and he let me live in it without rent. That was the first safety. Pacific Grove is on the sea. That was the second. People in inland cities or in the closed and shuttered industrial cemeteries had greater problems than I. Given the sea a man must be very stupid to starve. That great reservoir of food is always available. I took a large part of my protein food from the ocean. Firewood to keep warm floated on the beach daily, needing only handsaw and ax. A small garden of black soil came with the cottage. In northern California you can raise vegetables of some kind all year long. I never peeled a potato without planting the skins. Kale, lettuce, chard, turnips, carrots and onions rotated in the little garden. In the tide pools of the bay, mussels were available and crabs and abalones and that shiny kelp called sea lettuce. With a line and pole, blue cod, rock cod, perch, sea trout, sculpin could be caught.

I must drop the "I" for "we" now, for there was a fairly large group of us poor kids, all living alike. We pooled our troubles, our money when we had some, our inventiveness, and our pleasures. I remember it as a warm and friendly time. Only illness frightened us. You have to have money to be sick—or did then. And dentistry also was out of the question, with the result that my teeth went badly to pieces. Without dough you couldn't have a tooth filled.

It seems odd now to say that we rarely had a job. There just weren't any jobs. One girl of our group had a job in the Women's Exchange. She wasn't paid, but the cakes that had passed their salable prime she got to take home and of course she shared so that we were rarely without dry but delicious cakes. Being without a job, I went on writing—books, essays, short stories. Regularly they went out and just as regularly came back. Even if they had been good, they would have come back because publishers were hardest hit of all. When people are broke, the first things they give up are books. I couldn't even afford postage on the manuscripts. My agents, McIntosh & Otis, paid it, although they couldn't sell my work. Needless to say, they are still my agents, and most of the work written at that time has since been published.

Given the sea and the gardens, we did pretty well with a minimum of theft. We didn't have to steal much. Farmers and orchardists in the nearby countryside couldn't sell their crops. They gave us all the fruit and truck we could carry home. We used to go on walking trips carrying our gunnysacks. If we had a dollar, we could buy a live sheep, for two dollars a pig, but we had to slaughter them and carry them home on our backs, or camp beside them and eat them there. We even did that.

Keeping clean was a problem because soap cost

money. For a time we washed our laundry with a soap made of pork fat, wood ashes and salt. It worked, but it took a lot of sunning to get the smell out of the sheets.

For entertainment we had the public library, endless talk, long walks, any number of games. We played music, sang and made love. Enormous invention went into our pleasures. Anything at all was an excuse for a party: all holidays, birthdays called for celebration. When we felt the need to celebrate and the calendar was blank, we simply proclaimed a Jacks-Are-Wild Day.

Now and then there came a bit of pure magic. One of us would get a small job, or a relative might go insane and enclose money in a letter—two dollars, and once or twice, God help me, five. Then word would fly through the neighborhood. Desperate need would be taken care of first, but after that we felt desperate need for a party. Since our clothing was increasingly ratty, it was usually a costume party. The girls wanted to look pretty, and they didn't have the clothes for it. A costume party made all manner of drapes and curtains and tablecloths available.

Hamburger was three pounds for a quarter. One third of that weight was water. I don't know how the chain stores got so much water in the meat. Of course it cooked out, but only a fool would throw the juice away. Browned flour added to it and we had delicious gravy, particularly with fresh-gathered mushrooms or the big black ones we had gathered and dried. The girls shampooed their hair with soaproot, an onionshaped plant that grew wild; it works, too. We rarely had whisky or gin. That would have ruined the budget. There was local wine—and pretty good too; at least it didn't kill us. It was twenty cents a gallon—take your own jug. Sometimes we made it ourselves with grapes the vineyardists let us pick. And there you had a party. Often we made them quite formal, a kind of travesty on the kind of party we thought the rich gave. A windup phonograph furnished the music and the records were so worn down that it could be called Lo-Fi, but it was loud.

I remember one great meat loaf carried in shoulder high like a medieval boar's head at a feast. It was garnished with strips of crisp bacon cut from an advertisement in *The Saturday Evening Post*. One day in a pile of rubbish behind Holman's store I found a papier-mâché roast turkey, the kind they put in window displays around Thanksgiving. I took it home and repaired it and gave it a new coat of paint. We used it often, served on a platter surrounded with dandelions. Under the hollow turkey was a pile of hamburgers.

It wasn't all fun and parties. When my Airedale got sick, the veterinary said she could be cured and it would cost twenty-five dollars. We just couldn't raise it, and Tillie took about two weeks to die. If people sitting up with her and holding her head could have saved her, she would have got well. Things like that made us feel angry and helpless. But mostly we made the best of it because despondency, not prosperity, was just around the corner. We were more afraid of that than anything. That's why we played so hard.

It's not easy to go on writing constantly with little hope that anything will come of it. But I do remember it as a time of warmth and mutual caring. If one of us got hurt or ill or in trouble, the others rallied with what they had. Everyone shared bad fortune as well as good.

Relief came along and was welcomed. We got some food—blocks of cheese and canned Government beef. I remember the beef well. It tasted like boiled laundry and had about as much food value. Private enterprise processed it from Government-bought cattle. They processed the hell out of it and at that time a rich beef essence went on sale. We ate the boiled laundry from which it probably came.

When W.P.A. came, we were delighted because it offered work. There were even writers' projects. I couldn't get on one, but a lot of very fine people did. I was given the project of taking a census of all the dogs on the Monterey Peninsula, their breeds, weight and characters. I did it very thoroughly and, since I knew my reports were not likely to get to the hands of the mighty, I wrote some pretty searching character studies of poodles and beagles and hounds. If such records were kept, somewhere in Washington there will be a complete dog record of the Monterey Peninsula in the early Thirties.

All over the country the W.P.A. was working. They built many of the airports we still use, hundreds of schools, post offices, stadia, together with great and permanent matters like the stately Lake Shore Drive in Chicago.

By that time some business was beginning to recover and it was the fixation of businessmen that the W.P.A. did nothing but lean on shovels. I had an uncle who was particularly irritated at shovel-leaning. When he pooh-poohed my contention that shovel-leaning was necessary, I bet him five dollars, which I didn't have, that he couldn't shovel sand for fifteen timed minutes without stopping. He said a man should give a good day's work and grabbed a shovel. At the end of three minutes his face was red, at six he was staggering and before eight minutes were up his wife stopped him to save him from apoplexy. And he never mentioned shovel-leaning again. I've always been amused at the contention that brainwork is harder than manual labor. I never knew a man to leave a desk for a muckstick if he could avoid it.

Meanwhile, wonderful things were going on in the country: young men were reforesting the stripped hills, painters were frescoing the walls of public buildings. Guides to the States were being compiled by writers' projects, still the best source books on America up to the time they were printed.

A fabulous character named Hallie Flanagan was creating a National Theatre. And playwrights and actors were working like mad for relief wages. Some of our best people grew to stature during that time. We might still have a National Theatre if some highminded Senators had not killed the whole thing on the ground that *Getting Gertie's Garter* was an immoral play.

In Pacific Grove we heard that business was improving, but that hadn't much emphasis for us. One of the indices of improvement was that the men who had begged the Administration to take over and tell them what to do were now howling against Government control and calling Mr. Roosevelt highly colored names. This proved that they were on their feet again and was perfectly natural. You only tolerate help when you need it.

The factories were slowly coming to life again and the farmers were as optimistic as farmers can be, which isn't much. And then the weather gods reared back and let us have it. The rains simply went away. A weather map of 1934 is a dismal history—dry, poor, drought, arid—West, Middle West, Southwest—the great meat, cereal and vegetable area of the nation, shriveled and desiccated and cracked. Cows were racks of bones and pigs were shot to stop their hunger squeals. The corn came up and collapsed.

Prohibition had been repealed by then and crudely painted signs went up everywhere: "You gave us beer. Now give us water!" On the great plains, the root carpet of buffalo grass had been long plowed away and the earth lay bare and helpless under the sun. When the strong winds blew, the topsoil rose into the sky in gritty clouds, put out the sun and then drifted back against houses and fences like dark snow. Photographs taken then show our richest areas looking like moonscapes, desolate and frightening. Cattle died or were shot, and people fled to save themselves, abandoning everything they could not carry. They ran to the fringes of moisture—California, Oregon and Washington, where the cold of winter would not be an added problem. America was like a boxer, driven to the floor by left-hand jabs for a seven count, who struggles to his feet to catch a right-hand haymaker on the point of his chin.

In the early days of the migration, some groups got trapped by other kinds of weather. For example, about three thousand, encamped in King's County, California, were caught in a flood. They were huddled and starving on high ground surrounded by water and mud-logged fields.

I had a friend, George West of the San Francisco *News*, who asked me to go over there and write a news story—the first private-enterprise job I could remember. What I found horrified me. We had been simply poor, but these people were literally starving and by that I mean they were dying of it. Marooned in the mud, they were wet and hungry and miserable. In addition they were fine, brave people. They took me over completely, heart and soul. I wrote six or seven articles and then did what I could to try to get food to them. The local people were scared. They did what they could, but it was natural that fear and perhaps pity made them dislike the dirty, helpless horde of locusts.

The newspaper paid me some money and about that time I had a little windfall so I went to live with these migrant people, traveled back to their home base to see why they were leaving it. It wasn't philanthropy. I liked these people. They had qualities of humor and courage and inventiveness and energy that appealed to me. I thought that if we had a national character and a national genius, these people, who were begin-ning to be called Okies, were it. With all the odds against them, their goodness and strength survived. And it still does.

In Pacific Grove a part of our social life was politics; we argued and contended and discussed communism, socialism, labor organization, recovery. Conversation was a large part of our pleasure and it was no bad thing. With the beginning of recovery and the rebirth of private business, strikes began to break out. I went to see them to find out what it was about, felt them, tasted them, lived them, studied them and did quite a bit of writing about them. Fantastically, a few people began to buy and read my work even when they denounced it. I remember one book that got trounced by the Communists as being capitalist and by the capitalists as being Communist. Feelings as always were more potent than thought.

And feelings in the Thirties ran high. People were not afraid to express them as they have become recently. If you believed a thing, you shouted it. We lived or at least talked excitement.

We discussed what was happening in Europe. Hitler was rising on the despair of defeated ex-soldiers, Mussolini riding up on Italian poverty and confusion.

And in America maybe we were weary too. We had been up and down too many times in a short period. We have always had a tendency in confusion to call for a boss. A baseball scandal, a movie difficulty with morals, and we yell for one man to take over. Oddly enough we always call him a Czar, but, fortunately, so far we have never let him get very big.

But in the Thirties when Hitler was successful, when Mussolini made the trains run on time, a spate of would-be Czars began to arise. Gerald L. K. Smith, Father Coughlin, Huey Long, Townsend—each one with plans to use unrest and confusion and hatred as the material for personal power.

The Klan became powerful, in numbers at least. In Pacific Grove K.K.K. was painted in huge letters on the streets and several times a small red card was slipped under my door which read, "We are watching you," signed "K.K.K."

The Communists were active, forming united fronts with everyone. We had great shouting arguments about that. They were pretty clever. If you favored justice, or the abolition of poverty, or equality or even mother love, you were automatically in a united front with the Communists. There were also Love-stoneites and Trotskyists. I never could get them straight in my mind except that the Stalinists were in power in Russia and the others were out. Anyway, they didn't like each other. The Stalinists went about with little smiles of secret knowledge and gave the impression that they had sources of information not available to ordinary people. It was only later that I realized this was not so. We were all united in a dislike for dictators (Stalin was not a dictator if you were properly educated in dialectics).

When the stunning news of the Hitler-Stalin pact was printed, I came on one of my Communists friends in the street. He began shouting before I got near him: "Don't ask me. I don't know, Goddamn it. They didn't tell us." As it turned out, the Kremlin didn't tell the American Communists anything. Someone told me later they didn't trust them.

Except for the field organizers of strikes, who were pretty tough monkeys and devoted, most of the so-called Communists I met were middle-class, middle-aged people playing a game of dreams. I remember a woman in easy circumstances saying to another even more affluent: "After the revolution even we will have more, won't we, dear?" Then there was another lover of proletarians who used to raise hell with Sunday picnickers on her property.

I guess the trouble was that we didn't have any self-admitted proletarians. Everyone was a temporarily embarrassed capitalist. Maybe the Communists so closely questioned by investigation committees were a danger to America, but the ones I knew—at least they claimed to be Communists—couldn't have disrupted a Sunday-school picnic. Besides they were too busy fighting among themselves.

During the early years of the Thirties, my literary experience was unfortunate, but not unique. Every time a publisher accepted one of my books, he went bankrupt. One book was accepted by one publisher, printed by a second and issued under a third. But it didn't sell anyway. I began to feel like the Typhoid Mary of the literary world. But as the Thirties progressed, a little solvency began to creep in on me. I remember when a story of mine called *The Red Pony* was bought by the now defunct *North American Review*. They paid ninety dollars for it. I didn't believe there was that much money in the world. The pure sparkling affluence of it went to my head for weeks. I couldn't bear to cash the check, but I did.

By 1936 the country must have been on the upgrade. When a writer does well, the rest of the country is doing fine. A book of mine which had been trudging wearily from publisher to publisher was finally bought and brought out by Pat Covici. It sold well enough so that it was bought for motion pictures for $3,000. I had no conception of this kind of dough. It was like thinking in terms of light-years. You can't.

The subsequent history of that book is a kind of index of the change that was going on. The studio spent a quarter of a million dollars having my book rewritten before they abandoned it. Then they fired the man who had bought it in the first place. He bought it back for three thousand and later sold it for $90,000. It shows how values change. But I still think of that original $3,000 as about as much money as there is in the world. I gave a lot of it away because it seemed like too much to be in private hands.

I guess I wasn't cut out for a capitalist. I even remained a Democrat.

During the Depression years and the slow recovery, the world of gadgets called science had passed us by in Pacific Grove. One of our friends owned a Model T Ford, high ceiling, cut-glass vases, a fairly dangerous vehicle since its brake band was gone and the reverse band had been moved over to the high-low-forward drum. It could be used for emergencies if we could come by a quart of gasoline.

I had at one time come by a radio, tickler and crystal affair with headphones. But sitting tapping my foot to music or laughing at jokes no one else could hear caused my wife to threaten divorce. Now in my growing affluence I bought a magnificent secondhand radio for $15. Architecturally it was a replica of the Cathedral of Notre Dame, lacking only gargoyles. The set itself was good and still is. Now we had access to the great world of music and particularly to news. We gathered close to the speaker because a nearby X-ray machine had a way of coming on at the most vital times. On this set we heard Mr. Roosevelt's fireside chats, listened to the doom tones of Gabriel Heatter and the precise, clipped reporting of H. V. Kaltenborn. But also we heard the recorded voice of Hitler, a hoarse screaming and the thundering *Heils* of his millions. Also we listened with horror to the mincing sneers of Father Coughlin. One night we got Madison Square Garden, a Nazi meeting echoing with shrill hatred and the drilled litany of the brown-shirted audience. Then a dissenter's voice broke through and we could hear the crunch of fists on flesh as he was beaten to the floor and flung from the stage. America First came through our speaker and it sounded to us very like the Nazi approach. Lindbergh was proposed to ride the White Horse, which must have saddened him. We had also heard the trial of the man who had stolen and murdered his baby.

Prosperity had returned, leaving behind the warm and friendly associations of the dark days. Fierce strikes and retaliations raged in Detroit, race riots in Chicago: tear gas and nightsticks and jeering picket lines and overturned automobiles. The ferocity showed how frightened both sides were, for men are invariably cruel when they are scared.

The Spanish War split America's emotions. The people we knew favored the Republic. We could not see how justice could be on the side armed and supplied by Hitler and Mussolini. We watched with dismay while our Government cut off supplies to the Loyalists and forced them to turn to the Russians for help. It was a crazy time that came to us through that great episcopal radio.

Shirley Temple, then a little girl, was denounced by the Dies Committee for sending money for medical aid to Loyalist Spain. And I had one hilarious experience because I also had contributed toward an ambulance. Everyone knows at least one telephone joker. Ours was a woman who loved to call the zoo and ask for Mr. Bear. One day I answered the phone (oh! yes, we had a telephone by now). I thought it was our joker because the voice said: "This is the Monterey *Herald*. You were denounced before the Dies Committee today. Would you care to comment?"

And I, still thinking it was the joker, replied: "What's good enough for Shirley Temple is good enough for me."

But it was true. I had been denounced for giving money for medical aid to Spain. My reply got printed all over and apparently the Committee didn't think it as funny as many others did. They wouldn't even answer my wire asking to be heard. But from then on I was a Communist as far as the Dies Committee was concerned. It was at this time that everyone was a

Communist or a Fascist depending on where you stood.

My books were beginning to sell better than I had ever hoped or expected and while this was pleasing it also frightened me. I knew it couldn't last and I was afraid my standard of living would go up and leave me stranded when the next collapse came. We were much more accustomed to collapse than to prosperity. Also I had an archaic angry-gods feeling that made me give a great lot of my earnings away. I was a push-over for anyone or any organization asking for money. I guess it was a kind of propitiation. It didn't make sense that a book, a humble, hat-in-hand, rejected book, was now eagerly bought—even begged for. I didn't trust it. But I did begin to get around more.

I met Mr. Roosevelt and for some reason made him laugh. To the end of his life, when occasionally he felt sad and burdened, he used to ask me to come in. We would talk for half an hour and I remember how he would rock back in his chair behind his littered desk and I can still hear his roars of laughter.

One night at John Gunther's apartment in New York I met Wendell Willkie who was running for the Presidency. I liked him very much, although I was opposed to him politically. He seemed a warm and open man. Very late at night after a number of whiskeys I brought up something that had always interested me. I asked him why he wanted to be President. It seemed the loneliest and most punishing job in the world. He rolled his highball glass slowly between his palms and stared into it. And finally he said: "You know—I haven't the slightest idea."

I liked him even more then. He didn't give me any bull.

The strange parade of the Thirties was drawing toward its close and time seemed to speed up. Imper-ceptibly the American nation and its people had changed, and undergone a real revolution, and we were only partly aware of it while it was happening.

Now war was coming. You didn't have to be an expert to know that. It was patent in every news report, in the clanging steps of goose-stepping Nazis. It had been in the cards since the first German put on his brown-shirted uniform. The practice wars—Ethiopia, Spain, the Ruhr, the Czech border—we had watched with paralyzed attention. At any early moment it could have been stopped—or could it? America knew it was coming even while we didn't believe it. We watched the approach of war as a bird helplessly watches an approaching rattlesnake. And when it came, we were surprised as we always are.

But the strange design-like quality of the Thirties continued to the end. It was as though history had put up markers, dramatic milestones at either end of the decade. It started with the collapse not only of financial structure, but of a whole way of thought and action. It ended with perhaps the last Great War.

A few weeks ago I called on a friend in a great office building in midtown New York. On our way out to lunch he said, "I want to show you something."

And he led me into a broker's office. One whole wall was a stock-exchange trading board. Two young men moved back and forth swiftly filling in changes, rises, falls, buying, selling. Behind an oaken rail was a tight-packed, standing audience, clerks, stenographers, small businessmen. Most of them munched sandwiches as they spent their lunch hour watching the trading. Now and then they made notations on envelopes. And their eyes had the rapt, glazed look one sees around a roulette table.

William Styron:

My Generation

The Forties: The whole point was to survive and <u>then</u> begin

Let me try to define my generation—rather narrowly, but in a way similar to Fitzgerald's—as those of us who approached our majority during World War II, and whose attitudes were shaped by the spirit of that time and by our common initiation into the world by that momentous event. For a slightly earlier generation the common initiation was the Spanish Civil War; for us it somehow simultaneously ended and began when Harry Truman announced the destruction of Hiroshima. I wish I could say that in 1945—at the end of *our* war—I did anything so blissfully adventurous as to steal a locomotive as had Scott Fitzgerald. That distant war in Europe had had its own terrible ferocity but mainly for Europeans; as Fitzgerald says, it left America and Americans generally intact. By contrast our war, despite a nervous overlay of the usual frivolity (do you recall *Rosie the Riveter* and *Slap the Jap* or aching erotic schmaltz that suffused those "Back Home For Keeps" ads?), was brutally businesslike and anti-romantic, a hard-boiled matter of stamping out a lot of very real and nasty totalitarianism in order to get along with the business of the American Way of Life, whatever that is. Our generation was not only not intact, it had been in many places cut to pieces. The class just ahead of me in college was virtually wiped out. Beautiful fellows who had won basketball championships and Phi Beta Kappa keys died like ants in the Normandy invasion. Others only slightly older than I—like myself young Marine Corps platoon leaders, primest cannon fodder of the Pacific war—stormed ashore at Tarawa and Iwo Jima and met ugly and horrible deaths on the hot coral and sands.

I was lucky and saw no battle, but I had the wits scared out of me more times than I could count, and so by the time the bomb dropped on Hiroshima, thus circumventing my future plans (I was on my way; "You can figure that four out of five of you will get your asses shot off," I can recall some colonel telling

us, as he embroidered dreamily about the coming invasion of the Japanese mainland), an enormous sense of relief stole over my spirit, along with a kind of dull weariness that others of that period have recalled and which, to a certain offshoot of my generation, later came to be characterized as "beat." I disclaim any literary link with this splinter group but certainly the "beat" sensation was all too real, and though it may have sent Kerouac off on the road in search of kicks, to others of us it was a call to quiet pursuits: study and the square rewards of family and rather gloomy stocktaking. I think most of us were in a way subtly traumatized, which is why we didn't steal any locomotives or pull off any of the wild capers that so richly strew the chronicles of Fitzgerald's jazz age. We were traumatized not only by what we had been through and by the almost unimaginable presence of the bomb, but by the realization that the entire mess was not finished after all: there was now the Cold War to face, and its clammy presence oozed into our nights and days. When at last the Korean War arrived, some short five years later (it was this writer's duty to serve his country in the Marines in that mean conflict, too), the cosmos seemed so unhinged as to be nearly insupportable. Surely by that time—unlike Fitzgerald's coevals, "born to power and intense nationalism"—we were the most mistrustful of power and the least nationalistic of any generation that America has produced. And just as surely, whatever its defects may have been, it has been this generation's interminable experience with ruthless power and the loony fanaticism of the military mind that has by and large caused it to lend the most passionate support to the struggle to end war everywhere. We have that at least in our favor.

I think that the best of my generation—those in their late thirties or early forties—have reversed the customary rules of the game and have grown more radical as they have gotten older—a disconcerting but healthy sign. To be sure, there are many youngish old fogies around and even the most illustrious of these, William Buckley, is blessed by a puzzling, recondite but undeniable charm, almost as if beneath that patrician exterior an egalitarian was signaling to

Not a few artists who came of age in the Forties were obliged to improvise their lives. A Southerner established in New England, William Styron is a case in point. His essay on the war years and their aftermath first appeared in our thirty-fifth anniversary issue.

get out. We seem to be gradually shaking loose of our trauma (which for some of us, by the way, also includes the remembered effect of the Depression) and one has only to flourish the picture of an embattled Norman Mailer on the steps of the Pentagon to put down the claim that political activism is the purview of the very young. Perhaps the act of participating in one horrendous war, or two, has allowed most of us to sympathize with young people and be bitterly troubled by much of the shit they have to put up with. Having been pushed around by bullyboys and sub-cretins, by commissioned shoe clerks and *salauds* of every stripe and gauge, we tend toward more than a twinge of empathy at the sight of youth struggling with the managerial beast, military, secular, or scholastic.

In 1944, as a Marine recruit, I was shanghaied into the "clap shack," the venereal-disease ward of the Naval Hospital at Parris Island, South Carolina. There at the age of eighteen, only barely removed from virginhood, I was led to believe that blood tests revealed I had a probably fatal case of syphilis—in those pre-penicillin days as dread a disease as cancer—and was forced to languish, suicidal, for forty days and forty nights amid the charnel-house atmosphere of draining buboes, gonorrhea, prostate massages, daily short-arm inspections, locomotor ataxia, and the howls of poor sinners in the clutch of terminal paresis, until at last, with no more ceremony than if I were being turned out of a veterinary clinic, I was told I could go back to boot camp: I would not die after all, *it was all a mistake*, those blood tests had turned up a false reaction to an old case of trench mouth. I could have wept with relief and hatred. Such experiences have given our generation, I believe, both the means and the spirit to bridge the generation gap.

Literary sweepstakes are a bore, especially when this is a matter of comparing generations, and the situation is not enhanced in this case by Fitzgerald's boast, with its implication that the men of his era produced achievements in prose writing that would cause those who followed after to feel like scared epigones. The stature of Faulkner alone would have been enough to cow any young writer, all the more if he were Southern; as Flannery O'Connor remarked so wonderfully: "No one wants to get caught on the tracks when the Dixie Special comes through." Yet it has been a rich time for writing, I think, richer than may be imagined. Certainly, whether or not as a group we shall receive posterity's sweet kiss—whether our names will date as sadly as Cyril Hume and Edward Hope Coffey—no gathering ever comprised a clutch of talents so remarkably various: Mailer, Baldwin, Jones, Capote, Salinger, the incomparably infuriating Gore Vidal, John Barth, Terry Southern, Heller (where's that second book, Joe?), Walker Percy, Peter Matthiessen—who would survive as the finest writer on nature since John Burroughs even if he never found due recognition for his badly under-estimated fiction—William Gaddis, Richard Yates, Evan Connell, George Mandel, Herbert Gold, Jack Kerouac, Vance Bourjaily, John Clellon Holmes, Calder Willingham, Alan Harrington, John Phillips,

William Gass, and, honorifically, George Plimpton.

To this roll must be added, incidentally, the name of Richard Howard, the city of Cleveland's gift to France and the most elegant translator from the French tongue writing in English.

Catalogs like the foregoing are at best an amusement, surely a trifle silly, so I won't make another quite as extensive, but a list of the poets of this generation would sparkle brightly, from Simpson to Merwin, James Dickey to Anthony Hecht, Snodgrass to Allen Ginsberg.* There are, obviously, quite a few others of equivalent stature. As John Hollander, himself a fine poet, has written about their best poems: "[They] stand as some sort of testament to the continuing spiritual revolution to which poetry in English has been committed for more than a century and a half, and to the ancillary struggle to redeem poetry itself, as the product of imaginative creation, from the sickness with which Literature as a realm is too often infected."

So all in all a pretty good show, I would say, for a crowd that started out with the blind staggers—with the disease of McCarthy and the drug of Eisenhower —one that some ineffably fatuous critic long ago dismissed with the tag, "the Silent Generation." And let us brood for a moment on our predecessors. Despite the buoyancy with which Fitzgerald commences his reflections on his own brothers in art, there is something dispirited, tired, elegiac about that little memoir. There is an odor of the grave about it. Faced with the sure prospect of a cataclysmic war and—who knows?—a premonition of his own imminent death, perhaps this fading tone, this pervasive mood of fare-well was inevitable. Wolfe, Hemingway, Dos Passos, Faulkner, Wilder, all his peers—Fitzgerald had truly been born into noble company. But the best, the greatest work of all these men was long behind them, including Faulkner, who was the only one of them capable of a sustained level of quality until the very end. It is perhaps this knowledge, an instinctive sense of decline, that causes a mood of sadness to overlay this essay of Fitzgerald, who knew no better than the rest of us why whole groups of talents will burst into thrilling efflorescence, and then as mysteriously fade away. Writing now at roughly the same age as Fitzgerald, I can say that I feel no such a falling off, no similar sense of loss about my own generation. Revolution rends the air, the world around us shivers with the brave racket of men seeking their destiny, with the invigorating noise of history in collision with itself. This generation, once so laggardly, now confronts a scene astir with great events, such a wild dynamo of dementedly marvelous transactions that merely to be able to live through them should be cause for jubilation. *Mes amis, aux barricades!* I would not be astonished if our truly most precious flowering lay in the time to come. As for myself—reflecting upon the way in which we all started out—I have never felt so young. ⌗

Chronologically, Richard Wilbur should be included here, but he started publishing very young, and might be considered an influence on, rather than a member of, this generation.

Garry Wills:

The Sixties

Something happened, but what happened?

A decade has soft boundaries; but the kernel is hard, if you can find it. For me, it was a three-hour secret meeting—not that anyone cared enough to spy on or prevent it. The Sixties kept elaborate secrets no one wanted to hear. The press was ostentatiously banned from radical meetings, more out of psychic revenge for a lack of interest than to pique its interest. When reporters did bother to infiltrate such meetings, they suffered harangues they could have read at leisure in their homes, simply by leafing through underground papers. I remember "penetrating" a New Haven strike meeting, and being forced to read the mass of handbills drifting by, for sheer relief, tossed from one boredom to another.

But there was excitement, at times; and always the promise of it, the hope for a secret worth keeping. So I went, when a black activist called to let me in on something "hot." The arrangements were absurd—a meeting on "neutral turf," a hotel room rented for our conversation (with my money, of course); no tape recorder allowed, no notes to be taken. And come alone. It took me back to my Junior G-Man days of World War II, when we kids learned to identify enemy planes by their silhouettes and German spies by their accent.

This was not my first or last such meeting with a radical con man. They haunted every "movement," and were especially (stylishly) abundant in civil-rights organizations, where the assumed tradition of fooling whitey and making a buck reinforced an overt purpose of helping the brothers. Making a buck along the way added to the joy of social revenge; the con had become a crusade. Even religion could be fit into the pattern. One black preacher came to our home and thundered at my wife and me, all one evening, trying to peddle his particular hustle. When it didn't work, he folded up his rhetoric like a salesman briskly snapping shut his case of wares, got up, and left without a word. You win some, you lose some—con some, but never get conned. Yet, after a while, suckers got so low in supply the conners worked on each other, out of pure love for their art.

Garry Wills came to prominence as a journalist in the Sixties, with reportage on Catholicism, Nixon, Nixon's dog, Agnew, Buckley, Jack Ruby, and Martin Luther King. His review of his generation was written especially for the October 1973 issue of Esquire.

The man I finally met in the hotel was different, a white hustler of hip young blacks. It is no mean achievement to chisel money out of hard-core militants and live to tell (while embroidering) the tale. As I checked up on him, he began to sound larger than life, in a low and shady way. Now he was back in Washington, and at it again; the friend who had called me held him in awe, like some black messiah arrived in mocking whiteface.

We met in the lobby—he was chubby, improbable, furtive; he demanded we ride an empty elevator, searched me at the door, checked the room out, crab-worked his way backward across the wall bed into a corner, and theatrically laid out his square handgun on the bedspread, in loving proximity to his gestures, which hovered and darted and spread outward from its hokey implied menace. *Oh god*, I thought, *trapped again, and no handbills to read this time*.

His scheme was so elaborate, meant to gain conviction by sheer detail and nicety, that I remember only its large outline. All its charm resided in the loving care with which he lied. Roughly, it went like this. Riots were coming in Washington (this was early in 1968). Fat Demagogue across from me would organize a paramilitary police force, supported by a protection scheme for ghetto merchants. When the riot occurred, and regular police had lost control, he would bring in his troops and make peace, but on a set of political conditions—among them the summoning of Nelson Rockefeller as an outside observer and negotiator (this was three years before Attica). I would be chief propagandist for his troops, making them look noble instead of venal, writing books and articles (splitting my royalties fifty-fifty with him), and lionizing Rockefeller as the black man's savior. Rockefeller would be nominated and elected President, and we would be joint kingmakers and secret powers at the White House. We would end the race war, do good and be praised, gain power and yet tame it to constructive purposes—fulfill all those promises with which the decade began, and which must not be allowed to die with Kennedy.

It sounds too idiotic even to be interesting, transmitted thus through my blunting haze of incredulity. But it came from him all vivid with a mad conviction. Its power lay precisely in its craziness—the Sixties were especially vulnerable to "crazies," as they de-

fiantly called themselves, to self-confessed "freaks" as well as inconspicuous "loners." They were all silly, like this man with his stage-prop gun. But one had to remember, in that period, that Ruby's and Oswald's guns had been unbelievable too. The nuts' schemes might miscarry; but, in the very process of miscarrying, it was as easy for a nut to make history as to make a buck.

My Fat Demagogue was the kernel. He scared me despite his absurdity, or because of it. He couldn't, after all, be more unlikely than, say, New Orleans' Jim Garrison, that burbly "Green Giant" of prosecutorial fantasy, hatcher of great assassination hustles, who turned a large city's powers of law against convenient targets. Garrison probably meant to be President, if not a rescuing Dictator. His plan miscarried, too; but that is small comfort to Clay Shaw. Garrison, like many in that decade, lived off the startled large hates and loves that Kennedy had kindled, feelings bigger than Americans had thought themselves capable of. All those summoned emotions drifted objectless, looking for someplace to go, after Kennedy was shot; and they found some very weird places to go. There were many people anxious to avenge the Prince's death on someone or other, something or other—on L.B.J., or the C.I.A., or Texas, or Cuba, or the Birchers. The thing was too big to be caused by a single punk like Oswald—and that very suspicion bred power for other punks, beginning with Ruby; continuing down to my Fat Demagogue—and not ending there. Not even ending yet, as Bremer reminds us.

This was the authentic Sixties feeling, of being locked up with a madman whose power made no sense. He could tickle the resulting hyperkinesis expertly. His pitch was based on idealism (we were out to help the blacks); but with realism (one has to be as "hard-nosed" as a Bobby), a whiff of venality (we'll do well by doing good), and vanity (no one can pull this off but you—writing about me). He was, as the bargaining began in his own mind, willing to compromise—an hour or so into the struggle, he was ready to give me seventy-five percent of the royalties; his despairing offer at the end gave me *all* the writing income. His moods changed often, in the reeling strobe lights of his rhetoric. When he was not coaxing or flattering, he was probing and insulting. He played games—one-upmanship (the "two Big Jims" of the black movement would come along, they were his friends; did *I* know them?). If I called some part of his plan unworkable, he spun out obscure tales of wilder plots that had worked in the guerrilla warfare of the ghettos. He used even his failed arguments as levers to pry information out of me—sizing up his prey. As soon as he learned my religion, he gave me a touching story of how he tamed a class of black militants for some troubled inner-city nuns. He played me against my hypnotized friend, asking if I doubted *him*, using the black's credulity, stirring up fights between us. He was all energy and conviction, never letting up, though I was soon worn down by the emotional attrition. Every time I tried to ease my way out the door, he loomed up with new giant claims or some belligerent challenge—was I calling him a liar? Like all spell-

binders, he was clearly convincing himself at least part of the time, trying to believe, with an actor's wish to measure up to the part. Or, alternately, he would so taunt me with undisguised lies that he made me respond—and had me hooked again. The weird fascination of Hitler became comprehensible at last. Much as I tried to stay clinical and observant, he involved me, made me angry, or sympathetic, or frightened; ashamed for him, or ashamed of myself for letting his emotional bullying work. He was the voice of all that Sixties mystique of "the confrontation"—the belief that sheer conflict will somehow purify, as when people in encounter groups screamed, criticized, fatigued each other down to some ultimate capitulation —and called their stripped-bare cell of exhaustion "reality." The street theatre of shouts and trashing, tear gas and taunting the pigs, was a way of moving these "encounters" out onto the public stage. My Demagogue had brought the process full circle around, taking the inflated political rhetoric back into the ego's echo chamber. The Sixties experience—"mind-blowing," consciousness-altering—was always some kind of "trip."

He was, of course, a media freak, my Fat One. He needed a writer to make his dream real, to make him a reality (Bremer wrote his own press notices in his mind while stalking Wallace). Protests had always to be timed for TV coverage, and sympathetic newsmen sought out. This led to the criticism of manufactured Movement heroes. Agnew told us the press created a Rap Brown. He does not know how many of my Fat Demagogues tried to capture the press's attention and failed. The ones who got heard had normally done something constructive, formed a constituency, suffered for their ideals—even Abbie Hoffman and Jerry Rubin served their obscure apprenticeship in the South as civil-rights volunteers.

But I won't protest too much the charge of media inflation. Remember, however, that L.B.J. was our leading media freak. He lived in a hall of mirrors, each mirror a TV screen on which he wanted to see himself projected, looking noble, smiling that perfect smile of beatific idiocy. My Demagogue was trying to float a hoax; but Johnson did it, when he conned the whole Senate (all but two) into the Tonkin Gulf resolve. The Pentagon public-relations officers were media freaks, pouring cosmetic money all over their armaments. The "creations of the media" were responding to a voracious audience. Without its appetites, no hustle could be worked. We wooed our demagogues, who only reciprocated. Middle Americans did not admire Jerry Rubin? Maybe not. But who was buying all those fan and fashion magazines filled with pictures of the President's wife? Jackie dressed as carefully for the cameras as Jerry Rubin; and we made sure the cameras were there to see her. Americans led an intense vicarious life, sharing instant tragedy or adventure— rocketing along on various trips, "spaced out" with John Glenn or Tim Leary. We rolled on the cameras' wheels down into a police garage, and waited there for Oswald, shoulder to shoulder with Jack Ruby. A tourist named Zapruder shot the hottest news film of the decade. To be on the streets was to be in history, part of the decade's street theatre, blinking at the tear gas.

Tom Wolfe took us on the road with Kesey. *Life* solaced astronauts' wives at lift-off. A journalist sat at the lawyers' table during Sirhan's trial. Another one kept Bobby Kennedy informed at Justice. Mailer was sent off with his cameras to jail, while Edgar Smith wrote himself out of it. Even Attica rioters would later call for Tom Wicker of The *Times*. We all found out what Jackie wore, or didn't wear. Capote astounded Kansans amid their native corn, then wafted some back with him to "the party of the century"—much as L.B.J. brought the camel driver home to dinner. People kept wandering into each other's stories; we were all one jumbled story we kept telling ourselves— the novelist as participant, the audience as actors; events first aimed at the TV mirrors as "news," and played out as theatre; then replayed, by instant nostalgia, as camp. The time seemed set on illustrating the maxim that history plays through its tragedies again as farce. On a Baltimore street, they restaged the Dallas motorcade for an underground movie, and police watched as placidly as at the original scene. Only when the actors stripped themselves nude did policemen move in. And, after a while, even Keystone Kops no longer chased the bathing beauties at each demonstration's ideological skinny dip.

The fads and tragedies came and went, barely distinguishable. We had camp weddings—Tiny Tim's on the Johnny Carson show. Camp assassination— the S.C.U.M. woman's attempt on Andy Warhol. Camp patriotism—Abbie Hoffman in flag drag. Camp religion—Billy Graham going disguised in fright wig to a rock show. And it grew harder to find a difference between the camp and straight versions of—what? Reality? Between Billy Graham with a wig and without one; between Abbie's flag and Anita Bryant's anthem; between Valerie Solanas and Lee Oswald; Johnny Carson's bridegroom and Johnny Carson.

My Demagogue was a hustler. But the New Frontier was a hustle—aimed at the Sea of Tranquillity, it veered first into the Central Highlands. All that Kennedy Kulcher of a manipulated Frost and the Casals night (Franco's revenge). 007. Air Force One. James Bond. Jack Kennedy. "Eyeball to eyeball, and the other fellow blinked." Susan Sontag called camp "style without content"—and historians have made that the judgment on Kennedy's regime. He put the concept of "image" at the heart of Sixties concerns.

The Great Society was a hustle. The great con man of the Senate who committed the hustler's one crime, of getting conned himself. And by Harvard sharpies at that—by computers and kill counts; running endlessly down a tunnel after nonexistent light.

Woodstock was a hustle, and The Beatles, along with Haight-Ashbury and Con III. Smoking banana peels, spiking sugar cubes, trying to turn Chicago on by way of its reservoir. Mary Quant, Carnaby Street, rummaging for a Barbra Streisand wardrobe in the junk shops. The frug and the twist. Political conventions were a hustle, just like the counter conventions—you got Pigasus either way. Day-Glo politics.

TV was a hype, but so was Newton Minow (liberal fashion of one season). What passed for profundity was Marshall McLuhan. For comedy, Peter Sellers. For art, *The Graduate*. For poetry, Bob Dylan. Short shorts, minis, midis, hot pants came and went. Bras went. Sex came, and stayed. And the Commissions— ah, the Commissions; on assassination, riots, race, drugs, pornography, violence. They were all dismissed before they could be delivered. The New York *Herald Tribune* went. Biafra. And the U.N.—shaken by Khrushchev's shoes on the table (early guerrilla theatre); and shattered when poor Adlai had to mouth falsehoods (another literate victim of White House Kulcher). Gene McCarthy. Mark Lane. Mark Rudd. Teach-ins. Be-ins. *Laugh-In*. General Bullroar. General Walker. Where is the *nudzh d'antan*?

Was it all a deception? If so, what made us so easily deceivable? Perhaps it was the quest for a cheap intensity not paid for, indulged in through a surrogate. TV took us everywhere. People lived the Kennedys' lives. "Participation" meant parasitism. A whirl of over-vivid borrowed experience seemed to empty people of their own existence. We were made ghostly with secondhand fulfillments. A thousand intrusive stories every night reduced all violence to a kind of neutral hum. The nation freaked out on "trips" at a safe remove—as when each TV detective show filmed an LSD experience hoked up from "inside" a character. We even managed to have a safe civil war of the generations, in which hard-hats could get back at their own kids by killing surrogate Asians in Vietnam. Cool J.F.K. promised some heat of immediacy if people could just press up close enough to him. Norman Mailer was our delegate from the audience jumping onto the stage. Kids lived out at the edge of The Beatles' manic careering. Marilyn Monroe hustled the intellectuals, who hustled her back, turning her into a plaything of the mind—every desiccated don's vision of a succulent disciple. Street theatre led to street tragedy in Dallas, followed by the greatest scene of all —the prancing horse and panoply, dip of jet wings, lighting fire to withstand eternity.

The kids' "Movement" burned itself out in destroying other things—some pretensions of the racists, militarists, authoritarians; while destroying the peace of parents, the rhetoric of school administrators, and the liberalism of editors. It was mainly destructive— little thought, and much inveighing. Perhaps we are fortunate it lacked long-term force. The father of street theatre was Hitler, and social recrimination is tugged always toward nihilism. With nothing to confront, the Movement did not exist—fell into postcoital lassitude. Fires burn themselves out; one cannot stay passionate forever—which leads to a new sentimentalism of the young, tears being shed for the tear-gas days, for glad cries about offing the pigs. But it is better, in the long run, to get out of a room with screaming people and guns too handy. I remember the relief and sheer drained thankfulness with which I at last escaped Fat Demagogue. He said I must never reveal his plans, or someday he would get me. I confess I half believed him—how predict what a crazy man will do? You notice I have not given his name here—though I am undoubtedly safe. The Sixties are over. ⧘

THE FITZGERALD HEMINGWAY EPOCH

When F. Scott Fitzgerald and Ernest Hemingway first met in 1925, Fitzgerald had just completed *The Great Gatsby* and Hemingway *In Our Time*. Fitzgerald was the better known of the two but by October, 1933, when Esquire was founded, Hemingway had become the most prominent author of his time while Fitzgerald had started down the long reverse slope of his career, or so it then seemed. The founding editor of Esquire, before he had a magazine to edit, was a fan of both. As a collector of Hemingway's first editions, he had corresponded with the author and met him one day, in the flesh, in Captain L. H. Cohn's bookshop in New York City, where Hemingway astonishingly agreed on the spot to contribute a series of "outdoor letters" for the new magazine (an example of which appears on the next page). Hemingway was in the first issue, Fitzgerald came along in 1934, having sent material at the suggestion of H. L. Mencken, former editor of *The American Mercury*. In 1936, within a period of six months, both men published in Esquire some of their finest writing, curiously, in the case of each, reflecting his measure of the other—envy on Fitzgerald's part, contempt on Hemingway's. Fitzgerald's was *The Crack-Up*, a series of three brilliant essays describing his creative exhaustion. In one passage, he contrasted indirectly his impotence to Hemingway's vitality. Hemingway, in Bimini, read Fitzgerald's confessions of failure and registered his reaction in *The Snows of Kilimanjaro*, perhaps his most accomplished story, which appeared in August of '36: "He remembered poor Scott Fitzgerald and his romantic awe of [the rich] and how he had started a story once that began 'The very rich are different from you and me.' And how someone had said to Scott, Yes they have more money. But that was not humorous to Scott. He thought they were a special glamorous race and when he found they weren't it wrecked him just as much as any other thing that wrecked him." In a letter to Hemingway, Fitzgerald complained of the liberty taken with his name and reputation and the reference was deleted from later publications of the story. Their friendship survived the event, but barely. Fitzgerald died in 1940, by his own measure a failure; Hemingway in 1961, a winner of the Nobel Prize and America's preeminent man of letters. But at no other time in their respective careers did their talents so sharply intersect as in those six months of 1936, within the pages of Esquire. The editor survived them both, and in 1965 sought to place in perspective the character of both men as he had known them.

Ernest Hemingway:

On the Blue Water

A Gulf Stream Letter

Certainly there is no hunting like the hunting of man and those who have hunted armed men long enough and liked it, never really care for anything else thereafter. You will meet them doing various things with resolve, but their interest rarely holds because after the other thing ordinary life is as flat as the taste of wine when the taste buds have been burned off your tongue. Wine, when your tongue has been burned clean with lye and water, feels like puddle water in your mouth, while mustard feels like axle grease, and you can smell crisp, fried bacon, but when you taste it, there is only a feeling of crinkly lard.

You can learn about this matter of the tongue by coming into the kitchen of a villa on the Riviera late at night and taking a drink from what should be a bottle of Evian water and which turns out to be *Eau de Javel*, a concentrated lye product used for cleaning sinks. The taste buds on your tongue, if burned off by *Eau de Javel*, will begin to function again after about a week. At what rate other things regenerate one does not know, since you lose track of friends and the things one could learn in a week were mostly learned a long time ago.

The other night I was talking with a good friend to whom all hunting is dull except elephant hunting. To him there is no sport in anything unless there is great danger and, if the danger is not enough, he will increase it for his own satisfaction. A hunting companion of his had told me how this friend was not satisfied with the risks of ordinary elephant hunting but would, if possible, have the elephants driven, or turned, so he could take them head-on, so it was a choice of killing them with the difficult frontal shot as they came, trumpeting, with their ears spread, or having them run over him. This is to elephant hunting what the German cult of suicide climbing is to ordinary mountaineering, and I suppose it is, in a way, an attempt to approximate the old hunting of the armed man who is hunting you.

This friend was speaking of elephant hunting and urging me to hunt elephant, as he said that once you took it up no other hunting would mean anything to you. I was arguing that I enjoyed all hunting and shooting, any sort I could get, and had no desire to wipe this capacity for enjoyment out with the *Eau de Javel* of the old elephant coming straight at you with his trunk up and his ears spread.

"Of course you like that big fishing too," he said rather sadly. "Frankly, I can't see where the excitement is in that."

"You'd think it was marvelous if the fish shot at you with Tommy guns or jumped back and forth through the cockpit with swords on the ends of their noses."

"Don't be silly," he said. "But frankly I don't see where the thrill is."

"Look at so and so," I said. "He's an elephant hunter and this last year he's gone fishing for big fish and he's goofy about it. He must get a kick out of it or he wouldn't do it."

"Yes," my friend said. "There must be something about it but I can't see it. Tell me where you get a thrill out of it."

"I'll try to write it in a piece sometime," I told him.

"I wish you would," he said. "Because you people are sensible on other subjects. Moderately sensible I mean."

"I'll write it."

In the first place, the Gulf Stream and the other great ocean currents are the last wild country there is left. Once you are out of sight of land and of the other boats you are more alone than you can ever be hunting and the sea is the same as it has been since before men ever went on it in boats. In a season fishing you will see it oily flat as the becalmed galleons saw it while they drifted to the westward; white-capped with a fresh breeze as they saw it running with the trades; and in high, rolling blue hills the tops blowing off them like snow as they were punished by it, so that sometimes you will see three great hills of water with your fish jumping from the top of the farthest one and if you tried to make a turn to go with him without picking your chance, one of those breaking crests would roar down in on you with a thousand tons of water and you would hunt no more elephants, Richard, my lad.

There is no danger from the fish, but anyone who goes on the sea the year around in a small power boat does not seek danger. You may be absolutely sure that

Ernest Hemingway's "Letters" were written from the regions of his interest, beginning in 1933 and continuing through 1936. This one is typical except for the fact that the eighteenth paragraph is the basis for The Old Man and the Sea, *which, eighteen years later, helped win him the Nobel Prize.*

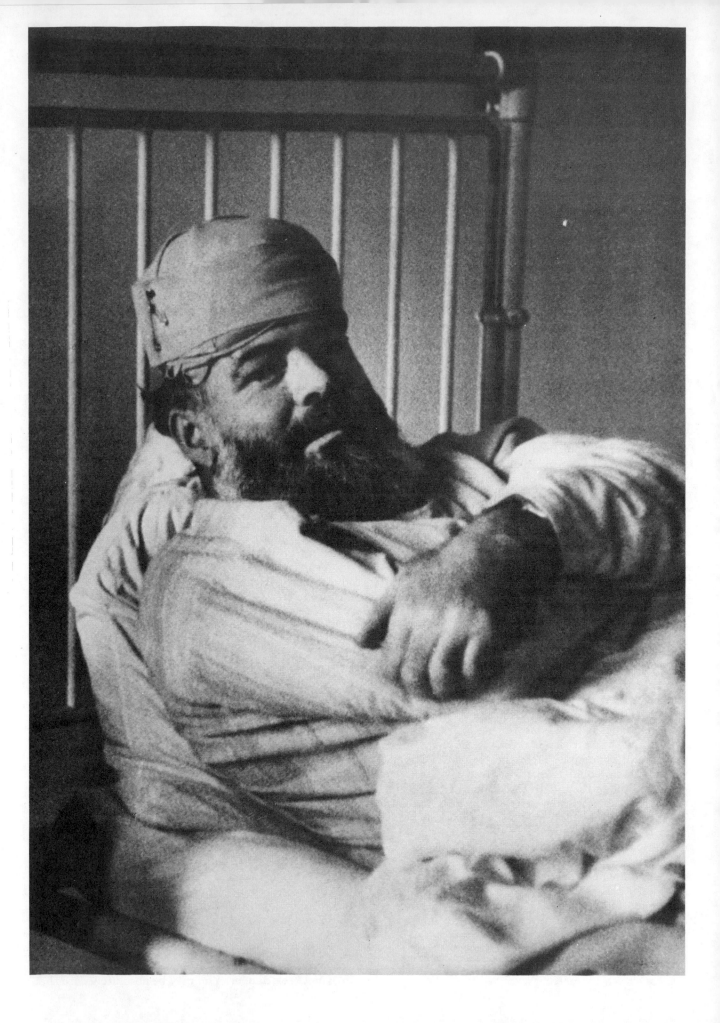

in a year you will have it without seeking, so you try always to avoid it all you can.

Because the Gulf Stream is an unexploited country, only the very fringe of it ever being fished, and then only at a dozen places in thousands of miles of current, no one knows what fish live in it, or how great size they reach or what age, or even what kinds of fish and animals live in it at different depths. When you are drifting, out of sight of land, fishing four lines, sixty, eighty, one hundred and one hundred fifty fathoms down, in water that is seven hundred fathoms deep you never know what may take the small tuna that you use for bait, and every time the line starts to run off the reel, slowly first, then with a scream of the click as the rod bends and you feel it double and the huge weight of the friction of the line rushing through that depth of water while you pump and reel, pump and reel, pump and reel, trying to get the belly out of the line before the fish jumps, there is always a thrill that needs no danger to make it real. It may be a marlin that will jump high and clear off to your right and then go off in a series of leaps, throwing a splash like a speedboat in a sea as you shout for the boat to turn with him watching the line melting off the reel before the boat can get around. Or it may be a broadbill that will show wagging his great broadsword. Or it may be some fish that you will never see at all that will head straight out to the northwest like a submerged submarine and never show and at the end of five hours the angler has a straightened-out hook. There is always a feeling of excitement when a fish takes hold when you are drifting deep.

In hunting you know what you are after and the top you can get is an elephant. But who can say what you will hook sometime when drifting in a hundred and fifty fathoms in the Gulf Stream? There are probably marlin and swordfish to which the fish we have seen caught are pygmies; and every time a fish takes the bait drifting you have a feeling perhaps you are hooked to one of these.

Carlos, our Cuban mate, who is fifty-three years old and has been fishing for marlin since he went in the bow of a skiff with his father when he was seven, was fishing drifting deep one time when he hooked a white marlin. The fish jumped twice and then sounded and when he sounded suddenly Carlos felt a great weight and he could not hold the line which went out and down and down irresistibly until the fish had taken out over a hundred and fifty fathoms. Carlos says it felt as heavy and solid as though he were hooked to the bottom of the sea. Then suddenly the strain was loosened but he could feel the weight of his original fish and pulled it up stone dead. Some toothless fish like a swordfish or marlin had closed his jaws across the middle of the eighty pound white marlin and squeezed it and held it so that every bit of the insides of the fish had been crushed out while the huge fish moved off with the eighty-pound fish in its mouth. Finally it let go. What size of a fish would that be? I thought it might be a giant squid but Carlos said there were no sucker marks on the fish and that it showed plainly the shape of the marlin's mouth where he had crushed it.

Another time an old man fishing alone in a skiff out of Cabañas hooked a great marlin that, on the heavy sash-cord handline, pulled the skiff far out to sea. Two days later the old man was picked up by fishermen sixty miles to the eastward, the head and forward part of the marlin lashed alongside. What was left of the fish, less than half, weighed eight hundred pounds. The old man had stayed with him a day, a night, a day and another night while the fish swam deep and pulled the boat. When he had come up the old man had pulled the boat up on him and harpooned him. Lashed alongside the sharks had hit him and the old man had fought them out alone in the Gulf Stream in a skiff, clubbing them, stabbing at them, lunging at them with an oar until he was exhausted and the sharks had eaten all that they could hold. He was crying in the boat when the fishermen picked him up, half crazy from his loss, and the sharks were still circling the boat.

But what is the excitement in catching them from a launch? It comes from the fact that they are strange and wild things of unbelievable speed and power and a beauty, in the water and leaping, that is indescribable, which you would never see if you did not fish for them, and to which you are suddenly harnessed so that you feel their speed, their force and their savage power as intimately as if you were riding a bucking horse. For half an hour, an hour, or five hours, you are fastened to the fish as much as he is fastened to you and you tame him and break him the way a wild horse is broken and finally lead him to the boat. For pride and because the fish is worth plenty of money in the Havana market, you gaff him at the boat and bring him on board, but the having him in the boat isn't the excitement; it is while you are fighting him that is the fun.

If the fish is hooked in the bony part of the mouth I am sure the hook hurts him no more than the harness hurts the angler. A large fish when he is hooked often does not feel the hook at all and will swim toward the boat, unconcerned, to take another bait. At other times he will swim away deep, completely unconscious of the hook, and it is when he feels himself held and pressure exerted to turn him, that he knows something is wrong and starts to make his fight. Unless he is hooked where it hurts he makes his fight not against the pain of the hook, but against being captured and if, when he is out of sight, you figure what he is doing, in what direction he is pulling when deep down, and why, you can convince him and bring him to the boat by the same system you break a wild horse. It is not necessary to kill him, or even completely exhaust him to bring him to the boat.

To kill a fish that fights deep you pull against the direction he wants to go until he is worn out and dies. It takes hours and when the fish dies the sharks are liable to get him before the angler can raise him to the top. To catch such a fish quickly you figure, by trying to hold him absolutely, which direction he is working (a sounding fish is going in the direction the line slants in the water when you have put enough pressure on the drag so the line would break if you held it any tighter); then get ahead of him on that direction and he can be brought to the boat without killing him.

You do not tow him or pull him with the motor boat; you use the engine to shift your position just as you would walk up or down stream with a salmon. A fish is caught most surely from a small boat such as a dory since the angler can shut down on his drag and simply let the fish pull the boat. Towing the boat will kill him in time. But the most satisfaction is to dominate and convince the fish and bring him intact in everything but spirit to the boat as rapidly as possible.

"Very instructive," says the friend. "But where does the thrill come in?"

The thrill comes when you are standing at the wheel drinking a cold bottle of beer and watching the outriggers jump the baits so they look like small live tuna leaping along and then behind one you see a long dark shadow wing up and then a big spear thrust out followed by an eye and head and dorsal fin and the tuna jumps with the wave and he's missed it.

"Marlin," Carlos yells from the top of the house and stamps his feet up and down, the signal that a fish is raised. He swarms down to the wheel and you go back to where the rod rests in its socket and there comes the shadow again, fast as the shadow of a plane moving over the water, and the spear, head, fin and shoulders smash out of water and you hear the click the closepin makes as the line pulls out and the long bight of line whishes through the water as the fish turns and as you hold the rod, you feel it double and the butt kicks you in the belly as you come back hard and feel his weight, as you strike him again and again, and again.

Then the heavy rod arc-ing out toward the fish, and the reel in a band-saw zinging scream, the marlin leaps clear and long, silver in the sun long, round as a hogshead and banded with lavender stripes and, when he goes into the water, it throws a column of spray like a shell lighting.

Then he comes out again, and the spray roars, and again, then the line feels slack and out he bursts headed across and in, then jumps wildly twice more seeming to hang high and stiff in the air before falling to throw the column of water and you can see the hook in the corner of his jaw.

Then in a series of jumps like a greyhound he heads to the northwest and standing up, you follow him in the boat, the line taut as a banjo string and little drops coming from it until you finally get the belly of it clear of that friction against the water and have a straight pull out toward the fish.

And all the time Carlos is shouting, "Oh, God the bread of my children! Oh look at the bread of my children! Joseph and Mary look at the bread of my children jump! There it goes the bread of my children! He'll never stop the bread the bread the bread of my children!"

This striped marlin jumped, in a straight line to the northwest, fifty-three times, and every time he went out it was a sight to make your heart stand still. Then he sounded and I said to Carlos, "Get me the harness. Now I've got to pull him up the bread of your children."

"I couldn't stand to see it," he says. "Like a filled pocketbook jumping. He can't go down deep now. He's caught too much air jumping."

"Like a race horse over obstacles," Julio says. "Is the harness all right? Do you want water?"

"No." Then kidding Carlos, "What's this about the bread of your children?"

"He always says that," says Julio. "You should hear him curse me when we would lose one in the skiff."

"What will the bread of your children weigh?" I ask with mouth dry, the harness taut across shoulders, the rod a flexible prolongation of the sinew pulling ache of arms, the sweat salty in my eyes.

"Four hundred and fifty," says Carlos.

"Never," says Julio.

"Thou and thy never," says Carlos. "The fish of another always weighs nothing to thee."

"Three seventy-five," Julio raises his estimate. "Not a pound more."

Carlos says something unprintable and Julio comes up to four hundred.

The fish is nearly whipped now and the dead ache is out of raising him, and then, while lifting, I feel something slip. It holds for an instant and then the line is slack.

"He's gone," I say and unbuckle the harness.

"The bread of your children," Julio says to Carlos.

"Yes," Carlos says. "Yes. Joke and no joke yes. *El pan de mis hijos*. Three hundred and fifty pounds at ten cents a pound. How many days does a man work for that in the winter? How cold is it at three o'clock in the morning on all those days? And the fog and the rain in a norther. Every time he jumps the hook cutting the hole a little bigger in his jaw. Ay how he could jump. How he could jump!"

"The bread of your children," says Julio.

"Don't talk about that any more," said Carlos.

No it is not elephant hunting. But we get a kick out of it. When you have a family and children, your family, or my family, or the family of Carlos, you do not have to look for danger. There is always plenty of danger when you have a family.

And after a while the danger of others is the only danger and there is no end to it nor any pleasure in it nor does it help to think about it.

But there is great pleasure in being on the sea, in the unknown wild suddenness of a great fish; in his life and death which he lives for you in an hour while your strength is harnessed to his; and there is satisfaction in conquering this thing which rules the sea it lives in.

Then in the morning of the day after you have caught a good fish, when the man who carried him to the market in a handcart brings the long roll of heavy silver dollars wrapped in a newspaper on board it is very satisfactory money. It really feels like money.

"There's the bread of your children," you say to Carlos.

"In the time of the dance of the millions," he says, "a fish like that was worth two hundred dollars. Now it is thirty. On the other hand a fisherman never starves. The sea is very rich."

"And the fisherman always poor."

"No. Look at you. You are rich."

"Like hell," you say. "And the longer I fish the poorer I'll be. I'll end up fishing with you for the market in a dinghy."

"That I never believe," says Carlos devoutly. "But look. That fishing in a dinghy is very interesting. You would like it."

"I'll look forward to it," you say.

"What we need for prosperity is a war," Carlos says. "In the time of the war with Spain and in the last war the fishermen were actually rich."

"All right," you say. "If we have a war you get the dinghy ready."

Ernest Hemingway: THE SNOWS OF KILIMANJARO

A Long Story

Kilimanjaro is a snow-covered mountain 19,710 feet high, and is said to be the highest mountain in Africa. Its western summit is called by the Masai "Ngàje Ngài," the House of God. Close to the western summit there is the dried and frozen carcass of a leopard. No one has explained what the leopard was seeking at that altitude.

The marvelous thing is that it's painless," he said. "That's how you know when it starts."

"Is it really?"

"Absolutely. I'm awfully sorry about the odor though. That must bother you."

"Don't! Please don't."

"Look at them," he said. "Now is it sight or is it scent that brings them like that?"

The cot the man lay on was in the wide shade of a mimosa tree and as he looked out past the shade onto the glare of the plain there were three of the big birds squatted obscenely, while in the sky a dozen more sailed, making quick-moving shadows as they passed.

"They've been there since the day the truck broke down," he said. "Today's the first time any have lit on the ground. I watched the way they sailed very carefully at first in case I ever wanted to use them in a story. That's funny now."

"I wish you wouldn't," she said.

"I'm only talking," he said. "It's much easier if I talk. But I don't want to bother you."

"You know it doesn't bother me," she said. "It's that I've gotten so very nervous not being able to do anything. I think we might make it as easy as we can until the plane comes."

"Or until the plane doesn't come."

"Please tell me what I can do. There must be something I can do."

"You can take the leg off and that might stop it, though I doubt it. Or you can shoot me. You're a good shot now. I taught you to shoot didn't I?"

"Please don't talk that way. Couldn't I read to you?"

"Read what?"

"Anything in the book bag that we haven't read."

"I can't listen to it," he said. "Talking is the easiest. We quarrel and that makes the time pass."

"I don't quarrel. I never want to quarrel. Let's not quarrel anymore. No matter how nervous we get. Maybe they will be back with another truck today. Maybe the plane will come."

"I don't want to move," the man said. "There is no sense in moving now except to make it easier for you."

"That's cowardly."

"Can't you let a man die as comfortably as he can without calling him names? What's the use of slanging me?"

"You're not going to die."

"Don't be silly. I'm dying now. Ask those bastards." He looked over to where the huge, filthy birds sat, their naked heads sunk in the hunched feathers. A fourth planed down, to run quick-legged and then waddle slowly toward the others.

"They are around every camp. You never notice them. You can't die if you don't give up."

"Where did you read that? You're such a bloody fool."

"You might think about someone else."

"For Christ's sake," he said, "That's been my trade." He lay then and was quiet for a while and looked across the heat shimmer of the plain to the edge of the bush. There were a few Tommies that showed minute and white against the yellow and, far off, he saw a herd of zebra, white against the green of the bush. This was a pleasant camp under big trees against a hill, with good water, and, close by, a nearly dry water hole where sandgrouse flighted in the mornings.

"Wouldn't you like me to read?" she asked. She was sitting on a canvas chair beside his cot. "There's a breeze coming up."

Hemingway's best-known story, The Snows of Kilimanjaro, *figured prominently in the lives of all three authors within this section. It was published in August, 1936.*

"No thanks."

"Maybe the truck will come."

"I don't give a damn about the truck."

"I do."

"You give a damn about so many things that I don't."

"Not so many, Harry."

"What about a drink?"

"It's supposed to be bad for you. It said in Black's to avoid all alcohol. You shouldn't drink."

"Molo!" he shouted.

"Yes Bwana."

"Bring whiskey-soda."

"Yes Bwana."

"You shouldn't," she said. "That's what I mean by giving up. It says it's bad for you. I know it's bad for you."

"No," he said. "It's good for me."

So now it was all over, he thought. So now he would never have a chance to finish it. So this was the way it ended in a bickering over a drink. Since the gangrene started in his right leg he had no pain and with the pain the horror had gone and all he felt now was a great tiredness and anger that this was the end of it. For this, that now was coming, he had very little curiosity. For years it had obsessed him; but now it meant nothing in itself. It was strange how easy being tired enough made it.

Now he would never write the things that he had saved to write until he knew enough to write them well. Well, he would not have to fail at trying to write them either. Maybe you could never write them, and that was why you put them off and delayed the starting. Well he would never know, now.

"I wish we'd never come," the woman said. She was looking at him holding the glass and biting her lip. "You never would have gotten anything like this in Paris. You always said you loved Paris. We could have stayed in Paris or gone anywhere. I'd have gone anywhere. I said I'd go anywhere you wanted. If you wanted to shoot we could have gone shooting in Hungary and been comfortable."

"Your bloody money," he said.

"That's not fair," she said. "It was always yours as much as mine. I left everything and I went wherever you wanted to go and I've done what you wanted to do. But I wish we'd never come here."

"You said you loved it."

"I did when you were all right. But now I hate it. I don't see why that had to happen to your leg. What have we done to have that happen to us?"

"I suppose what I did was to forget to put iodine on it when I first scratched it. Then I didn't pay any attention to it because I never infect. Then, later, when it got bad, it was probably using that weak carbolic solution when the other antiseptics ran out that paralyzed the minute blood vessels and started the gangrene." He looked at her, "What else?"

"I don't mean that."

"If we would have hired a good mechanic instead of a half-baked kikuyu driver, he would have checked the oil and never burned out that bearing in the truck."

"I don't mean that."

"If you hadn't left your own people, your goddamned old Westbury, Saratoga, Palm Beach people to take me on—"

"Why I loved you. That's not fair. I love you now. I'll always love you. Don't you love me?"

"No," said the man. "I don't think so. I never have."

"Harry, what are you saying? You're out of your head."

"No. I haven't any head to go out of."

"Don't drink that," she said. "Darling, please don't drink that. We have to do everything we can."

"You do it," he said. "I'm tired."

Now in his mind he saw a railway station at Karagatch and he was standing with his pack and that was the headlight of the Simplon-Orient cutting the dark now and he was leaving Thrace then after the retreat. That was one of the things he had saved to write, with, in the morning at breakfast, looking out the window and seeing snow on the mountains in Bulgaria and Nansen's secretary asking the old man if it were snow and the old man looking at it and saying, No, that's not snow. It's too early for snow. And the secretary repeating to the other girls, No, you see. It's not snow and them all saying, It's not snow we were mistaken. But it was the snow all right and he sent them on into it when he evolved exchange of populations. And it was snow they tramped along in until they died that winter.

It was snow too that fell all Christmas week that year up in the Gauertal, that year they lived in the woodcutter's house with the big square porcelain stove that filled half the room, and they slept on mattresses filled with beech leaves, the time the deserter came with his feet bloody in the snow. He said the police were right behind him and they gave him woolen socks and held the gendarmes talking until the tracks had drifted over. In Schruns, on Christmas day, the snow was so bright it hurt your eyes when you looked out from the weinstube and saw everyone coming home from church. That was where they walked up the sleigh-smoothed urine-yellowed road along the river with the steep pine hills, skis heavy on the shoulder, and where they ran that great run down the glacier above the Madlener-haus, the snow as smooth to see as cake frosting and as light as powder and he remembered the noiseless rush the speed made as you dropped down like a bird. They were snowbound a week in the Madlener-haus that time in the blizzard playing cards in the smoke by the lantern light and the stakes were higher all the time as Herr Lent lost more. Finally he lost it all. Everything, the skischule money and all the season's profit and then his capital. He could see him with his long nose, picking up the cards and then opening, "Sans Voir." There was always gambling then. When there was no snow you gambled and when there was too much you gambled. He thought of all the time in his life he had spent gambling. But he had never written a line of that, nor of that cold, bright Christmas day with the mountains showing across the plain that Barker had flown across the lines to bomb the Austrian officers' leave train, machine-gunning them as they scattered and ran. He remembered Barker afterwards coming into the mess and starting to tell about it. And how quiet it got and then somebody saying, "You bloody, murderous bastard." Those were the same Austrians they killed then that he skied with later. No not the same. Hans, that he skied with all that year, had been in the Kaiser-Jägers and when they went hunting hares together up the little valley above the sawmill they had talked of the fighting on Pasubio and of the attack on Pertica and Asalone and he had never written a word of that. Nor of Monte Corno, nor the Siete Communi, nor of Arsiero. How many winters had he lived in the Vorarlberg and the Arlberg? It was four and then he remembered the man who had the fox to sell when they had walked into Bludenz, that time to buy presents, and the cherry pit taste of good kirsch, the fast-slipping rush of running powder-snow on crust, singing "Hi Ho said Rolly!" as you ran down the last stretch to the steep drop, taking it straight, then running the orchard in three turns and out across the ditch and onto the icy road behind the inn. Knocking your bindings loose, kicking the skis free and leaning them up against the wooden wall of the inn, the lamplight coming from the window where inside, in the smoky, new-wine smelling warmth, they were playing the accordion.

"Where did we stay in Paris?" he asked the woman who was sitting by him in a canvas chair, now, in Africa.

"At the Crillon. You know that."

"Why do I know that?"

"That's where we always stayed."

"No. Not always."

"There and at the Pavillion Henri-Quatre in St. Germain. You said you loved it there."

"Love is a dunghill," said Harry. "And I'm the cock that gets on it to crow."

"If you have to go away," she said, "is it absolutely necessary to kill off everything you leave behind? I mean do you have to take away everything? Do you have to kill your horse, and your wife and burn your saddle and your armour?"

"Yes," he said. "Your damned money was my armour. My Swift and my Armour."

"Don't."

"All right. I'll stop that. I don't want to hurt you."

"It's a little bit late now."

"All right then. I'll go on hurting you. It's more amusing. The only thing I ever really liked to do with you I can't do now."

"No, that's not true. You liked to do many things and everything you wanted to do I did."

"Oh for Christ sake stop bragging will you?"

He looked at her and saw her crying.

"Listen," he said. "Do you think that it is fun to do this? I don't know why I'm doing it. It's trying to kill to keep yourself alive I imagine. I was all right when we started talking. I didn't mean to start this, and now I'm crazy as a coot and being as cruel to you as I can be. Don't pay any attention, darling, to what I say. I love you, really. You know I love you. I've never loved anyone else the way I love you." He slipped into the familiar lie he made his bread and butter by.

"You're sweet to me."

"You bitch," he said. "You rich bitch. That's poetry. I'm full of poetry now. Rot and poetry. Rotten poetry."

"Stop it. Harry, why do you have to turn into a devil now?"

"I don't like to leave anything," the man said. "I don't like to leave things behind."

* * *

It was evening now and he had been asleep. The sun was gone behind the hill and there was a shadow all across the plain and the small animals were feeding close to camp; quick dropping heads and switching tails, he watched them keeping well out away from the bush now. The birds no longer waited on the ground. They were all perched heavily in a tree. There were many more of them. His personal boy was sitting by the bed.

"Memsahib's gone to shoot," the boy said. "Does Bwana want?"

"Nothing."

She had gone to kill a piece of meat and, knowing how he liked to watch the game, she had gone well away so she would not disturb this little pocket of the plain that he could see. She was always thoughtful, he thought. On anything she knew about, or had read, or that she had ever heard.

It was not her fault that when he went to her he was already over. How could a woman know that you meant nothing that you said; that you spoke only from habit and to be comfortable. After he no longer meant what he said, his lies were more successful with women than when he had told them the truth.

It was not that he lied as that there was no truth to tell. He had had his life and it was over and then he went on living it again with different people and more money, with the best of the same places, and some new ones. You kept from thinking and it was all marvelous. You were equipped with good insides so that you did not go to pieces that way, the way most of them had, and you made an attitude that you cared nothing for the work you used to do, now that you could no longer do it. But, in yourself, you said that you would write about these people; about the very rich; that you were really not of them but a spy in their country; that you would leave it and write of it and for once it would be written by someone who knew what he was writing of. But he would never do it, because each day of not writing, of comfort, of being that which he despised, dulled his ability and softened his will to work so that, finally, he did no work at all. The people he knew now were all much more comfortable when he did not work. Africa was where he had been happiest in the good time of his life so he had come out here to start again. They had made this safari with the minimum of comfort. There was no hardship; but there was no luxury and he had thought that he could get back into training that way. That in some way he could work the fat off his soul the way a fighter went into the mountains to work and train in order to burn it out of his body.

She had liked it. She said she loved it. She loved anything that was exciting, that involved a change of scene, where there were new people and where things were pleasant. And he had felt the illusion of returning strength of will to work. Now if this was how it ended, and he knew it was, he must not turn like some snake biting itself because its back was broken. It wasn't this woman's fault. If it had not been she it would have been another. If he lived by a lie he should try to die by it. He heard a shot beyond the hill.

She shot very well this good, this rich bitch, this kindly caretaker and destroyer of his talent. Nonsense. He had destroyed his talent himself. Why should he blame this woman because she kept him well? He had destroyed his talent by not using it, by betrayals of himself and what he believed in, by drinking so much that he blunted the edge of his perceptions, by laziness, by sloth, and by snobbery, by pride and by prejudice, by hook and by crook. What was this? A catalog of old books? What was his talent anyway? It was a talent all right but instead of using it, he had traded on it. It was never what he had done, but always what he could do. And he had chosen to make his living with something else instead of a pen or a pencil. It was strange too, wasn't it, that when he fell in love with another woman, that woman should always have more money than the last one? But when he no longer was in love, when he was only lying, as to this woman, now, who had the most money of all, who had all the money there was, who had had a husband and children, who had taken lovers and been dissatisfied with them, and who loved him dearly as a writer, as a man, as a companion and as a proud possession; it was strange that when he did not love her at all and was lying, that he should be able to give her more for her money than when he had really loved. We must all be cut out for what we do, he thought. However you make your living is where your talent lies. He had sold vitality, in one form or another, all his life and when your affections are not too involved you give much better value for the

money. He had found that out but he would never write that, now, either. No, he would not write that, although it was well worth writing.

Now she came in sight, walking across the open toward the camp. She was wearing jodphurs and carrying her rifle. The two boys had a Tommie slung and they were coming along behind her. She was still a good-looking woman, he thought, and she had a pleasant body. She had a great talent and appreciation for the bed, she was not pretty, but he liked her face, she read enormously, liked to ride and shoot and, certainly, she drank too much. Her husband had died when she was still a comparatively young woman and for a while she had devoted herself to her two just-grown children, who did not need her and were embarrassed at having her about, to her stable of horses, to books, and to bottles. She liked to read in the evening before dinner and she drank scotch and soda while she read. By dinner she was fairly drunk and after a bottle of wine at dinner she was usually drunk enough to sleep.

That was before the lovers. After she had the lovers she did not drink so much because she did not have to be drunk to sleep. But the lovers bored her. She had been married to a man who had never bored her and these people bored her very much.

Then one of her two children was killed in a plane crash and after that was over she did not want the lovers, and drink being no anaesthetic she had to make another life. Suddenly she had been acutely frightened of being alone. But she wanted someone that she respected with her.

It had begun very simply. She liked what he wrote and she had always envied the life he led. She thought he did exactly what he wanted to. The steps by which she had acquired him and the way in which she had finally fallen in love with him were all part of a regular progression in which she had built herself a new life and he had traded away what remained of his old life. He had traded it for security, for comfort too, there was no denying that, and for what else? He did not know. She would have bought him anything he wanted. He knew that. She was a damned nice woman too. He would as soon be in bed with her as anyone; rather with her, because she was richer, because she was very pleasant and appreciative and because she never made scenes. And now this life that she had built again was coming to a term because he had not used iodine two weeks ago when a thorn had scratched his knee as they moved forward trying to photograph a herd of waterbuck standing, their heads up, peering while their nostrils searched the air, their ears spread wide to hear the first noise that would send them rushing into the bush. They had bolted, too, before he got the picture.

Here she came now.

He turned his head on the cot to look toward her. "Hello," he said.

"I shot a Tommie ram," she told him. "He'll make you good broth and I'll have them mash some potatoes with the Klim. How do you feel?"

"Much better."

"Isn't that lovely. You know I thought perhaps you would. You were sleeping when I left."

"I had a good sleep. Did you walk far?"

"No. Just around behind the hill. I made quite a good shot on the Tommie."

"You shoot marvelously you know."

"I love it. I've loved Africa. Really. If *you're* all right it's the most fun that I've ever had. You don't know the fun it's been to shoot with you. I've loved the country."

"I love it too."

"Darling you don't know how marvelous it is to see you feeling better. I couldn't stand it when you felt that way. You won't talk to me like that again, will you? Promise me?"

"No," he said. "I don't remember what I said."

"You don't have to destroy me. Do you? I'm only a middle-aged woman who loves you and wants to do what you want to do. I've been destroyed two or three times already. You wouldn't want to destroy me again, would you?"

"I'd like to destroy you a few times in bed," he said.

"Yes. That's the good destruction. That's the way we're made to be destroyed. The plane will be here tomorrow."

"How do you know?"

"I'm sure. It's bound to come. The boys have the wood all ready and the grass to make the smudge. I went down and looked at it again today. There's plenty of room to land and we have the smudges ready at both ends."

"What makes you think it will come tomorrow?"

"I'm sure it will. It's overdue now. Then, in town, they will fix up your leg and then we will have some good destruction. Not that dreadful talking kind."

"Should we have a drink? The sun is down."

"Do you think you should?"

"I'm having one."

"We'll have one together. *Molo, letti dui whiskey-soda!*" she called.

"You'd better put on your mosquito boots," he told her.

"I'll wait till I bathe. . . ."

While it grew dark they drank and just before it was dark and there was no longer enough light to shoot, a hyena crossed the open on his way around the hill.

"That bastard crosses there every night," the man said. "Every night for two weeks."

"He's the one makes the noise at night. I don't mind it. They're a filthy animal though."

Drinking together, with no pain now except the discomfort of lying in the one position, the boys lighting a fire, its shadow jumping on the tents, he could feel the return of acquiescence in this life of pleasant surrender. She *was* very good to him. He had been cruel and unjust in the afternoon. She was a fine woman, marvelous really. And just then it occurred to him that he was going to die.

It came with a rush; not as a rush of water nor of wind; but of a sudden evil-smelling emptiness and the odd thing was that the hyena slipped lightly along the edge of it.

"What is it, Harry?" she asked him.

"Nothing," he said. "You had better move over to the other side. To windward."

"Did Molo change the dressing?"

"Yes. I'm just using the boric now."

"How do you feel?"

"A little wobbly."

"I'm going in to bathe," she said. 'I'll be right out. I'll eat with you and then we'll put the cot in."

So, he said to himself, we did well to stop the quarreling. He had never quarreled much with this woman, while with the women that he loved he had quarreled so much they had finally, always, with the corrosion of the quarreling, killed what they had together. He had loved too much, demanded too much, and he wore it all out.

He thought about alone in Constantinople that time, having quarreled in Paris before he had gone out. He had whored the whole time and then, when that was over, and he had failed to kill his loneliness, but only made it worse, he had written her, the first one, the one who left him, a letter telling her how he had never been able to kill it. . . . How when he thought he saw her outside the Regence *one time it made him go all faint and sick inside, and that he would follow a woman who looked like her in some way, along the Boulevard, afraid to see it was not she, afraid to lose the feeling it gave him. How everyone he had slept with had only made him miss her more. How what she had done could never matter since he knew he could not cure himself of loving her. He wrote this letter at the Club, cold sober, and mailed it to New York asking her to write him at the office in Paris. That seemed safe. And that night missing her so much it made him feel hollow sick inside, he wandered up past Taxim's, picked a girl up and took her out to supper. He had gone to a place to dance with her afterward, she danced badly, and left her for a hot Armenian slut, that swung her belly against him so it almost scalded. He took her away from a British gunner subaltern after a row. The gunner asked him outside and they fought in the street on the cobbles in the dark. He'd hit him twice, hard, on the side of the jaw and when he didn't go down he knew he was in for a fight. The gunner hit him in the body, then beside his eye. He swung with his left again and landed and the gunner fell on him and grabbed his coat and tore the sleeve off and he clubbed him* twice behind the ear and then smashed him with his right as he pushed him away. When the gunner went down his head hit first and he ran with the girl because they heard the M. P.'s coming. They got into a taxi and drove out to Rimmily Hissa along the Bosphorus, and around, and back in the cool night and went to bed and she felt as overripe as she looked but smooth, rose-petal, syrupy, smooth-bellied, big-breasted and needed no pillow under her, and he left her before she was awake looking blousy enough in the first daylight and turned up at the Pera Palace with a black eye, carrying his coat because one sleeve was missing. That same night he left for Anatolia and he remembered, later on that trip, riding all day through fields of the poppies that they raised for opium and how strange it made you feel finally and all the distances seemed wrong, to where they had made the attack with the newly arrived Constantine officers, that did not know a god-damned thing, and the artillery had fired into the troops and the British observer had cried like a child. That was the day he'd first seen dead men wearing white ballet skirts and upturned shoes with pompons on them. The Turks had come steadily and lumpily and he had seen the skirted men running and the officers shooting into them and running then themselves and he and the British observer had run too until his lungs ached and his mouth was full of the taste of pennies and they stopped behind some rocks and there were the Turks coming as lumpily as ever. Later he had seen the things that he could never think of and later still he had seen much worse. So when he got back to Paris that time he could not talk about it or stand to have it mentioned. And there in the café as he passed was that American poet with a pile of saucers in front of him and a stupid look on his potato face talking about the Dada movement with a Roumanian who said his name was Tristan Tzara, who always wore a monocle and had a headache, and, back at the apartment with his wife that now he loved again, the quarrel all over, the madness all over, glad to be home, the office sent his mail up to the flat. So then the letter in answer to the one he'd written came in on a platter one morning and when he saw the hand-writing he went cold all over and tried to slip the letter underneath another. But his wife said, "Who is that letter from, dear?" and that was the end of the beginning of that. He remembered the good times with them all, and the quarrels. They always picked the finest places to have the quarrels. And why had they always quarreled when he was feeling best? He had never written any of that because, at first, he never wanted to hurt anyone and then it seemed as though there was enough to write without it. But he had always thought that he would write it finally. There was so much to write. He had seen the world change; not just the events; although he had seen many of them and had watched the people, but he had seen the subtler change and he could remember how the people were at different times. He had been in it and he had watched it and it was his duty to write of it; but now he never would.

"How do you feel?" she said. She had come out from the tent now after her bath.

"All right."

"Could you eat now?" He saw Molo behind her with the folding table and the other boy with the dishes.

"I want to write," he said.

"You ought to take some broth to keep your strength up."

"I'm going to die tonight," he said. "I don't need my strength up."

"Don't be melodramatic, Harry, please," she said.

"Why don't you use your nose? I'm rotted half way up my thigh now. What the hell should I fool with broth for? Molo, bring whiskey-soda."

"Please take the broth," she said gently.

"All right."

The broth was too hot. He had to hold it in the cup until it cooled enough to take it and then he just got it down without gagging.

"You're a fine woman," he said. "Don't pay any attention to me."

She looked at him with her well-known, well loved face from *Spur* and *Town and Country*, only a little the worse for drink, only a little the worse for bed, but *Town and Country* never showed those good breasts and those useful thighs and those lightly small-of-back-caressing hands and as he looked and saw her well-known pleasant smile, he felt death come again. This time there was no rush. It was a puff, as of a wind that makes a candle flicker and the flame go tall.

"They can bring my net out later and hang it from the tree and build the fire up. I'm not going in the tent tonight. It's not worth moving. It's a clear night. There won't be any rain."

So this was how you died, in whispers that you did not hear. Well, there would be no more quarreling. He could promise that. The one experience that he had never had he was not going to spoil now. He probably would. You spoiled everything. But perhaps he wouldn't.

"You can't take dictation, can you?"

"I never learned," she told him.

"That's all right."

There wasn't time, of course, although it seemed as though it telescoped so that you might put it all into one paragraph if you could get it right.

There was a log house, chinked white with mortar, on a hill above the lake. There was a bell on a pole by the door to call the people in to meals. Behind the house were fields and behind the fields was the timber. A line of lombardy poplars ran from the house to the dock. Other poplars ran along the point. A road went up to the hills along the edge of the timber and along that road he picked blackberries. Then that log house was burned down and all the guns that had been on deer foot racks above the open fireplace were burned and afterwards their barrels, with the lead melted in the magazines, and the stocks burned away, lay out on the heap of ashes that were used to make lye for the big iron soap kettles, and you asked Grandfather if you could have them to play with, and he said, no. You see they were his guns still and he never bought any others. Nor did he hunt anymore. The house was rebuilt in the same place out of lumber now and painted white and from its porch you saw the poplars and the lake beyond; but there were never any more guns. The barrels of the guns that had hung on the deer feet on the wall of the log house lay out there on the heap of ashes and no one ever touched them.

In the Black Forest, after the war, we rented a trout stream and there were two ways to walk to it. One was down the valley from Triberg and around the valley road in the shade of the trees that bordered the white road, and then up a side road that went up through the hills past many small farms, with the big Schwartzwald houses, until that road crossed the stream. That was where our fishing began. The other way was to climb steeply up to the edge of the woods and then go across the top of the hills through the pine woods, and then out to the edge of a meadow and down across this meadow to the bridge. There were birches along the stream and it was not big, but narrow, clear and fast, with pools where it had cut under the roots of the birches. At the Hotel in Triberg the proprietor had a fine season. It was very pleasant and we were all great friends. The next year came the inflation and the money he had made the year before was not enough to buy supplies to open the hotel and he hanged himself.

You could dictate that, but you could not dictate the Place Contrescarpe where the flower sellers dyed their flowers in the street and the dye ran over the paving where the autobus started and the old men and the women, always drunk on wine and bad marc; and the children with their noses running in the cold; the smell of dirty sweat and poverty and drunkenness at the Café des Amateurs and the whores at the Bal Musette they lived above. The Concierge who entertained the trooper of the Garde Republicaine in her loge, his horsehair plumed helmet on a chair. The locataire across the hall whose husband was a bicycle racer and her joy that morning at the Cremerie when she had opened L'Auto and seen where he placed third in Paris-Tours, his first big race. She had blushed and laughed and then gone upstairs crying with the yellow sporting paper in her hand. The husband of the woman who ran the Bal Musette drove a taxi and when he, Harry, had to take an early plane the husband knocked upon the door to wake him and they each drank a glass of white wine at the Zinc of the bar before they started. He knew his neighbors in that quarter then because they all were poor. Around that Place there were two kinds; the drunkards and the sportifs. The drunkards killed their poverty that way; the sportifs took it out in exercise. They were the descendants of the Communards and it was no struggle for them to know their politics. They knew who had shot their fathers, their relatives, their brothers, and their friends when the Versailles troops came in and took the town after the Commune and executed anyone they could catch with calloused hands, or who wore a cap, or carried any other sign he was a working man. And in that poverty, and in that quarter across the street from a Boucherie Chevaline

and a wine cooperative he had written the start of all he was to do. There never was another part of Paris that he loved like that, the sprawling trees, the old white plastered houses painted brown below, the long green of the autobus in that round square, the purple flower dye upon the paving, the sudden drop down the hill of the rue Cardinal Lemoine to the River, and the other way the narrow crowded world of the rue Mouffetard. The street that ran up toward the Pantheon and the other that he always took with the bicycle, the only asphalted street in all that quarter, smooth under the tires, with the high narrow houses and the cheap tall hotel where Paul Verlaine had died. There were only two rooms in the apartment where they lived and he had a room on the top floor of that hotel that cost him sixty francs a month where he did his writing, and from it he could see the roofs and chimney pots and all the hills of Paris.

From the apartment you could only see the wood and coal man's place. He sold wine too, bad wine. The golden horse's head outside the Boucherie Chevaline where the carcasses hung yellow gold and red in the open window, and the green painted cooperative where they bought their wine; good wine and cheap. The rest was plaster walls and the windows of the neighbors. The neighbors who, at night, when someone lay drunk in the street, moaning and groaning in that typical French ivresse that you were propaganded to believe did not exist, would open their windows and then the murmur of talk.

"Where is the policeman? When you don't want him the bugger is always there. He's sleeping with some concierge. Get the Agent." Till someone threw a bucket of water from a window and the moaning stopped. "What's that? Water. Ah, that's intelligent." And the windows shutting. Marie, his femme de menage, protesting against the eight-hour day saying, "If a husband works until six he gets only a little drunk on the way home and does not waste too much. If he works only until five he is drunk every night and one has no money. It is the wife of the working man who suffers from this shortening of hours."

"Wouldn't you like some more broth?" the woman asked him now.

"No thank you very much. It is awfully good."

"Try just a little."

"I would like a whiskey-soda."

"It's not good for you."

"No. It's bad for me. Cole Porter wrote the words and the music. This knowledge that you're going mad for me."

"You know I like you to drink."

"Oh yes. Only it's bad for me."

When she goes, he thought. I'll have all I want. Not all I want but all there is. Ayee he was tired. Too tired. He was going to sleep a little while. He lay still and death was not there. It must have gone around another street. It went in pairs, on bicycles, and moved absolutely silently on the pavements.

No, he had never written about Paris. Not the Paris that he cared about. But what about the rest that he had never written?

What about the ranch and the silvered grey of the

sagebrush, the quick, clear water in the irrigation ditches, and the heavy green of the alfalfa. The trail went up into the hills and the cattle in the summer were shy as deer. The bawling and the steady noise and slow moving mass raising a dust as you brought them down in the fall. And behind the mountains, the clear sharpness of the peak in the evening light and, riding down along the trail in the moonlight, bright across the valley. Now he remembered coming down through the timber in the dark holding the horse's tail when you could not see and all the stories that he meant to write.

About the half-wit chore boy who was left at the ranch that time and told not to let anyone get any hay, and that old bastard from the Forks who had beaten the boy when he had worked for him stopping to get some feed. The boy refusing and the old man saying he would beat him again. The boy got the rifle from the kitchen and shot him when he tried to come into the barn and when they came back to the ranch he'd been dead a week, frozen in the corral, and the dogs had eaten a big part of him. But what was left you packed on a sled wrapped in a blanket and roped on and you got the boy to help you haul it, and the two of you took it out over the road on skis, and sixty miles down to town to turn the boy over. He having no idea that he would be arrested. Thinking he had done his duty and that you were his friend and he would be rewarded. He'd helped to haul the old man in so everybody could know how bad the old man had been and how he'd tried to steal some feed that didn't belong to him, and when the sheriff put the handcuffs on the boy he couldn't believe it. Then he'd started to cry. That was one story he had saved to write. He knew at least twenty good stories from out there and he had never written one. Why?

"You tell them why," he said.

"Why what, dear?"

"Why nothing."

She didn't drink so much, now, since she had him. But if he lived he would never write about her, he knew that now. Nor about any of them. The rich were dull and they drank too much, or they played too much backgammon. They were dull and they were repetitious. He remembered poor Julian and his romantic awe of them and how he had started a story once that began, "The very rich are different from you and me." And how someone had said to Julian, Yes they have more money. But that was not humorous to Julian. He thought they were a special glamorous race and when he found they weren't it wrecked him just as much as any other thing that wrecked him.

He had been contemptuous of those who wrecked. You did not have to like it because you understood it. He could beat anything, he thought, because no thing could hurt him if he did not care.

All right. Now he would not care for death. One thing he had always dreaded was the pain. He could stand pain as well as any man, until it went on too long, and wore him out, but here he had something that had hurt frightfully and just when he had felt it breaking him, the pain had stopped.

He remembered long ago when Williamson, the bombing officer, had been hit by a stick bomb some-one in a German patrol had thrown as he was coming in through the wire that night and, screaming, had begged everyone to kill him. He was a fat man, very brave, and a good officer, although addicted to fantastic shows. But that night he was caught in the wire, with a flare lighting him up and his bowels spilled out into the wire, so when they brought him in, alive, they had to cut him loose. Shoot me, Harry. For Christ sake shoot me. They had had an argument one time about our Lord never sending you anything you could not bear and someone's theory had been that meant that at a certain time the pain passed you out automatically. But he had always remembered Williamson that night. Nothing passed out Williamson until he gave him all his morphine tablets that he had always saved to use himself and then they did not work right away.

Still this now, that he had, was very easy; and if it was no worse as it went on there was nothing to worry about. Except that he would rather be in better company.

He thought a little about the company that he would like to have.

No, he thought, when everything you do, you do too long, and do too late, you can't expect to find the people still there. The people all are gone. The party's over and you are with your hostess now.

I'm getting as bored with dying as with everything else, he thought.

"It's a bore," he said out loud.

"What is, my dear?"

"Anything you do too bloody long."

He looked at her face between him and the fire. She was leaning back in the chair and the firelight shone on her pleasantly lined face and he could see that she was sleepy. He heard the hyena make a noise just outside the range of the fire.

"I've been writing," he said. "But I got tired."

"Do you think you will be able to sleep?"

"Pretty sure. Why don't you turn in?"

"I like to sit here with you."

"Do you feel anything strange?" he asked her.

"No. Just a little sleepy."

"I do," he said.

He had just felt death come by again.

"You know the only thing I've never lost is curiosity," he said to her.

"You've never lost anything. You're the most complete man I've ever known."

"Christ," he said. "How little a woman knows. What is that? Your intuition?"

Because, just then, death had come and rested its head on the foot of the cot and he could smell its breath.

"Never believe any of that about a scythe and a skull," he told her. "It can be two bicycle policemen as easily, or be a bird. Or it can have a wide snout like a hyena."

It had moved up on him now, but it had no shape anymore. It simply occupied space.

"Tell it to go away."

It did not go away but moved a little closer.

"You've got a hell of a breath," he told it. "You stinking bastard."

It moved up closer to him still and now he could not speak to it, and when it saw he could not speak it came a little closer, and now he tried to send it away without speaking, but it moved in on him so its weight was all upon his chest, and while it crouched there and he could not move, or speak, he heard the woman say, "Bwana is asleep now. Take the cot up very gently and carry it into the tent."

He could not speak to tell her to make it go away and it crouched now, heavier, so he could not breathe. And then, while they lifted the cot, suddenly it was all right and the weight went from his chest.

It was morning and had been morning for some time and he heard the plane. It showed very tiny and then made a wide circle and the boys ran out and lit the fires, using kerosene, and piled on grass so there were two big smudges at each end of the level place and the morning breeze blew them toward the camp and the plane circled twice more, low this time, and then glided down and leveled off and landed smoothly and, coming walking toward him, was old Compton in slacks, a tweed jacket and a brown felt hat.

"What's the matter, old cock?" Compton said.

"Bad leg," he told him. "Will you have some breakfast?"

"Thanks. I'll just have some tea. It's the Puss Moth you know. I won't be able to take the Memsahib. There's only room for one. Your lorry is on the way."

Helen had taken Compton aside and was speaking to him. Compton came back more cheery than ever.

"We'll get you right in," he said. "I'll be back for the Mem. Now I'm afraid I'll have to stop at Arusha to refuel. We'd better get going."

"What about the tea?"

"I don't really care about it you know."

The boys had picked up the cot and carried it around the green tents and down along the rock and out onto the plain and along past the smudges that were burning brightly now, the grass all consumed, and the wind fanning the fire, to the little plane. It was difficult getting him in, but once in he lay back in the leather seat, and the leg was stuck straight out to one side of the seat where Compton sat. Compton started the motor and got in. He waved to Helen and to the boys and, as the clatter moved into the old familiar roar, they swung around with Compie watching for warthog holes and roared, bumping, along the stretch between the fires and with the last bump rose and he saw them all standing below, waving, and the camp beside the hill, flattening now, and the plain spreading, clumps of trees, and the bush flattening, while the game trails ran now smoothly to the dry

water holes, and there was a new water that he had never known of. The zebra, small rounded backs now, and the wildebeeste, big-headed dots seeming to climb as they moved in long fingers across the plain, now scattering as the shadow came toward them, they were tiny now, and the movement had no gallop, and the plain as far as you could see, grey-yellow now and ahead old Compie's tweed back and the brown felt hat. Then they were over the first hills and the wildebeeste were trailing up them, and then they were over mountains with sudden depths of green-rising forest and the solid bamboo slopes, and then the heavy forest again, sculptured into peaks and hollows until they crossed, and hills sloped down and then another plain, hot now, and purple brown, bumpy, with heat and Compie looking back to see how he was riding. Then there were other mountains dark ahead. And then instead of going on to Arusha they turned left, he evidently figured that they had the gas, and looking down he saw a pink sifting cloud, moving over the ground, and in the air, like the first snow in a blizzard, that comes from nowhere, and he knew the locusts were coming up from the South. Then they began to climb and they were going to the East it seemed, and then it darkened and they were in a storm, the rain so thick it seemed like flying through a waterfall, and then they were out and Compie turned his head and grinned and pointed and there, ahead, all he could see, as wide as all the world, great, high, and unbelievably white in the sun, was the square top of Kilimanjaro. And then he knew that there was where he was going.

Just then the hyena stopped whimpering in the night and started to make a strange, human, almost crying sound. The woman heard it and stirred uneasily. She did not wake. In her dream she was at the house on Long Island and it was the night before her daughter's debut. Somehow her father was there and he had been very rude. Then the noise the hyena made was so loud she woke and for a moment she did not know where she was and she was very afraid. Then she took the flashlight and shone it on the other cot that they had carried in after Harry had gone to sleep. She could see his bulk under the mosquito bar but somehow he had gotten his leg out and it hung down alongside the cot. The dressings had all come down and she could not look at it.

"Molo," she called, "Molo! Molo!"

Then she said, "Harry, Harry!" Then her voice rising, "Harry! Please, Oh Harry!"

There was no answer and she could not hear him breathing.

Outside the tent the hyena made the same strange noise that had awakened her. But she did not hear him for the beating of her heart.

F. Scott Fitzgerald:

Pasting It Together

Shoring up the fragments against the ruin left in the wake of that psychophysical storm: a crack-up

In a previous article this writer told about his realization that what he had before him was not the dish that he had ordered for his forties. In fact—since he and the dish were one, he described himself as a cracked plate, the kind that one wonders whether it is worth preserving. Your editor thought that the article suggested too many aspects without regarding them closely, and probably many readers felt the same way—and there are always those to whom all self-revelation is contemptible, unless it ends with a noble thanks to the gods for the Unconquerable Soul.

But I had been thanking the gods too long, and thanking them for nothing. I wanted to put a lament into my record, without even the background of the Eugenean Hills to give it color. There weren't any Eugenean Hills that I could see.

Sometimes, though, the cracked plate has to be retained in the pantry, has to be kept in service as a household necessity. It can never again be warmed on the stove nor shuffled with the other plates in the dishpan; it will not be brought out for company, but it will do to hold crackers late at night or to go into the ice box under leftovers. . . .

Hence this sequel—a cracked plate's further history.

Now the standard cure for one who is sunk is to consider those in actual destitution or physical suffering—this is an all-weather beatitude for gloom in general and fairly salutory daytime advice for everyone. But at three o'clock in the morning, a forgotten package has the same tragic importance as a death sentence, and the cure doesn't work—and in a real dark night of the soul it is always three o'clock in the morning, day after day. At that hour the tendency is to refuse to face things as long as possible by retiring into an infantile dream—but one is continually startled out of this by various contacts with the world. One meets these occasions as quickly and carelessly as possible and retires once more back into the dream, hoping that things will adjust themselves by some great material or spiritual bonanza. But as the withdrawal persists there is less and less chance of the bonanza—one is not waiting for the fade-out of a single sorrow, but rather being an unwilling witness of an execution, the disintegration of one's own personality. . . .

Unless madness or drugs or drink come into it, this phase comes to a dead end, eventually, and is succeeded by a vacuous quiet. In this you can try to estimate what has been sheered away and what is left. Only when this quiet came to me, did I realize that I had gone through two parallel experiences.

The first time was twenty years ago, when I left Princeton in junior year with a complaint diagnosed as malaria. (It transpired, through an X ray taken a dozen years later, that it had been tuberculosis—a mild case, and after a few months of rest I went back to college.) But I had lost certain offices, the chief one was the presidency of the Triangle Club, a musical comedy idea, and also I dropped back a class. To me college would never be the same. There were to be no badges of pride, no medals after all. It seemed on one March afternoon that I had lost every single thing I wanted—and that night was the first time that I hunted down the specter of womanhood that, for a little while, makes everything else seem unimportant.

Years later I realized that my failure as a big shot in college was all right—instead of serving on committees, I took a beating on English poetry; when I got the idea of what it was all about, I set about learning how to write. On Shaw's principle that "If you don't get what you like, you better like what you get," it was a lucky break—at the moment it was a harsh and bitter business to know that my career as a leader of men was over.

Since that day I have not been able to fire a bad servant, and I am astonished and impressed by people who can. Some old desire for personal dominance was broken and gone. Life around me was a solemn dream, and I lived on the letters I wrote to a girl in another city. A man does not recover from such jolts—he becomes a different person and, eventually, the new person finds new things to care about.

The other episode parallel to my current situation took place after the war, when I had again over-extended my flank. It was one of those tragic loves doomed for lack of money, and one day the girl closed it out on the basis of common sense. During a long summer of despair I wrote a novel instead of letters, so it came out all right, but it came out all right for a different person. The man with the jingle of money in his pocket who married the girl a year later would always cherish an abiding distrust, an animosity,

"I can't write anymore," Fitzgerald told the editor. Then write about why you can't, he suggested; and this, the less-well-known sequel to The Crack-Up *(February, 1936), appeared in March, 1936.*

35

toward the leisure class—not the conviction of a revolutionist but the smouldering hatred of a peasant. In the years since then I have never been able to stop wondering where my friends' money came from, nor to stop thinking that at one time a sort of *droit de seigneur* might have been exercised to give one of them my girl.

For sixteen years I lived pretty much as this latter person, distrusting the rich, yet working for money with which to share their mobility and the grace that some of them brought into their lives. During this time I had plenty of the usual horses shot from under me— I remember some of their names—*Punctured Pride, Thwarted Expectation, Faithless, Show-off, Hard Hit, Never Again*. And after a while I wasn't twenty-five, then not even thirty-five, and nothing was quite as good. But in all those years I don't remember a moment of discouragement. I saw honest men through moods of suicidal gloom—some of them gave up and died; others adjusted themselves and went on to a larger success than mine; but my morale never sank below the level of self-disgust when I had put on some unsightly personal show. Trouble has no necessary connection with discouragement—discouragement has a germ of its own, as different from trouble as arthritis is different from a stiff joint.

When a new sky cut off the sun last spring, I didn't at first relate it to what had happened fifteen or twenty years ago. Only gradually did a certain family resemblance come through—an overextension of the flank, a burning of the candle at both ends; a call upon physical resources that I did not command, like a man overdrawing at his bank. In its impact this blow was more violent than the other two but it was the same in kind—a feeling that I was standing at twilight on a deserted range, with an empty rifle in my hands and the targets down. No problem set—simply a silence with only the sound of my own breathing.

In this silence there was a vast irresponsibility toward every obligation, a deflation of all my values. A passionate belief in order, a disregard of motives or consequences in favor of guesswork and prophecy, a feeling that craft and industry would have a place in any world—one by one, these and other convictions were swept away. I saw that the novel, which at my maturity was the strongest and supplest medium for conveying thought and emotion from one human being to another, was becoming subordinated to a mechanical and communal art that, whether in the hands of Hollywood merchants or Russian idealists, was capable of reflecting only the tritest thought, the most obvious emotion. It was an art in which words were subordinate to images, where personality was worn down to the inevitable low gear of collaboration. As long past as 1930, I had a hunch that the talkies would make even the best-selling novelist as archaic as silent pictures. People still read, if only Professor Canby's book of the month—curious children nosed at the slime of Mr. Tiffany Thayer in the drugstore libraries —but there was a rankling indignity, that to me had become almost an obsession, in seeing the power of the written word subordinated to another power, a more glittering, a grosser power. . . .

I set that down as an example of what haunted me during the long night—this was something I could neither accept nor struggle against, something which tended to make my efforts obsolescent, as the chain stores have crippled the small merchant, an exterior force, unbeatable—

(I have the sense of lecturing now, looking at a watch on the desk before me and seeing how many more minutes—)

Well, when I had reached this period of silence, I was forced into a measure that no one ever adopts voluntarily: I was impelled to think. God, was it difficult! The moving about of great secret trunks. In the first exhausted halt, I wondered whether I had ever thought. After a long time I came to these conclusions, just as I write them here:

(1) That I had done very little thinking, save within the problems of my craft. For twenty years a certain man had been my intellectual conscience. That was Edmund Wilson.

(2) That another man represented my sense of the "good life," though I saw him once in a decade, and since then he might have been hung. He is in the fur business in the Northwest and wouldn't like his name set down here. But in difficult situations I had tried to think what *he* would have thought, how *he* would have acted.

(3) That a third contemporary had been an artistic conscience to me—I had not imitated his infectious style, because my own style, such as it is, was formed before he published anything, but there was an awful pull toward him when I was on a spot.

(4) That a fourth man had come to dictate my relations with other people when these relations were successful: how to do, what to say. How to make people at least momentarily happy (in apposition to Mrs. Post's theories of how to make everyone thoroughly uncomfortable with a sort of systematized vulgarity). This always confused me and made me want to go out and get drunk, but this man had seen the game, analyzed it and beaten it, and his word was good enough for me.

(5) That my political conscience had scarcely existed for ten years save as an element of irony in my stuff. When I became again concerned with the system I should function under, it was a man much younger than myself who brought it to me, with a mixture of passion and fresh air.

So there was not an "I" anymore—not a basis on which I could organize my self-respect—save my limitless capacity for toil that it seemed I possessed no more. It was strange to have no self—to be like a little boy left alone in a big house, who knew that now he could do anything he wanted to do, but found that there was nothing that he wanted to do—

(The watch is past the hour and I have barely reached my thesis. I have some doubts as to whether this is of general interest but if anyone wants more, there is plenty left, and your editor will tell you. If you've had enough, say so—but not too loud, because I have the feeling that someone, I'm not sure who, is sound asleep—someone who could have helped me to keep my shop open. It wasn't Lenin, and it wasn't God.) ⧢

Arnold Gingrich:

Scott, Ernest and Whoever

When Fitzgerald and Hemingway both
sat at the moveable feast,
where was the head of the table?

Scott Fitzgerald draws the finest and purest tone from the English language of any writer now alive—in fact, *I* think, of any writer since Walter Pater."

It was a late June night in Bimini in 1936 and Janie, who had just turned twenty-seven, shushed me as if I were an unruly kid making rude noises in church. She was Mrs. G. Grant Mason Jr. then, and I had met her only a matter of hours before. Now she was looking at me as if she thought even that had been too soon.

"We don't say things like that around here," she said.

"Who doesn't?"

"None of us." I thought the stress on the "us" was just a touch heavier than it had been on the "none," and since there are some skins thicker than mine, I was ready to take instant umbrage. I thought it could be interpreted as meaning that I was certainly not one of "us," and I remember thinking of what my mother had always told me when I was very small, "Now don't you hang around one minute after you see you're not wanted," but this was once I disobeyed my mother. I hung around, and we got to know each other a little bit better and in fact, almost twenty years later, and after four marriages to other people, we got married ourselves. But that night she was just a member in high standing of the Hemingway camp, warning me that if I valued my own much more recent membership in his circle, I'd better not mention Fitzgerald or I might be out on my ear the next day.

I thought the warning was exaggerated, and reminded her that Hemingway had asked me to bring Fitzgerald down to fish with him when the *Pilar* was first acquired, only a little over a year earlier. (This wasn't exactly true. I had suggested bringing Scott down, and Ernest had said fine, and it was Scott who had refused, saying he couldn't face Ernest again, while Ernest was such a success and he was such a

The three preceding contributions were received, edited and published by Gingrich, Esquire's founding editor and present publisher. In 1966, after the posthumous publication of Hemingway's Paris memoirs, A Moveable Feast, *A. G. wrote his impressions of both Hemingway and Fitzgerald.*

failure.) I asked her if she knew Fitzgerald and she said she "didn't think so," which I thought a damned peculiar answer.

"But can't we talk about somebody else? I don't want to draw you any diagrams, but he's just not a good topic."

There were people still coming in and out of the lounge in The Compleat Angler, where we sat. The Hemingways had all retired to the "college," which was what the Mouse, little Patrick, had called the cottage where they were staying, but Pauline's sister Ginny was still dropping around now and then, and so was Dick Cooper, a great friend of Jane's, who had an African plantation.

So I suppose I must finally have taken the hint, and probably with something heavily if belatedly gallant, like "Sure, let's talk about you," because ultimately of course that's what we did wind up talking about. But Fitzgerald was abandoned, as an unsafe topic, as long as there were people around.

Thinking back on it now, it occurs to me that at that very moment the presses were turning, back in Chicago, with the August '36 issue of Esquire containing the first printed appearance of *The Snows of Kilimanjaro* with its line, later changed, referring to "poor Scott Fitzgerald," but I'm sure I never gave that a thought at the time.

Sometime within the last couple of years, having occasion to look something up in *Tender Is the Night*, I found a copy on our shelves at home, inscribed in Scott's unmistakable hand and apparently with an eyebrow pencil of a rather light brown shade, as follows: "Now to all the other charms there is a physical one—and so now I may cease trying to please you and will only (glow) quite (naturally) from myself. As this delight in me comes from you it is very good." The "glow" could have been "flow" and the "naturally" could have been "rationally," and there was a faint line, as if to cross out, drawn through the "only" and part of the "glow" or "flow."

Janie's books and mine have become higgledy-piggledy, especially in the course of our last couple of moves, and when I showed it to her at the time, she couldn't imagine where it had come from.

"Hell, I thought you told me you never knew Scott!"

"Did I ever say that? I must have known him sometime around Paris. I never liked him. I still think you're wrong, with this great Fitzgerald thing of yours. He had nothing to say, and he kept insisting on saying it."

"You said you 'didn't think' you knew him, and I thought it was damned funny at the time."

"What time was that?"

"In Bimini in '36. Besides, if you'd known him around Paris, you'd have been about fourteen, *Tender* wasn't published until '34, Scott wasn't around Paris after—"

"Your memory! My god, I can't remember what I said last week and you expect me—hey, you know what? Maybe it was Dorothy Hale's book. I used to have a lot of her things. . . ."

"Dorothy jumped out of that Hampshire House window in '38—well, yeah, it could have been, at that—this was published in '34 and. . . ."

"Your memory again. Have you ever thought of teaching elephants? Retarded elephants, of course, something like these remedial reading classes. . . ."

Well, I suppose it is too much to expect a woman to remember everybody who ever made any sort of pass at her, even with an eyebrow pencil, but still—could anybody not remember, if it was Scott Fitzgerald?

He was the idol of my high-school days, right after the poets, like Rupert Brooke, Ezra Pound, and e. e. cummings, and a good six years before I'd ever heard of Hemingway.

In Central High School in Grand Rapids in 1920 I remember confiding in Margaret Robinson, a young teacher of French, to the extent of telling her I found it hard to understand how F. Scott Fitzgerald, in *This Side of Paradise*, had been able to read my inmost thoughts and ascribe them to a fictional character called Amory Blaine, and how dashed I was when she said she was sure that lots of boys had felt that way about lots of books, ever since books began to be printed, though it was the best excuse she'd heard that year for why one boy was behind

in his written French exercises.

Later, Fitzgerald himself told me something somewhat similar, when we were talking about Rupert Brooke, saying:

"Of course, he was the idol of all of us; I was not too old, just as you were not too young, back there around 1917, to have fallen under his spell."

Scott's own most enduring idol, though, next after Hobey Baker, must have been Ernest Hemingway. One of his last letters, in the Fall of '40 before he died, was to Ernest, a warm letter, full of ungrudging admiration for *For Whom the Bell Tolls*, the book that had the kind of huge popular success that Scott had himself hoped to obtain with *Tender Is the Night*. And although in the decade before that Hemingway had done and said, and even written, many things to hurt him, throughout that time Scott had always expressed, both to Ernest and about him to others, the same unstinted enthusiasm for his work that had impelled him to bring Hemingway to Scribner's attention at a time when he himself was a hot literary property for any publisher and Hemingway was still, after one abortive appearance under the Boni & Liveright banner, relatively unknown.

After an article of Scott's had appeared that Ernest thought was too cry-babily self-revelatory, he wrote Scott about it in the most brutal way, using language that you'd hesitate to use on a yellow dog. It can't be quoted, because none of Hemingway's letters can be, under the terms of his will, but Scott let me see it, and it was shameful.

The most that Scott ever let himself say against Ernest, and I know how strong the provocation must have been, was that one wonderful crack that "Ernest was always ready to lend a helping hand to the one on the rung above him," and it was mild compared to what he would have been fully justified in saying.

When *A Moveable Feast* came out, with its large sections about both Scott and Zelda, I was prepared to hate it, because I had always felt that Scott brought out the bully in Ernest, and I had resented bitterly for years the way Hemingway treated Fitzgerald in life, at a time when it mattered and had a direct bearing on Scott's own professional scorecard.

Scott had died in '40 at low ebb, his books out of print, his last novel unfinished and thinking of himself as an utter failure. His last letter to me, written not long after the one to Hemingway about *For Whom the Bell Tolls*, referred to

The Last Tycoon, the book on which he was then engaged, as "a book I confidently expect to sell all of a thousand copies." In contrast, he thought of Hemingway as at the flood tide of success.

By the time Hemingway shot himself, in 1961, the tables had begun to turn, and Fitzgerald's literary standing had soared, on the wings of several "revivals" from 1945 on, while Ernest's had begun to ebb.

So when I first heard there was anything about Scott in *A Moveable Feast*, I expected the worst, thinking that if Ernest had been catty and cruel about him when Scott was down and he was up, there was no telling how vicious he could be after the score had changed.

But I soon saw, after reading a few pages of *A Moveable Feast*, that this was the old Ernest speaking, probably because he had sense enough not to kill with improvements the old notes from the Twenties on which it was based, and by the time I came to the Fitzgerald parts I felt like cheering where I had expected to swear.

Of course, by the time *A Moveable Feast* was published it was all academic anyway, as Scott and Ernest were both dead. Still, in fairness, I did feel impelled to correct in print, as soon as possible, one imputation that I knew was wrong.

In general, I felt that Hemingway's portrayal of Fitzgerald was the best portrait of him ever done in print, for as I read it there Scott stood again alive, at his inimitably exasperating best and worst. It simply *is* Scott, to the last breath and the least bat of an eyelash, and Scott would have recognized himself in every line, something that is true of only a very few of the things that have been written about him.

There was, however, that one exception, the matter of Scott's being ill-equipped, or insufficiently equipped, as a man. Ordinarily, that's not a question you write about for general print, about anybody, dead or alive, but *A Moveable Feast* had given the matter a certain ineffable currency.

So I recalled the day in the early Spring of '35 when, having flown down to Baltimore from New York, I arrived at 1307 Park Avenue at the approximate time of the milkman's morning rounds, and found a note pinned to the front door bidding me to come right on up to the top floor. There Scott was working, clad in a grubby, faded-plaid flannel bathrobe, perched on a high stool and with a row of empty tumblers ranged alongside and away from his elbow.

"I will greet the editor of Esquire," he said, crawling rather shakily down, "ceremoniously," he added, essaying as he said the last a courtly bow worthy of Cyrano making a ground-sweeping gesture with his plume. The one hitch was that the cord of the bathrobe was caught in the grand downward swoop of the right arm, revealing all that F. Scott Fitzgerald had to reveal.

It was unimportant then, and would be now, had *A Moveable Feast* not raised the question. So I chose to answer it, from eyewitness authority, the way Rolls-Royce always answered all inquiries as to just how much horsepower they hide under their distinctive hood, with just one word: *adequate*.

Scott in my eyes, and even in such dégagé attire, always had an elegance surpassing even that of the Arrow Collar Man who had been the model we all grew up admiring. So I can see him now in my mind's eye, even more vividly, as he looked that day just before we were sitting down to lunch, four of us, with his daughter Scottie, then fourteen, and a Virginia friend, Elizabeth Lemmon.

Typically, because my memory always astonishes me more by its sharp-focus selectivity than by its tenacity, I can't remember a damn thing that the other three of us wore, but I can see every detail of what Scott was wearing, as he turned away to put on an old heather-tweed jacket, and they are as plain to me now as if I were looking at them in a shop window: white shoes with a dark brown saddle, pipe-clayed like a British soldier's belt, grey flannel slacks, venerable but gracefully aged and still supremely well cut, and a black pullover that, aside from being vastly becoming, contrived to make him look, though he was then thirty-eight, as if he could never seem to be more than six or seven years out of Princeton.

(In contrast, a mental snapshot of Ernest at about the same time, pulled at random from memory's file, shows a hulking creature looking as if he were about to burst the seams of a blue tweed suit [cut by O'Rossen in the Place Vendôme—a ladies' tailor, for god sake] with the sleeves and the pant legs both too short, an oatmeal flannel shirt with the collar unevenly turned down and a russet wool tie askew, with pebbly-grained thick-soled shoes of a wrong shade of liverish brown. The general effect is that of items left over from a rummage sale.)

Scottie was the most beguiling of children. When I think of her as she was then the phrase that comes to mind is that of the headstone that used to be up near Grant's Tomb, commemorating "an amiable child." She struck me then, and for that matter does all over again whenever I see her now, as the most supremely normal creature imaginable, and I marvel that she could be the product of a pair as zany in their different ways as Scott and Zelda.

But as a father Scott was so impossibly exacting and demanding that no child, actual or even fictional, could ever have come up to his perfectionist standards of behavior to be expected of others.

I really think that this, more than alcohol, was the key to most of his troubles. The great tragedy of Scott Fitzgerald's life, it seems to me, was not any one of the several minor tragedies on which, successively, he was wont to blame the wreckage of his life. Other writers have lived lives more sorrow-filled and disappointment-packed than his, from Charles Lamb to Clarence Day, to cite only the first two that come to mind.

But his big trouble was that he was a perfectionist in his living as much as in his writing. He wanted to live his best stories more than he wanted to write them. And in a sense he almost always wrote for his living, at least whenever it came to a choice between that and living for his work.

Then, too, Scott had that strange, almost mystic Celtic tendency to enjoy ill luck as some people enjoy ill health. He liked to dramatize to himself the inevitability of his latest and his next defeats.

If anything was wrong in his life, and something always seemed to be, even during his Long Island and Riviera days, when the world appeared to be his oyster, then everything was all wrong, and he seemed rather to enjoy saying so. It could be something as tragic as Zelda's failure to return more than momentarily to sanity, or as trivial as Scottie's failure, at fourteen, to pick up the right fork without a momentary hesitation, or to react instantly, and precisely as he thought she should, to a given set piece of reading that he had chosen for her.

He was the same way about a story of his own. At a time when everything was askew, when his Hollywood-contract options had been dropped and his freelance film work had been one disappointment after another, when his health was febrile and his fiscal situation precarious, he niggled over trifling details of the Pat Hobby stories, revising some of them four times and sometimes even as much as a week after they had achieved print.

In life and in letters Scott was such a perfectionist that he was prone to exaggerate minor excellences and minor defects away out of their proportionate importance to the average perception.

Failure always fascinated him. I think that's why he enjoyed writing about Pat Hobby more than almost any other character that came out of his pen since that first far-off Amory Blaine back at the beginning of his writing career.

And if through most of his life as a writer it could be said that he wrote for his living, rather than living for his work, more perhaps than any other author of our time, then paradoxically it could be said that the two exceptions were at the end and at the beginning—when he was frantically racing time to get the reject *Romantic Egoist* rewritten as *This Side of Paradise*, to get to be a success in time to win Zelda, and again at the end, in his Pat Hobby period, those last two desperately difficult years of life, when he was racing time to finish *The Last Tycoon*.

As Scottie said of the Pat Hobby stories, when she had at last prevailed upon Scribner's to publish them after I had failed for eleven years to get anybody else to do so, "In those dark, grim days, when life was such a struggle for Daddy, the fact that the old humor came out so strong in these stories was reassurance that somehow things would turn out right in the end."

Things did turn out right, of course, though not in time for him to know it. Scott died thinking that Ernest was the greatest of successes, and that he was himself a failure, an example, an exhibit of the topic that for so long had held his interest, like the man in the O. Henry story who went around trying to find out the meaning of the phrase, "man about town," and could never learn it, only to have it applied to himself in his obituary.

His own obits were perfunctory. As estimates of his stature in American letters, they ranged from niggardly to nonsensical, and almost without exception everybody seemed bent on remembering him for his worst book, *Flappers and Philosophers*, and forgetting all about the book for which he is today best remembered, *The Great Gatsby*. In most of the newspapers at the time, that was given mere passing mention, if any at all, while most of the space went to *This Side of Paradise* which compares to *The Great Gatsby* about as George Moore's *Confessions of a Young Man* (with its sentence about "the young actress with whom I used to sit on the stairs at midnight with") compares to his *Esther Waters*.

And it took *The New Yorker* to tell the great grey and always oh so accurate New York *Times* that *The Beautiful and Damned* was not "a book of short stories" nor was its name *The Beautiful and THE Damned*.

Scott himself, in those kidding letters he used to write when he was in his nearest to total eclipse of both fame and fortune, answering routine inquiries with made-up citations of nonexistent tomes about aspects of his work, was much closer to the mark. Some of those scholarly works that have already appeared must be only harbingers of the minute dissection to which his *oeuvre* is ultimately destined.

But most of his worries, like most worries, were vain. He worried so about Scottie, as his letters to her show, and today she is about as successful as a woman can be, in every way, and as a person one he could only have been proud of.

Remembering how much more he enjoyed living than writing, before the first of those emotional blackouts that used to leave him unfit to enjoy either, and remembering how the bent of his wild and willful nature always inclined to defeatism, frustration, negation and failure, it is a matter of wonder that he left any perfectly realized work at all and not that he left so little. The five novels (and by no means least *The Beautiful and Damned*) will always be worth reading, though it is doubtful that more than one of them will always be read. *The Great Gatsby* will undoubtedly be both read and studied a century hence, as it is today, when *Gone With the Wind* will in all probability long since have lived up to its title, as it almost has already. Among the half-dozen volumes of short stories, there are probably not more than a half-dozen tales that will appeal to anthologists of our great-grandchildren's day as being (to use Scott's own early phrase) "worth preserving until the ennui of changing fashions suppresses me, my books, and them together."

Oddly enough, or perhaps appropriately enough in view of his long fixation on failure, his most beautiful book, *Tender Is the Night*, was in a sense the most ugly and was the least perfectly realized piece of work of all five of his novels. It was a magnificent failure in many ways, and it contains passages of haunting loveliness, but it suffered from the very phenomenon with which it was concerned, a split personality. It was really the malformed twin embryo of two books, one of which might well have been a masterpiece. That book, which ought to have a prominent place on the shelf of the great unwritten books of lost time, was to have been titled simply *Dick Diver*. Scott was aiming high at the time. He obviously wanted to leave the world a *Tom Jones*. It might just possibly have been an even better book than *The Great Gatsby*, but the story got lost and twisted and came out imperfectly and misshapenly as an unassimilated half of *Tender Is the Night*.

For about eight years or so, along with *The Compleat Angler*, I reread both *The Great Gatsby* and *A Farewell to Arms* once a year. The one that made me give up the habit was not *The Great Gatsby*, which I feel sure I could reread every year for the rest of my life. But the set pieces began to obtrude from *A Farewell to Arms*, and coincidences began to stick out like exposed plumbing, of which I had hardly been aware the first few times. So I had to give up, and decide to reread Scrope's *Days and Nights of Salmon Fishing in the Tweed*, as *The Compleat Angler*'s one lone companion.

So where is Ernest's Gatsby now, hardly more than one scant lustrum after his death? In contrast to the ripple caused at the time by Scott's passing, Hemingway's was the shot quite literally heard round the world.

I honestly think now that in the long run he will have to rest his chances on his first real novel—not the Sherwood Anderson parody *The Torrents of Spring* that is still so listed—but that book from the Autumn of '26, *The Sun Also Rises*. That one will bear the repeated rereadings that form the kind of test none of the others can pass.

Scott would not have enjoyed the last laugh. He could write Ernest, as he did both early and late in his career, that "I envy you like hell," and mean it. But he simply could not have embraced the thought that he himself might ultimately emerge as a better writer than Hemingway. He saw himself as, at best, a sort of John the Baptist, foretelling the Coming. He was so "gone" on Ernest, from the early Twenties on, when he began trying to enlist other writers into a sort of great unpaid claque (I remember Glenway Wescott as one who refused to join) that the degree of his admiration for Hemingway was, as among grown men, almost embarrassing. He so palpably modeled his medieval hero on Ernest, for the abortive serial that ran for a few numbers in *Redbook*, that even Edwin Balmer, himself one of the early admirers and encouragers of Hemingway, must have been glad when the series came to a halt. To anyone who knew both Scott and Ernest, the effect was as mawkish as would be the unwitting reading, before realizing what one was doing, of the "crush" notes between schoolchildren.

Of the two of them, I had always thought Scott was the one who might kid himself, that Ernest never would. When I first knew him, in '31 and '32, Ernest seemed an almost-hermit, basically interested in the only changeless things there are, the woods, waters and the denizens thereof, and filled with both suspicion and contempt for the fickle and evanescent "tea-drinking, back-scratching, logrolling literary world." He used to brag about being possessed of an infallible and built-in shit-detector, and boast about his ability to spot a phony of any kind from a mile away. When we used to talk on the runs back and forth to the fishing grounds, and I would ask him about this one or that one, I soon saw that the men of his acquaintance were instantly classifiable into only three categories, shits, or rummies, or pretty good citizens.

"You and I are the only peasants here," he said in '36 in Bimini, indicating with a hint of a wave of one hand the cluster of the rich and fashionable, the wealthy sportsmen types, who were in sight at the time. I took it for humility, but before very long I wasn't so sure. Within the year the nickname "Papa" had begun to spread well outside the immediate circle of his acquaintance. It had begun through his habit of calling women "Daughter," thus practically insuring the appropriate response. Nobody, except possibly from Oak Park High days, ever called him Ernie. And few except Scott, of those who had known him in the Twenties in Paris, called him anything but Hem. Scott always called him Ernest, and so did the members of his family, including his brother Leicester (Lester the Pester, Ernest always called *him*), although Pauline fell in with the growing Papa phase.

Within another year or so after that, I began to feel that the old humility, the "to thine own self be true" stuff that I had really always thought he believed, was being eroded by more than a touch of what Knute Rockne used to warn the Notre Dame team against between halves, the tendency toward "believing your own press clippings."

This cropped up once during a week when we were fishing out of Key West, when I had flown down from Chicago to do battle with him over the completed manuscript of *To Have and Have Not*. Next only to *Across the River and Into the Trees* (which I thought Janie summed up well at the time as *Across the Liver and Into the Crise*), his worst book, certainly, was *To Have and Have Not*, and I always felt guilty about it, because when he sent me the finished script I felt, based only on my own hard-earned knowledge of what is and what isn't libelous, that large gobs of this were libel *per se*. Three people were libeled right up to their eyebrows. They were Dos Passos, and Janie, and her then husband, Grant Mason. Since I knew all three, I could see through every reference to them as if through a screen door, and suggested that all the portions in which they were involved would have to be heavily reworked, if allowed to stand at all.

On the phone Ernest said that if I would come down to go over the parts I felt had to be changed, he'd get Moe, his lawyer, to come down from New York at the same time.

"It isn't that I don't respect your experience," he said; "on this subject I'm sure you're as great an expert as the burnt monkey on the subject of hot soup, but after all you're not a lawyer and he is, and I'd like the added security of somebody to check the checker."

The week was funny. It was like those Paris riots, where the rioters and the cops would lay down their brickbats and nightsticks respectively, and adjourn two hours for lunch, then come back and pick them up again. It was just like that with us. Ernest and Pauline and Moe and I would "riot" all morning, then Ernest and I would go out fishing for the afternoon, then in the evening we would "riot" again.

It was the first time I had ever had any kind of quarrel with Ernest, as in dealing with his copy for the magazine we had always operated on the basis that I would make no changes of any kind, but would suggest changes, by wire or telephone, only if impelled to do so by considerations of libel, invasion of privacy, obscenity (then much stricter than now, when anything goes). Nothing had ever come up that couldn't be settled on one quick and always amiable exchange. He had always behaved like "the old pro" that he prided himself on being.

But now he began behaving like a stuck pig, squealing his head off. The parts about Dos Passos which, now that I think of it, were really no worse than the Pilot Fish portions of the last chapter of *A Moveable Feast*, he undertook to solve by a neat stratagem:

"You know all I have to do to get Dos to okay everything in here that you object to about him? All I have to do is tell him *you* don't like it! That shakes *you* up a little, doesn't it? Moe, you draw up the tightest-ass release you can dream up, and I'll get it signed."

Then to me again: "You know what Dos thinks of you? He thinks you're a shit, that's what he thinks of you. Who had to get Dos into your magazine in the first place? Who had to get Dos to let you have the piece about the Quintanilla exhibition that he and I did together—when Dos had promised his part to *The New Republic*? For chris'sake, come down here and try to tell me how to write about one of my oldest friends!"

"But Ernest, I thought your defense of that part was that it *isn't* about Dos Passos. I frankly don't see how I can draw up a release for a man to sign that isn't *about* him—" This from Moe, the lawyer, who was quickly cut off:

"*Defense*, for chris'sake, so now I'm the defendant. Jesus Christ, between a lawyer and an editor, a poor working stiff hasn't got a chance."

Changing tactics, and apparently on the ground that the best defense is a good offense, he let me have it next on the Janie parts, shrewdly sensing that my interest in them might not be altogether academic.

"Goddamn editor comes down to Bimini and sees a blonde, and he hasn't been the same since! Here I thought we had a Mennonite editor."

"Oh, come on, Ernest, Arnold's *wife's* a blonde." This from Pauline.

I was on a sticky wicket and afraid I showed it. I didn't see how Ernest or Pauline could know that I had been seeing Janie in New York, until suddenly I remembered that after the first time Jane had gone on to Acapulco with Pauline's sister Ginny. Maybe what one knew they all knew.

"Gotta come into court with clean hands, doesn't he, counselor?" But Moe seemed to have lost the thread of the argument.

"But I won't be the one to come into court," I tried to riposte, feebly.

"Court, my ass. You know yourself, Pauline, that Jane was flattered when people took her for Mrs. Macomber in that story. Didn't she tell you so?"

"Well, not in so many words, but I can't imagine that her husband would exactly feel set up about it."

"Maybe I could fix up the parts about him—not that I admit that there are any—you understand this is all privileged conversation, without prejudice, isn't that the term you used, Moe?"

"Oh, for god's sake Papa you don't think *Arnold's* going to sue you do you? Now, really...." That from Pauline.

And so it went, morning after morning and night after night, with the afternoons providing the only peaceful interludes.

But one of those afternoons, while Ernest was at the wheel of the *Pilar*, he reverted to the thing about people being flattered at being used as prototypes in his work.

"It's a little like having Cézanne include your features in a village scene," he pointed out modestly.

I thought he was kidding, so I said, "You aren't mixing your métiers, by any chance?"

"Not really," he went on evenly. "After all, what I can't seem to get through your Pennsylvania Dutch skull is that you're not dealing with some little penny-a-liner from the sports department of the Chicago *Daily News*. You're asking for changes in the copy of a man who *has* been likened to Cézanne, for bringing 'a new way of seeing' into American literature."

I almost fell out of the boat. This outsized ham was quoting *me* to my face, and without giving me any credit. I couldn't believe that it wasn't an elaborate spoof and that any second the big wide mouth would bust open in laughter. But he was completely deadpan and, most unbecoming, even a little prim.

"For chris'sake, that was *me*, that Cézanne stuff."

He looked honestly surprised, then sheepish. "Oh, was it? I ought to know better than to go up against your memory. Anyway, I thought it was pretty good in there."

Later, I looked it up and sent it to him, but of course that's the point. He had seen it before, he who always prided himself on slogans like "Keep your head down and never look at the scoreboard," and professed not to pay any attention to what anybody ever wrote about him. Characteristically, he had remembered only the bit he liked. Some of the rest set him off, as he himself expressed it, like a set piece of fireworks, and he accused me of getting too big for my britches.

Maybe I was, but since I had dug it out only to settle a bet, as it were, I still didn't think it was very sporting of him to start picking the other parts to pieces. However, after killing large portions of the *Have* sections of *To Have and Have Not*, which I had not expected him to do, I thought he might be smarting a bit, and more anxious than usual to try to put me back in my place.

The book, as it came out, was rather malformed as the result of such major excisions without any sort of replacement of the deleted elements. I thought the least he might have done would have been to change the title, because, as the book appeared, the title applied about like the "fifty-fifty" recipe for hamburger: one horse, one rabbit.

It was a little disillusioning, after believing for so long that he started every day's work by rereading everything that had been written up to that point and, as he put it, "challenging every word's right to be there," to find him chopping whole hunks out of a book, and not bothering to put one damn word back in.

I suppose he rationalized it on some such basis as that the value of any work increases in proportion to how much can be left out of it—a writer's version of the Mies van der Rohe dogma on architecture: less is more.

But that's one book I certainly don't think the treatment improved.

The passage relevant to Cézanne was this, and after thirty years, I still think it's relevant:

"For like Cézanne, Hemingway not only worked out a new way of setting things down but, far more important, he worked out a new way of looking at things before setting them down. And that is something in which the countless writers of the Hemingway school have neglected to follow their master. It's no trick to copy the Hemingway style. It's almost as easy to duplicate it as it is to parody it. But it is the trick of a lifetime to duplicate the method of seeing with the Hemingway eye for significant and selective detail, to achieve the all-important pattern down to which to strip the so-called 'stripped style.' "

But the piece in which it was contained went on less favorably, or at least so he thought, to say this:

"The old man himself, surefooted as he is on his own ground, is none too sharp in detecting in the work of others this all-important difference between the solid substance and the empty shell. An excellent, even sometimes a scholarly, appraiser of the works of writers dead and gone, he is not a good critic of contemporary writers. The very intensity with which he has worked out his way of writing for himself has given his subconscious mind an inclination to think of his way as the only way. For him, of course, it is. . . . In the process he has acquired a blind spot. Things that are said his way, by others, are apt to fool him into thinking they are better than they are. Only this way can one account for his going out of his way to praise such a wholly fortuitous performance as *Appointment in Samarra*."

Ouch. The fur flew after that. Just because I had written a novel, I suddenly thought I was a critic. Maybe I'd better just spit it all up in Papa's hand, and I'd feel better.

Maybe I did. But I doubt that he did. I think my membership in The Ex-Friends of Hemingway must have been put up for the first time not long after that.

Moe, the lawyer, was not the lawyer that Hemingway later had representing him both as lawyer and as literary agent. Moe had meanwhile died. The agent lawyer got into some very peculiar difficulties, occasioned by the awkward necessity of wearing two hats.

As agent, for instance, he gave me permission to include a Hemingway story in *The Armchair Esquire*, an anthology we got out some years back. Then to his own very evident embarrassment, he had to switch hats and, as lawyer, threaten to sue me for what he had just arranged with me as agent. The newspapers had a field day over it, and *The Wall Street Journal* ran what I consider an excellent exhibit of the ease of parodying the Hemingway style. Here it is, by permission:

THE OLD MAN AND THE FEE

"The writer has served with honor in many wars and he does not care what people think about his politics. He does not want a magazine to reprint two of his stories about the Spanish Civil War in *The Armchair Esquire*, an anthology, because he wants to revise them. It is not true that the writer is worried about a change in public sentiment toward Russia in our time. The writer does not worry about such things. The lawyer misbehaved badly in saying the writer does worry about such things.

"The writer wishes to protect his reprint rights. The mistake reflects badly on his courage. What a way to be wounded!

"The publisher wondered if he was to have or have not. But the writer did not bid farewell to *The Armchair Esquire*. One Spanish war story will be printed in the book by a magazine not noted for men without women.

"The publicity is not too bad. The people now know the book and many will buy it. Do not believe the winner takes nothing. When you hear the bookstore cash registers ring, don't ask for whom the bell tolls. Just know that the sum also rises."

In the item, like faces in a rebus, are five Hemingway book titles and puns on three others. At the risk of elucidating the obvious, I will spell them out, with the warning that they are coming, here below, if you want to look back first and see if you can find the two you might have missed out of the eight.*

I never heard from Ernest again after that episode, which was in '58, and within three years he was dead.

I can't say I ever felt too good about the way our friendship ended, never with a real bang, but just a gradual petering out that was, in Ezra's old phrase, like "the slow cooling of a bathtub."

If friendship is scored in acts of befriending, then Ernest was way ahead of me. He was a far better friend to me, if I keep the scorecard absolutely straight, for many years than Scott ever was. But I was a far better friend to Scott than I ever was to Ernest. Ernest helped me, much more, in the beginning days of the magazine, than Scott ever did. (He lined up a lot of people for me, and helped me line up a lot of others, though oddly enough, he never once suggested, in the magazine's prenatal days, my trying to get anything from Scott.)

---

*All right. Here they are: 1. *The Old Man and the (Sea)* 2. *In Our Time* 3. *To Have (and) Have Not* 4. *(A) Farewell to (Arms)* 5. *Men Without Women* 6. *Winner Take(s) Nothing* 7. *For Whom the Bell Tolls* 8. *The (Sun) Also Rises*.

In fact, looking back, it seems now that almost from the beginning, and certainly after the first year, when Scott was in such a bitter state of dejection over the failure of *Tender Is the Night* to achieve a success of smash-hit proportions, I was always helping Scott and Scott was always needing help. And I somehow always found, or made, the time to help him, even when I was in some pretty bad jams myself.

But after I had obliged him with the financing of the *Pilar* when he couldn't swing it himself, Ernest never again needed the kind of help that I could give him, unless you want to count the rather dubious benefit of getting him to mutilate *To Have and Have Not*, just to avoid getting his ass in a sling over libel problems. But he was chartering planes to bring me down from Miami to Key West, and telling me I was one of the three or four people he cared about pleasing in print, and really going far out of his way, time and again, to be helpful.

In '35, when my third son was born, and I'd been hoping as always for a girl, and even had the name Laurian Jane all printed in readiness for "her," Ernest wired to ask to be allowed to stand godfather to him, while Scott contented himself with a couplet:

> *My advice is you still should strive*
> *For Laurian Jane who didn't arrive.*

But Scott and I were friends until he died, and would be now, I am morally certain, whereas Hemingway and I were no longer friends after, well, come to think of it, about when Scott died. In recent years I have read so much about each of them, written all of a sudden by everybody and his brother, except by those who knew both of them, that I am almost beginning to doubt that I knew either of them.

They were both changing when I knew them, but I felt that Scott was changing for the better, while Ernest was changing for the worse. Aside from two major lapses, both well-publicized, one in *Beloved Infidel* (in the scene where I met Sheilah Graham, as she entered Scott's Drake Hotel room, with the mem-

orable phrase "the son of a bitch just bit my finger") and the other in the Dartmouth Winter Festival scene in *The Disenchanted*, Scott hadn't had a drink in three years before he died. On the other hand Ernest, from all I heard after that, was in the process of crossing the great divide between great drinkers and great drunks.

Scott had the better excuse, of the two, for his drinking, because it is a matter of medical record that he had functional *hypoglycemia*, or *hyperinsulinism*, the opposite of diabetes, a condition that Janie, who has it too, has always said constitutes a great sodality whose spokesman might well be considered O. Henry, with his immortal summary of it as "I was born eight drinks below par."

When I think back on the way they were thirty years ago, before either had begun to be distorted by legend or disfigured by myth, I see them as two enormously attractive and gifted men, both of whom I admired and liked. Each of them seemed to me then to be completely sure of his own talent, though the one seemed even more respectful of the other's than of his own. I thought of each of them as simply loaded with personality and charm. But even then, Ernest was always the sore loser, blustering when he couldn't be first in anything and everything, while Scott with a certain jaunty blend of insouciance and despair was always both gracious and graceful in defeat, perhaps because Scott was always fascinated by failure and Ernest always enamored of success.

The irony is that the one who had appeared, while they were both living, to be the big success really died a failure, while the one who appeared to die a failure has since achieved such resounding success.

There may yet have to be a Hemingway revival, just as I feel pretty sure a Dreiser revival is about due. But there will never have to be another Fitzgerald revival, as he's had as many by now as he will ever need. He is established now, in a way that Hemingway has yet to be.

It's a jest he would have relished, but not gloated over, for he was never one to gloat.

SHOW BIZ

The inclusion of Theodore Dreiser and John Dos Passos in a section dealing with show business in general and movies in particular may come as a surprise to all but the most devoted fans of these writers. Yet they do deserve to be here. Both paid more than passing attention to Hollywood and both worked in films, though, fortunately, neither's literary reputation rests heavily on the results. When Dreiser went to Hollywood in 1919 as a story editor, his major novel *An American Tragedy* still lay ahead, while *Sister Carrie* and the editorships of *Broadway* magazine and a women's publication, *Delineator*, were behind. He was among the first wave of talented novelists to be attracted by the possibilities of the relatively new art and the promise of a generous salary. Others—Dos Passos, Fitzgerald, Faulkner—followed in the Thirties, and, like Dreiser, were disappointed with the treatment they and their work received from the former glove salesmen and penny-arcade owners who controlled the studios. In 1935, Dos Passos wrote the screenplay of *The Devil Is a Woman*, an unsuccessful film most notable as the last Dietrich-von Sternberg collaboration for Paramount Studios. It was also Dos Passos' first and last feature-film script, although he continued applying movie techniques to his important writing. By this time, both Dreiser and Dos Passos were submitting material regularly to Esquire. Dreiser continued until his death in 1945. Dos Passos contributed partially out of friendship for Hemingway until 1938, when the two authors disagreed bitterly over politics. He returned to Esquire in the Fifties with two pieces, one of which was the retrospective profile of actor James Dean that appears in this section.

The other writers presented here first converged on the magazine in the Sixties, each bringing with him a rare sensibility and commitment to his area of special interest. They are in order of their appearance: Dwight Macdonald, cineaste and journalist, who served as Esquire's film critic for six years and with a distinction that made him, in the vernacular of show biz, a very tough act to follow. Nevertheless, Wilfrid Sheed, who up to that time had been occupied primarily as a literary and theatre critic, took over Films in what might be termed the best show-must-go-on tradition. Thomas Berger had been contributing fiction to Esquire for a decade, beginning with excerpts from *Reinhart in Love* and *Little Big Man*. When he accepted the film column in 1972, he told the editor that he was bored with establishment stuff and would deal with offbeat subjects that would come naturally to him as a novelist and that would help him make the column uniquely his own. The editor nodded and Berger proceeded to make the column uniquely his own for more than a year. Robert Alan Aurthur has the most checkered show-business background of any contributor to Esquire, having been associated with every entertainment medium at one time or another, and having written about almost everyone remotely connected therewith—including Harry Truman *and* Zero Mostel. Peter Bogdanovich claims he was a movie fan practically from birth. He's also an actor, writer and director. As a writer he favors directors as subjects, and as a director he prefers to make the simple, clearly defined films he enjoyed as a fan. Finally, how could any expedition into the dark continent of Hollywood go without the excellent company of Orson Welles, who knows where the snakes hide and the lions feed?

Theodore Dreiser:
Myself and the Movies

The great American novelist,
who has emerged as victor from
counters with the film industry,
defends Hollywood

My first personal contact with Hollywood and the Movies was in September, 1919. It was an extremely pleasing place and I liked it enormously, so much so that once I was permitted to come to look over the Paramount lot and, possibly, make some realistic suggestions in connection with pictures, I stayed three years. It was either Mr. Jesse Lasky or Famous Players Lasky or certainly some Hollywood magnate who bought the Mirror Films from under me (I was then the prospective editor in chief of Mirror Films of Corona, Long Island, which, after the purchase, became an eastern branch of Famous Players Lasky); for some reason, possibly kindness of heart, Mr. Lasky offered me a lump sum to come to Hollywood to do exactly what I have stated above.

I never truly hated Hollywood as a whole—merely certain aspects of it which ran counter to my own ego, which for one reason and another (the sale of a novel like *An American Tragedy* for one thing) caused me to feel that a percentage of consideration, not always at the fingertips of busy men, was due me. Perhaps the most disturbing thing was that, having been called to Hollywood for a job I was never allowed to perform, and having for that reason time on my hands, I was soon in a position not only to hear about all Hollywood characteristics, but to observe the difficult strugglings of the aspirants of that day—girls and boys, men and women—who hurried to Hollywood to display their charms or talents, and to seek the public's recognition of the same.

But, oh, the difference between the dreams and the reality. On the one hand a few hundreds, at the most, strutting their talents before the growing movie audiences of the nation, and being paid, even then, enormous salaries; whereas for the other thousands there remained but a weary parade, day after day, from casting office to casting office, bearing photos of themselves, which brought them nothing. Also to the habitats of a swarm of lying moving-picture fakirs, who, well dressed and having a little money, pretended to connections with one and another of the

Dreiser's recollection of Hollywood was published in July, 1943, two years before he joined the Communist Party and twenty-nine months before his death. Had Dreiser lived another few years he might have questioned the kindness of the film industry.

great studios, yet without a trace of such between the lot of them.

I watched it with interest because, as fortune would have it, I was identified with one who, possessing exceptional beauty, was too attractive to be ignored, and so was making her way briskly enough. On the other hand, as a writer I had plenty to do working on such books as *Newspaper Days*, *Moods* and *The Color of a Great City*. Yet often I was advised that if I wished to see something startling, and at the same time pitiable, I should arise at six a.m. and let her drive me to the particular spot or gate where extras apply.

I was not only startled but, from a humanitarian, economic and social point of view, really infuriated by the crass indifference displayed by these already then arriving picture magnates, who, having stumbled upon a social gold mine, could so swiftly and greedily seize upon the endless male and female aspirants as to compel them to arise as early as five or six in the morning and travel miles—private cars being out of the question—in order to reach a certain distant movie gate to be looked over by some young moving-picture assistant as one would look over cattle or sheep. And this in order to find among the hundreds assembled there some twenty or thirty "types" for the particular wild-west or city mob or country farm festival for which at most some forty or fifty were required. As for the other hundreds advertised for, and then and there swarming around the gate in the hope of a day's work—they had their early rising and their long walk for nothing.

And then the mourning mob!

"And me getting up at five and walking seven miles!"

"And look at my shoes!"

"And now I got to go back again."

"And no telling whether the work is good for more than one day after you get it. You're in big luck if it lasts a few days."

On more than one occasion I watched these depressing mobs of the disappointed—their slow discouraged steps, their depressed, almost shrunken faces. After a time, irritated by this phase and that—the spendthrift gaiety on the one hand (do you remember Fatty Arbuckle?) and the endless waves of disappointed aspirants on the other, I sat down and painted a word picture of it which, to my surprise, was printed in some Eastern publication—possibly the first article of its kind. The result was public anti-reaction on the part of the moving-picture organization or their press agents to me personally. At any rate I found myself being denounced as a disappointed sorehead, which most certainly I was not. For the Lasky invitation to come West—although I never got to see him—had netted me several thousand in cash to live on, to say nothing of the sale of my books thus far. No, it was not hatred of the movies as such. I liked them as a new art. Nor was I down on any particular magnate—not even Mr. Lasky. The truth was, as someone has since amusingly but perhaps correctly put it, I was "in leash to the underdog" and, alas, still am.

When I left Hollywood in 1922 and returned to New York to write *An American Tragedy*, I carried no hatred for, as all know, I subsequently sold *An American Tragedy* and later *Jennie Gerhardt* to Paramount, as well as *Sister Carrie* to R.K.O. and *My Gal Sal* to West Coast Fox.

It is true that after buying *An American Tragedy*, for what was then the silent movies, Famous Players Lasky, which later became Paramount, shelved that work until 1930—then announced that it was about to be done as a talkie. I would have thought nothing of this if immediately thereafter I had not been approached by a friend of mine—one J. G. Robin, lawyer, banker, businessman, as well as dramatist, author of *Jesus* and *Caius Gracchus*, who said to me: "Didn't you sell that to them back in 1926 before talking pictures came in?"

"Yes," I said.

"But then what right have they to produce it as a talking picture? Silent rights are one thing. These new talking rights are another and buying one does not mean you have bought the other. Why should you let them buy it and shelve it for four years and then produce it as a talkie for nothing? Why not let me get you up a letter stating that you wish to go into court?"

Having been disappointed by the company's long delay of the picture, I felt in the mood to punish them at least to the degree they had punished me. And, as Liveright had later confided to me, if they had picturized the book in 1926, or simultaneously with Patrick Kearney's dramatization of the book in 1927, the sale of the book would no doubt have been enormous.

For the third time—Mr. Lasky and I met. The meeting took place in my studio in New York, at which time, at Mr. Robin's suggestion, I demanded and received $55,000 for the talking rights of the four years delayed *Tragedy*.

My fourth meeting with Mr. Lasky was in a Beverly Hills garden where an afternoon tea was being held, and where, reasonably enough, we got along most pleasantly—not a trace of resentment or ill feeling on either side. All old bets seemed off and there we were, smiling and enjoying the sunshine, the tea, the this and that. And not a mention of any one of our previous meetings. Not a mention!

Social courtesy is certainly a great thing.

But now as to other so-called Hollywood ills or "hatreds" (that last makes me laugh) if there were any, I have recovered from the same. The moving-picture industry has changed greatly. It has grown enormously and in consequence new blood has come into it—so much so that one feels today a fresher and more sensitive attitude to what must truly be said is not only the American but the world scene. I am thinking of such pictures as *Little Women*, *Good-Bye Mr. Chips*, *How Green Was My Valley*, *Ladies in Retirement*, *Sullivan's Travels*, *The Great McGinty*, *Grapes of Wrath*, *Now Voyager* and many others which were quite taboo when I first sold *An American Tragedy*.

It is not at all as it was twenty or even ten years ago. The entire industry is more friendly and more courteous, to me at least—only I hear others say the same thing.

Of course there are charges now by this person and that—they have been blacklisted, for instance; that without rhyme or reason their contracts have been broken; that they are dealing with creatures who do not understand the first letter of the word art.

Well, it may be so. Some of my early experiences were certainly disagreeable. Nonetheless I insist that I feel new blood, better and fresher American understanding, new courtesy and a lot of other things that make me feel that the Hollywood of 1943 is by no means the Hollywood of 1920–21–22–23 and later. And so I cannot possibly hate it or the industry.

In truth, I never have.

John Dos Passos:

THE DEATH OF JAMES DEAN

The sinister adolescents,
class of '59, as seen through
the newsreel style of the
author of <u>U.S.A.</u>

BRONX YOUTH 16 SEIZED IN
TEEN-AGE GANG KILLING

Woman Fights for Life with Child's Kidney

Royally beautiful former Queen Soraya of Iran arrived in Genoa tonight en route to the United States saying she feels "that life starts anew for me today." Soraya talked between bites from a salami sandwich, which she washed down with synthetic orange juice from a bottle.

TEEN-AGE DANCES SEEN THREATENED
BY PARENTS' FAILURE TO COOPERATE

MOST OFFENDERS EMULATE ADULTS

James Dean is three years dead but the sinister adolescent still holds the headlines.

James Dean is three years dead;

but when they file out of the close darkness and the breathed-out air of the second-run motion-picture theatres where they've been seeing James Dean's old films

they still line up:

the boys in the jackboots and the leather jackets, the boys in the skintight jeans, the boys in broad motorbike belts,

before the mirrors in the restroom
to look at themselves
and see
James Dean;
the resentful hair,
the deep eyes floating in lonesomeness,
the bitter beat look,
the scorn on the lip.

Their pocket combs are out; they tousle up their hair and pat it down just so;

make big eyes at their eyes in the mirror
pout their lips in a sneer,
the lost cats in love with themselves,
just like James Dean.

The girls flock out dizzy with wanting
to run their fingers through his hair, to feel that

Dos Passos appeared in the first issue of Esquire with a short story, later incorporated in The Big Money. *Appropriately, his* The Death of James Dean, *which appeared in the twenty-fifth anniversary issue, uses the same techniques as* The Big Money.

thwarted maleness; girl-boy almost, but he needs a shave. . . . "Just him and me in the back seat of a car. . . ." Their fathers snort,

but sometimes they remember: "Nobody understood me either. I might have amounted to something if the folks had understood."

The older women struggle from their seats wet-eyed with wanting

to cuddle, to mother (it's lack of mother love makes delinquents), to smother with little attentions the poor orphan youngster,

the motherless, brotherless, sisterless, lone-wolf brat strayed from the pack,

the poor mixed-up kid.

LACK OF PARENTAL LOVE IS
BLAMED IN SLAYING

Niagara Falls, N.Y. (AP): Judge Frank J. Kronenberg says the slaying of Johnny Stompanato by Lana Turner's daughter is a *"perfect* example" of the juvenile-delinquency situation in this country. "I think the facts in this case cry out for the American public to be more discriminating in the purchase of a movie ticket."

LANA BARES HEARTBREAK IN
LOVE LETTERS TO PAPITO

From her lofty pinnacle as reigning movie queen and one of the world's most envied women, Lana Turner, rich and beautiful, reached down into the back alleys of Hollywood to surrender her heart to the strange and mysterious John Stompanato.

The press agents told us James Dean lacked parental love, that he was an orphan, a farm boy who couldn't get along at school, a poor mixed-up kid from the black-soil belt in Indiana. (He never could quite get rid of that Hoosier twang . . .

. . . Hoosier ghosts of forgotten Penrods, cracker-barrel reveries. . . . *"The thoughts of youth are long, long thoughts"* . . . *"For I was once a barefoot boy"* . . . *Life on the Mississippi. The Arkansas Traveller.* Hundred-year-old Huck Finn drifting with runaway Jim downriver on their eternal raft.) The young used to be comical in America. Not often anymore.

(Continued on page 248)

TEEN-AGERS TERRORIZE
CALIFORNIA TOWN

Hollister, Calif.: A swarm of motorcyclists descended today on this quiet California town, breaking windows, tearing down signs, wrecking bars in an orgy of vandalism that drove the inhabitants to take refuge in their homes.

"I'm a serious-minded and intense little devil," the movie magazines quoted James Dean as saying, "terribly gauche and so tense I don't see how people stay in the same room with me. I know I wouldn't tolerate myself."

The teen-agers approve: "Everything he said was cool."

In mid-century America the barefoot boys are all shod in loafers.

The Hoosier farm boys have no cows to milk before day, no wood to chop, no horses to currycomb or oats to measure out into the manger, no coal-oil lamps to fill, no chores—"If it's housework let mother do it"—no chapter of the Bible to read every night,

no roaring preachers to remind them from the pulpit every Sunday that good is Heaven and bad is Hell,

no examiners to ask hard questions;

only perhaps an occasional package to carry out from the A & P, or maybe the family car to wash

before driving down to the drugstore for a Coke and a cigarette of some advertised brand, and a comic book (nothing in mid-century America is less comical than a comic) diagraming murder and mayhem and rape, tirelessly strumming on the

> raw nerves
> for kicks.

8 INDICTED IN SALE OF
SMUT RECORDS

Daytona Beach, Fla., Feb. 26: National Guard troops with loaded carbines moved in early today to help break up a riot of teen-agers. The mob had flouted police authority and milled through a business section near the ocean beach for more than four hours. The riot stemmed from efforts of the police to stop a group of youths from racing their cars on ramps leading to the beach and from signal lights on the city streets. Instead of dispersing, the youths slashed the tires of two police cars and started throwing rocks. They seemed to have an idea a teen-ager had been arrested and kept calling: "Bring him back. Bring him back."

Kicks are big business: the sallow hucksters needle the nerves. Through radios drumming rock 'n roll and blurred girls crooning on TV

> they hammer on the wracked nerves:
> buy,

buy speed, buy horsepower, buy chromium, buy happiness in a split-level ranch house, elegance in shocking-pink lipstick, passion in a jar of Parisian perfume,

> or that portable transistor set
> you can take along on your vacations
> so that even beside the thunderous ocean, or

camping out in some hidden intervale green in a notch of the hills, you'll never be free

> from the clamor of salesmen.

Why not resentful? There's more to life; the kids know it. Their fathers won a war, but weren't men enough to keep the peace; they let the pundits and the politicians wheedle them into defeat; they let the goons pilfer their pay checks, too busy watching TV to resent oppression. . . . (Freedom, What good is it? Let's have social security

> and welfare and tailfins on our cars
> and packaging)

. . . There's no cellophane can protect the glory of life when you've lost it; the kids know it.

"When we spotted 'Killer' on the stoop of his home, he kicked Candelaria in the leg and ran for the roof. We took after him. When we reached the top landing 'Killer' leaned down from the roof and let go with his shotgun twice."

Why not resentful? Even in success James Dean was resentful. This kid had talent. That's how he differed from the general run of drugstore cowboys. The critics said he had the makings of a great film actor. He won awards. Even after he was dead the audiences voted him the best actor of the year.

> "Rare mixture of truth, beauty and
> fun."

> James Dean was resentful, we were
> told,

because he came from a broken home. "My mother died on me when I was nine years old. What does she expect me to do? Do it all myself." His father married again. An aunt and uncle raised him on their neat farm in Fairmount, Indiana. He was a moody boy. He was terribly nearsighted. He did poorly in his studies,

but in high school he played baseball, basketball, led the track team and excelled in dramatics. They gave him a medal for the best all-around athlete, senior year.

His elocution teacher took a fancy to him. She spotted the talent. She coached him in parts in school plays and had him win a statewide contest in public speaking

> reading *The Madman*, by Dickens.

When she induced him to enter a national contest held out in Colorado, the judges passed him over. He resented that. He never forgave that poor teacher.

His father worked as a dental technician in Los Angeles. After young Dean graduated he went out to stay with his father. There he met a fellow who was taking a course in acting with a retired motion-picture performer. James Dean tagged along; he panicked the class acting the part of a pine tree in a storm. Now he knew he wanted to act.

CITY TO ADD POLICE AT
SUMMER SPOTS

He hung around L.A., broke most of the time, working as an usher in movie theatres, getting an occasional part as an extra on the lots, or a bit on TV,

dreaming and yearning and hungry,
eating cold spaghetti out of the can.
Dirty shirt, never a haircut, needed a shave, the
grubbiest guy in town. Sometimes he got a job parking cars in a parking lot to earn the two bits he
needed for a hamburger and a cup of coffee.

HOUSEWIFE'S DOLLAR SHRINKS
SOME MORE

RESERVE BANK'S HEADS SAY
CONSUMER'S RECOVERY IS KEY

The three juvenile gangs involved in the arrest
yesterday of a 20-year-old boy on charges of killing
a rival gang member have a characteristic in common.
They are the "shook-up generation" in sections of the
city undergoing their own profound shake-ups in
social patterns.

James Dean was impatient. He was stagnating
in L.A. He made a break for New York, rode east all
the way on the bus. For a year he hung around
Broadway with the out-of-work actors.

ONE WORKER IN FOUR FOUND
DEPENDENT ON FOREIGN TRADE

As he mounted the steps a photographer said,
"Look up."
"You are not the Sinners," the youth replied.
"I don't have to look up to you." Inside the station,
however, the prisoner told the police: "I'm sorry I
shot him. I didn't mean to pull the trigger. I only
meant to cock the gun."

"New York is vital, above all, fertile," James
Dean used to tell the reporters. "I fit into cadence
and pace better here."
He developed a lingo
out of tearoom talk about be-bop and Bach,
and stale shards of Freud,
existentialism,
and scraps out of translations of Jean Genêt sold
under the counter:
—"Our Lady of the Flowers"—
include me out: self-expression.

In the drab summer desert of New York, James
Dean lacked friends; he lacked girls, he lacked dough;
but when the chance comes he knows how to
grab it; a young director takes an interest, invites
him out sailing on a sloop on the Sound, gives him a
part in a show which immediately flops;
but he's been seen on the stage. He plays the
blackmailing Arab in a dramatization of André Gide's
Immoralist. He walks out on the part, the play closes,
but he's been seen by people who know show business: rave write-ups: he's an actor.
Live the part, Stanislavsky told his actors.
Dean does just that. He's obstreperous as hell.
"I can't divert into being a social human being," he
snarls at the reporters through the butt that dangles
from his lip, "when I'm working on a hero like Cal
who's essentially demonic."

The tall muscular youth was arrested as the
result of a trap set for him by the police. They had
the cooperation of his girl friend who was among the
fifty youngsters questioned by the police yesterday
morning. Two detectives accompanied the girl to
their usual meeting place. They hid in two hallways.
The other detectives also kept out of sight. When
Serra walked to the girl the detectives surrounded
him.
He was wearing a narrow-striped red-and-grey
blazer. A tiny gold cross was attached to the lobe of
his left ear.
Demonic, but lovable under it all.
The sinister adolescent is box office. Long before
his first picture is released James Dean is besieged by
Hollywood agents, promoters, feature writers, photographers.
He is serious about self-expression. "Acting is
the most logical way for people's neuroses to express
themselves." As soon as he's in the money he buys
himself a good camera and photographs himself in
melancholy moods,
sad and resentful and sorry, so soon to die,
but lovable under it all. Sharp lights and shadows, his head in a noose, a kitchen knife shot for a
dagger. He talks a lot about wanting to sculpt.
He's crazy about racing cars. Speed's how to
die. He makes up his own mobiles. He's planning to
be a bullfighter: "Death in the Afternoon."
"Cool," echo the teen-agers. "Everything he said
was cool."
In Hollywood he goes on playing the part he
plays on the screen. "A wary suspicious loner," one
director calls him. Another is more forgiving: "Just
a boy on the rise."
"Rebel Without a Cause."
The teen-agers saw themselves in James Dean.
Everything he said was cool.

Screening Giant,
he was already beginning not to like it much
if people didn't look up when he slouched into the
Villa Capri that was his hangout. Wasn't he James
Dean?
He was handy with the mambo drum. His
bachelor actor's home was loud with hi-fi. He had to
pick an isolated location so that the neighbors
wouldn't complain about the rock 'n roll. . . .

7 TEEN KILLERS IN JURY'S
HANDS AFTER NINETY-FIVE DAYS

The king of the disc jockeys was throwing a ball
so I decided to ankle along. There must have been a
thousand more cats than they had seats for. They
started off with cool numbers, but pretty soon they
speeded up. As the music got warmer so did the cats.
They started climbing out of their seats, running up
and down the aisles screaming to their buddies. One
kid dressed in a leather jacket and paratroop boots
stood up in his seat and started to wave his arms.
Four cops tried to take him out. Before long, twenty
or thirty kids had pitched in to help him and every-

body else was yelling like crazy and tossing things at the cops.

James Dean is made. In quiet moods he likes to be seen in Hollywood night spots with another celebrity. He plays around with the girl who acts Vampira on TV, the ghoul who gives people, right in their own homes, their daily creeps,

like a Charles Addams cartoon. (No romance, say their friends, and how she was real warmhearted underneath and understood his resentments.) He tells her everything.

A few days before his death she sends him a postcard picture of herself posed beside an open grave. "Come join me," it reads.

TWO THEORIES OFFERED AS CLUES TO ALL MATTER

Dean owned a horse, but racing cars was his public hobby. He'd won a race for novices at some meet. His racing had given the producers fits. He teased them by telling them that racing was a glorious way to die. (Life can't be all Social Security and safety first. The kids know that. It's glory a man has to have.) Some friends furnished him with a St. Christopher medal, but the studio had written it into his contract that he wasn't to race a car until the picture was ready for release.

By September 30, 1955, he was free from that clause in his contract. There was to be a meet at Salinas. Instead of taking his white Porsche Spyder with the 130 painted on its side over to the track on a truck like most of the contestants,

he had to drive it over himself. His German mechanic went along. A photographer followed in a station wagon.

He wanted to feel her speed.

Already at Bakersfield a traffic cop gave him a ticket for doing sixty through a forty-mile zone.

The sun was setting. It was nearly dusk. He wanted to feel her speed. He was making seventy-five, eighty, a hundred—accounts differ—when near Paso Robles on the empty highway he collided head on with a car turning in from an intersection,

a Ford driven by a young man named Donald Turnupseed.

James Dean was killed. The steering wheel went through him: Turnupseed and the mechanic were hurt but recovered.

Fairmount, Indiana, October 8: James Dean, the motion-picture actor, was buried today in a quiet country ceremony in the community where only six years ago he had been an outstanding high-school athlete. A crowd estimated at 3000 milled quietly about this little town of 2600 people as final services were read.

Dead at twenty-four:

"James Dean can't be dead," the girls told each other, "he's in the hospital undergoing facial surgery." It would take a long time, but someday they would see him slouching out onto the screen again.

People paid fifty cents a head to see the wreck of his car.

In L.A. the clairvoyants and psychics did a land-office business interviewing James Dean in the spirit world. Some interviews were printed. "Everything he said was cool," the teen-agers said.

At Warner Brothers the requests for photographs, which had merely been average, went up by the time he'd been dead a year to seven thousand letters a month. Everybody from his grandmother to the waiters at the Villa Capri was interviewed by the motion-picture press. The pulp merchants sold one-shot lives of him in hundreds of thousands of copies. Bronze heads and plaster masks were marketed in bulk.

One popular item was made of a plastic supposed to feel like human skin when you stroked it.

Candelaria was found moaning on the fifth-floor landing of the Fox Street tenement. Mrs. Retorico, a registered nurse, almost fainted when she heard her son named as the gunman, but she said nothing and concentrated on giving the victim first aid. "He could hardly whisper," Chavez said, "his clothes and body were torn to shreds. But he recognized that we were trying to help him. 'Help me, I'm going to die.'"

"The Killer" was taken to the Simpson Street Station for booking. He glowered behind dark glasses.

The sinister adolescents come to various ends.

They found it hard to believe that James Dean was dead. There he was right on the screen when they saw his old pictures. The promoters had been struggling hard to blow up the story that millions wouldn't believe he was dead, but when they released a picture on his life nobody went to see it. When a man's dead, he's dead. His competitor, Elvis Presley, continued the rage, bumping his guitar with his rump,

until his draft board one day

drafted him into the Army.

U.S. CAN HIT MOON IN '58 OFFICER SAYS

The sinister adolescents come to various ends; sometimes they grow up.

SHOW
PEOPLE

From Dreiser's *Myself and the Movies* (1943) to Aurthur in the present day, these seven writers covered the field of show business for Esquire.One article by each is included in this section.

Theodore Dreiser

Wilfrid Sheed

Thomas Berger

John Dos Passos

Dwight Macdonald

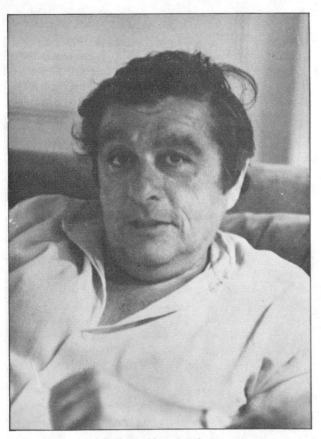

Robert Alan Aurthur

Peter Bogdanovich

Dwight Macdonald:

A FEW WELL-CHOSEN WORDS ABOUT BEN-HUR

Ho hum

Ben-Hur, as everyone knows, cost $15,000,000 to make, runs for almost four hours, has a cast variously estimated at 50,000 (by Metro-Goldwyn-Mayer) and at 10,400 (by *Time*), was directed by William Wyler, and has had the biggest advance sale ($500,000) in film history. But what no one knows who hasn't seen it is that it is lousy. The secret was well kept by the New York newspaper critics: "a remarkably intelligent and engrossing human drama . . . real excitement . . . sober meaning . . . plain integrity" (*Times*), "squirms with energy . . . acting good to excellent" (*Tribune*), "a classic peak" (*Post*), "stupendous" (*News*), "extraordinary cinematic stature" (*Journal-American*), "massive splendor in overwhelming force roars from the screen" (*World-Telegram*). Even *Time*, which used to be sophisticated about films, went overboard: "The script is well ordered and its lines sometimes sing with good rhetoric and quiet poetry. . . . Director Wyler's wit, intelligence, and formal instinct are almost everywhere in evidence and he has set a standard of excellence by which coming generations of screen spectacles can expect to be measured."

Against these bellows of approval, which might have been emitted by the M-G-M lion himself, I can only pipe that I found *Ben-Hur* bloody in every way—bloody bloody and bloody boring. Watching it was like waiting at a railroad crossing while an interminable freight train lumbers past, often stopping completely for a while. Because they had to spend that $15,000,000, every dramatic point is stated, restated, then hammered home with a dozen more inept speeches. The three main characters are played by Charlton Heston, the poor man's Gregory Peck, as Ben-Hur; Stephen Boyd, a stolid Western-type villain, as Messala; and a young Israeli actress, if one may use the term for courtesy, named Haya Harareet, who as Esther maintains an admirable composure through many harrowing situations. They are at no point in danger of lawsuits for impersonating real people. The tender passages between Heston and Miss Harareet make Joan Crawford's love scenes look positively animated. Misdirected by Wyler, Heston throws all his punches in the first ten minutes (three grimaces and two intonations) so that he has nothing left long before he stumbles to the end, four hours later, and has to react to the Crucifixion. (He does

Macdonald was Esquire's film reviewer from 1960 to 1966. This, a portion of his second column, ran in March, 1960. Many of the critical selections included in the anthology Dwight Macdonald on Movies *(1969) came from his monthly column.*

make it clear, I must admit, that he quite disapproves of it.)

But *Ben-Hur* is a "spectacle" and so, one gathers from the critics, must be judged by modest aesthetic standards. (Though, as I recall, *Intolerance*, *The Birth of a Nation*, and *Potemkin* were also "spectacles.") Very well. The big spectacular moments—the sea fight, the Roman triumph, the chariot race—all failed because Wyler doesn't know how to handle crowds nor how to get a culminating rhythm by cutting. He tries to make up for this lack, as De Mille did, by huge sets and thousands of extras, but a Griffith can make a hundred into a crowd while a Wyler-De Mille can reduce a thousand to a confused cocktail party. The sets, furthermore, are glossily new; the galleys look as if they were built yesterday, as indeed they were; the armor and helmets are shiny tin foil, and the columns of ancient Rome are of sleekest, smoothest plastic. The chariot race, long on gore and short on excitement, takes place under three gigantic statues of a majestic phoniness (M-G-M claims they used one million pounds of plaster in the production; I believe it). The color photography was the glaring kind that makes the people stand out like waxworks, with no relation to the background. There was not even a decent, or rather an indecent, Roman orgy, the only valid excuse for making a Biblical picture.

Instead of sex, *Ben-Hur* gives us sadism. As G. Legman demonstrated ten years ago in *Love and Death* (published by the wonderfully named Breaking Point Press), our mass culture compensates for its prudery about sex by a uniquely American license in portraying violence. *Ben-Hur* carries this principle to its extreme—De Mille, after all, gave us *both* orgies and bloodshed—omitting Roman eroticism but dwelling on Roman brutality with pornographic realism. We are treated to close-ups of the galled ankles of galley slaves, of their writhings under the lash of the overseers, of their gasping struggles as they drown. We are left in no doubt as to what a leper's face looks like, on a Panavision screen. We see exactly what happens when a man is run over in the chariot race, and we are treated to a good ten minutes of stimulating close-ups of Messala's bloody, crusted, broken face and torso while he is dying after being dragged face-down in such an accident, all in full color and all suggesting a most insanitary butcher shop. (Any parent who takes a child to see *Ben-Hur* is irresponsible.) The Crucifixion opens with a shot of the nails being hammered into Christ's hands that is really quite graphic; it differs from similar shots in such Old

Masters as Grunewald in lacking any sense of tragedy or religious awe, in being simply—graphic. (Christ wears a long auburn hairdo and is seen only from the back, a bit of reverence that reminds me of the modest gestures of a striptease.)

In short, here is a film that debauches—or tries to —whatever taste, feeling or simple common sense Hollywood and television have left us. Here is blood blood blood—the brook running from the Cross is full of it. Here is a mad jumble of talents transmuted by Hollywood's alchemy into solid lead. Let us pass over the musical director, "the world-famous Dr. Miklos Rozsa," let us even pass over such extras, doubtless as eminent in the *haut monde* as Dr. Rozsa is in the musical world, as Prince Emanuele Ruspoli of Italy, Count Santiago Oneto of Spain, Princess Irina Wassilchikoff of Russia, let us even pass over the Baroness Lilian del Balzo of Hungary. Still, William Wyler has made some not-bad movies, and the script was worked on by, among others, Maxwell Anderson, Gore Vidal, Christopher Fry and S. N. Behrman. Quite a galaxy to produce this sputtering little Roman candle. Here is, finally, a blasphemous falsification of the Bible—I wonder what the Legion of Decency will say about it—in which not the Jews but the Romans are responsible for Christ's martyrdom. According to Matthew, Mark, Luke and John, it wasn't that way at all. *"Then said Pilate to the chief priests and the people, 'I find no fault in this man.' And they were the more fierce, saying, 'He stirreth up the people. . . . Crucify him, crucify him!'"* But in this film, we see merely Pilate washing his hands and delivering Christ over to the brutal soldiery; ain't nobody here but just us Romans.

I apologize for so tedious an explication of the obvious. My only excuse is that none of my fellow critics seems to have noticed this, any more than the plastic columns, the feeble crowd scenes, the sadism or any of the other obvious points about *Ben-Hur*. Assuming they are not moronic, which I am sure is the case, the only explanations are (1) that it would be un-American to suggest you could spend $15,000,000 on a turkey, and (2) a feeling, perhaps justified, that *Ben-Hur* will be a smash, in which case, also, it would be un-American to cavil. But I don't see what either point has to do with film criticism.

To conclude on a more positive and American note, let me admit, and indeed insist, that this *Ben-Hur* makes a real contribution to international amity. All the Romans are portrayed by English—or at least by British Commonwealth—actors, while all the Hebrews except Miss Harareet of Israel (using her for Esther was a really inspired bit of public relations) are Americans. M-G-M attributes this to "Mr. Wyler's determination not to have a clash of accents," but this explanation is at the least confusing. I suggest that M-G-M, in a most tactful gesture, gave the colonial parts to the country that is now acquiring an empire and the imperial parts to the country that has recently lost one. Jolly decent, *I* say.

Wilfrid Sheed:

The Graduate and Other Strangers

Youth is not only wasted
on the young
but on the moviegoer

Recent bulletins on today's youth reveal him to be, among other things, brutal, callow, cynical, trusting, lovable and desperately honest. It is good to know these things about today's youth in case you ever actually meet him. You will know right away to pull a knife and hand him a lump of sugar.

This year's stretch-your-mind-with-a-new-idea prize, bestowed for seizing every characteristic known to mankind since the Flood and identifying it with modern youth, goes to a breathy little item called *The Hippie Revolt*. This one will certainly jerk you alert on your prayer mat: it shows scenes of wild dancing, and body painting, and flower-picking, and peace rallies as if they were all being done by the same kids on the same day. A hectic schedule, this copping out.

Such giddy roundups are best left to the news-magazines where they are neutralized by the hopeless prose. Film impresses without trying; and it is getting to be a bad joke setting the old folk atremble once more with flashing images and howling sound tracks. It might be explained that at least some of the kids in this film are trying to get away from the noise the other ones are making.

The Kingdom of Cop Out has many mansions, and it is unclean billiards to lump the recluses with the exhibitionists, the nature crowd with the electricians, and then accuse them all of being conformists. You might as well say that Bertrand Russell and Dwight Eisenhower are typical examples of older men. On top of that, such socio-hokum movies tend to seek out the most cretinous spokesmen from each group and encourage them to mumble stray nothings about, you know, the scene and what's happening, baby, and the other chin dribble we've come to insist on.

The Graduate is a species of satirical cartoon, featuring Youth as Adam's apple, too choked to speak, confronted by unspeakable adults bent on making him One of Them with greed injections. In line with a growing Hollywood tradition, it puts

"Following Dwight Macdonald is a dirty trick," Wilfrid Sheed remarked in his first column, when, in 1967, Macdonald decided to forsake Films for Politics. The editor thought it a neat trick and Sheed continued to write the column for more than two years. This one was published in April, 1968.

the ideas in one part and the pretty photography in the other. Everything interesting you're going to learn is over by the first reel, and after that we get lots of driving and running, brooding and loping, so expressive of today's youth (see *You're A Big Boy Now*), plus some lackluster variations on the original theme.

Here, in retaliation, is our own graceful, loping run-down: young man comes home from college to be initiated into dreadful grown-up life. (How he's missed it so far is his secret.) As "Youth," he is big American thing: but he must be right kind of youth. Corruption is offered to him—very bad form to refuse it. Older woman (Anne Bancroft) seduces him: Okay, kid—get your experience, and keep quiet about it. (When he wishes to exchange thoughts with her during one of their intermissions, she says, in effect, "Shut up and keep rowing." American youth is adorable, American youth is a frigging bore.)

What happens of course is that our boy breaks the code by acting decently and spontaneously. But somebody must have set fire to the script at this point, because the working out of this is random and scratching. Our boy falls in love with his mistress' daughter. This would have been socially appropriate at one time, but now mistress gets mad and blows the whistle on him, proving the sneaky unreliability of adults, I suppose, and he pursues the girl all over Northern California, to the booming strains of Simon and Garfunkel, singing eighty-seven brand-new verses of *Scarborough Fair*, and any satirical point is lost forever. Marrying this girl is not a sufficient resolution to the problems raised in the opening minutes.

None of which would matter, except that the movie *is* a cartoon, not a real story, and a cartoon demands a certain tightness and consistency of intention. On the credit side, director Mike Nichols has contrived a blend of sight and sound that conveys the graduate's world, and another for the slick grown-up world, and these two do battle behind the story's back, to some effect. The film has an audiovisual impact independent of the screenplay; if you aren't tired of these tricks—well, see *The Graduate*, and start getting tired.

Dustin Hoffman is a slight disappointment in the lead. He has done some extraordinarily fine work on Broadway, but it seems that when he tried to do likewise on film, Mr. Nichols told him to cut that out, and do nothing. So nothing is what he does. And it's too little by half. There is a superstition going around that stage actors have to drop everything down to the smallest twitch for the cameras, and it has resulted in some uncommonly wooden performances. (Anyone remember Jason Robards in *The Journey*? Deborah Kerr had told him that film acting was like paring a fingernail.) I should like to have seen Mr. Hoffman give it the works, instead of standing around with his mouth open. This Richard Lester business of using actors as gadgets backfires when the actor consciously holds back too much.

Final youth movie, before returning to our checkers over the cracker barrel. Albert Camus' *The Stranger*, the prophetic masterpiece about cool and honesty and all the other postwar surplus. Marcello Mastroianni is a mite old and shaggy-looking for the part of Meursault. But we have seen, since Camus started this particular ball rolling, so many burned-out, fresh-frozen late adolescents, that it is high time they were played by older men. (Sir John Gielgud would make a much more convincing adolescent than most of the ones you see around these days.)

To match Mastroianni's natural air of exhausted befuddlement, Luchino Visconti has reconceived all the book's main scenes slightly. But he has kept the two main things—the setting and the weather. A movie cannot show the inside of a man's mind, but it can show what he sees, and this can be decoded and arranged into thoughts. Meursault's indifference to what society assures him is important comes to us in the form of a weather report: it is a species of sunstroke. His refusal to pretend is partly a heat-drugged laziness, partly a bleaching clarity of mind, like the harsh whiteness of Moorish architecture.

Visconti has conveyed marvelously well, with splendid use of color and lighting, at least some hint of Camus' obsession with the Algerian sun. When Meursault commits his absurd crime, it is in a shimmer of heat. Languid, restless, hallucinating just a touch, Meursault empties his whole gun into the victim, where one bullet would have sufficed, or none. He does not know why. It was the sun, he explains. Society can make nothing of such answers, society doesn't recognize crimes of weather.

The courtroom scene is extravagantly ridiculous, but with, I believe, a possible purpose. A colonial courtroom has a peculiar unreality about it. Colonial institutions are usually parodies of the real thing, just as Colonel Blimp is a parody of an Englishman, or as, let's say, a Philippine version of Groton School would be a monstrosity. An imported culture is a distorted one, and the courtroom scene is hardly more bizarre than a Pakistani talking BBC English. Furthermore, a colonial citizen has an absurd relation to government power. Meursault's judge represents a ramshackle society, held together with sticking plaster and menace. This is the society in which Meursault has been formed. Now it is come to judge its baby. This slightly overdone scene reminds us how hard Visconti had to squeeze the book to find cinematic equivalents for Meursault's sense of absurdity, and how shrewdly he has used what was there.

The chic thing now in movies is to show a man's interior by frisking the camera around like a puppy, as he walks, trots, or canters past buildings, blurred crowds, etc. *The President's Analyst*, *The Producers* and *Sebastian* are just three recent examples of this pretty device. This does establish mood, often the wrong one, and sometimes situation, but no one ever got far inside a character that way. Visconti does it the old way with concrete scenes, and by using an actor with an actual face (Mastroianni) to help him along. The result is one of the best films of last year.

Thomas Berger:
Candy Darling Is (Almost) All Girl

An appealing and revealing look at one of Warhol's superstars

Candy Darling has a cloud of Harlow hair, milk-white shoulders, and a svelte body made for the red chiffon in which, on and off screen, she frequently swathes herself. She plays prominent roles in a picture called *Some of My Best Friends Are . . .* and another entitled *Sex* (at the moment; the latest word is that it may be released as *Women In Revolt*). As of the time I write, the former has disappeared from New York theatres and the latter can be seen only at private screenings at Andy Warhol's film Factory on Union Square, which is no longer as accessible as it was before a young woman walked in several years back and shot Mr. Warhol in the alleged interests of a militant-feminist organization named S.C.U.M., an acronym which I think I remember as standing for "Society for Cutting Up Men."

(For persons with a ghoulish interest in Mr. Warhol's damage, which was certainly no joke and almost did him in, his chest, bandaged just below the dugs, is on view in another motion picture, *Tits*, made by the distinguished painter Larry Rivers and one of the few films that live up absolutely to their titles, being about an hour's worth of mammaries, female, male, child, animal, real, prosthetic.)

As to Candy Darling, the only deficiency I can find in her arsenal of feminine attributes, or at any rate those available for public judgment, switching the metaphor (as well as, very soon now, the gender), is in the milk-fund department. Her chest is considerably flatter than that of an old boxer gone to seed.

I hasten to say that I did not ascertain this with my own ape-like paw. It is on record in *Some of My Best*, etc., in which a lust-maddened stud, in self-hating reaction against having previously sold himself to a flabby, middle-aged individual of his own sex, seizes this delicate girl, rips away her bodice and padded bra, and reveals her to be, underneath it all, just another guy. Then he beats hell out of her —I mean, him.

But even when bare-chested and, divested of her wig, close-cropped, Candy is still somehow all girl, a vulnerable maiden being brutalized by a sadistic male. This may be why the scene is actually very moving, in more ways than one, *natürlich, mein Herr*—but to put kinkiness aside for a moment, if that can be done when talking about, my God, a man who is girlier than many contemporary women, what one feels most here is the old moral shock of seeing an impostor, in whatever realm, unmasked. Reality, which is to say the injustice of Nature, wins again.

The rest of *Some of My Best Friends Are . . .* did not stir me unduly, being a rather slick account of what could occur in a homosexual bar on Christmas Eve: comedy, venality, melancholy, and of course the usual pain that is the concomitant of passion.

Sex, the Warhol picture, is another thing altogether and one that I might, if pressed, be prepared to call a masterpiece of wit. But to make a straightforward judgment on any product of Mr. Warhol's is to make an ass of yourself. He is so ruthlessly literal that one must approach him deviously. He has stopped painting because "all the other painters are so good nowadays." He recently designed a dollar bill which could be easily counterfeited "because everybody should have money."

I think it would be as much of a mistake to see these statements as disingenuous as it would be to consider *Sex* a vengeful answer to S.C.U.M. Mr. Warhol is not exactly innocent, but neither is he corrupt. Think about that, maybe for the first time. There might well be more to art, and life, than disjunctive propositions.

An added moral, aesthetic, and probably metaphysical complication is that Mr. Warhol may have had nothing to do with the making of *Sex*, except to lend his aura to the production. It is alleged that the Warhol films are really the product of genial, modest Paul Morrissey. I have abstained, on grounds of irrelevance, from pursuing the matter with either of them. I did ask Mr. Warhol for his opinion of another movie, not his or Morrissey's, and he said he thought it was very good. "But don't go by me," he added. "I like everything." He then proceeded to take Polaroid snapshots of everybody at the dinner table.

Berger chose Candy Darling as the subject for his first film column (April, 1972) because "as a novelist who started out very obscurely I have a soft spot in my heart for people who are obscure and struggling for recognition."

Sex is the story of three young ladies involved in the women's liberation movement. The roles are played by the Misses Holly Woodlawn, Jackie Curtis, and the heroine of these notes, Candy Darling, a trio of male transvestites. And here nobody gets unmasked—well, none of these three anyway. Holly Woodlawn at one point is stripped to the waist and shows a pair of small but seemingly real breasts. She looks like a real but plain woman, whereas Jackie Curtis looks like a man in drag, the Milton Berle or college-follies, falsetto-voiced kind of thing.

Candy Darling, ravishing as always, plays a rich man's daughter in the Forties style of Joan Bennett, whom in these passages she also resembles in clothes and coiffure. Holly lives with a man who exploits her, then moves into a Village pad with Jackie, a virgin who dreams of being deflowered.

For a time the girls make common cause with a women's lib group, at the meetings of which as in all the Warhol films the conversation is largely *ad* lib, maddeningly banal and hilarious, but they get nowhere and eventually drift apart, Holly to become a Bowery wino, Jackie to marry the weight lifter called Mr. America, bear his child, and stay home all day with dirty diapers and canned beer. But Candy achieves the dream of every old-style American girl. She becomes a love-goddess movie star. Not by reason of talent alone, or in fact at all, but rather by balling an entire roster of famous directors.

The sequence in which her career is summarized during an interview with a parody of Rex Reed is a comic gem. He becomes increasingly enraged at her failure to give candid answers to his aggressive questions and concludes by, yes, beating the hell out of her, in the course of which commotion his own wig falls off, revealing him to be a woman.

If Candy Darling can survive the punishments with which her appearances are invariably accompanied, and which indeed seem, if undeserved, peculiarly appropriate, he might well prove a world-beater. Whatever, whoever Candy Darling *really* is, are, they are

remarkably talented, perhaps as much in life as in art. He/she would like next to play the feminine role in one of the classic love stories. I suggested *Mayerling*. Miss Sylvia Miles, who is certainly all woman, conjured up the name of Madame Lupescu, mistress of the late King Carol of Rumania. We were rewarded with Candy's Gioconda smile, the inscrutable eyes, the crimson mouth like a wound.

Another newcomer to me is a massive, gifted actress named Wini Bryan, who could be seen in the aforementioned *Tits*, displaying you know what in her two hands and discoursing extravagantly and sometimes even profoundly on racial matters as they pertain to breasts and vice versa, and also in a picture that accompanied the aforementioned in a short run on Bleecker Street, Charles Rydell's *School Play*. The latter is a crazy creation that straddles the line between underground films and home movies, like Warhol's in its use of impromptu dialogue and naïve camera work, but utterly original in wit and esprit. I suppose it might be described as a pastiche of the legends of Western civilization and the films which derive from them, so that fairy godmothers, howling cannibals, and the siren whose song drives men mad fade in and out; there are endless chases and magical transformations and an extraordinarily funny scene in which Cinderella, played by an enormous, amorphous white actress named Brigid Polk (who also exposes herself in Rivers' film), converses with her mother as represented by Miss Bryan, who is black and weighs two hundred and fifty pounds. Dressed in similar dark-red dresses with white accents, they sit at a table the entire surface of which is covered with guttering candles, and they rant and bicker while the camera turns.

By now you surely must know that *A Clockwork Orange* is well worth the price of a ticket. But have you heard of Candy Darling, Wini Bryan, Brigid Polk? They are fine performers, and they are unique. I'd like to see them up there with the biggies.

Robert Alan Aurthur:

Hanging Out with Zero Mostel

If he were a rich man,
he'd hate himself

I wait in a cab outside an apartment building on Central Park West, and at the exact appointed moment Zero Mostel, full-bearded, massive, bursts from the foyer to the sidewalk. Flailing a cane, he is a sighted Mr. Muckle, sweeping all from his way, and the thought occurs that here may be the only existing performer who on stage or screen has always been smaller than life. Convoyed by a stoic doorman, Zero pummels his case-hardened victim while loudly proclaiming him guilty of ten- and twelve-letter perversions. A standard Mostel entrance.

Our eventual goal is Zero's studio on Twenty-eighth Street, but first we will join friends for lunch at a midtown restaurant. In the cab we talk about his latest film, one I'd seen the night before, a thoroughly rotten picture that Zero had previously warned me was "appalling." Somewhat saddened to find I agreed with him, he eyes me balefully, then says, "I've never done anything for money that turned out good." And while I, unsuccessfully, try to think of an exception, he adds, "That's because moneymen, not artists, are in charge."

The conflict between art and money had plagued Zero Mostel ever since, as the youngest easel painter on the W.P.A., he was repeatedly lopped off the project, or, as a lesser evil, converted to a snow shoveler. Whatever he has done since as an actor-entertainer, Zero has never surrendered the conviction that he is primarily a painter. From the hard times in the Thirties when he did funny bits in union halls and at left-wing meetings for $10 a night ("The promise of ten meant maybe you got eight"), to a recent run as Tevye at the Westbury Music Fair from where he brought home better than $25,000 a week, his first priority has always been to buy paints.

It was painting that sustained Zero during the devastating years of the 1950's political blacklist, a time of trouble for many, shame for a few. Zero bore his piece of the trouble, none of the shame. Banned from films and television, found suddenly to be unemployable in nightclubs where he'd been earning up to $5,000 a week, not yet an attraction

Aurthur had been hanging out as a writer, director and producer of films and TV plays for twenty years, and as an occasional contributor to Esquire for ten, when the editor persuaded him to write a monthly column about show business. This one ran in June, 1972.

in the Broadway theatre which, alone, ignored the right-wing Neanderthals, Zero painted while witches were burned. In 1955, ultimately subpoenaed as a most reluctant witness, Mostel defied H.U.A.C., at the same time telling the absolute truth. In response to Counsel Tavenner's question, "You are also known by 'Zero' as a nickname, are you not?," he answered, "Yes, sir. After my financial standing in the community—sir."

Sharing the back seat of a taxi with Zero Mostel, or in fact being anywhere with him, I find the past and present merging into a single canvas, which like some of his paintings has a multicolored abstract background through which burst sharp, mostly grotesque images, all of them somehow resembling Mostel himself. There's the first time I ever saw him—it must have been 1942—he was a coffeepot and a butterfly-at-rest, performing at Café Society Downtown, his first proper professional engagement. Initially signed for two weeks at $40 per, he remained to earn a salary of $450. Four years passed before I saw him again: he'd become a star at La Martinique, a wildly cavorting zoot-suiter, a brilliant satirist of the truly insane among us. Remember, then, his performance in the 1950 film *Panic In The Streets*, not in the least funny. Sleazy, sweating, distorted; a whining creep. Remember, too, his Bloom. He stands limned in a pin spot in a crummy off-Broadway house, reads Joyce's soliloquies, and the poetry melts walls. And, later, the moment in the Ionesco play when the mincing bourgeois transmutes into a roaring, raging rhinoceros, a heavy warning to us all. And, most recently, his Tevye when you didn't even have to be Jewish to love him. His role in *Fiddler* was not just a sentimental journey. No, it was a creation, his own, that earned for Zero an audience for all time.

Right! I am a fan, but look at it this way: in a lifetime of theatregoing you might remember an actor for one transcendent moment, maybe two. Three? With Zero, for me, at least six. If I had to pick a seventh it would be his benefit appearance for H.U.A.C., and forced to go to eight, I would choose another unpaid moment, not long after the confrontation with the committee, this time in a friend's living room. Among the guests was Senator Jacob Javits, for

61

whom Zero quite possibly had not voted. Nonetheless, in high spirits, Mostel, suddenly transformed into a simpering queen, sashayed his way through a crowd, limply took the Senator's hand and said, "Sir, I want you to know I'm honored to head up Homosexuals for Javits. We'll soon have our own pin." Mr. Javits laughed nervously, moved to another room.

The ten-minute cab ride to the restaurant has become a whole different kind of trip for me, but now we've arrived, and Zero insists on paying the driver in return for my promise that never, in print, will I describe him as "elfin." I say that's his word, not mine, and not in ten million years. . . .

Another Mostel entrance. Recognized and greeted by restaurant personnel, Zero becomes manic, draping hat and coat onto the headwaiter, wrapping his arms and one leg around the manager, then bellowing his way into the main room. He holds center stage, all attention riveted. Three friends are waiting; as Zero collapses onto a banquette in his version of killer-whale-at-rest, someone says, "Okay, Zee, you've been noticed; everyone knows who you are," and there's an instantaneous transition to the man of dignity, the cultured artist. His voice softens to a charming French accent as he slides into a long story told him by Jean Renoir about the director's painter-father and Gauguin. No one questions how we got to Impressionist France, but sometimes it's hard to keep up. It's also hard to discuss any subject that does not star Zero Mostel, not because he always demands attention among friends, but because at this lunch we are interested. He tells of his next film, soon to be made in Mexico, then the possibility of a Broadway musical: good score, book needs work. The role will be especially demanding, a stretch for Zero, calling for great style and discipline. No one at the table questions his ability to achieve the style, but one tentative voice murmurs something about discipline. Zero changes the subject, and the lunch comes to an end soon after.

We are again in a cab heading downtown. Another Renoir story, then a description of a visit Zero had once made to Goya's grave, bringing flowers, the caretaker saying he was the first to pay homage in recent memory. Zero is pleased at this; somehow he is thus connected to Goya, but, more important, is reassured that he is not of the yahoos who ignore, forget or disparage great artists.

From Fifth Avenue and Twenty-eighth Street we walk west; Zero strides briskly, swinging his cane, not using it as an aid. In 1959 he'd been sideswiped by a bus, his left leg—and his career—saved only through innovative surgery by Dr. Joseph Wilder, an old friend of Zero's and a summer neighbor of mine in East Hampton. Five major operations were required, and the leg, though eminently usable, is without feeling, heavily scarred. I'm about to ask Zero about a story I'd heard regarding Joe Wilder and a convention of surgeons, but we are near the studio, and Zero tells me that this block, now the center of the flower market, was once the actual Tin Pan Alley. His old studio on the north side of the street had housed the music firm where young George Gershwin had dem-

onstrated his songs. The drab buildings, all converted to industrial lofts, are today without distinction, but as we turn through the door into one of them Zero explains that this building was the former home of vaudevillians Weber & Fields.

The studio occupies the entire top floor, a cheery, clean, organized place of work. Overlooking Twenty-eighth Street is a sitting area: comfortable chairs and a couch, shelves of books, tables laden with magazines and objects, mostly found or camp. The walls are filled with more found objects, some Americana. The loft, narrowing in the center, is lined with racks of paintings on one side, stacks on the other. Great piles of drawings and sketches. The main work area, almost half the loft, contains several easels, drafting tables, a small raised stage for his model—Zero always works from a model—and an intricate lighting system. In the rear we come to an area featuring a large, much-used poker table and a spotlessly clean kitchen and bath, both with shiny new equipment.

We sit at the poker table. Zero has the look of a man about to be interviewed, but I tell him he should simply go about his ordinary business, that my game is only to hang out and observe. He says he saves Fridays (and this is a Friday) for reading and talking with friends. I say I'll watch him read. "We'll talk," he says. A long moment of silence. I remember I meant to ask him about the Joe Wilder story, but before I can become a regular interviewer we're interrupted by Zero's younger son Tobias, twenty-three, himself a painter, with his own studio across the street. In what nearly becomes a ballet—and from Zero's attitude I may be witnessing a first—Toby replays a ten-dollar touch, the ceremony ending with the bill tucked into his father's shirt pocket. On his way out Toby says he'll sell me any of the paintings in the place at cut rates, conveying the impression that whatever I pay will be too much. Zero throws him out. He tells me that Toby is a talented painter and that son Josh, twenty-five, is off pursuing a promising acting career. Speaking of his sons, Zero is both a proud, loving father and a fugitive with savage wolves nipping his flanks.

He confirms the Joe Wilder story, which goes back to a time when Zero was still hospitalized. At an international meeting of surgeons Joe would describe his unprecedented work on Zero's left leg, and it would be to Wilder's advantage if the patient, designated only by a number, would then demonstrate the results. Anonymity was guaranteed. Gratefully, Zero promised he'd do anything for the pal who'd virtually saved his life. At the meeting, attended by surgeons from all over the world, Joe Wilder delivered his paper, with Zero at the ready. Now the clincher: "Patient X," said Dr. Wilder, "please show the leg." Shuffling forward, humble Patient X lifted his right pajama leg, revealing a healthy, seamless, if somewhat hairy, limb. A standing ovation, during which Joe Wilder was heard to say, "You miserable bastard, I'll kill you!" "Oops!" said Patient X, apologetically switching pajama pant legs to show the scarred mess. Still a miracle, but greeted with scattered applause from a disappointed group. A subsequent miracle is that Wilder and Zero are still close friends.

Another visitor, this time old friend Herbie Kallem, the sculptor whose studio is on the floor beneath Zero's. Many of the objects in Mostel's studio were given him by Herbie in a reciprocal arrangement where each strives to please and outdo the other. The two artists talk in a code that's evolved over more than thirty-five years, but I'm able to gather that Kallem has bought some clothes that need Zero's approval, and after Zee has seen the clothes modeled at six o'clock Herbie will drive us both uptown. The sculptor is ready to settle down for "a cold drink," but when, haughtily, Zero tells him I'm here not as a friend but as an interviewer, Kallem hustles downstairs to take a nap.

Smouldering irritation stemming from the casual remark at lunch about Zero's alleged lack of discipline now surfaces, but in a most devious way. "Have you any idea how much I hate rich people?" he suddenly demands. I allow that over the years I've had several clues. He summons up his current case, an aggrieved witness in a People's Court.

"A few Sundays ago my wife Kate"—Kate Mostel, his sainted spouse for twenty-eight years, was once a Rockette, now has her own poker game—"dragged me to some afternoon party given by *her* rich friends. I didn't want to go, but you know Kate. So I made the best of it and swore I'd be dignified and charming. We got there early, and I asked for a tomato juice. The host says there's no tomato juice, only champagne. I said in that case I'll have a seltzer. The host said no seltzer, only champagne. Okay, I'll die of thirst—but with dignity. I go to sit on a chair. The hostess yells, 'Don't sit there, it's an antique.' I turn to another chair; same thing: 'Don't break the antique!'

"I wander into the television room, turn on a ball game, and just as I'm about to sit down, the host runs in, screaming, 'Watch out for the chair, you'll break it!' So I scream back, 'Watch out for *me*, I'm going to break every focking thing in this focking house!'

"People lead me to a couch in the living room, I can't even see the ball game. Nothing to drink, not a mouthful of food, and the hostess sits down next to me and says, 'The trouble with you, Zero, is you have no discipline on the stage.' In all my dignity I say to her, 'You don't know the first focking thing about acting, much less the focking stage!' Kate takes me home early."

His case against all rich people made, we share a moment of understanding. "You know what they mean by discipline, don't you?" he asks. "They mean English acting, technique without any life. Stand up, look thirty degrees right, take two steps front, say the words, turn left, sit down. That's discipline? That's crap; I *relate*! Acting is living; it's experience. It's *relating*! Every night the actors come to the theatre different people than they were the night before. You look into their eyes, they look back, and you connect. Something happened that day: their kid is sick, they had a fight at home. Something.

They lived that day, so of course it changes. But not with technical actors like the English. Play a scene with them, you can't make them look into your focking eyes. No connection; they look *through* you, for crissake. Focking zombies!

"I'll tell you about relating. One night in *Rhinoceros* there was some drunken schmock in the second row who kept talking back to Eli [Wallach], making his life miserable, telling Eli he hated him. Between acts Eli was practically in tears, and I said, 'Leave the schmock to me.' So when I became the rhinoceros, without breaking out of character, I lean forward and *"roarrr"* right at him, blowing the poor schmock half out of his seat. He's petrified. He wiggles his fingers at me, and he whispers, 'I like you,' and not a peep from then on. That's *relating*!"

He'll surely get no argument from me. Instead, I'm reminded by his references to the English that several years ago Zero had been invited to play a season of rep with the Royal Shakespeare Company.

"I'll tell you what happened with that," Zero says. "They wanted me to play the two Falstaffs. Fine. So I went to London to make plans, and because there wasn't much money I stayed with Peter Hall when he was still married to Leslie Caron. A tiny house, one bathroom. *She* was in the john most of the time, so generally I had to pee outside. And *no food!* For dinner maybe you'd get one chop like this"—he indicates a circle the size of a nickel—"and four peas. One night Joan Littlewood came over, she was supposed to direct one of the plays. She tells us she wants the play to be 'a statement for peace.' Okay, we're all for peace, but I asked where in the play does Shakespeare make such a statement? 'Oh, Zero,' she said, 'we'll just forget about Shakespeare.' *Forget about Shakespeare!* She disappeared to make her statement somewhere else.

"A few nights later we're at dinner, I've eaten my four peas, and Peter Hall asked me if I thought I could play Falstaff in the manner of an English gentleman. Quietly, I told him I had the idea I'd bring other qualities to the part. 'No, no,' Hall said. 'I want you to play the English gentleman.'

"I rose from the table and said, 'You want an English gentleman, *get an English fag!*' I then went upstairs, packed my bag and left. Fock 'em!"

All afternoon Zero had been promising—or threatening—to show me paintings; now it was time, but first he served me a roundabout warning. "You know Harold Rosenberg, don't you?" And when I nodded: "Well, he came up here once. A fine critic, knows his field, and his work on action painting was most important. I showed him a painting, and he said, 'I don't like it.' I showed him another, he said, 'I don't like that one either.' I pulled out a third, he said, 'I'm not crazy about that one.' I had it with him. 'Harold,' I said, 'I don't need you as a focking critic. *Just look at the paintings!*' I took out another painting; he looked at it a long time. 'That one I like very much,' he said."

Forewarned, I start looking at paintings, beginning with the latest on the easels, then working back to the stacks. In response to each, I react with pleasure and delight, murmuring things like, "Marvelous. . . . Great. . . . I love that. . . . Fantastic work, Zee. . . ." Or just nodding my head in amazement. Intimidated, I'm not seeking to be "related" to. Not a complete sell-out, however; I do find myself impressed with the work, reacting to the power, the vivid colors, the imagination. The paintings are Zero. Apparently pleased by my response, he shows me more and more, but it's nearly time to go downstairs to awaken Herbie Kallem. Zero pulls one last picture from the racks: black, jagged figures against a blue background, splashes of bright colors, some objects quite specific. I'm truly moved by the painting, remark that it would seem to be somewhere out in space.

"I wanted to say something about the Universe," Zero says. "There's God, angels, planets . . . and horseshit." Our eyes make contact, two actors—one a genius—playing their parts, sharing a life experience. "It's *all* horseshit," Zero says, and then we go down to see Herbie's clothes.

Peter Bogdanovich:
THE LUBITSCH LEGACY

When comedy was king,
he was an emperor

I was speaking with Jack Benny the other day and he told me about working with Ernst Lubitsch. The director had called Benny in 1939 and asked if he'd be available to do a film. "I said, 'I'll do it!' And he said, 'But you haven't read the script?' And I said, 'I don't *have* to read the script. If you want me for a picture, I want to be in it!' I'd have been an *idiot* to say anything else. It was always impossible for comedians like me or Hope to get a good director for a movie—that's why we made lousy movies—and here was *Ernst Lubitsch*, for God's sake, calling to ask if *I'd* do a picture with him. Who *cares* what the script is!"

The film became *To Be or Not To Be* (Carole Lombard's last—she died in a plane crash before release) and it caused not a little controversy at the time for being a purportedly frivolous look at Nazism, dealing as it did with a troupe of Polish actors in occupied Warsaw and their comical confrontations with Hitler's gauleiters. But those who objected missed the point, having forgotten Thomas De Quincey's famous maxim: "If once a man indulges himself in murder, very soon he comes to think little of robbing; and from robbing he comes next to drinking and Sabbath-breaking, and from that to incivility and procrastination." For Lubitsch, the Nazis' most damning sin was their bad manners, and *To Be or Not To Be* survives not only as satire but as a glorification of man's indomitable good spirits in the face of disaster—survives in a way that many more serious and high-toned works about the war do not. Lubitsch had a habit of establishing his European locales by showing a series of stores, each featuring a more unpronounceable name on its facade. He does this in *To Be or Not To Be*, then follows it with an identical sequence of the same shops as they looked after the bombing. The simplicity of this is deeply affecting, especially realizing the significance it must have held for Lubitsch, who was, after all, a European and to whom those "funny" names—like his own—meant more than the easy laugh he enjoyed giving his American audiences.

"The Lubitsch Touch"—it was as famous a moniker

Coincidentally, Peter Bogdanovich was born the year Lubitsch made Ninotchka, 1939. *He has seen all of Lubitsch's films plus 6000 or so more. His tribute to Lubitsch appeared first as a column,* Hollywood, *November, 1972.*

as Hitchcock's "Master of Suspense"—but perhaps not as superficial. The phrase does connote something light, strangely indefinable. yet nonetheless tangible, and seeing Lubitsch's films—more than in almost any other director's work—one can feel this spirit: not only in the tactful and impeccably appropriate placement of camera, the subtle economy of his plotting, the oblique dialogue which had a way of saying everything through indirection, but also—and particularly—in the performance of every single player, no matter how small the role. Jack Benny told me that Lubitsch would act out in detail exactly how he wanted something done—often broadly but always succinctly—knowing, the comedian said, that he would translate the direction into his own manner and make it work. Clearly, this must have been Lubitsch's method with all his actors because everyone in a Lubitsch movie—whether it's Benny or Gary Cooper, Lombard or Kay Francis, Maurice Chevalier or Don Ameche, Jeanette MacDonald or Claudette Colbert—performs in the same unmistakable *style*. Despite their individual personalities—and Lubitsch never stifled these—they are imbued with the director's private view of the world, which made them behave very differently than they did in other films.

This was, in its own way, inimitable—though Lubitsch has had many imitators through the years—yet none has succeeded in capturing the soul of that attitude, which is as difficult to describe as only the best styles are, because they come from some fine inner workings of the heart and mind and not from something as apparent as, for instance, a tendency to dwell on inanimate objects as counterpoint to his characters' machinations. Certainly Lubitsch was famous for holding on a closed door while some silent or barely overheard crisis played out within, or for observing his people in dumb show through closed windows. This was surely as much a part of his style as it was an indication of his sense of delicacy and good taste, the boundless affection and respect he had for the often flighty and frivolous men and women who played out their charades for us in his glorious comedies and musicals.

No, closer to the heart of it (but not the real secret, because that, I believe, died with him—as every great artist's secret does) was his miraculous ability to mock and celebrate both at once and to such perfection that it was never quite possible to tell where the satirizing ended and the glorification began—so inseparably were they combined in Lubitsch's attitude and manner. In *Monte Carlo*, alone in her train compartment, Jeannette MacDonald sings "Beyond the Blue Horizon" in that pseudo-operatic, sometimes not far from ludicrous way of hers, and you feel right from the start that Lubitsch loves her not despite the fragility of her talents but *because* of it—because her way of singing was something irrevocably linked to an era that would soon be dead and whose gentle beauties Lubitsch longed to preserve and to praise, though he could also transcend them. For while her singing may be dated (but see her in the Nelson Eddy pictures she did and note the difference), Lubitsch's handling of the number is among the greatest of movie sequences. As she leans out the train window, her scarf wafting in the wind, she waves to the farmers along the countryside and they—in a magical display of art over reality—wave back and join in the chorus to her song. Of course, Lubitsch is making fun of it as much as he is *having* fun with it—indeed, it's this tension between his affection for those old-fashioned operetta forms and his awareness of their absurdity that gives his musicals such unpretentious charm, as well as a wise and pervasive wit. And he is never patronizing, either to his audience or to his characters, and when Miss MacDonald and the brittle and ingratiating Jack Buchanan sing a reprise of that song at the close of *Monte Carlo*—leaning together now from their train window—their fond wave to the people they pass can be enjoyed both for its innocence and gaiety as for the deeper sense of farewell to old times that Lubitsch's ineffable touch imparts.

Of course, it follows that Lubitsch made the very best of musical movies—not just the first great one in the first full year of sound—*The Love Parade* (1929)—but also just the best period—*Monte Carlo, The Smiling Lieutenant, One Hour with You, The Merry Widow*: no one has quite equaled or surpassed their special glow. (I guess *Singin' in the Rain*, directed by Stanley Donen and Gene Kelly and written by Comden and Green, is the best of the "modern" ones, and I love it, but really it's of another breed.) Truth to tell, no one even came close: the Astaire-Rogers shows of the Thirties—and I'm quite fond of Mark Sandrich's *Top Hat* and George Stevens' *Swing Time*—seem tawdry by comparison, and Rouben Mamoulian's *Love Me Tonight*—a forthright imitation of Lubitsch with his usual stars, Chevalier and MacDonald—though remembered fondly by many, looks pretty labored today next to the genuine article.

Lubitsch had a terrific impact on American movies. Jean Renoir was exaggerating only slightly when he told me recently, "Lubitsch invented the modern Hollywood," for his influence was felt, and continues to be, in the work of many of even the most individualistic directors. Hitchcock has admitted as much to me and a look at Lubitsch's *Trouble in Paradise* and Hitchcock's *To Catch A Thief* (both plots deal with jewel thieves so the comparisons are easy) will reveal how well he learned, though each is distinctly the work of the man who signed it. Billy Wilder, who was a writer on a couple of Lubitsch films—including the marvelous *Ninotchka*—has made several respectful forays into the world of Lubitsch, as have many others, with less noteworthy results. Even two such distinctive film makers as Frank Borzage and Otto Preminger, directing pictures which Lubitsch only produced—*Desire* (Borzage), *A Royal Scandal* and *That Lady in Ermine* (Preminger)—found themselves almost entirely in the service of his unique attitudes and these movies are certainly far more memorable for those qualities than for ones usually associated with their credited directors. (Actually, Lubitsch *is* credited for *That Lady in Ermine*, but this was a sentimental gesture since he suffered a fatal heart attack and only shot eight days of it before Preminger took over.)

Lubitsch brought a maturity to the handling of sex in pictures that was not dimmed by the dimness of the censors who took over in the early Thirties because his method was so circuitous and light that he could get away with almost anything. And that was true in everything he did. No other director, for example, has managed to let a character talk directly to the audience (as Chevalier did in *The Love Parade* and *One Hour with You*) and pull it off. There is always something coy and studied in it, but Lubitsch managed just the right balance between reality and theatricality—making the most outrageous device seem natural and easy; his movies flowed effortlessly and though his hand was felt, even seen, it was never intrusive.

But finally, of course, it was another world; it's no coincidence that several of Lubitsch's films were set in mythical Ruritanian countries, and that those set in "real" places have the same fanciful quality. Lubitsch achieved what only the best artists can—a singular universe where he sets all the rules and behavior. As Jean Renoir said in a recent interview: "Reality may be very interesting, but a work of art must be a creation. If you copy nature without adding the influence of your own personality, it is not a work of art. . . . Reality is merely a springboard for the artist. . . . But the final result must not be reality. It must only be what the actors and the director or author of the film selected of reality to reveal." Lubitsch had his own way of putting it; he once told Garson Kanin, "I've been to Paris, France, and I've been to Paris, Paramount. I think I prefer Paris, Paramount. . . ."

Lubitsch had also the unique ability to take the lightest of material and give it substance and resonance far beyond the subject. *The Shop Around the Corner*, a charming story of love and mistaken identities in a Budapest department store, becomes under Lubitsch's hand both a classic high comedy and a remarkably touching essay on human foibles and folly. Another movie, *In the Good Old Summertime*, and a stage musical, *She Loves Me*, both used the same story but they are to Lubitsch as George S. Kaufman is to Molière. The most profound expression of this particular aspect of his work is in *Heaven Can Wait*, which tells a ridiculously simple and unassuming story of one fairly insignificant man's life —from birth to death—which Lubitsch turns into a moving testament to the inherent beauty behind our daily frivolousness and vanity, our petty crises, our indiscretions, our deep vulnerability. It is Lubitsch's "divine comedy," and no one has ever been more gentle or bemused by the weaknesses of humanity. When the hero of the picture dies behind (of course) a closed door, Lubitsch's camera slowly retreats to take in a ballroom, and an old waltz the man loved begins to play, and death has no dominion. No other image I can think of more aptly conveys Lubitsch's generosity or tolerance: the man has died—long live man.

After Lubitsch's funeral in 1947, his friends Billy Wilder and William Wyler were walking sadly to their car. Finally, to break the silence, Wilder said, "No more Lubitsch," and Wyler answered, "Worse than that—no more Lubitsch films." The following year, the French director-critic, Jean-Georges Auriol, wrote a loving tribute that made the same point; titled "Chez Ernst," it can be found in Herman Weinberg's affectionate collection, *The Lubitsch Touch* (Dutton). After comparing the director's world to an especially fine restaurant where the food was perfect and the service meticulous, the piece ends this way: "How can a child who cries at the end of the summer holidays be comforted? He can be told that another summer will come, which will be equally wonderful. But he cries even more at this, not knowing how to explain that he won't be the same child again. Certainly Lubitsch's public is as sentimental as this child; and it knows quite well that 'Ernst's' is closed on account of death. This particular restaurant will never be open again."

Orson Welles:

Twilight in the Smog

Solemn suburbia crowds out the raucous old circus

It used to be easy to hate Hollywood. For me it was no trouble at all. But that was years ago. I don't think either of us have mellowed very much since then; but we are getting on a bit and our feelings for each other are scarcely as passionate as they were. For one thing, I no longer live there; I'm not just saying this—I really don't. Formerly this claim was the purest affectation; now it's a fact. It was my melancholy pretense that I was a transient, temporarily employed. There was nothing original about this self-deception. In the film colony a good half of the working population, including many of the oldest inhabitants, keep up their spirits by means of the same ruse. People buy houses and spend half their lives in them without unpacking all their bags. By now, however, I think it's safe to announce that I am one of those who got away. I chose freedom—and that was quite a while ago. Nowadays, if I do venture back behind the chromium curtain, it's never without a return ticket to the outside world. Also, I'm very careful about sitting down. This is important. In that peculiar climate one is haunted with the possibility that standing up again might suddenly exceed one's aspirations. Hollywood is a place where a youngish man is ill-advised to indulge in a siesta. Leaving a call for four-thirty won't do him any good. The likelihood remains that when he wakes up he'll be sixty-five.

It was Fred Allen who said, in his fair-minded way, that "California is a wonderful place if you're an orange." I guess what Fred was actually referring to was the general region of Los Angeles, or, as it's called, Greater Los Angeles (greater than what?). Like so many of us, this was the part of the state he knew best and liked least. Anyway, as the citrus people are the first to admit, smog has taken the fun out of life even for the oranges.

When we speak of Hollywood we take in, of course, more than the community of that name: we mean the movie and TV studios in the San Fernando Valley; we

include the beach houses, villas and palazzi in Santa Monica and Malibu. We mean the film colony which is spread so wide and thin, and the "industry" itself, which no longer dominates the scene as it once did. In the stately homes of Bel Air and Beverly Hills, oil millionaires are at least as numerous as movie stars, and nowadays the luckier studios bristle with oil pumps.

According to the map, Hollywood is a district attached but not belonging to the City of Los Angeles. But this is not strictly accurate: Los Angeles—though huge, populous and rich—has never quite made it as a city. It remains a loose and sprawling confederation of suburbs and shopping centers. As for downtown Los Angeles, it's about as metropolitan as Des Moines or Schenectady.

The metropolitan air is what one misses. Neither the theatre nor its artists are at their best in a suburb. Or a gigantic trailer camp. Whether we work before a camera or behind the footlights, actors are, by nature, city people. Hollywood is most precisely described as a colony. (Colonies are notoriously somewhat cut off from reality, insular, bitchy and cliquish, snobbish—a bit loose as to morals but very strict as to appearances.) One expects a colony to be an outpost of empire. Hollywood might be called an outpost of civilization (a word which means, after all, "city culture"), but it's also the heart of its own empire of the movies: a capital without a city, yet among its colonies are numbered the great cities of the world.

What is best in any branch of theatre must always have a certain flavor of tradition. Dear, shabby old Times Square, for instance, has its roots in Rome and the Middle Ages. It was, after all, a kind of market-place, and in the old tradition. The saloons and bars of the Broadway area are still the sorts of places where show folk have always gathered in Athens and Madrid, in London and Paris and Peking. But Hollywood, which boasts the largest population of actors ever concentrated in a single community, is also the first show town in history without a pub or a bistro in the traditional sense. In California the tradition of

An intermittent Hollywood resident during the Forties and Fifties, Welles, still in demand for acting roles in Hollywood when this piece was written for the March, 1959, issue, had recently completed two films, The Long Hot Summer *and* Compulsion.

the Mermaid Tavern has given way to the country club. A rigidly standardized middle-class suburbia is replacing the raucous and circusy traditions of the recent past.

Is Hollywood's famous sun really setting? There is certainly a hint of twilight in the smog and, lately, over the old movie capital there has fallen a grey-flannel shadow. Television is moving inexorably westward. Emptying the movie theatres across the land, it fills the movie studios. Another industry is building quite another town; and already, rising out of the gaudy ruins of screenland, we behold a new, drab, curiously solemn brand of the old foolishness.

There must always be a strong element of the absurd in the operation of a dream factory, but now there's less to laugh at and even less to like. The feverish gaiety has gone, a certain brassy vitality drained away. TV, after all, is a branch of the advertising business, and Hollywood behaves increasingly like an annex of Madison Avenue.

Television—live, taped or on film—is still limited by the language barrier, while by nature and economics moving pictures are multilingual. Making them has always been an international affair. Directors, writers, producers and, above all, the stars come to Hollywood from all over the world and their pictures are addressed to a world public. The town's new industry threatens its traditional cosmopolitanism and substitutes a strong national flavor. This could not be otherwise since our television exists to sell American products to American consumers.

And there's the question of money.

Millions of dollars are being made in television, but a million dollars has never been spent on any television show. Some few of the most lavish "spectaculars" are budgeted at the cost of a B-picture. All the rest of the TV product is made for "quickie" prices, the big money being spread thin to cover the whole season. If there's any conspicuous waste in this new industry it's only in the area of talent. A half-hour television western multiplied by three equals the playing time of a "program picture." But add the total price of all three and you have less than half the minimum budget for a negotiable second feature. Some TV stars are paid about as much for a week's solo appearance in Las Vegas as the complete production cost of one of their TV programs—and this includes full cast and crews, script, sets, photography, raw stock, wardrobe, music, scoring, mixing, processing, insurance—even their own star salaries. This penny-pinching grind runs counter to the town's most venerable instincts, but now, with the biggest of the big film studios limping along on economy programs administered by skeleton staffs, the gold-rush atmosphere which once was Hollywood's own dizzy brand of charm is just a memory.

In its golden age—in the first years of the movie boom—the mood and manner were indeed much like that of a gold rush. There was the frenzy and buccaneering hurly-burly of an earlier California: the vast fortunes found in a day and squandered in a night; the same cheerful violence and cutthroat anarchy. All of that Western turbulence has been silenced now; the wild and woolly charm is just a memory.

Architectural fantasy is in decline, the cheerful gaudiness is mostly gone, the more high-spirited of the old outrages have been razed or stand in ruins. In the "better" residential and business districts a kind of official "good taste" has taken charge. The result is a standardized impeccability, sterile and joyless, but it correctly expresses the community's ardent yearnings toward respectability.

Right down to this last moment in a long, long history, show folk have been kept quite firmly segregated from respectability. Significantly, the theatre profession had no contact (or contamination) with the middle class. Indeed, it's just recently that we began to employ that very middle-class word, "profession." This was when the mention of art began to embarrass us, and this was the beginning of our fall from grace: when we suddenly aspired to the mediocre rank of ladies and gentlemen. Before that, and in common with all other artists, we had no rank at all, and stood in our own dignity outside of protocol.

Something of what's ailing the new Hollywood, its movies, and us who make them can be traced, I think, back to that first fatal descent into polite society. It really started on that disastrous morning in the last century when the great English tragedian Henry Irving knelt before Queen Victoria to accept the theatre's first accolade. For Irving, knighthood seemed a giant step out of the old gypsydom, a deliverance from vagabondage; he thought of it as dignifying his "profession"—as sanctifying it with respectability. We can't rebuke him from this distance for imagining that the receipt of royal honors immeasurably elevated the social status of the theatre. Too many of his compatriots today agree with him. For my part, I'm convinced that this famous elevation was, in its consequences, nothing less than an abdication from royalty. I don't think that the great leaders of the stage in any country deserve to be ranked with the minor nobility. I think they deserve more. Sir Henry, rising from his knee a dubbed knight, dragged us all, not upward, but sideways—into another dimension, embedding us squarely and forevermore in the middle class.

What had been invulnerable in our position was the fact that we really had no position whatsoever. For just as long as there was no proper place for us —neither above nor below the salt—an actor was at liberty to sit wherever he was welcome, and this way very often next to the king. (It may be noted that our most distinguished cousins in the British theatre are not today the easy intimates of royalty.) I hold that we had more to give our art and to our audiences when we ourselves were royal bums, draped in our own brand of imperial purple. Our crown was tin, but it was a crown, and we wore it, with a difference, among such other diadems as happened to be gold.

For decades after Irving, the new stage gentry on both sides of the Atlantic made private imitation and public representation of the bourgeois their paramount concern. Then came the movies.

This was an institution "legitimate" actors could

look down on with all the priggish contempt formerly lavished by middle-class respectability on the playhouse itself. Hollywood became a word in the language, and in this unlikely outpost—unfettered, unbracketed and largely unconsidered—a motley crew of show folk, in spirit far closer to the circus, to burlesque and the commedia dell'arte than to the starchy stage world of that epoch, was gaily producing a new art form, and celebrating in the process a brief but exciting renaissance of the old royal nonsense and glory.

That glory had all but died out as the theatre reduced itself into a mere profession. Now—as the making of motion pictures began to be spoken of and to be organized as a mere industry—the glory started dimming in Hollywood.

What's valid on the stage or screen is never a mere professional effort and certainly not an industrial product. Whatever is valuable must, in the final analysis, be a work of art. There should be no need to repeat that originality is one of the essential definitions of any work of art, and that every artist is an individual. Just as obviously, the industrial system cannot accommodate originality. A genuine individual is an outright nuisance in a factory.

There's Method in Their Madness

There used to be something spoken of as "the Hollywood influence." What is more noticeable today is that the rest of America is influencing Hollywood.

As always, much fun is provided by the current sex symbols, but Jayne and Elvis are too patently creatures of the publicity experts—fuzzy carbon copies of the old freewheeling originals, the vamps and sheiks who invented themselves and lived up so gorgeously to their own legends. The recent crop of "Method actors" and the official representatives of the beatnik constituency are rather too sullen in their personal style to add much color to the pallid scene. The biggest noise they make is on their bongo drums and their gestures of protest are no less standardized than the conformist patterns they pretend to reject. They have their own conformism, these eagle scouts of The Actors Studio—there is no madness in their method.

Of the authentic mavericks the youngest, men like Mitchum and Sinatra, are in their forties. Rock 'n' roll throws up an occasional oddball of a minor sort, but such types are "cool" in the dictionary sense of the word and do nothing to the tepid temperature of the new Hollywood one way or another. Their kind of egotism rages in a sort of monotone and with no exuberance. They hold the mirror up to their own generation. So do their pseudosuburbanite elders in the film colony. These two groups, the T-shirts and the sports jackets, are more accurate reflections of today's America than were those dazzling pioneers who blazed screenland's frontiers.

One of our producers, by way of explaining the school of neorealism in the Italian cinema, told me that over there, instead of actors, they use people. For good or evil it's certain that the town is overrun with characters who are quite reasonable facsimiles of today's people. It's a solemn thought, but maybe that's what's wrong with Hollywood.

NEW YORK, NEW YORK

In Esquire's special "New York" issue of July, 1960, Arnold Gingrich wrote in his Publisher's Page column: "New York is where you can find the best and the worst of practically anything you're looking for." Indeed, in the scores of articles Esquire has published about New York, we have considered it both our pleasure to hail its glories and our duty to report its failings. The four articles which follow have been chosen as a representative cross section of our forty years running the Gotham gamut: a paean to New York by Gay Talese; James Baldwin's *Fifth Avenue, Uptown,* a bitter foretaste of his *The Fire Next Time*; an uncharacteristically mellow mood piece by the late Dorothy Parker; and, finally, a loving but firm renunciation of the city by John Cheever. Since each of these pieces appeared a number of years ago, it seemed only appropriate by way of preface to contact the various contributors where possible for an update on their personal feelings about New York. Gay Talese spoke feelingly about the people in his article on the next page. "That was the New York I knew when I was twenty-eight," Talese said. "The people I wrote about, many of them, are people I still know. My view of New York is really the city of side streets and unnoticed people who are taken for granted, who are never interviewed by anyone but me. The people whose voices I try to reecho on paper are the small people, yet representative of what makes the city big and magnificent. The people I am attracted to and write about are not the super achievers, but they are, to me, in the way they live, fas-

cinating. I have tried to get a sense of history from the people historians ignore—bridge builders, charwomen, doormen, electric-light-bulb changers in the I.R.T., designers of store window mannequins, retired cops on Staten Island." Regarding his feelings about New York today, Talese says simply, "New York is my home. The fact that it's home to eight million others does not make it any less mine." Echoing Talese's view is the noted artist John Koch, whose evocative paintings are the subject of Dorothy Parker's *New York at 6:30 P.M.* "During the forty years I've lived here," said Koch in his apartment on Central Park West, "New York has become for me so essential that I am afraid that I have developed a kind of gradual provincialism in reverse. In all ways, New York is my home." Unfortunately, we were unable to contact James Baldwin, who is currently living in France; however, Saul Leiter, whose brilliant documentary photographs of Harlem originally accompanied Baldwin's article (an example of which appears on page 77), told us from his Manhattan studio, "For people with a sense of adventure and a spirited view of life, New York is a great place to live. Cowards usually prefer London or Vermont. What spoils New York for me sometimes is not the city itself but the many people who hate it." Finally, John Cheever, who writes on *Moving Out* and who remains a dropout to this day, said from his home in Ossining, New York, that he still has no regrets about moving away. "I'm very happy," Cheever said. "It's a nice, reclusive and boozy life with trees and dogs."

Gay Talese:
NEW YORK

"The offbeat wonders of a town without time"

New York is a city of things unnoticed. It is a city with cats sleeping under parked cars, two stone armadillos crawling up St. Patrick's Cathedral, and thousands of ants creeping on top of the Empire State Building. The ants probably were carried up there by wind or birds, but nobody is sure; nobody in New York knows any more about the ants than they do about the panhandler who takes taxis to the Bowery; or the dapper man who picks trash out of Sixth Avenue trash cans; or the medium in the West Seventies who claims, "I am clairvoyant, clairaudient and clairsensuous."

New York is a city for eccentrics and a center for odd bits of information. New Yorkers blink twenty-eight times a minute, but forty when tense. Most popcorn chewers at Yankee Stadium stop chewing momentarily just before the pitch. Gumchewers on Macy's escalators stop chewing momentarily just before they get off—to concentrate on the last step. Coins, paper clips, ball-point pens, and little girls' pocketbooks are found by workmen when they clean the sea lion's pool at the Bronx Zoo.

A Park Avenue doorman has parts of three bullets in his head—there since World War I. Several young gypsy daughters, influenced by television and literacy, are running away from home because they don't want to grow up and become fortune-tellers. Each month a hundred pounds of hair is delivered to Louis Feder on 545 Fifth Avenue, where blond hairpieces are made from German women's hair; brunette hairpieces from Italian women's hair; but no hairpieces from American women's hair which, says Mr. Feder, is weak from too frequent rinses and permanents.

Some of New York's best informed men are elevator operators, who rarely talk, but always listen—like doormen. Sardi's doormen listen to the comments made by Broadway's first-nighters walking by after the last act. They listen closely. They listen carefully. Within ten minutes they can tell you which shows will flop and which will be hits.

On Broadway each evening a big, dark, 1948 Rolls-Royce pulls into Forty-sixth Street—and out hop two little ladies armed with Bibles and signs reading, "The Damned Shall Perish." These ladies proceed to stand on the corner screaming at the multitudes of Broadway sinners, sometimes until three a.m., when their chauffeur in the Rolls picks them up and drives them back to Westchester.

By this time Fifth Avenue is deserted by all but a few strolling insomniacs, some cruising cabdrivers, and a group of sophisticated females who stand in store windows all night and day wearing cold, perfect smiles. Like sentries they line Fifth Avenue—these window mannequins who gaze onto the quiet street with tilted heads and pointed toes and long rubber fingers reaching for cigarettes that aren't there.

At five a.m. Manhattan is a town of tired trumpet players and homeward-bound bartenders. Pigeons control Park Avenue and strut unchallenged in the middle of the street. This is Manhattan's mellowest hour. Most *night* people are out of sight—but the *day* people have not yet appeared. Truck drivers and cabs are alert, yet they do not disturb the mood. They do not disturb the abandoned Rockefeller Center, or the motionless night watchmen in the Fulton Fish Market, or the gas-station attendant sleeping next to Sloppy Louie's with the radio on.

At five a.m. the Broadway regulars either have gone home or to all-night coffee shops where, under the glaring light, you see their whiskers and wear. And on Fifty-first Street a radio press car is parked at the curb with a photographer who has nothing to do. So he just sits there for a few nights, looks through the windshield, and soon becomes a keen observer of life after midnight.

"At one a.m.," he says, "Broadway is filled with wise guys and with kids coming out of the Astor Hotel in white dinner jackets—kids who drive to dances in their fathers' cars. You also see cleaning ladies going home, always wearing kerchiefs. By two a.m. some of the drinkers are getting out of hand, and this is the hour for bar fights. At three a.m. the last show is over in the nightclubs, and most of the tourists and out-of-town buyers are back in hotels. And small-time comedians are criticizing big-time comedians in Hanson's Drugstore. At four a.m., after the bars close, you see the drunks come out—and also the pimps and prostitutes who take advantage of drunks. At five a.m., though, it is mostly quiet. New York is an entirely different city at five a.m."

At six a.m. the early workers begin to push up from the subways. The traffic begins to move down Broadway like a river. And Mrs. Mary Woody jumps out of bed, dashes to her office and phones dozens of

Talese was a reporter for The New York Times when he wrote about his city in July, 1960, with a magpie researcher's eye. Many of the names and addresses of businesses have changed since that time, but we have chosen to present the article as it was written.

sleepy New Yorkers to say in a cheerful voice, rarely appreciated: "Good morning. Time to get up." For twenty years, as an operator of Western Union's Wake-Up Service, Mrs. Woody has gotten millions out of bed.

By seven a.m. a floridly robust little man, looking very Parisian in a blue beret and turtleneck sweater, moves in a hurried step along Park Avenue visiting his wealthy lady friends—making certain that each is given a brisk, before-breakfast rubdown. The uniformed doormen greet him warmly and call him either "Biz" or "Mac" because he is Biz Mackey, a ladies' masseur *extraordinaire*. He never reveals the names of his customers, but most of them are middle-aged and rich. He visits each of them in their apartments, and has special keys to their bedrooms; he is often the first man they see in the morning, and they lie in bed waiting for him.

The doormen that Biz passes each morning are generally an obliging, endlessly articulate group of sidewalk diplomats who list among their friends some of Manhattan's most powerful men, most beautiful women and snootiest poodles. More often than not, the doormen are big, slightly Gothic in design, and the possessors of eyes sharp enough to spot big tippers a block away in the year's thickest fog. Some East Side doormen are as proud as grandees, and their uniforms, heavily festooned, seem to come from the same tailor who outfitted Marshal Tito.

Shortly after seven-thirty each morning hundreds of people are lined along Forty-second Street waiting for the eight a.m. opening of the ten movie houses that stand almost shoulder-to-shoulder between Times Square and Eighth Avenue. Who are these people who go to the movies at eight a.m.? They are the city's insomniacs, night watchmen, and people who can't go home, do not want to go home, or have no home. They are derelicts, homosexuals, cops, hacks, truck drivers, cleaning ladies and restaurant men who have worked all night. They are also alcoholics who are waiting at eight a.m. to pay forty cents for a soft seat and to sleep in the dark, smoky theatre. And yet, aside from being smoky, each of Times Square's theatres has a special quality, or lack of quality, about it. At the Victory Theatre one finds horror films, while at the Times Square Theatre they feature only cowboy films. There are first-run films for forty cents at the Lyric, while at the Selwyn there are always second-run films for thirty cents. But if you go to the Apollo Theatre you will see, in addition to foreign films, people in the lobby talking with their hands. These are deaf-and-dumb movie fans who patronize the Apollo because they read the subtitles. The Apollo probably has the biggest deaf-and-dumb movie audience in the world.

New York is a city of 38,000 cabdrivers, 10,000 bus drivers, but only one chauffeur who has a chauffeur. The wealthy chauffeur can be seen driving up Fifth Avenue each morning, and his name is Roosevelt Zanders. He earns $100,000 a year, is a gentleman of impeccable taste and, although he owns a $23,000 Rolls-Royce, does not scorn his friends who own Bentleys. For $150 a day, Mr. Zanders will drive

anyone anywhere in his big, silver Rolls. Diplomats patronize him, models pose next to him, and each day he receives cables from around the world urging that he be waiting at Idlewild, on the docks, or outside the Plaza Hotel. Sometimes at night, however, he is too tired to drive anymore. So Bob Clarke, his chauffeur, takes over and Mr. Zanders relaxes in the back.

New York is a town of 3000 bootblacks whose brushes and rhythmic rag-snaps can be heard up and down Manhattan from midmorning to midnight. They dodge cops, survive rainstorms, and thrive in the Empire State Building as well as on the Staten Island Ferry. They usually wear dirty shoes.

New York is a city of headless men who sit obscurely in subway booths all day and night selling tokens to people in a hurry. Each weekday more than 4,500,000 riders pass these money changers who seem to have neither heads, faces, nor personalities—only fingers. Except when giving directions, their vocabulary consists largely of three words: "How many, please?"

In New York there are 200 chestnut vendors, and they average $25 on a good day peddling soft, warm chestnuts. Like many vendors, the chestnut men do not own their own rigs—they borrow or rent them from pushcart makers such as David Amerman.

Mr. Amerman, with offices opposite a defunct public bathhouse on the Lower East Side, is New York's master builder of pushcarts. His father and grandfather before him were pushcart makers, and the family has long been a household word among the city's most discriminating junkmen, fruit vendors and hot-dog peddlers.

In New York there are 500 mediums, ranging from semi-trance to trance to deep-trance types. Most of them live in New York's West Seventies and Eighties, and on Sundays some of these blocks are communicating with the dead, vibrating to trumpets, and solving all problems.

The Manhattan Telephone Directory has 776,300 names, of which 3316 are Smith, 2835 are Brown, 2444 are Williams, 2070 are Cohen—and one is Mike Krasilovsky. Anyone who doubts this last fact has only to look at the top of page 876 where, in large black letters, is this sign: "There is only one Mike Krasilovsky. Sterling 3-1990."

In New York the Fifth Avenue Lingerie shop is on Madison Avenue; The Madison Pet Shop is on Lexington Avenue; the Park Avenue Florist is on Madison Avenue, and the Lexington Hand Laundry is on Third Avenue. New York is the home of 120 pawnbrokers and it is where Bishop Sheen's brother, Dr. Sheen, shares an office with one Dr. Bishop.

New York is a town of thirty tattooists where interest in mankind is skin-deep, but whose impressions usually last a lifetime. Each day the tattooists go pecking away over acres of anatomy. And in downtown Manhattan, Stanley Moskowitz, a scion of a distinguished family of Bowery skin-peckers, does a grand business.

When it rains in Manhattan, automobile traffic is slow, dates are broken and, in hotel lobbies, people slump behind newspapers or walk aimlessly about with no place to sit, nobody to talk to, nothing to do. Taxis are harder to get; department stores do between fifteen and twenty-five percent less business, and the monkeys in the Bronx Zoo, having no audience, slouch grumpily in their cages looking more bored than the lobby-loungers.

While some New Yorkers become morose with rain, others prefer it, like to walk in it, and say that on rainy days the city's buildings seem somehow cleaner—washed in an opalescence, like a Monet painting. There are fewer suicides in New York when it rains. But when the sun is shining, and New Yorkers seem happy, the depressed person sinks deeper into depression, and Bellevue Hospital gets more suicide calls.

New York is a town of 8485 telephone operators, 1364 Western Union messenger boys, and 112 newspaper copyboys. An average baseball crowd at Yankee Stadium uses over ten gallons of liquid soap per game—an unofficial high mark for cleanliness in the major leagues; the stadium also has the league's top number of ushers (360), sweepers (72), and men's rooms (34).

New York is a town in which the brotherhood of Russian Bath Rubbers, the only union advocating sweatshops, appears to be heading for its last rubdown. The union has been going in New York City for years, but now most of the rubbers are pushing seventy and are deaf—from all the water and the hot temperatures.

Each afternoon in New York a rather seedy saxophone player, his cheeks blown out like a spinnaker, stands on the sidewalk playing *Danny Boy* in such a sad, sensitive way that he soon has half the neighborhood peeking out of windows tossing nickels, dimes and quarters at his feet. Some of the coins roll under parked cars, but most of them are caught in his outstretched hand. The saxophone player is a street musician named Joe Gabler; for the past thirty years he has serenaded every block in New York and has sometimes been tossed as much as $100 a day in coins. He is also hit with buckets of water, empty beer cans and eggs, and chased by wild dogs. He is believed to be the last of New York's ancient street musicians.

New York is a town of nineteen midget wrestlers. They all can squeeze into the Hotel Holland's elevator, six can sleep in one bed, eight can be comfortably transported to Madison Square Garden in the chauffeur-driven Cadillac reserved for the midget wrestlers.

In New York from dawn to dusk to dawn, day after day, you can hear the steady rumble of tires against the concrete span of George Washington Bridge. The bridge is never completely still. It trembles with traffic. It moves in the wind. Its great veins of steel swell when hot and contract when cold; its span often is ten feet closer to the Hudson River in summer than in winter. It is an almost restless structure of graceful beauty which, like an irresistible seductress, withholds secrets from the romantics who gaze upon it, the escapists who jump off it, the chubby girl who lumbers across its 3500-foot span trying to reduce, and the 100,000 motorists who each day cross it, smash into it, shortchange it, get jammed up on it.

When street traffic dwindles and most people are sleeping in New York, some neighborhoods begin to crawl with cats. They move quickly through the shadows of buildings; night watchmen, policemen, garbage collectors and other nocturnal wanderers see them—but never for long.

There are 200,000 stray cats in New York. A majority of them hang around the fish market, or in Greenwich Village, and in the East and West Side neighborhoods where garbage cans abound. No part of the city is without its strays, however, and all-night garage attendants in such busy neighborhoods as Fifty-fourth Street have counted as many as twenty of them around the Ziegfeld Theatre early in the morning. Troops of cats patrol the waterfront piers at night searching for rats. Subway trackwalkers have discovered cats living in the darkness. They seem never to get hit by trains, though some are occasionally liquidated by the third rail. About twenty-five cats live seventy-five feet below the west end of Grand Central Terminal, are fed by the underground workers, and never wander up into the daylight.

New York is a city in which large, cliff-dwelling hawks cling to skyscrapers and occasionally zoom to snatch a pigeon over Central Park, or Wall Street, or the Hudson River. Bird watchers have seen these peregrine falcons circling lazily over the city. They have seen them perched atop tall buildings, even around Times Square. About twelve of these hawks patrol the city, sometimes with a wingspan of thirty-five inches. They have buzzed women on the roof of the St. Regis Hotel, have attacked repairmen on smokestacks, and, in August, 1947, two hawks jumped women residents in the recreation yard of the Home of the New York Guild for the Jewish Blind. Maintenance men at the Riverside Church have seen hawks dining on pigeons in the bell tower. The hawks remain there for only a little while. And then they fly out to the river, leaving pigeons' heads for the Riverside maintenance men to clean up. When the hawks return, they fly in quietly—*unnoticed*, like the cats, the headless men, the ants, the ladies' masseur, the doorman with three bullets in his head, and most of the other offbeat wonders in this town without time.

Fifth Avenue, Uptown

*"There are few things under heaven more unnerving than the silent,
accumulating contempt and hatred of a people"*

There is a housing project standing now where the house in which we grew up once stood, and one of those stunted city trees is snarling where our doorway used to be. This is on the rehabilitated side of the avenue. The other side of the avenue—for progress takes time—has not been rehabilitated yet and it looks exactly as it looked in the days when we sat with our noses pressed against the windowpane, longing to be allowed to go "across the street." The grocery store which gave us credit is still there, and there can be no doubt that it is still giving credit. The people in the project certainly need it—far more, indeed, than they ever needed the project. The last time I passed by, the Jewish proprietor was still standing among his shelves, looking sadder and heavier but scarcely any older. Further down the block stands the shoe-repair store in which our shoes were repaired until reparation became impossible and in which, then, we bought all our "new" ones. The Negro proprietor is still in the window, head down, working at the leather.

These two, I imagine, could tell a long tale if they would (perhaps they would be glad to if they could), having watched so many, for so long, struggling in the fishhooks, the barbed wire, of this avenue.

The avenue is elsewhere the renowned and elegant Fifth. The area I am describing, which, in today's gang parlance, would be called "the turf," is bounded by Lenox Avenue on the west, the Harlem River on the east, 135th Street on the north, and 130th Street on the south. We never lived beyond these boundaries; this is where we grew up. Walking along 145th Street —for example—familiar as it is, and similar, does not have the same impact because I do not know any of the people on the block. But when I turn east on 131st Street and Lenox Avenue, there is first a soda-pop joint, then a shoeshine "parlor," then a grocery store, then a dry cleaners', then the houses. All along the street there are people who watched me grow up, people who grew up with me, people I watched grow up along with my brothers and sisters; and, sometimes in my arms, sometimes underfoot, sometimes at my shoulder—or on it—their children, a riot, a forest of children, who include my nieces and nephews.

In 1960, when James Baldwin found that a housing project had supplanted his childhood home, he wrote this essay. We have left it unchanged, although its details bear no relation to current conditions. (The photograph on the following page is by Saul Leiter.)

When we reach the end of this long block, we find ourselves on wide, filthy, hostile Fifth Avenue, facing that project which hangs over the avenue like a monument to the folly, and the cowardice, of good intentions. All along the block, for anyone who knows it, are immense human gaps, like craters. These gaps are not created merely by those who have moved away, inevitably into some other ghetto; or by those who have risen, almost always into a greater capacity for self-loathing and self-delusion; or yet by those who, by whatever means—War II, the Korean war, a policeman's gun or billy, a gang war, a brawl, madness, an overdose of heroin, or, simply, unnatural exhaustion—are dead. I am talking about those who are left, and I am talking principally about the young. What are they doing? Well, some, a minority, are fanatical churchgoers, members of the more extreme of the Holy Roller sects. Many, many more are "moslems," by affiliation or sympathy, that is to say that they are united by nothing more—and nothing less—than a hatred of the white world and all its works. They are present, for example, at every Buy Black street-corner meeting—meetings in which the speaker urges his hearers to cease trading with white men and establish a separate economy. Neither the speaker nor his hearers can possibly do this, of course, since Negroes do not own General Motors or RCA or the A&P, nor, indeed, do they own more than a wholly insufficient fraction of anything else in Harlem (those who *do* own anything are more interested in their profits than in their fellows). But these meetings nevertheless keep alive in the participators a certain pride of bitterness without which, however futile this bitterness may be, they could scarcely remain alive at all. Many have given up. They stay home and watch the TV screen, living on the earnings of their parents, cousins, brothers, or uncles, and only leave the house to go to the movies or to the nearest bar. "How're you making it?" one may ask, running into them along the block, or in the bar. "Oh, I'm TV-ing it"; with the saddest, sweetest, most shamefaced of smiles, and from a great distance. This distance one is compelled to respect; anyone who has traveled so far will not easily be dragged again into the world. There are further retreats, of course, than the TV screen or the bar. There are those who are simply sitting on their stoops, "stoned," animated for a moment only, and hideously, by the approach of someone who may lend them the

1783

the
UNSeeN
eye
IS WatCHING
YOU

money for a "fix." Or by the approach of someone from whom they can purchase it, one of the shrewd ones, on the way to prison or just coming out.

And the others, who have avoided all of these deaths, get up in the morning and go downtown to meet "the man." They work in the white man's world all day and come home in the evening to this fetid block. They struggle to instill in their children some private sense of honor or dignity which will help the child to survive. This means, of course, that they must struggle, stolidly, incessantly, to keep this sense alive in themselves, in spite of the insults, the indifference, and the cruelty they are certain to encounter in their working day. They patiently browbeat the landlord into fixing the heat, the plaster, the plumbing; this demands prodigious patience; nor is patience usually enough. In trying to make their hovels habitable, they are perpetually throwing good money after bad. Such frustration, so long endured, is driving many strong, admirable men and women whose only crime is color to the very gates of paranoia.

One remembers them from another time—playing handball in the playground, going to church, wondering if they were going to be promoted at school. One remembers them going off to war—gladly, to escape this block. One remembers their return. Perhaps one remembers their wedding day. And one sees where the girl is now—vainly looking for salvation from some other embittered, trussed, and struggling boy—and sees the all-but-abandoned children in the streets.

Now I am perfectly aware that there are other slums in which white men are fighting for their lives, and mainly losing. I know that blood is also flowing through those streets and that the human damage there is incalculable. People are continually pointing out to me the wretchedness of white people in order to console me for the wretchedness of blacks. But an itemized account of the American failure does not console me and it should not console anyone else. That hundreds of thousands of white people are living, in effect, no better than the "niggers" is not a fact to be regarded with complacency. The social and moral bankruptcy suggested by this fact is of the bitterest, most terrifying kind.

The people, however, who believe that this democratic anguish has some consoling value are always pointing out that So-and-So, white, and So-and-So, black, rose from the slums into the big time. The existence—the public existence—of, say, Frank Sinatra and Sammy Davis Jr. proves to them that America is still the land of opportunity and that inequalities vanish before the determined will. It proves nothing of the sort. The determined will is rare—at the moment, in this country, it is unspeakably rare—and the inequalities suffered by the many are in no way justified by the rise of a few. A few have always risen—in every country, every era, and in the teeth of regimes which can by no stretch of the imagination be thought of as free. Not all of these people, it is worth remembering, left the world better than they found it. The determined will is rare, but it is not invariably benevolent. Furthermore, the American equation of success with the big time

reveals an awful disrespect for human life and human achievement. This equation has placed our cities among the most dangerous in the world and has placed our youth among the most empty and most bewildered. The situation of our youth is not mysterious. Children have never been very good at listening to their elders, but they have never failed to imitate them. They must, they have no other models. That is exactly what our children are doing. They are imitating our immorality, our disrespect for the pain of others.

All other slum dwellers, when the bank account permits it, can move out of the slum and vanish altogether from the eye of persecution. No Negro in this country has ever made that much money and it will be a long time before any Negro does. The Negroes in Harlem, who have no money, spend what they have on such gimcracks as they are sold. These include "wider" TV screens, more "faithful" hi-fi sets, more "powerful" cars, all of which, of course, are obsolete long before they are paid for. Anyone who has ever struggled with poverty knows how extremely expensive it is to be poor; and if one is a member of a captive population, economically speaking, one's feet have simply been placed on the treadmill forever. One is victimized, economically, in a thousand ways— rent, for example, or car insurance. Go shopping one day in Harlem—for anything—and compare Harlem prices and quality with those downtown.

The people who have managed to get off this block have only got as far as a more respectable ghetto. This respectable ghetto does not even have the advantages of the disreputable one, friends, neighbors, a familiar church, and friendly tradesmen; and it is not, moreover, in the nature of any ghetto to remain respectable long. Every Sunday, people who have left the block take the lonely ride back, dragging their increasingly discontented children with them. They spend the day talking, not always with words, about the trouble they've seen and the trouble—one must watch their eyes as they watch their children—they are only too likely to see. For children do not like ghettos. It takes them nearly no time to discover exactly why they are there.

The projects in Harlem are hated. They are hated almost as much as policemen, and this is saying a great deal. And they are hated for the same reason: both reveal, unbearably, the real attitude of the white world, no matter how many liberal speeches are made, no matter how many lofty editorials are written, no matter how many civil-rights commissions are set up.

The projects are hideous, of course, there being a law, apparently respected throughout the world, that popular housing shall be as cheerless as a prison. They are lumped all over Harlem, colorless, bleak, high, and revolting. The wide windows look out on Harlem's invincible and indescribable squalor: the Park Avenue railroad tracks, around which, about forty years ago, the present dark community began; the unrehabilitated houses, bowed down, it would seem, under the great weight of frustration and bitterness they contain; the dark, the ominous schoolhouses from which the child may emerge maimed, blinded, hooked, or enraged for life; and the churches, churches, block upon block of churches, niched in the walls like cannon in the walls of a fortress. Even if the administration of the projects were not so insanely humiliating (for example: one must report raises in salary to the management, which will then eat up the profit by raising one's rent; the management has the right to know who is staying in your apartment; the management can ask you to leave, at their discretion), the projects would still be hated because they are an insult to the meanest intelligence.

Harlem got its first private project, Riverton—which is now, naturally, a slum—about twelve years ago because at that time Negroes were not allowed to live in Stuyvesant Town. Harlem watched Riverton go up, therefore, in the most violent bitterness of spirit, and hated it long before the builders arrived. They began hating it at about the time people began moving out of their condemned houses to make room for this additional proof of how thoroughly the white world despised them. And they had scarcely moved in, naturally, before they began smashing windows, defacing walls, urinating in the elevators, and fornicating in the playgrounds. Liberals, both white and black, were appalled at the spectacle. I was appalled by the liberal innocence—or cynicism, which comes out in practice as much the same thing. Other people were delighted to be able to point to proof positive that nothing could be done to better the lot of the colored people. They were, and are, right in one respect: that nothing can be done as long as they are treated like colored people. The people in Harlem know they are living there because white people do not think they are good enough to live anywhere else. No amount of "improvement" can sweeten this fact. Whatever money is now being earmarked to improve this or any other ghetto might as well be burnt. A ghetto can be improved in one way only: out of existence.

Similarly, the only way to police a ghetto is to be oppressive. None of Commissioner Kennedy's policemen, even with the best will in the world, have any way of understanding the lives led by the people they swagger about in two's and three's controlling. Their very presence is an insult, and it would be even if they spent their entire day feeding gumdrops to children. They represent the force of the white world, and that world's real intentions are, simply, for that world's criminal profit and ease, to keep the black man corralled up here, in his place. The badge, the gun in the holster, and the swinging club make vivid what will happen should his rebellion become overt. Rare, indeed, is the Harlem citizen, from the most circumspect church member to the most shiftless adolescent, who does not have a long tale to tell of police incompetence, injustice, or brutality. I myself have witnessed and endured it more than once. The businessmen and racketeers also have a story. And so do the prostitutes. (And this is not, perhaps, the place to discuss Harlem's very complex attitude toward black

policemen, nor the reasons, according to Harlem, that they are nearly all downtown.)

It is hard, on the other hand, to blame the policeman, blank, good-natured, thoughtless, and insuperably innocent, for being such a perfect representative of the people he serves. He, too, believes in good intentions and is astounded and offended when they are not taken for the deed. He has never, himself, done anything for which to be hated—which of us has?—and yet he is facing, daily and nightly, people who would gladly see him dead, and he knows it. There is no way for him not to know it: there are few things under heaven more unnerving than the silent, accumulating contempt and hatred of a people. He moves through Harlem, therefore, like an occupying soldier in a bitterly hostile country; which is precisely what, and where, he is, and is the reason he walks in two's and three's. And he is not the only one who knows why he is always in company: the people who are watching him know why, too. Any street meeting, sacred or secular, which he and his colleagues uneasily cover has as its explicit or implicit burden the cruelty and injustice of the white domination. And these days, of course, in terms increasingly vivid and jubilant, it speaks of the end of that domination.

The white policeman who is standing on a Harlem street corner finds himself at the center of the revolution now occurring in the world. He is not prepared for it—naturally, nobody is—and, what is possibly much more to the point, he is exposed, as few white people are, to the anguish of the black people around him. Even if he is gifted with the merest mustard grain of imagination, something must seep in. He cannot avoid observing that some of the children, in spite of their color, remind him of children he has known and loved, perhaps even of his own children. He knows that he certainly does not want *his* children living this way. He can retreat from his uneasiness in only one direction: into a callousness which very shortly becomes second nature. He becomes more callous, the population becomes more hostile, the situation grows more tense, and the police force is increased. One day, to everyone's astonishment, someone drops a match in the powder keg and everything blows up. Before the dust has settled or the blood congealed, editorials, speeches, and civil-rights commissions are loud in the land, demanding to know what happened. What happened is that Negroes want to be treated like men.

Negroes want to be treated like men: a perfectly straightforward statement, containing only seven words. People who have mastered Kant, Hegel, Shakespeare, Marx, Freud, and the Bible find this statement utterly impenetrable. The idea seems to threaten profound, barely conscious assumptions. A kind of panic paralyzes their features, as though they found themselves trapped on the edge of a steep place. I once tried to describe to a very well-known American intellectual the conditions among Negroes in the South. My recital disturbed him and made him indignant; and he asked me in perfect innocence, "Why don't all the Negroes in the South move North?" I tried to explain what *has* happened, unfailingly, whenever a significant body of Negroes moves North. They do not escape jim-crow: they merely encounter another, not-less-deadly variety. They do not move to Chicago, they move to the South Side; they do not move to New York, they move to Harlem. The pressure within the ghetto causes the ghetto walls to expand, and this expansion is always violent. White people hold the line as long as they can, and in as many ways as they can, from verbal intimidation to physical violence. But inevitably the border which has divided the ghetto from the rest of the world falls into the hands of the ghetto. The white people fall back bitterly before the black horde; the landlords make a tidy profit by raising the rent, chopping up the rooms, and all but dispensing with the upkeep; and what has once been a neighborhood turns into a "turf." This is precisely what happened when the Puerto Ricans arrived in their thousands—and the bitterness thus caused is, as I write, being fought out all up and down those streets.

Northerners indulge in an extremely dangerous luxury. They seem to feel that because they fought on the right side during the Civil War, and they won, they have earned the right merely to deplore what is going on in the South, without taking any responsibility for it; and that they can ignore what is happening in Northern cities because what is happening in Little Rock or Birmingham is worse. Well, in the first place, it is not possible for anyone who has not endured both to know which is "worse."

I know some Negroes who prefer the South and white Southerners, because "At least there, you haven't got to play any guessing games!" The guessing games referred to have driven more than one Negro into the narcotics ward, the madhouse, or the river. I know another Negro, a man very dear to me, who says, with conviction and with truth, "The spirit of the South is the spirit of America." He was born in the North and did his military training in the South. He did not, as far as I can gather, find the South "worse"; he found it, if anything, all too familiar. In the second place, though, even if Birmingham *is* worse, no doubt Johannesburg, South Africa, beats it by several miles, and Buchenwald was one of the worst things that ever happened in the entire history of the world. The world has never lacked for horrifying examples; but I do not believe that these examples are meant to be used as justification for our own crimes. This perpetual justification empties the heart of all human feeling. The emptier our hearts become, the greater will be our crimes. Thirdly, the South is not merely an embarrassingly backward region, but a part of this country, and what happens there concerns every one of us.

As far as the color problem is concerned, there is but one great difference between the Southern white and the Northerner: the Southerner remembers, historically, and in his own psyche, a kind of Eden in which he loved black people and they loved him. Historically, the flaming sword laid across this Eden is the Civil War. Personally, it is the Southerner's sexual coming of age, when, without any warning, unbreakable taboos are set up between himself and his past. Everything, thereafter, is permitted him except the love he remembers and has never ceased to need. The resulting, indescribable torment affects every Southern mind and is the basis of the Southern hysteria.

None of this is true for the Northerner. Negroes represent nothing to him personally, except, perhaps, the dangers of carnality. He never sees Negroes. Southerners see them all the time. Northerners never think about them whereas Southerners are never really thinking of anything else. Negroes are, therefore, ignored in the North and are under surveillance in the South, and suffer hideously in both places. Neither the Southerner nor the Northerner is able to look on the Negro simply as a man. It seems to be indispensable to the national self-esteem that the Negro be considered either as a kind of ward (in which case we are told how many Negroes, comparatively, bought Cadillacs last year and how few, comparatively, were lynched), or as a victim (in which case we are promised that he will never vote in our assemblies or go to school with our kids). They are two sides of the same coin and the South will not change—*cannot* change—until the North changes. The country will not change until it reexamines itself and discovers what it really means by freedom. In the meantime, generations keep being born, bitterness is increased by incompetence, pride, and folly, and the world shrinks around us.

It is a terrible, an inexorable law that one cannot deny the humanity of another without diminishing one's own: in the face of one's victim, one sees oneself. Walk through the streets of Harlem and see what we, this nation, have become.

John Cheever:

Moving Out

"...the rich of the city were getting richer and the friable middle ground where we stood was vanishing"

The war was over; so was the shortage of building materials and from the windows of our apartment near Sutton Place we could see the horizon beginning to change. Everybody was home who was coming back, the girls still had their dewy furlough looks and, after the smoking and carious ruins of Manila, the City of New York with the sky pouring its light onto the rivers looked like a vision of enlightenment. My children were young and my favorite New York was the one they led me through on Sunday afternoons. A girl in high heels can show you Rome, a drinking companion is the best for Dublin, and I enjoyed the New York my children knew. They liked the Central Park lion house at four o'clock on February afternoons, the highest point of the Queensboro Bridge, and a riverside dock in the East Forties, long gone, where I once saw a couple of tarts playing hopscotch with a hotel room key. Oh, it was a long time ago. You could still hear the *Oklahoma!* score during drinking hours, the Mink Decade was just taking hold and the Third Avenue El still rattled the dishes in Bloomingdale's. The East River views were broader then and there was an imposing puissance to those reaches of light and water. We used to ride and play touch football in Central Park and, in October, with the skiing season in mind, I used to climb the ten flights of stairs to our apartment. I used the back stairs, the only stairs, and I was the only one to use them. Most of the kitchen doors stood open and my

John Cheever, a native New Yorker, won the 1958 National Book Award for his novel, The Wapshot Chronicle. *This reminiscence of his leaving the city and moving to Wapshot territory was published in July, 1960.*

climb was a breach of privacy, but what could I do? I used to whistle and sometimes sing to warn the tenants of my approach, but in spite of these precautions I once saw a lady wearing nothing but a girdle while she basted a leg of lamb, a cook drinking whiskey out of a bottle, and a housewife sitting on the lap of the sallow-faced delivery boy from the corner butcher's. On Christmas Eve my children and their friends used to sing carols on Sutton Place—mostly to butlers, everyone else having gone to Nassau, which may have been the beginning of the end.

It was a wonderful life and it didn't seem that it would ever end. In the winter there were those days with a smart polish on the air and the buildings, and then there were the first south winds of spring with their exciting and unclean odors of backyards and all the women shoppers walking east at dusk, carrying bunches of apple blossom and lilac that had been trucked up from the Shenandoah Valley the night before. A French-speaking panhandler used to work Beekman Place (*Je le regrette beaucoup, monsieur . . .*), and going out to dinner one night we ran into a bagpiper on the Lexington Avenue subway platform who played a Black Watch march between trains. New York was the place where I had met and married my wife, I had dreamed of its streets during the war, my children had been born here and it was here that I had first experienced the feeling of being free from social and parental strictures. We and our friends seemed to improvise our world and to meet society on the most liberal and spontaneous terms. I don't suppose there was a day, an hour, when the middle class got their marching orders, but toward the end of the 1940's the middle class began to move. It was more of a push than a move and the energy behind the push was the changing economic character of the city. It would all be easier to describe if there had been edicts, proclamations and tables of statistics, but this vast population shift was forced by butcher's bills, tips, increased rental and tuition costs and demolitions. Where are the Wilsons? you might ask. Oh, they've bought a place in Putnam County. And the Renshaws? They've moved to New Jersey. And the Oppers? The Oppers are in White Plains. The ranks were thinning and we watched them go with commiseration and some scorn. They sometimes returned for dinner with mud on their shoes, the women's faces red from weeding the vegetable garden. My God, the suburbs! They encircled the city's boundaries like enemy territory and we thought of them as a loss of privacy, a cesspool of conformity and a life of indescribable dreariness in some split-level village where the place name appeared in The New York *Times* only when some bored housewife blew off her head with a shotgun.

That spring, at the closing assembly of my daughter's school, the headmistress took the lectern and announced: "Now school is over and we are *all* going to the country!" We were not going to the country and the exclamation fascinated me because hidden somewhere in her words was a sense, an apprehension of the fact that the rich of the city were getting richer and the friable middle ground where we stood was vanishing. The river views at any rate were vanishing and so were most of the landmarks. Down went a baronial old brewery, up went a deluxe apartment house. Building began on a lot where we used to run the dog and most of the small and pleasant houses in the neighborhood, where people who were less than rich could live, were marked for demolition and would be replaced by the glass towers of a new class. I could see the landscape of my children's youth destroyed before my eyes; and don't we impair the richness of our memories with this velocity of reconstruction? The apartment house where we lived changed hands and the new owners prepared to turn the building into a cooperative, but we were given eight months to find another home. Most people we knew by then lived either in River House or in downtown tenements where you had to put out pots to catch the leaks when it rained. Girls either came out at the Colony Club or came out, so to speak, on the river embankments, and my sons' friends either played football for Buckley or practiced snap-knife shots in the shadows of the bridge.

That was the winter when we never had enough money. I looked for another apartment, but it was impossible to find a place for a family of five that suited my wife and my income. We were not poor enough for subsidized housing and not anything like rich enough for the new buildings that were going up around us. The noise of wrecking crews seemed aimed directly at our residence in the city. In March one of the obligations that I couldn't—or at least neglected to—meet was the electric bill and our lights were turned off. The children took their baths by candlelight and, while they enjoyed this turn of events, the effect of the dark apartment on my own feelings was somber. We simply didn't have the scratch. I paid the light bill in the morning and went out to Westchester a week later and arranged to rent a little frame house with a sickly shade tree on the lawn.

The farewell parties were numerous and sometimes tearful. The sense was that we were being exiled, like so many thousands before us, by invincible economic pressures and sent out to a barren and provincial life where we would get fat, wear ill-fitting clothes and spend our evenings glued to the television set. What else can you do in the suburbs? On the night before we left we went to Riverview Terrace for dinner where I jumped, in an exuberance of regret, out of a first-story window. I don't think you can do that anymore. After the party I walked around the city, beginning my farewells. The customary tinder lights beat up from the streets onto the low clouds overhead. On a sidewalk somewhere in the Eighties I saw a Cuban going through the steps of a rumba, holding a baby in his arms. A dinner party in the Sixties was breaking up and men and women were standing in a lighted doorway calling good-bye and good-night. In the Fifties I saw a scavenger pushing an enormous English perambulator—a carriage for a princess—from ash can to ash can. It was part of the city's imprimatur. It was in the spring and there was a heady, vernal fragrance from Central Park, for in New York the advance of the seasons is not forgotten but intensified. Autumn thunderstorms, leaf fires, the primeval stillness that comes after a heavy snowfall and the ran-

dy smells of April all seem magnified by the pavings of the greatest city in the world.

The moving men were due at noon and I took another melancholy walk. I had my shoes shined by a pleasant Italian who always described himself as a dirty-minded man. He blamed it on the smell of shoe polish which he claimed had some venereal persuasions. He had, like many men of his kind, a lively mind and possessed, along with the largest collection of nudist magazines I have ever seen, some exalted memories of Laurence Olivier as Hamlet, or Omletto as he called him. Standing in front of our apartment house was an old lady who not only fed and watered the pigeons that then lived around the Queensboro Bridge, but whose love of the birds was jealous. A workman had put the crusts of his meal onto the sidewalk for the birds and she was kicking the crusts into the gutter. "*You* don't have to feed them," she was telling him. "*You* don't have to worry about them. *I* take care of them. I spend four dollars a week on grain and stale bread and in the summer I change their water twice a day. I don't like strangers to feed them. . . ." The city is raffish and magnificent and she and the shoeshine man would be advocates of its raffishness—those millions of lonely but not discontented men and women who can be overheard speaking with great intimacy to the chimpanzee in the zoo, the squirrels in the park and the pigeons everywhere. That morning the air of New York was full of music. Bessie Smith was singing *Jazzbo Brown* from a radio in the orange-drink stand at the corner. Halfway down Sutton Place a blind man was playing *Make Believe* on a sliding trombone. Beethoven's *Fifth Symphony*, all threats and revelations, was blowing out of an upstairs window. Men and women were sunning themselves on Second Avenue and the vision of urban life seemed to be an amiable one, a bond of imponderables, a shared risk and at least a gesture toward the peaceableness of mankind, for who but a peaceable species could live in such congestion? Fredric March was sitting on a bench in Central Park. Igor Stravinsky was waiting at the corner for the light to change. Myrna Loy was coming out of the Plaza and on lower Sixth Avenue E. E. Cummings was buying a bunch of bananas. It was time to go and I got a cab uptown. "I'm not sleeping," the driver said. "I'm not sleeping anymore. I'm not getting my rest. Spring! It don't mean nothing to me. My wife, she's left me. She's shacked up with this fireman, but I told her I'll wait for you, Mildred, I'll wait for you, it's nothing but bestiality you feel for this fireman and I'm waiting for you, I'm keeping the home fires burning. . . ." It was the idiom of the city and one of its many voices, for where else in the world will strangers bare their intimate secrets to one another with such urgency and such speed—and I would miss this.

Like so much else in modern life the pathos of our departure was concealed by a deep cartilage of decorum. When the moving van had closed its doors and departed, we shook hands with the doorman and started for the country ourselves, wondering if we would ever return.

As it happened we returned the next week for dinner and continued to drive back into town regularly to see our friends. They shared our prejudices and our anxieties. "Can you bear it?" we would be asked. "Are you all right out there? When do you think you can get back?"

And we found other evacuees in the country who sat on their suburban lawns, planning to go back when the children had finished college; and when the rain fell into the leaves of the rock maples they asked: "Oh, Charlie, do you think it's raining in New York?"

Now on summer nights the smell of the city sometimes drifts northward on the waters of the Hudson River, up to the wooded, inland banks where we live. The odor is like the stales from some enormous laundry, although I expect that an incurable evacuee could detect in it Arpege, stone-cold gin, and might perhaps even imagine that he heard music on the water; but this is not for me. I sometimes go back to walk through the ghostly remains of Sutton Place where the rude, new buildings stand squarely in one another's river views and where the rents would make your head swim, but now my old friends seem insular in their concern about my exile, their apartments seem magnificent but sooty, like the scenery for the national or traveling company of a Broadway hit, and their doormen only remind me of the fact that I don't have to tip a staff of twenty at Christmas and that in my own house I can shout in anger or joy without having someone pound on the radiator for silence. The truth is that I'm crazy about the suburbs and I don't care who knows it. Sometimes my sons and I go fishing for perch in the Hudson, and when the trains for the city come bowling down along the riverbanks I salute the sometimes embarrassed passengers with my beer can, wishing them Godspeed and prosperity in the greatest city in the world, but I see them pass without a trace of longing or envy.

Dorothy Parker:

New York at 6:30 P.M.

"If you can get through the twilight, you'll live through the night"

To write about art now gives me a feeling of deep embarrassment which, in the long ago, I kept hidden under what was known then as "She's having one of her difficult days again, ma'am—screaming and spitting and I don't know what all."

But that, unhappily, was too easy; we outgrow such simple masquerades, and all there is left for the likes of me is a silence not even silver. This occurs when the subject of the adjacent conversation is Art. Oh, I can go as far as "Of course, I don't know anything about painting"—but I cannot even stumble on through the rest of it. Lower you cannot get.

Well, yes, you really can. For here I am burbling on of an American artist and his works, as if—God grant—I knew what I was talking about. The American artist is John Koch; he is just about to crash his middle years, and he is, I should think, as nearly happy as anyone ever gets to be. I know that few of the gifted can accept that as a compliment ("So she says I'm shallow, does she?"), but I mean it to please, and that is why I envy him.

Well, anyway, I know Mr. Koch only through his paintings, and through the almost lyrical tributes to his works. I do not know what school of painting he belongs in; he is not, I believe, avant-garde, and he is, I gather, though I have to strain to take it in, a realist —but not of the ashcan school of the Glackens, Luks, Sloan group. He takes his realism out on the rich. His lovely ladies step out of Edith Wharton, and his graceful gentlemen come from Henry James (whenever you say Edith Wharton, you have to say Henry James right after. If you don't, you'll have bad luck all day).

Mr. Koch, so far as I can pluck from his ungenerous snatches of biography, paints of his times—it seems as if of the times through which he must have been growing up. His pictures are a delight to the eye and a joy to the memories, in case you have such well-bred memories. His favorite time is the autumn of the day —the late afternoon. It was then, in the Old Days, that gracious people gathered together, to speak wittily in soft voices and laugh gently no matter how

funny somebody was. Nobody seemed to be exerting himself and the ladies could take it just as easily, never showing appreciation in a giggle or a screech. They were exquisite people, considerate, one of another, and delicate of tread as cats. One of their sweetest attributes was that they could always be found when you wanted them—they were at home in the late afternoon, and there you could go without a date or an appointment. Theirs were never parties—the cocktail party was not yet alive. I misremember who first was cruel enough to nurture it into life. But perhaps it would be not too much to say, in fact it would be not enough to say, that it was not worth the trouble.

I am jumping a great many of John Koch's paintings when I deal only with the soft spirit of late afternoon in New York, when the sky was Renoir blue and a fire—a real fire—whispered gently under the classic mantelpiece—for he chose many other subjects. He did a succession of still lifes (that looks odd but "still lives" looks even worse). At any rate they somehow never were permanently still. Always the lady, probably the hostess, sat immovable, her back of the straightness achieved by hours of walking about the house with a heavy book on her head; but you had no feeling that she remained motionless. Mr. Koch seemed to have caught her just as she stopped speaking and was about to speak again as soon as she could do so without interrupting.

The regulation still lifes—oh, all right, then, "still lives"—are of furniture, walls and curtains, but somehow John Koch brought his own gift to them; the rooms empty only for a moment, the curtains had just been drawn by accomplished fingers, the vases of flowers were not "arranged"—simply the blossoms had found the exact place for themselves.

I am always a little sad when I see a John Koch painting. It is nothing more than a bit of nostalgia that makes my heart beat slower—nostalgia for those rooms of lovely lights and lovelier shadows and loveliest people. And I really have no room for the sweet, soft feeling. Nor am I honest, perhaps, in referring to it. For it is the sort of nostalgia that is only a dreamy longing for some places where you never were.

And, I never will be there. There is no such hour on the present clock as six-thirty, New York time. Yet, as only New Yorkers know, if you can get through the twilight, you'll live through the night. ⧺

When Dorothy Parker wrote on John Koch's New York paintings (examples of which appear opposite), the works were on exhibit at the Museum of the City of New York. Parker wrote directly from the paintings themselves, without access to any facts about them. The article was published in November, 1964.

OF NATIONAL MOMENT

Plus ça change is right up there among the iron laws of life. When Esquire was but an infant, the war clouds were gathering, as they used to say, between the Soviet Union and its mighty neighbor to the east, and Esquire got Leon Trotsky to write about it; now there's a new neighbor in 1973, but the clouds are of the same shape and consistency, and the outcome no more discernible than in 1934. Esquire isn't, wasn't and never can be a news-magazine, but this qualification has never hindered its access to significant, or indeed worldwide, issues. Certain of these issues, cases, commotions have been recognizable to the running reader by the yards of headlines they generated as they rose; such were the decline and fall of Joe McCarthy and the assassination of President Kennedy. Others were much smaller at first than a man's hand, as in the case of Sinclair Lewis' farsighted anticipation of the Black Revolution. Sometimes, alas, Esquire's contribution has been merely to set the record straight, and that in vain—in spite of Laurence Stallings' counterargument, the world is still full of people who believe that Hitler danced at Compiègne.

Leon Trotsky:

Clouds in the Far East

The creator and first commander
of the Red Army summarizes the Russian
chances in case of war

At first sight one becomes astonished by the insignificance of those military forces which were concentrated in the Far East during the months of extreme tension in Soviet-Japanese relations. On February 3, the Japanese Minister of War, Hayashi, declared that his government had only 50,000 soldiers in Manchuria, while the Soviets had concentrated 100,000 men and 300 planes on their nearest border. Bluecher, the commander-in-chief of the special Far Eastern army, refuted Hayashi, stating that the Japanese had actually concentrated in Manchuria 130,000 men, more than one third of their regular army, plus 115,000 Manchukuo soldiers—all told 245,000 men and 500 planes. At the same time, Bluecher added reassuringly that the Soviet armed forces were not inferior to the Japanese. On the scale of a major war, we are dealing here, one may say, with partisan detachments.

The concentration of masses of millions, an unbroken and deep front and a positional war are excluded by the properties of the Far Eastern arena (immense and sparsely populated areas, extremely broken terrain, poor means of communication, remoteness from the key bases). In the Russo-Japanese war of 1904-05, 320,000 soldiers participated on the Russian side; and toward the end, i.e., when the Czarist army was completely routed—500,000. The Japanese hardly numbered as many. The Czarist army lacked not transport, not numbers, but ability. Since that time, the technology of war has changed beyond recognition. But the basic properties of the theatre of war in the Far East have remained the same. To Japan, Manchuria is an intermediate base, separated from the key bases by sea. The Japanese fleet rules on sea, but not under sea or in the air. Sea transport is bound up with dangers. The Chinese population of Manchuria is hostile to the Japanese. Like the Soviets, Japan will be unable to concentrate masses of millions on the Far Eastern front. The most modern technology must, of necessity, be correlated with the tactical methods of the past. The

Esquire's founding editor Arnold Gingrich began negotiations with Trotsky for this article in 1933, while Esquire was being started. Dealing with Trotsky was complicated by his efforts to avoid being located by the European press (he was living secretly in France at the time), but the story finally appeared after a year in August, 1934.

strategy of Napoleon, and even of Hannibal, remains to a large measure in force for the Trans-Baikal and the Maritime Provinces. Large-scale cavalry raids will introduce decisive changes into the map of war. The Japanese railroads in Manchuria will be subjected to greater dangers than the Soviet line running along the Amur. In the operations of isolated detachments, in cavalry raids at the enemy's rear, colossal work will entail upon modern technology in the form of aviation as the means of scouting, of maintaining connections of transport, and of bombing. Insofar as the war in the Amur and Maritime Provinces will bear, in general, a mobile and maneuvering character, its outcome will depend to a decisive degree upon the ability of isolated detachments to operate independently; upon the initiative of the lowest ranking officers; and upon the resourcefulness of every soldier who is left to act on his own. In all these respects, the Soviet army, in my opinion, will prove superior to the Japanese, at least by as much as the Japanese army proved superior to the Czarist in 1904-05.

As the events of last year have demonstrated, Tokyo cannot make up her mind to begin right now. And in the meantime, with every additional year, the interrelation of forces will not change in favor of Japan. The development of the Kuznietsk military-industrial base has already freed the Far Eastern front from the necessity of depending upon the European rear. The radical reconstruction of the carrying capacity of the Moscow-Khabarovsk railway, by double-tracking the line, was set by the Soviet government as one of the principal tasks for 1934. Conjointly work was begun on the railroad from Lake Baikal to the lower Amur regions, 1400 kilometers long. The new main line will tap the richest coal regions of Bureya and the mines of Khingan. The Bureya region—which is only 500 kilometers from Khabarovsk, i.e., one tenth the distance to the Kuznietsk region—will be transformed by the program of industrial construction into an independent industrial military-technological base for the Far East. The correlation of the gigantic undertakings in transportation and industry with the substantial economic privileges extended to the population of the Far East must lead to a rapid settlement of this territory—and this will cut the ground completely from under the Siberian plans of Japanese Imperialism.

Nevertheless Japan's internal situation makes war almost inevitable, just as thirty years ago there was no forestalling Czarism from it, despite all the voices of warning. There is no paradox in the statement that after the war has broken out in the Far East, it will be either very short, almost instantaneous, or very, very long. Japan's goal—the seizure of the Far East, and if possible, of a considerable section of the Trans-Baikal territory—requires of itself very long periods of time. The war could end quickly only provided the Soviet Union will be able to shatter at the very outset the Japanese offensive, decisively and for a long time to come. For the solution of this defensive task, aviation provides the Soviets with a weapon of inestimable power.

One need not be a devotee of "integral" aerial warfare, i.e., believe in the transference of the decisive military operations to the air, in order to realize that, under certain conditions, aviation is unquestionably capable of solving the war problem by radically paralyzing the offensive operations of the enemy. Such is precisely the case in the Far East. In his complaint about the concentration of Soviet air forces in the Maritime Provinces, Hayashi divulged the easily understood alarm of Japan's ruling circles, whose political centers, whose military industrial combines and whose most important war bases are exposed to the blow of the Red Air fleets. With the Maritime Provinces as a base, it is possible to spread the greatest havoc among the vital centers of the Island Empire by means of long-range planes. Even should one concede what is hardly likely, that Japan will be able to muster an equal or superior air force, the danger to the islands will only be lessened but not eliminated. There is no creating an impassable aerial barrier; breaches will be only too frequent, and every breach is pregnant with great consequence. In this duel, the decisive importance will be borne not by the material technological preponderance, which unquestionably lies on the side of Soviet aviation, and which can only increase in the immediate future, but by the relative geographic position of the two sides.

While almost all the Japanese centers are exposed to attack from the air, the Japanese air forces cannot retaliate with blows anywhere nearly equivalent: not only Moscow but also the Kuznietsk basin (6-7000 kilometers away!) cannot be reached without a landing. At the same time, neither in the Maritime Provinces nor in Eastern Siberia are there centers so vital that their destruction could exert a decisive or even a telling influence on the course of the war. The advantages of position multiplied by a more powerful technology will give the Red Army a preponderance which is difficult to express in terms of a precise coefficient, but which may prove of decisive importance.

Should the Soviet aviation, however, prove unprepared for the solution of the grandiose task of the third dimension, the center of gravity would revert to the two-dimensional plane, where the laws of the Far Eastern theatre would enter into full force; and the principal law reads: Slowness. The time has obviously elapsed for the sudden seizure of the Maritime Provinces. Vladivostok today represents a strongly fortified position which may become the Verdun of the Pacific Coast. The attempt to capture a fortress can be made only by land; and would require, say, a dozen divisions—two and a half to three times more than are required for the defense. Even in the event of complete success this operation would consume months, and thereby leave at the disposal of the Red Army an invaluable supplementary period of time. The westward movement of the Japanese would require colossal preparatory labors: intermediate bases must be fortified; railways and roads must be built. Japan's very successes in this line would create increasing difficulties for her, because the Red Army would retreat to its own bases while the Japanese would become dispersed within inhospitable territories having behind their backs enslaved Manchuria, crushed Korea and hostile China. A protracted war would open up the possibility of forming, in the deep rear of the Japanese, a Chinese army with the aid of Soviet technology and Soviet instructors.

But here, we already enter into the sphere of world relations, in the true sense of the word, with all the possibilities, dangers and unknown quantities latent in them. Many of the considerations and estimates which were stated above would, of course, be eliminated should the war last a number of years and force the Soviets to place twenty million men under arms. In such a case, the weakest link after transport, or together with transport, would probably prove to be the Soviet rural economy, the fundamental problems of which are still far from solution. However, it is precisely in the perspective of a major war that it is absolutely impermissible to take the question of U.S.S.R. in an isolated form, i.e., without direct connection with the entire world situation. What will

be the groupings of countries in the East and the West? Will the military coalition of Japan and Germany be realized? Would the U.S.S.R. find allies, and precisely whom? What will happen to the freedom of the seas? What will be the subsistence level, and, in general, the economic position of Japan? Will Germany find itself within a new blockading ring? What will be the relative stability of the regimes of the warring countries? The number of such questions could be multiplied indefinitely. All of them will flow inevitably from the conditions of a world war; but no one can answer them a priori. The answer will be found during the actual course of the mutual destruction of peoples, and this answer may turn out to be a merciless sentence upon our entire civilization.

The Abraham Lincoln Brigade

They thought it was, back then, the only good fight in the world.
The facts were clear:
Franco was wrong and Left was right

Among the many medallions struck in honor of this century's bloody conflicts, there is one, uncataloged, that has already worn almost indistinguishably smooth. After twenty-five years, the faceless alloy exposed beneath its vanished silvering proves too soft ever to have held any lasting stamp, but, more important, the idea behind it now seems almost too immense to begin with, as if it had forced too many symbols into the medal's shallow, unfirm relief: an outline map of Spain, a fist clenched in salute to international solidarity, guns challenging both flanks, the round world, the five-pointed Red star within it, the dates 1936-1937, and the circlet motto, VOLUNTARIOS INTERNACIONALES DE LA LIBERTAD. It was once known as the I.B. medal, issued to members of the Spanish Loyalists' International Brigades, which included—besides the Poles, the Czechs, the Hungarians, the anti-Hitler Germans, the anti-Mussolini Italians, the anti-appeasement English, and anti-Fascist Europe in general—thirty-two hundred Americans. "Tourists," according to their passports (whenever they had them), who picked up a cardboard suitcase, a Paris address, and sometimes passage money from the "Committee for Technical Assistance to the Spanish Loyalist Government" in New York City and shipped out a quarter of a century ago to fight fascism in Spain. A little over half of them survived, and today some still have the medal somewhere around the house ("I've got two at home. Not one, but two"), some never bothered to get it, more threw it away, most can't remember *what* happened to it, and a handful, like Alvah Bessie, have it tissued like a rare Spanish coin—tucked inside a wallet, something of the past they keep forgetting to leave with the jeweler for repairs. Long ago, the veterans officially adopted a civilian insignia, one of those nondescript lapel pins: a familiar three-pointed star. "We always claimed Mercedes-Benz stole it from us," says Moe Fishman, executive secretary of the veterans. "But actually they predate us. So we stole it from them, I guess." Either way, it looks as rotarian as any automobile emblem, and

seems to stand much more for what's left now of "a group of guys"—as Fishman occasionally calls the Veterans of the Abraham Lincoln Brigade—than for the struggle itself. The old medal is the struggle—what was meant whenever the cry of *Spain!* went up in the Thirties—and both have suffered a harsh and abrasive fate. As Fishman says of his own I.B. medal, long gone, "I wore it out."

Idealistically, something like that has happened to the men who fought in Spain. They had (and still have, many believe) an irreducible cause, one that everybody from Harold Ickes to John Osborne has admired; and from February, 1937, to September, 1938, they fought for it as the frontline shock troops of the XVth International Brigade of the Spanish Republican Army. They were nicknamed the "Lincolns," for the Abraham Lincoln Battalion; the "Washingtons," for the George Washington Battalion, which was so decimated during its first and only action at Brunete that the survivors had to join with the few Lincolns left standing to become an effective fighting force again; the "Mac-Paps," for the part-Canadian Mackenzie-Papineau Battalion; and even the "John Brown Battery," an artillery group. The names are almost farcical—like something out of proletarian literature—but the dead are very much the real dead. "I was a company commander," says one vet. "But that's only because if you lived long enough, you were bound to end up one." Yet long after the undeniable heroism of Jarama River, Brunete, Quinto, Belchite, Teruel, the Aragón retreats, the final futile counterattack across the Ebro River, and the last motley parade in Barcelona ("They learned to fight before they had time to learn to march," The New York *Times*'s Herbert Matthews wrote of them), they found themselves forced onto a last indefensible height—a redoubt located, according to the rhetoric of certain analphabetic patriots, "right at the top of the Attorney General's list."

They never expected anything quite like that. As Matthews says in candid recollection of those days, "Eighty percent of them, I figured, were Communists, but regardless of whether they were Communists or not, they sincerely considered themselves to be as good Americans as anybody else. Maybe better." They had Ernest Hemingway for a friend, who knew

Long before the extravagant fancies of the Weathermen, Brower (March, 1962) reported on the Brigade as the only group of American leftists with experience in a violent revolution. Time has made the personal data obsolete, but the historical moral is as valid as ever.

most of them personally; his suite at the Hotel Florida in Madrid was kept open to them for hot baths and plenty of stiffener during leaves from the front. Hemingway shared with them the passionate conviction, in a time when slogans had a bite to them that they have never since recovered in this Agitprop-ed century, that they would make of Spain the tomb of fascism. "It's something that's burnt into me," Steve Nelson, once political commissar of the XVth I.B., says even now.

What it all adds up to at present, however, is evidence placed before the Subversive Activities Control Board, which ruled in 1955 that the Veterans of the Abraham Lincoln Brigade must register with the Attorney General as a Communist-front organization. The case is still on appeal, but the ruling is the latest in a series of crippling blows to what little mutual contact the V.A.L.B. has been able to maintain among the scattered veterans over recent years. They are kept apart by the usual hindrances of distance, age, and dimming memory, such as might bother even an American Legion post. "It's getting so when I see a guy at a vets' affair," remarks Nelson, "I can't remember whether I met him first at Jarama or Pittsburgh." But they are further sundered by a growing political reticence.

"A guy comes in here the other day, all the way from California; haven't seen him since Spain," Fishman recalls. "'Hello, how are you?' Fine. 'What are you doing now?' He's a TV repairman. 'Do you want us to send you any mail?' He'd prefer not. I offered to send it in a plain envelope but he feels no, the kids bring in their friends, you know how kids are, they might see something lying around the house. 'Some people know,' he says, 'but we don't make a big thing of it that I fought in Spain.'" If the present S.A.C.B. ruling sticks, there won't even be any more plain envelopes, because the Internal Security Act of 1950 requires that all mail from any proscribed group be stamped on the outside wrapper: "Disseminated by [name of organization], a Communist-front organization." "When that happens," concludes Fishman, "then we go out of business."

Business is already near marginal. Fishman, who, until 1956, was employed full time by the V.A.L.B., now keeps office hours Wednesday evenings from six to eight, free. The vets have offices on Twenty-first Street, $35 a month for rent and telephone, an obligation met by Fishman's asking the members every so often, "How about some dough for the outfit?" They use a couple of desks, a file cabinet, a chain, and a padlock. Otherwise, the only important chattel seems to be a legal notebook that contains the membership.

Only: "We don't have a membership. I used to send out membership cards all during the Forties, but the response was so sporadic that it wasn't worth it." The ledger is "as much of a list as we have of all the guys who were in Spain." And it isn't any big secret; the V.A.L.B. hopes, in fact, to publish the list someday. Unfortunately, with only one man, Moe Fishman again, serving as an entire Veterans Administration, and with some of the war dead remembered by their first names only, it's a hard list to compile. Frequently Moe can't give a really straight answer to inquiring relatives—*We're not in a position to honor our dead the way we would like*—and new addresses, even recent deaths, often reach him only via the grapevine. He figures he is in touch with about four hundred and fifty of some one thousand surviving vets. "A guy gets mail if he wants, and he does something about it if he wants."

The last time he canvassed them, it was for money to send packages to the families of political prisoners in Spain. "Don't make any big point of it. We're not becoming a big welfare agency." Only a few packages then, but they represented the vets' continuing interest in some six thousand Spaniards in Franco's prisons, some of whom have been there since the civil war started. They hope to do what they can as part of a worldwide effort to bring about an amnesty. That is, if they can escape the present consequences of the Internal Security Act themselves.

And it is a study in personal chagrin to watch Fishman leaf through a copy of the Internal Security Act, shaking his head over the steeper passages. *Organizations, commonly known as "Communist fronts," which in most instances are created and maintained, or used, in such a manner as to conceal the facts as to their true character and purposes and their membership. . . .* "How are we going to restrict our membership? Any guy who fought in Spain is a vet. About forty percent of them were Communists. Now—who knows? I know some are, some aren't. Some guys, I don't know, but I'll tell you this, I'd cut my tongue out before I'd ask them." *One result of this method of operation is that such affiliated organizations are able to obtain financial and other support from persons who would not extend such support if they knew the true purposes of. . . .* "We're talking about peanuts! Twenty-five, thirty dollars maybe. The highest I ever collected was two hundred dollars, and when I got two hundred dollars, I'd like to see anybody, *including* the Communist Party, get it away from me."

He is a cocky guy, who went to Spain right out of the laundry workers' union and the discussion groups that used to be held at the Ninety-second Street "Y." Age twenty-one. He fought as far as Cañada. "I never made those last two hundred yards." He was shot in the left leg, and the damaged knee gives him a sort of dog-trot limp. He tried to get into World War II, but the best he was able to do was to ship out with the Merchant Marine in 1945 as a radio operator, after taking a course in it at the "Y" again. He now works "allied to the printing trade," and devotes to the vets the time others might spend on bowling and the Community Chest.

"I'm the organization," he says. "There's no other thing. If there's something to decide, I talk it over with the guys, and then decide what I'm going to do. Cockeyed, but that's the way it is."

It would be a mistake, however, to suggest that the Veterans of the Abraham Lincoln Brigade is all that's left of life for the Americans who fought in Spain.

It was a long time ago, and even Fishman has other things to do now and again. It would be like judging all Americans who fought in World War II on the basis of the American Legion. What touches men is war itself, not its later regroupings; and what distinguished the war experience in Spain was individual commitment. It was so much more each man's own doing—a matter of personal conviction, pushed to the point of going into the Loyalist trenches with a Russian rifle (often the American Springfields that were first imported by the Czar), having sometimes never fired *any* rifle at all—that it was bound to have a more profound effect on combatants than the organized, G.I. warfare of the later conflict. Blood and commitment ran too deep for easy memories. Certainly the V.A.L.B. reflects this intense feeling—even hoards it to an extent—but it exists equally as strong in veterans of Spain who haven't been near the V.A.L.B. in years.

Alvah Bessie, for instance, got the first hint of this when his friend Aaron Lopoff, who died on Hill 666 in the Sierra Pandols of Catalonia, said to him, "You really started something when you came over here, baby." "I thought he meant I wouldn't get out alive," Bessie recalls—a thought they all had at one time or another—"but now I realize he meant something much different. It's subjective as hell. You see, I had something of a reputation as a writer when I left. But that vanished. And ever since, everything that's happened to me personally has happened in one way or another because of Spain." In small part, Spain got him to Hollywood to write films during the war when anti-fascism was the best story line; and in large part, Spain got him before the House Un-American Activities Committee five years later as one of the Unfriendly Hollywood Ten, and thence to jail for contempt of Congress; in some part, Spain got him a job after jail covering the waterfront for Harry Bridges' union newspaper; and, in a big part, Spain has him knocked down now to working as the electrician and offstage voice of San Francisco's hungry i, where, in part, Spain gets him an invitation from Arthur Miller to sit down at the table, chat awhile, and, in part, a tip of $75 from Mort Sahl. You really started something, baby. . . .

And the end—or what little of it is now in sight—has been, for most American veterans, just such a similar falling off. From the European battalions, a later history spins out like an engulfing web over the entire map of Europe. The partisans who shot Mussolini were once members of the Garibaldi Battalion. The present chief of the East Berlin *volkspolizei* is a former lieutenant colonel in the Ernst Thaelmann Battalion. Togliatti was in Spain as "Alfredo" and "Ercoli," directing tactics for the Spanish Communist Party, and the man who ran the "secret railroad" in Paris for East Europeans to fight in Spain turns up eventually in his native Yugoslavia as Tito. But history seems to quit the Lincoln Battalion right at the Spanish border.

Premier Juan Negrín ordered the withdrawal of all I.B.'s, including the Lincoln, in the vain hope that it might also force Germany and Italy to cease intervention; but Hitler's Condor Legion and Mussolini's

200,000 Black Arrows stayed put, substantially aiding Franco's victory and ending the peninsular stage of the great battle for the heartland of Europe. Two years later, everybody was in it, including six hundred vets, and it was then that the surrealistic confusion over their loyalty to country really began.

The irony is that the last place they were allowed to go was the one area in which they'd had the most experience: the front lines. Entire outfits would be shipped overseas, minus two or three men, who'd scratch their heads in puzzlement, get acquainted, and find out, sure enough, they'd all been in Spain together and didn't know it. Eventually some of them did make it to the real war, the one they'd helped start. John Gates jumped into France on D-Day. Robert Thompson won the Distinguished Service Cross in the Pacific, which later cut two years off a five-year sentence for a conviction under the Smith Act. The vets' most famous World War II hero, however, was Sergeant Hermann Bottcher, an early refugee from the Nazis, who won the D.S.C. and a captaincy in the field for his work at "Bottcher's corner," a salient that he and a couple of men held against the Japanese during the Papuan campaign in Australasia. Jungle warfare with Captain Bottcher was "just like cops and robbers," said one of his men, who always felt strangely safe with him. He was finally killed by a mortar shell at Leyte.

After the war—conclusive of the struggle, but somehow inconclusive for the vets, who saw Franco surviving Hitler and Mussolini—they seemed to set their lives on either of two completely separate courses. Either a militantly political one, in which case they became inextricably involved in the fate of the Party during the late Forties and early Fifties; or a private one, in which case their concerns avoided—or at least drifted away from—the issues of Spain almost entirely. Of the Party stalwarts, Thompson and Gates, among the so-called "top leadership," the Foley Square Eleven, went to jail; and in 1958, Gates, out of jail, went out of the Party, a little before, mostly long after other, lesser-known vets had quietly left "the Movement," helping to reduce it over the past five years to a tiny extremist sect barely a part of American political life. Some of the vets are still openly Communists, but their sectarian lives seem to have even less fascination than those of the vets who have deliberately disappeared into the political woodwork, unaligned, private, and a little remiss—they sometimes feel—in their duties to Spain.

For the past eleven years, for instance, one vet has been quietly running his own travel agency in New York City. He "knew somebody in the business," started up from scratch, and now has enough of a going concern to allow him to take a couple of trips back to Spain, courtesy of the airlines. "I went," he says in happy surprise, "like a tourist." Back in 1937, he went like a guerrilla, though the I.B.'s were pulled out before he was actually committed behind enemy lines. He'd already seen battle at Jarama, Brunete, Belchite. Jarama was the worst, maybe because he had to ask somebody else to load his rifle for him, not knowing how to do it himself, but "it was rough all the time. After all, we were on the losing side."

Another vet who's also been back to Spain recently as a tourist describes himself "more or less a half-assed photographer." In 1936, his first idea was to go over as a photographer, but "they already had Klein and Capa." So he fought instead, from Quinto right on through the war, as infantryman, company clerk, and then ambulance driver after he was wounded at Belchite. He had his camera along, but the bellows of its old butterfly lens cracked, and most of the pictures ended up sunstruck, as if taken during shell bursts. In 1959, however, he went back to Spain with his wife, a Citroën *deux chevaux*, and a much better camera. To visit the old fronts. "If you go anywhere near the war front—if you know where to go—you'll find it just like it was. Bombed out." The church at Belchite ("It was always the church you got it from") where machine-gun fire caught him in the leg. "It's a ruin. In fact, that town was so cut up that they just built another Belchite behind it." Tarazona, where the Lincolns trained. "I remembered the bread was delicious, and I wanted to see if I'd just been hungry back then, or if it was really good bread. It's really good bread." The bridge near Mora de Ebro. "Of course, the Ebro. The Ebro! I went across it as an ambulance driver, God knows how many times I went across. You know, on one side I picked up a leather jacket—sheepskin—I still have." ("I've got it," corrects his wife, patting his girth. "You outgrew it." "Okay. She's got it then.") The villa at Benicasim, where he was hospitalized, now a hotel, where he and his wife stayed overnight. "The only difference was the beach is much smaller, and the pool has mosquito larvae in it." ("No mosquitoes under the Republic!" adds his wife.)

"That was the greatest experience I've had," he says of Spain. "And it wasn't the Depression. I felt it was my duty. To myself. If Hitler could've been stopped then, there wouldn't have been a Second World War. It wasn't the Depression. I was doing fine. Thirty bucks a week as a locksmith up in Harlem. A lot of money then. I had a Model-A Ford. (Hey—why'd I go?) Sure, when the bullets are flying, you say, *Why did I come?* But later, no." He hasn't taken much part ever in official vets' affairs. "But if there is a group of guys who were in Spain getting together, I'll join 'em. One guy I know, you couldn't drag him to a meeting now, but he says himself it was his proudest moment."

Then again, not very many vets were buying Model-A Fords back in 1936, or even *deux chevaux*'s now. Maybe twenty percent of the volunteers were students, or such; but most of them were involved in the first stirrings of trade unionism—furniture workers, cafeteria workers, laundry workers, leatherworkers, merchant seamen, and longshoremen—and they often chose to go to Spain for little more cogent reason than that they'd heard "the unions are in trouble in Spain." When the wars were over, they went right back on the labor market, many eventually working their way up to decent positions within their unions, others moving only sideways, or down, from job to job.

Johnny Toutloff, who lost a finger dragging a wounded International off Hill 381, "the Pimple" of Gandesa, has been just about everything semiskilled a man can be in life: sandhog, gandy dancer, ride man and whip man in the carnival, dishwasher, metalworker, migratory laborer, hobo, and in Spain a *cabo*, or corporal. He never had "any respect for any kings or the exploiting class." In fact, he says he has "a rather contemptuous attitude toward 'em." In the late Thirties, he hoboed across the country to New York, headed for Europe, but ended up in Childs instead. Then Horn and Hardart. And then Spain.

Spain because, politically, he found that "the enemies of my enemies happened to become my friends," and the enemies of his enemies said the real enemy was Francisco Franco. "He was put into power by outside forces, and can only stay in power through the help of outside forces. And if this be treason. . . ." Johnny smiles and bumptiously twiddles his enormous thumbs. "My only regret is that we didn't win."

Right now, he has "no political connections. . . . I'm a rebel at heart. Most likely, if I were in the Soviet Union, I'd be considered an enemy of the state. I have a perfect right to dissent, and dissent I do."

But for the last ten years, he's been dissenting from a pretty much fixed position behind a pile of newspapers on Sixth Avenue. He's one of several vets who run newsstands in the City, this one down in the Village. Long hours, six a.m. to seven p.m. with two big rushes every day. "I wouldn't work this way for anybody else," he admits—shaking his head over the working conditions—but after all, the boss was in Spain *too*, "and you get stuck." With a girl sixteen and a boy twelve, he's "become engrossed in making a living. My hands are tied. Can't even build a bookcase I want to." The job demands courtesy—"it's not within my realm to be discourteous"—and a lot of physical labor. "And I've always been considered," he says with a final, class pride, "a good worker."

Perhaps the most curious fates, however, are reserved for those vets whose lives were the Party itself, and who have only just left it. Most of them have come to the end of militancy only in the last five years, and they are faced with a strange and sudden disjointure in time. Twenty, twenty-five years after the fact, they must decide what finally to do, now that they are home from Spain. John Gates—his newspaper, *The Daily Worker*, was folded right out from under him by the Party in 1957—is continuing his education. He was graduated from Brooklyn College last year, and is now a graduate student in economics and social science at the Massachusetts Institute of Technology. He is forty-eight years old. Steve Nelson has turned to his original union trade, carpentry. "I didn't know if I could do it again because electric tools have come in since my time, but it's working out okay." He will be sixty soon.

A younger veteran, now forty-four, who quit the Party in 1955, and this year quit his job as a laborer, has a completely new career as a salesman. "My great goal had always been to be a full-time organizer for the Communist Party, but I was never considered worthy of the position. So I had to go out and get bumped in the head by life." He started selling on the side when he began needing extra money to send his daughter to college. "And I found I was having a wonderful time doing it."

Back thirty years ago, he was having a wonderful time agitating for lower lunch prices and the removal of the principal at his Brooklyn high school. He was a member of the Young Communist League, and dying to go to Spain like the big kids on the block. The first time he tried to go, his mother got the word from a special agent and put a stop to that. But the next time he made it—returning to his native Spain on a Spanish passport—and landed right in the middle of the Aragón retreats. "I went into a state of shock when I arrived. 'Jesus Christ, I'm going to die. Twenty years old, I'm going to die.' And the food was terrible." The first thing he saw was the execution of three spies caught crossing the Ebro, which had a worse effect on him than later battle. "It was done with a typical Spanish flurry. A big speech before. A big speech after. It made me sick." But he stood up well under fire. "To me, it was always much more difficult to organize something, to think out a leaflet, than to go into action." He did his part—"Fantastico —you know him?—Luchell McDaniells?—I carried him out once"—and was finally hit by shrapnel in the legs. "I'm proud of myself that I was very devoted at the time."

Now: "I feel bad I didn't go to college, but that was one of the prices you paid for the period. At the time I had no desire to go to college because the revolution was coming, and I wanted to be in the elite. In a reverse way, you know." But he's surprised nowadays when Spain has "this melodramatic effect on people. . . . To me, it became just another incidental." And one he kept fairly quiet about. "I was afraid to tell a lot of people. The shops I worked, they knew it, but they never discussed it with me. It was like adultery." He never told his young nephew, for instance. "Then it happened to come out last Sunday, and right away he turns off Ed Sullivan and wants to know all about Spain."

Another younger veteran who left the Party in 1957 has gone to work down on Wall Street as head of a mail room at $67.50 a week. "I was in the Party for twenty years," he says, "and I'm still more or less Socialist-minded, but I found it was impossible to get ahead with my attitude. I felt that any party that was for socialism had to stand on its own two feet. You should be able to criticize Russia."

Spain remains for him, however, unsullied. "Whatever political mistakes I've made in the past, that was not one of them." In fact, after being sent home to Pittsburgh in 1937 because of his wounds, he went back to fight in Spain again—too late—in 1938. "I don't know how to put it in words. There was one great drawback. You were liable to get killed at any moment. But if you could forget that—it was one of the most satisfying experiences I've ever had." He actually gained weight. "When I went over, I weighed a hundred thirty-nine. When I got back, I weighed a hundred eighty-one. If I had to place anything as the highlight of my life, I'd say Spain was it. I'd like to live there right now."

Most vets feel this way, though some did come away deeply embittered. There were deserters, several of whom showed up much later to testify against the V.A.L.B. right to the escalation of investigations to the Subversive Activities Control Board. There were men who ended up with the bottle in hand as a life's occupation, and others who took the great moments of disillusionment (how could the world fail to come to their aid, many asked incredulously, after the inhuman destruction of Guernica as an "experiment" in aerial bombardment by the Condor Legion?) as the best way to take the world itself from then on. A very few turned renegade later, such as Mickey Mickenberg, the V.A.L.B.'s bête noire, who set up the Anti-Totalitarian Friends of Spain, an anti-Communist movement that reached a peak following of six other vets. But no vet has registered the kind of sobering dissent that George Orwell propounded in *Homage to Catalonia*, unless Sandor Voros' debunk of the I.B.'s in his *American Commissar*—an account more cynical than persuasive—is taken as one. In general, even among the somewhat soured vets, Spain was the one big moment.

So much so, in fact, that it raises an entirely different question. If personal fulfillment came that early on in life and so completely, what came after? Certainly no large measure of worldly success; and those careers that have prospered are very little aligned with the question of Spain. The medical students became doctors, and the art students became artists, but none of the politicals ever became Congressmen. Or dogcatchers, for that matter. Milton Robertson, who once wrote a radio ballad for Hermann Bottcher, is now a TV director on the West Coast. Alvah Bessie published his sixth book in 1957, a novel called *The Un-Americans*, which sold 10,000 copies and was a Liberty Book Club selection. It was adapted by Bessie himself for East German television. Dr. Edward K. Barsky—who set up a famous mobile medical unit with the Lincolns in Spain, and who has since been in jail for refusing to turn over the records of the Joint Anti-Fascist Refugee Committee to the H.U.A.C.—is considered one of New York's best surgeons, above anything else he may be politically. Such is the bubble reputation, e'en in the cannon's mouth. But most have found it hard to get good jobs, harder still to keep them, and almost impossible to pursue a career that puts their names before the public in any way. Right now, all they want to do is stay out of the papers; and if they are overly defensive—convinced that nobody will give them a fair hearing, so why open your mouth?—it's because they've had some bad experiences in the past trying to explain why they were glad to have new machine guns at the front, even if they did come from Joe Stalin. In the workaday world, there are a few reasons why the survivors of a lost cause can occasionally envy the dead.

In fact, perhaps the most "famous" American among the Lincolns was James Lardner, Ring Lardner's youngest son, and his fame rests upon his own very young death. He was twenty-four, fed up with Harvard, and even fed up with the Paris *Herald* where he'd gone as a reporter after leaving Harvard.

He joined the Lincoln Battalion during the final days —bringing along a Spanish-English dictionary and Edgar Snow's *Red Star Over China* in a knapsack— and, on the next-to-last day of action, he was killed on a patrol. There have been many elegies, including one by Vincent Sheean, another by his brother, Ring Lardner Jr., but the best way to hear it is from the vets themselves.

First of all, they didn't want him in the company. They knew the end was near—"What good's another guy losing his life? Sure, now it's supposed to be great for us—look, Jimmy Lardner died fighting for the Lincoln Battalion—but so what, what good's another guy losing his life?"

But he wanted desperately to join—"so what're you going to do"—and he was "a real Boy Scout about training." They concentrated on keeping him away from shots fired in anger, right up to the fatal day.

"I sent him on the patrol. It was such a simple job too. I had no qualms about it, no qualms at all. But he went northwest instead of north.

"It was as simple—and horrible—as that."

At this late date, it is hard to believe that anything about the Spanish Civil War was ever simple —considering the labyrinth of underlying commitments that has gradually been discovered beneath the duplicitous intervention, the fraudulent nonintervention, and the disruptive political strife within Republican Spain itself—or really horrible—now that Guernica (1654 dead, 889 wounded) can be seen in the glare of Hiroshima and Nagasaki. But such hindsight comes very near being "a case of rewriting history," according to Matthews, "and we ought to leave that to the Russians. . . . 1936–1939 had a reality that shouldn't be changed. It wasn't just Hitler and Stalin using the Spanish people. I didn't see it that way, and neither did Hemingway, I'm sure, though he can't speak for himself now." Men's motives should be taken a little more as what men actually said they were at the time. "We were there to influence our own people," says Fishman on that knotty question of intention. "At the time, it didn't look like anything could stand up to fascism. But the Spanish people proved that ordinary Joes *could* stand up to it—without guns, and without help—and we wanted our own people to see this." As another vet puts it, "The Spanish cause was so goddamn *pure* that everybody could see it." And everybody did, in one way or another. Bernard Baruch, for instance, gave $11,060 to help bring some wounded Lincolns home from Paris for rehabilitation, and Henry Luce contributed $250 and Clare Boothe Luce another $250. Only later did people begin second-guessing Spain, and the second-guessing explains in part why the vets guarded that reality so closely. They even guard it against objectivity. "This being objective is just lining us up to accept Franco," says one vet. "What you need is a partisan account because the guys who fought *were* partisan. Stalin was a part of this, and I wouldn't want him left out."

The one view the vets seem unable to entertain— put forward most recently by Hugh Thomas in his book, *The Spanish Civil War*—is that Stalin might not have wanted the Loyalists to win the war, wanted only to keep the Germans occupied for the time. "I know what a terrible guy Stalin was," says Nelson painfully, "but look, you're sitting at the front with a 1918 machine gun, and the barrel is worn out. Then suddenly brand-new Russian machine guns arrive, with the grease still on them. Now, wouldn't you have been happy to see an American gun arrive? *But they didn't come!*" That much of reality remains unshakable, and there is no use trying to de-Stalinize those years of Stalin, as far as they're concerned.

But on other matters of the past, there is "a wide divergence of opinion," according to one of the younger veterans, "which wouldn't have been true at one time." Or as Nelson puts it in his own bizarre metaphor, "In retrospect, you try to assemble the facts through a periscope you didn't have at the time." What this means is that they are able to see mistakes they made—or wrong views they took—without wanting to blacken the past as if they had led a life of total political sin. "I resent people who engage in shrieking at the past," says one ex-Communist vet. "I think the word is 'cynical laughter at others.' It's too much like the same laughter from *before*."

One mistake they would want to correct—if the man were still alive—is their latter-day attitude toward Hemingway. "We were wrong about Hemingway," says Harold Smith baldly, referring back to an old quarrel that began when Hemingway published *For Whom the Bell Tolls*. The vets objected violently at that time, 1940, to the portrait he drew of André Marty, the French Communist who had command at Albacete, the I.B. base, and after whom the Franco-Belge battalion had been named. Says Matthews, "He was poison"—a trigger-happy terrorist, who was at the same time pathologically suspicious of everybody as a possible agent of the Fifth Column, and Hemingway's brief sketch did him justice. Now Fishman can say: "There was much truth about what he said about Marty, but we didn't know. How could we? We never met Marty. To us, at the front, he was a big hero. We've talked this over among the guys, and the way we feel now, you're either anti-Franco, or pro-Franco. And Hemingway was anti-Franco. Obviously."

And this is really the only article of faith demanded, outside of feeling "responsible to the Spanish people." It's even allowable to let a little historical perspective creep in. "Regardless of whatever sentimentality or feeling of responsibility we have, it isn't such a big question anymore," says one of the vets. "We've got the H-bomb, and I don't think that Spain is the most important question in the world." Or, as even Fishman puts it, "The war used to get fought every time the guys got together, but not so much anymore."

But let there be any official call for a show of loyalty to the Spanish cause, and the vets will provision a force and march it stoutly out, right under the raking fire of the most aroused public criticism. They did this most recently in response to an invitation from the Anti-Fascist Committee in the East German Democratic Republic last summer. Fishman phrases the reasons for the trip very carefully: "East Germany was the only country in the world that had an official celebration commemorating the twenty-fifth anniversary of the fight against fascism in Spain. It was an *official* invitation of the Committee and we were asked to send a delegation. Nobody tried to stop us, coming or going."

Twenty-two vets went. With their wives and children, the party came to fifty-five. They paid their own fares over. The Anti-Fascist Committee of the East German Democratic Republic paid some of their fares back. For one week, July 18 to 25, they were part of the speeches, mass rallies, official receptions (in such places as Goering's old air ministry), and propaganda of the occasion. The rest of the time they toured.

As for their reactions, they varied as widely as they themselves obviously do now as individuals. The only thing they shared in common was this first chance "to see socialism at work," still a lifelong dream, however dimmed, for each of them: the proletarian tour-guide version of "see Venice and die." They all say they were "impressed"—a conclusion that "surprised" them, because they went over there "sympathetic but leery"—but what else could be expected from any tourist just back from his own particular tawdry Venice? The point is that a lot of *personal* things happened to each of them in Venice, and it's no use beginning with a direct question about the stinking canals.

One vet, for instance, finally made his peace with the cops. "All my life I've wondered if a cop came up to me, what did he want? But here, if a cop came up, he threw his arms around me! Turned out to be a guy who'd fought in Spain."

Johnny Toutloff found an old buddy. "A German fella who went over the Pyrenees with me. We recognized each other. I was so tickled. I've told my wife that story so many times—about these Germans I was with—and here I could *show* her one of them." And somebody recognized his I.B. medal. "I went to the Brecht theatre, and when I come out, this woman come out, and she saw I was wearing my brigade pin. She was a nurse in Spain herself."

And Moe Fishman got caught up emotionally in the affair. "You know that farewell speech to the International Brigades by La Pasionaria? I wasn't there then—I'd already been wounded—but they say guys cried. I heard it in German this time, in Berlin, recited by a German actress, and my German ain't too great, but *I* cried."

In short, a good time was had by all, and, except for the Berlin crisis, the border closing, the Cold War, and the resumption of testing, it might be just another veterans' convention in a rundown locale that was giving cut rates to get back the tourist trade. The absurdity of this—and yet the fact that it persists as a distinct impression: the vets and their families on the Big Golden Anniversary Outing—is perhaps a sign of the sheer quixotry of the whole experience, from 1937 straight on through. Certainly the vets were aware of the politics of the occasion. One of them, after paying several compliments to socialism-at-work, says frankly: "They tried to hide the fact that people were running to the West, when everybody in the street knew it. In the factories, they said they couldn't complete their quotas because of it. And right up until they closed the gates, they were assuring me they wouldn't because that would split up families in Berlin." And there certainly are some vets who would castigate this one for saying any of these heinous things about the "Free People's" Republic—their *host,* after all, and the people's protector against the Nazi scourge of West German capitalism. But somehow, dispute over these points misses what the vets really exemplify in an age that now has trouble taking them straight.

It's simply that they *volunteered.*

They actually volunteered to go all that way to Spain and fight. And they have been volunteering for one thing or another ever since. Wounded and returned from Spain, they volunteered to go back to Spain. Withdrawn from Spain, they volunteered for every kind of duty as soon as the United States got into the war. "I volunteered for the paratroops, the tank corps, infantry, and overseas in general," says one vet, "but the guy had a record of every street-corner speech and leaflet I'd ever done in my life." (He ended up a Link-trainer instructor in Reno, Nevada.) They've since volunteered for a lot of things that don't seem "so goddamn *pure*" to many people nowadays; few are likely, for instance, to praise them as goodwill ambassadors for their trip to East Germany. But there is no doubt that, regardless of the other political consequences, they have always chosen to fulfill their one outstanding commitment to oppose Franco in Spain, and, on every occasion, enough guys have stepped forward to give it another whirl. In a time when a volunteer is usually somebody who is still standing there when everybody else has taken a step *back,* this seems remarkable in its own right. It is their one common heritage, regardless of later politics, and if a number of vets have stopped volunteering altogether—even information—over recent years, it is still a deeply ingrained memory.

There is, for example, the case of one vet, who is now settled into a routine urban existence, who would not have gone on the recent junket to East Germany, even if asked, and who wants little to do with the V.A.L.B. at the moment. When he got back from Spain in 1938, for the first time in his life he was out of work and on relief. Nobody would give him a job, and the last miseries of Spain had turned into the hard times of the Depression of the late Thirties. He had a friend, Rudy, an Italian-American, who'd fought with the Garibaldis in Spain, and they used to get together and mull over what they ought to do now. "But what we were really thinking of doing, me and Rudy," the vet remembers now, "what we ought to do after Spain—was volunteer to go to fight fascism in China."

Laurence Stallings:
Hitler Did Not Dance That Jig

The secret behind a masterstroke of propaganda

There is no way to correct a trick of propaganda that fits a monstrous figure in history, even though it is a cunning blow struck at one of mankind's evil men. Nor is there any way to correct the belief that Hitler danced a protracted little jig when the French surrendered to him in that railway car at Compiègne. Hitler stood a moment in awe at his own distortion of history, and gave a small leap of astonishment at himself. Yet the world believes that Hitler staged a little war dance there; for a clever stroke by a film documentarian, and a wonderful Allied propaganda film making use of Nazi newsreel clips, had succeeded in making him the sissiest, most ludicrous conqueror that ever lived. It was not an accident, as was the case when a medieval translator succeeded in making Nero fiddle when Rome burned— when the manuscript said Nero fretted.

When I saw the Allied version of Hitler's protracted little jig, I knew I was witnessing one of the great hoaxes on film. I had just finished three years as editor in chief of the Movietone system, and I knew Hitler's image by heart. I had watched his beginnings on film, when he first marched six abreast with his bullies until there began to be only a triumvirate of Hitler, Goebbels and Goering. Then there was only one, Hitler, who led the parades. He had become monstrously divine, and the rest were dirt beneath his feet. He strode ten feet ahead of everyone, untouchable, unapproachable, as mad as a hatter. Gone were the almost comic rages, the sissy gestures. There was a demoniacal calm about him. And when I saw the celluloid jig, I knew that it was untrue.

A second look at the Allied documentary showed the trickery behind this jig. The film had been frozen —"looped" is a better word—which is to say that a

Laurence Stallings was coauthor with Maxwell Anderson of What Price Glory?, *the anti-war Broadway hit of 1924, and wrote the stage version of Hemingway's* A Farewell to Arms *in 1930. Like many talents of the era he found his way into films, where he scored this short but significant triumph of anti-propaganda; Esquire published it in October, 1958.*

few frames of the film, where he had made his involuntary leap, had been placed upon an optical printer, and duplicated many times. These identical frames had been spliced in sequence, and as a result the Allies had themselves a little wooden-soldier jig. Once Hitler had made his little leap, some genius of an Allied film documentarian had done the rest. I wondered how many film technicians must have recognized this as a phony clip, and who was its perpetrator. I had the answer one night in Claridge's Hotel in London, shortly after V-E day.

I was with John Grierson, film documentarian, and then General Manager of Wartime Information for the Dominion of Canada. I asked suddenly: "Who looped the Compiègne film and made Hitler dance that silly jig?"

"I did," he said quietly. "Hitler actually did a minute little jump of joy at Compiègne. The only trick was to freeze that little jump at the silliest point; that is, at the sissiest point. Because any little jump of joy is apt to give you at least one frame of a posture which is scarcely male." John Grierson then added, able to smile that night after six years of hell: "It gave a different emphasis to Hitler's victorious occasion."

John Grierson was kind enough to say I was the first ever to tax him with this trickery; but I disclaimed any priority, saying many technicians must have seen through the trick but, like myself, had relished the deceit.

"Tell me," John asked, "when you were at Movietone did you ever loop a piece of negative for trickery?"

"Only once," I replied. "When the Croat assassinated Alexander II of Yugoslavia at Marseilles, just before the king was killed, he looked aloft at a pretty girl on a balcony, and then settled back into the car cushions with a deep sigh. He died with that sigh in his breast, and I looped it, prolonging that sigh not so much for trickery as to give Lowell Thomas time to spot it in his commentary."

We agreed it was one of the great strips of film of all time, made by the French Movietone ace, Georges

Mejat, who ran into the scene with a hand camera the moment the Croat started blasting. It was remarkable that he caught so many shots in such a swift passage into eternity. Later, in Addis Ababa, I asked Mejat if he had not gone back afterward and faked one shot.

He smiled. "Which one?"

"The one where the assassin's straw hat is carried away by that gendarme."

"That is correct," Mejat said. "I saw it, but could not swerve from the main interest to photograph it. So, when the confusion was over, I got the gendarme to reenact it. Just a little five foot cut-in of that battered hat. But it was not a fake. It was a replica."

There in Claridge's we fell to talking of Hitlerian films again. "Your Hitler jig, John," I said, "is probably the greatest masterstroke of film propaganda. You made a great monster at the time of his greatest power into an object of ridicule. That's the way mankind wants it; that's the way it must be . . . and how you must have chuckled in that projection room."

"You don't chuckle," the great documentarian said soberly, "when you are trying to undo an S.O.B."

Sinclair Lewis:

Gentlemen, This Is Revolution

Discovered: the new and not surprising pattern of a universal revolt
against the old domination of white smugness

lack Boy, the story of his own youth in the South by Richard Wright, the enormously talented young Negro who also wrote *Native Son*, has been greeted by several placidly busy white reviewers and by a couple of agitated Negro reviewers as betraying too much "emotion," too much "bitterness."

Now this is the story of a colored boy who, just yesterday, found in his native community not merely that he was penalized for having the same qualities that in a white boy would have warmed his neighbors to universal praise—the qualities of courage, energy, curiosity, refusal to be subservient, the impulse to record life in words—but that he was in danger of disapproval, then of beatings, then of being killed, for these qualities, for being "uppity." Not bitterness but fear charges the book, and how this young crusader can be expected to look back only a few years to the quiet torture with anything except hatred is beyond me.

When we have a successful comedy by an ex-prisoner about the kindness and humor of the warders in a German concentration camp, then I shall expect Mr. Wright to mellow and to speak amiably of the teachers who flattened him, his colored neighbors and relatives who denounced him, the merchants who cheated him, the white fellow-mechanics who threatened him for wanting to learn their skills, and the librarian who suspected him—quite rightly—of reading that militant and bewhiskered Bolshevik, that polluter of temples and Chambers of Commerce, Comrade H. L. Mencken.

There has recently appeared, at the same time as *Black Boy*, the skilled and important report by the secretary of the National Association for the Advancement of Colored People, my friend Walter White, upon what has been happening to American Negro soldiers in our camps at home and in England, and at the battlefront in Italy and Africa. There are in this report numerous exact incidents of Jim Crowism lugged into our Army of Democracy. The main impressions that come out of reading it are the continued

Sinclair Lewis was Esquire's book reviewer from June to December, 1945, midway in a distinguished parade which includes James T. Farrell, Bennett Cerf, A.J. Liebling, Dorothy Parker and, now, Malcolm Muggeridge. This prophetic review of books by and about what was then called the Negro Problem seemed ahead of its time until around 1960, when events justified it.

segregation of Negro soldiers from their white comrades in Red Cross clubs and even in adjacent villages, and the fact that, except for a few sectors in which Negroes have brilliantly fought and flown, they have been restricted to labor units instead of being trusted as fighters.

Soldier workers, lugging supplies ashore during landings, or driving trucks or repairing roads under fire, get killed just as frequently—it may even be just as painfully—as the white fighters, but there is no credit in it. They are expected to live like dogs and not even to die as heroes.

The assertions of Mr. White are amply backed up by a woman, a white woman, a woman from a Navy family, in another just-issued book, *Jim Crow Grows Up*, by Ruth Danenhower Wilson.

If there had appeared only these three books, these three disturbing Border Incidents, they would still be enough to make the wise observer fear that a revolution in Negro affairs is threatened. But one may go beyond them to a score of other related books published in the past three years, and if America can possibly take the time from its study of comic strips to discover even the titles of these books, it may realize that this is a revolution, and that it is not coming—it is here.

The unwritten manifesto of this revolution states that the Negro, backed by a number of whites in every section of the land, is finished with being classed as not quite human; that he is no longer humble and patient—and unlettered; and that an astonishingly large group of Negro scholars and journalists and artists are expressing their resolution with courage and skill. They are no longer "colored people." They are *people*.

Lillian Smith's novel, *Strange Fruit*, still a best seller and as such revealing new audiences, is not merely a small tragedy about two lovers separated by a color line which bothered everybody except the lovers themselves. It is a condensation of the entire history of one tenth of our population.

That amusing and amazingly informative book, *New World A-Coming*, by Roi Ottley, published in 1943, is not just a report of the new Negro life in Harlem. It is a portent of an entire new life for all American Negroes, and it was written by what is naïvely known as a "colored man"—that is, a man who has by nature the fine rich skin that the rest of us try to acquire by expensive winter trips to Florida.

And the 1943 biography of Dr. George Washington Carver by Rackham Holt—who, like Lillian Smith, is very much the White Lady—portrays, on the positive side of the question, what one Negro could do, given any chance at all, even so small a chance that to a white man it would have seemed a balk. Dr. Carver, whose discovery of the food and the plastics to be found in the once disenfranchised peanut was salvation for large sections of the South, was the greatest agricultural chemist of our time. It is doubtful whether any flamboyant soldier or statesman or author has done more solid good for America than this Negro, the child of slaves.

But in one thing the intellectual or just the plain reasoning Negro today has broken away from the doctrines of Dr. Carver. This newcomer has progressed or seriously retrogressed, whichever you prefer. He is no longer, like Dr. Carver, ecstatic with gratitude to the white men who permit him the singular privilege of enabling them to make millions of dollars.

To such innocent readers as have not known that the Negro doesn't really like things as they are, such as have been shocked by the "bitterness" of Mr. Wright's *Black Boy*, there is to be recommended a book much more shocking. But here the shocks are communicated by graphs and columns of figures and grave chapters of sociology, which add up to exactly the same doctrines as Mr. Wright's.

This is *An American Dilemma*, a 1483-page treatise by Professor Gunnar Myrdal of Sweden and a staff of American assistants. Mr. Myrdal was invited by the Carnegie Corporation to come to America precisely because he was a foreigner, and less subject to our own prejudices.

Anyone who reads through this vast work will really know something about the identity and the social position of the Negro, and anyone who desires to "argue the question" is invited to read it, whether he was born in Maine or . Mississippi. Probably no other book has more exact information, more richness of Negro lore. Here is his complex origin, whereby the yardman whom you think so clownish may have in him the blood of Arabian princes as well as of Bantu warriors; here are his economic status today, his religion and culture, his past and present share in politics, his social conflicts, his actual and possible jobs, his dollars-and-cents budget today. It is all as impersonal as penicillin, and as powerful.

To this sober pair of volumes should be added the enlightenment and stimulation and considerable entertainment in a book published a few months ago by that excellent Southern institution, the University of North Carolina Press, at Chapel Hill; a book called *What the Negro Wants*. In this, fourteen distinguished Negro writers such as Langston Hughes, A. Philip Randolph, Dr. W. E. B. Du Bois, Mary Bethune, Roy Wilkins tell precisely what they think of it all.

They are all serious, honest, and informed, but among them I prefer George Schuyler of the Pittsburgh *Courier*, who, despite his wit and easy urbanity, is perhaps the most serious of the lot. How any person so cultured that he can add two and two and get as much as three out of it can read the deft pages of Mr. Schuyler and still accept any of the Comical Coon, the Dancing Dinge, the Grateful Bellhop, the "Mah brethrens, Ah absquatulates tuh consider" theory of Negro culture, I cannot understand.

His thesis, bland as dynamite soup, is that there is no Negro Problem at all, but there decidedly is a Caucasian Problem; that of the universal American-English-Belgian-Dutch-French-German-Portuguese exploiter who smugly talks about the "white man's burden" while he squats on the shoulders of all the "colored men" in the world. Mr. Schuyler suggests that in Kenya and Burma and Jamaica and Java and Peking just as much as in America these colored races are now effectively sick of it. He is, however, too polite to point up the facts that there are a lot more of them than there are of us, and that a machine gun does not inquire into the complexion of the man who uses it.

Here, all of these books begin to fit into a pattern. This suggestion of a universal revolt against the domination of white smugness is also the conclusion of *A Rising Wind*, even though the author is so gay and gentle a leader as Walter White. Quoting from Pearl Buck, another white woman who is not content to be nothing more than that, Mr. White indicates with what frightening care the entire "colored world" —including Japan—is watching and reporting upon our treatment of our own Negroes in Army and Navy, hotel and bus, in factory, pulpit and congressional committee room.

Gentlemen, my pukka English-Irish-Yank-Swede-Dutch brethren, it behooves us to find out what this larger part of the world is thinking and most articulately saying about us. A slight injection of knowledge may hurt our feelings, but it may save our lives.

I am delighted that in my first column for that stately household compendium, Esquire, I have been able to uphold the standards of refined and uncontaminated rhetoric and, here in my ivory tower in Duluth, to keep from taking sides and to conceal my personal views upon Messrs. White, Wright, Schuyler and Myrdal. Let us by all means avoid distasteful subjects and think only of the brightest and best.

Richard H. Rovere:

The Last Days of Joe McCarthy

Great was his fall, and there was no putting him together again

In the spring of the year, 1954, there was the televised rumble over Private Schine, Major Peress, General Zwicker, Secretary Stevens, and others then of disputed rank and now of rapidly dimming luster. In the late summer, there were the untelevised censure hearings presided over by Senator Arthur V. Watkins, a Mormon elder from Orem, Utah, who could play variations on the crack of doom with a chairman's gavel and who was so insistent on a pure, unclouded atmosphere that he posted No Smoking signs in the Senate Caucus Room—an act wholly without precedent. In the fall, there was the censure debate on the Senate floor—ending with a vote of sixty-seven for, twenty-two against a watered-down resolution of censure from which, at the very last moment and with a swift, concealed stroke of the pen, Vice-President Nixon struck the word "censure."

By winter, Joe McCarthy was through. He had not lost his following. He had not lost, so far as anyone knows, a single true friend. Lieutenant General George E. Stratemeyer headed up a committee of "Ten Million Americans Mobilizing for Justice"; all the old militants rallied round, and by the day of the censure vote over a million signatures to a protest petition had been delivered to the Senate by armored car. McCarthy had not lost any of the appurtenances of power. He still had his seat, his seniority, and his committee assignments. (In January, 1955, the Democrats organized Congress, and of course he lost his chairmanship of the Government Operations Committee. But it wasn't his fault that the Democrats had won the elections.) Exactly half his party in the Senate had stood by him and refused to support censure. Still and all, he was through, and everyone knew it. He had lost the power to panic the United States Senate and to shiver the White House timbers. Sixty-seven Senators, including twenty-two Republicans, had dared to vote against him, and the President had called in Senator Watkins, the Cato of Wasatch, to "congratulate him," in the words of James Hagerty, "for the splendid job he did." Far more important,

McCarthy had lost his nerve. His drive, his superb sense of timing, and even some of his meanness seemed to have gone from him. Where he had once been steely, he grew rubbery. He still knew what to do in a back-alley fight, but he seldom did it. He no longer clawed his antagonists but made wisecracks and played sophomoric jokes on them. Asked for comment on the Senate resolution, he said, "I wouldn't exactly say it was a vote of confidence." He added, "I don't feel I've been lynched." He struck back at Senator Wallace Bennett, the other Utah Senator and the author of the final draft of the resolution, when Bennett was assigned McCarthy's old office in a general shifting of quarters. In the refrigerator McCarthy had used to keep Milwaukee beer at a palatable temperature, Senator Bennett found, hanging from an ice-cube tray, a large, crudely lettered placard—WHO PROMOTED PERESS?

In the two and a half years that remained of his life, McCarthy made only a few spiritless attempts at a comeback. Now and then, he would get the Senate floor to denounce someone or something, but never with much force and never with much of an audience. When he rose, Senators would drift out of the chamber, and the reporters in the gallery would see a chance to catch lunch, play cards, or find out what Lyndon Johnson was up to. From time to time, McCarthy could be seen shambling (or lurching, for he was drinking more and holding it less well) down the corridors of the Senate Office Building en route to some committee room where photographers had been sighted. It wasn't of much use. The photographers knew he didn't have it. Mostly they ignored him; if, for old times' sake, they didn't, their editors filed the pictures. He got free television time every so often, generally on some panel or interview show with a low Trendex, and used it to call Paul Hoffman "a throwback on the human race," Sherman Adams a "pinhead," or Harold Stassen "one of the most contemptible politicians of our era." It was the old language, but in another voice and mood.

For a while, he tried statesmanship. He hired a bright and earnest young rightist, L. Brent Bozell, to write him some meaty speeches on foreign and military policy. Some of them were quite good. One, on April 25, 1956, described with remarkable prescience

Great was the fall of the Fifties' most controversial politician, and few paid much attention to the Senator afterward. One who did, to Esquire's advantage, was Mr. Rovere, now best known as The New Yorker's *Washington correspondent, but also a sometime staff member of* The Nation, *and others. This article ran in August, 1958.*

our lag in missile development and the political consequences of the lag; it may well have been the most prophetic speech of that year. But McCarthy felt as silly as he looked in a toga, and threw it aside. He made a pass at the farm vote. In the Administration and in Congress, there were arguments over whether agricultural price supports should assure 85 or 87.5 or 90 percent of parity. McCarthy said it was a lot of cheapskate talk and came out for 110 percent of parity. This was a promising line for a demagogue down on his luck, but he soon dropped it. He couldn't seem to stick to anything. In the 1956 election, he played hardly any role at all. After the censure vote, he had made a "public apology . . . to the American people" for having once believed that the President was anti-Communist. After Mr. Eisenhower's heart attack in 1955, McCarthy said he thought it would be "unkind" to ask the President to run again; he said he thought that either J. Edgar Hoover or Herman Welker would make a good Republican candidate. He did not attend the San Francisco convention in 1956. Early in 1957, when Senator McClellan of Arkansas, who had taken over as chairman of Government Operations, was getting high on the front pages by making life miserable for Dave Beck, McCarthy tried to get into the act—now by championing the Fifth Amendment teamster, now by bullyragging him. But he didn't work at it. He would come into the Caucus Room late, interrupt a line of questioning with questions of his own, some of which were incoherent, and after twenty minutes or so wander out in an almost trance-like state.

He was sick a lot of the time and frequently hospitalized, as a rule for the treatment of obscure ailments. The censure debate had been delayed for ten days because of one of these confinements. The Capitol physician, Dr. George Calver, explained that the Senator had "traumatic bursitis." Visited in the hospital, McCarthy said he had undergone surgery to have some pieces of glass removed from his elbow. (The story was that a Milwaukee admirer had shaken hands with him a bit too vigorously, pumping McCarthy's arm so hard his elbow cracked a glass-topped table.) The hospital doctors said there had been no surgery at all. It was always that way—mixed up. There was talk of back trouble, leg trouble, liver trouble, prostate trouble, lung trouble, heart trouble, and—always—bottle trouble. He would run alarmingly to fat, then he would grow gaunt. He lost forty-one pounds in a few weeks. Not even his closest friends knew what was wrong. "All I know is he always had a flaming belly," one of them has said. It was persistently rumored that he went to the hospital only to have the booze drained off. There have been descriptions of him as having spent his last years in an unbroken alcoholic stupor. These descriptions are inaccurate. He had always been a heavy drinker, and there were times in those seasons of discontent when he drank more than before. But he was not always drunk. He went on the wagon (for him, this meant beer in place of whiskey) for days and weeks at a time. The main trouble toward the end was that he couldn't hold the stuff. Where once he had been able to "belt a fifth"—as members of his set would put it—between midnight and five a.m., sleep for a couple of hours, and be at the office at eight-thirty or nine, he now went to pieces on the second drink.

Still and all, he did not devote his life to it. He was never a sot. He was as busy in that period as the average Senator and a lot busier than many. And he had a private life. He and his wife adopted a baby. He spent a good deal of time with his personal friends, a number of whom had never been his political friends. He went deer hunting, or at least he went into the Wisconsin woods, and once he got a deer with his car.

He became much interested in money. He had always liked it, just as he had always liked liquor, but he had liked to have it in order to get rid of it. Now he developed an obsession with financial security and investments. He began thinking in terms of a quiet, cozy, nonpolitical middle age. "Jean and I have enough money for a small cattle spread in Arizona," he said. "I might open a law office for friends and neighbors." The truth was that he didn't have enough money, but he figured he could get it. He knew people who knew the money game. On their advice, he took some fliers in oil and uranium. He made a sizable fraction of a million on paper. His smart friends egged him on. Visions of sugarplums danced in his head. He was on the wagon now, a dedicated speculator, all bear and no bull. Then some of the people who had been going along for the ride decided they had gone far enough. They quit while they were ahead and while McCarthy was in Wisconsin and, momentarily, not keeping up with his portfolio. He sustained heavy losses, not on paper but in legal United States tender. This was very close to the end. He fell off the wagon in a heap.

On April 28, 1957, he was admitted to Bethesda Naval Hospital. Mrs. McCarthy said he had gone for the treatment of a "knee injury." He was put in the neurological section. The Navy doctors announced that his condition had been diagnosed as "peripheral neuritis." Four days later, on May 2, he breathed his last, just in time for the seven o'clock news. ("In time for the seven o'clock news" was his favorite time for uncovering a new master spy, for blistering Sherman Adams, or for telling Eisenhower to watch his step.) The first obituaries gave no cause of death. They reported that he was forty-seven, having reached that age the preceding November 9. When someone checked his birth certificate in Grand Chute, Wisconsin, it was found that he had turned forty-eight the preceding November 14. Mrs. McCarthy wanted a posthumous triumph for him in the Senate. He got it. He was the first Senator in seventeen years—the last had been the old Idaho windbag, William Borah—to receive a state funeral in the Senate chamber. "This fallen warrior through death speaketh," the Reverend Frederick Brown Harris, the Senate chaplain, said, and the burden of his embarrassing message was that the prophet is not without honor except, etc. The flag-draped coffin was put on a plane with the late Herman Welker and two reporters aboard and flown to Green Bay, Wisconsin. The airborne wake was provisioned as the best wakes generally are. Grief was held at bay over—literally over—McCarthy's dead body. On May 7 the fallen warrior was given a Catholic funeral at St. Mary's Church in Appleton, then laid to rest in a cemetery on a bluff overlooking the Fox River.

Mystery still surrounds the cause of death. The Bethesda doctors said they had erred in their original diagnosis of peripheral neuritis, which is an inflammation of the nerve ends furthest from the central nervous system. They explained, after the fact, that on subsequent examination and consultation it had been found that McCarthy had been suffering from hepatitis, a chic malady formerly known as jaundice. They ascribed death to "acute hepatitic infection" and "hepatitic failure." Hepatitis and peripheral neuritis have about as much in common as Asian flu and a broken ankle. *Hepar* is Greek for liver. Hepatitis is an inflammation of that organ. It is debilitating but seldom fatal. *Time* reported that McCarthy had died of "cirrhosis of the liver." In cirrhosis, the liver turns into something the consistency of wet sawdust. The commonest agent for the transformation is alcohol. Many people are convinced that McCarthy drank himself to death. One way or another, he probably did—but not, perhaps, in the usual way. It is conceivable that years of drinking had given him a wet-sawdust liver, but the suddenness of his death suggests another possibility. He had had hepatitis, and for a victim of this disease alcohol even in small amounts is poison. The chances are that his last drinking bouts—begun when he got the bad news about his investments—did him in. Either way, liquor and the liver had something to do with it.

Life often hangs on desire

When he died, the true believers cried murder most foul. That is what true believers always do. They said, as one might have expected them to, that the Communists, the Truman-Acheson Democrats, the bleeding hearts, the eggheads, the Eisenhower Republicans, Americans for Democratic Action, the Army Department coddlers of Communists, the Adams-Brownell clique, all the forces of darkness, subversion, and betrayal had come together to crush this patriot and had succeeded in destroying his will to live. The McCarthyite publisher, William Loeb of Manchester, New Hampshire, said that McCarthy's enemies, among whom he numbered "that stinking hypocrite in the White House," had "worn down his adrenal and other glands." Others were less violent and less clinical. They said McCarthy had died of a broken heart, brought on by contemplation of a broken crusade. They would have said this if he had been struck by lightning or bitten by a rabid dog, but the known subjectivity of their judgment does not make it false. The will to live is, we know, a necessary condition of living. Life may endure when it is gone, but when life is challenged by disease or the ravages of time or a heedless mode of existence, it may hang on desire. There is reason to suppose that McCarthy's distress at the very end had more to do with a broken bankbook and a shattered dream of a cattle spread than

with a broken crusade, but that scarcely matters. The crusade, such as it was, had ended for him two and a half years earlier. And whether drinking was a primary or a secondary cause of his death, the fact remains that he could probably have held onto life by not drinking, and he elected to drink.

To acknowledge this much, though, is to raise a whole series of questions about McCarthy. Why was he undone by the events of 1954? What was his heart made of that it should break so easily? His defeats were real enough, but they were of the sort on which most leaders of mass movements thrive. Hitler, at one end of the moral spectrum, and Gandhi, at the other, rose phoenix-like from a half-dozen such defeats. What, after all, was so terrible about the events of 1954? He was in a brawl on television, and a lot of Americans got a close look at him and set him down as a plug-ugly. But the people who found him repulsive had never been his followers anyway, and never could have been. To the hard core, and to most of those who formed around it, his nastiness was part of his charm. The more he ranted, the more they loved him, and he was a Caruso among ranters. To be scorned by the respectable, disowned by Eisenhower, half-heartedly "censured" by the Senate—why should any of this have mattered? He wasn't left to rot in a dungeon. He retained his liberties and his office. His followers were still all about him—waiting, if they were of the authentic breed of those fetched by demagogues, for a rallying cry, an order to regroup and resume the attack. Their leader was young and vigorous.

If he had been a Hitler, he might have burned down the Senate. Being McCarthy, he hired a lawyer—one of the country's best, Edward Bennett Williams—and sought an acquittal. When he didn't get it, he buckled before respectable and official opinion. He shared its view that he hadn't much of a future. And he soon died because he could not lay off liquor. This, too, is odd. Historically, it is unheard of that the leader of a crusade, or any true fanatic, should die in this way. Normally, such men—the demonic and the saintly alike—are ascetics. Their dreams of power and glory are headier brews than anything fermented or distilled.

Such questions rest, of course, on the premise that McCarthy was a man of real stature in his field. I believe it can be demonstrated that he was not only the ablest demagogue of his time but the most gifted ever bred on these shores. Most of our demagogues, in this century and the last, have been provincial and parochial figures—their influence limited to a region or a sect. In the nineteenth century, abolition, secession, populism, and nativism produced a few rabble-rousers of proficiency, but none who left a lasting impact on the country and none who is widely remembered today. It may be too early to say that McCarthy's influence will still be felt twenty years from now, but the chances seem good that it will be. In any case, consider his achievements, or ravages, between 1950 and 1954:

—Unknown in 1950, he made himself a global figure by 1952. In many parts of the world, he was the personification of all that was held to be evil in American

policy and American life. He was one of the few Americans ever to be actively feared and hated by foreigners.

—Less than two years after his ascent from obscurity, he became a central issue in a Presidential campaign. He was still a first-term Senator in the minority party. He had no rank or power except that which he generated for himself, within himself.

—He gained enormous influence over American foreign policy at a time when American policy bore heavily on world history. Our diplomacy in the Far East, in many respects a key to our diplomacy elsewhere, might have borne a very different aspect if it had not been for McCarthy's power.

—He stamped with his name a tendency, a whole cluster of tendencies in American life. The name survives. To many Americans, whatever is illiberal, anti-intellectual, repressive, reactionary, totalitarian, or merely swinish will hereafter be "McCarthyism." The word is imprecise, but it conveys a meaning and a powerful image.

For all of the black arts that he practiced, McCarthy's natural endowments and his cultivated skills were of the highest order. "The qualities necessary to a demagogue," Aristophanes wrote, "are these: to be foul-mouthed, base-born, a low, mean fellow." McCarthy qualified handsomely. He was the master of the scabrous and the scatological. He understood the perverse appeal of the bum, the mucker, the dead-end kid, the James Jones-Nelson Algren hero to a nation in the midst of a vast leveling process in which everyone was sliding, from one direction or the other, into middle-class respectability, and he was quick to make it. He had some decent instincts—who hasn't?—and some yearnings of his own for lace-curtain, wall-to-wall respectability, but he overcame these with conspicuous ease. He was a fighter who used his thumbs, his teeth, and his knees. His style, I have always thought, owed a lot to that of a certain kind of American athlete: the kind who swaggers and exaggerates his swagger, the kind who looks ugly and talks ugly and earns such sobriquets as Killer or Slugger, the kind who attaches enough importance to winning the goddamned game to throw spitballs and rabbit punches and do a little work with knees and elbows in the pileups. He boasted of how he had been taught to go straight for the groin by an old north-woods scamp named Indian Charlie. The rank and file were pleased to know that the leader had been trained by this sage mentor.

Multiple lies and shell games

He had an extraordinary bag of tricks. Hitler discovered the uses of the Big Lie—the falsehood so large and round that reason, which deals in particulars, was almost powerless to combat it. McCarthy invented the Multiple Lie—the lie with so many particulars, so many moving and interchangeable parts, so many tiny gears and fragile connecting rods that reason exhausted itself in the effort to combat it. He said so many different things about so many different people (people, generally, of uncertain identity and even, so far as the public was concerned, of questionable ex-

istence) that no one could keep it all in focus.

He brought to perfection a kind of shell game to be played with facts, or what George Orwell called "unfacts." He flummoxed me with it the first time I met him, which was a year or so before he discovered communism. I wished to get certain information about one of his undertakings, and he brought me into his office to show me some "documents" that would, he said, be TNT. "Wait'll you get a load of this," he said. "It's going to rock the country." All eager, I began to look at his photostats, his clippings, his "confidential" reports, his copies of other people's correspondence. A feeling of foolishness—mine, not his—came over me when I was unable to see that any of them proved anything about anything. No TNT. "But I don't quite get it," I would say. "It doesn't seem to have much to do with what I'm after." "It has a lot to do with it," he would say, "but naturally those bastards were trying to cover up. Now look at this one, it will make the others clear. We've got a jigsaw puzzle here, see, and we've got to put the pieces together." I thought he was making sense and that my perceptions were at fault. "Please explain this," I would ask, and he would answer, "It'll all be clear when you've studied a few more of these documents." He would deal some from the bottom of the deck, and I would curse myself for my obtuseness. It was not until I had spent hours with him that it dawned on me that I was being switched, double-shuffled, and conned by one of the masters.

The cloak of sovereignty

There was an audacity about him, a sweep to his imagination that was quite simply beyond the comprehension of most of those with whom he had to deal. He cloaked himself in sovereignty—diplomatic, political, moral. He was not bound by the Constitution, the party system, or any version of the categorical imperative. In May, 1953, he advised the world of the fact that he had negotiated an agreement with the Greek maritime interests that would result in denying to Communist China goods delivered in Greek bottoms. And though he exaggerated wildly in his descriptions of what had occurred, the fact remained that he had constituted himself an agency for the conduct of foreign relations. When it suited his purposes, which was most of the time, he was an open seditionist. In 1952, 1953, and 1954, he organized among government workers a Loyal American Underground. This was an insurrectionist cabal that reported directly to McCarthy and his lieutenants and gave him their primary loyalty. McCarthy was, as all great demagogues are, a revolutionist.

He operated far outside the framework of American political morality. This is not to say that he was immoral or amoral rather than moral; it is rather to say that he ignored the conventions of American politics. Cheating of one sort or another is, of course, tolerated in politics. But there are limits of tolerance, and it was one of McCarthy's distinctions—one of the marks, if you will, of his greatness—that he simply did not consider that the No Trespassing signs were for him.

It is, for example, within limits to misrepresent a fact; but the convention holds that it must be a *fact* that is misrepresented. For McCarthy, this silly rule had no meaning. When he wished to have it believed that Senator Tydings of Maryland consorted with Communists, he was not embarrassed by lack of the kind of evidence that could be manipulated in such a way as to leave this impression. He fabricated the evidence: a photograph of Millard Tydings and ·a photograph of Earl Browder, the Communist leader, taken at a different time in a different place were mounted together and offered as a photograph of the two consorting.

I recall him once, early in his career, rising to the Senate floor and announcing that he was going to quote a letter from one government official to another. What he read had a very fishy sound, and a couple of other Senators interrupted to say they thought McCarthy must be "quoting out of context." They asked that the entire letter be made part of the record, so that Senators could judge its import for themselves. McCarthy said he would get around to that later; meanwhile, he wished to exercise his privilege of quoting what he wished to quote. When, eventually, the letter did get into the record, it turned out that he had not been quoting out of context—*for he had not been quoting at all*. What he had held in his hand might have been a picture of Zsa Zsa Gabor; he had simply invented, standing there on the Senate floor, lines that served his purpose at the moment. Within the framework of political morality, it is permitted for a man to deal in half-truths, words wrenched from context, and so forth, but not to deal, as he did, in wholly imaginary texts.

And of course he was a genius at that essential American strategy—publicity. He knew what it was made of, the very texture of it. He knew the newspapermen and how and when they worked and what their deadlines were, what made a "lead," what made an "overnight," what made a good "sidebar." He knew, in his good days, how to get into the news even on those rare occasions when invention failed him and he had no unfacts to give out. For example, he would call a press conference in the morning for the purpose of announcing that he was going to call a press conference in the afternoon. The reporters would come in, and McCarthy would say that he just wanted to give them the word that he was going to make a shattering announcement in the afternoon for use in the morning papers. Headline in the afternoon papers: NEW McCARTHY REVELATIONS AWAITED IN CAPITAL. When the appointed hour came, the reporters as often as not found McCarthy nowhere around. He had given his secretary a note saying that he had to delay his shattering revelation in order to get some "documents"—documents, documents, documents, how well he knew what suckers Americans are for "documents"—that would make it even more shattering, when it came.

He brought himself to public notice by one of his most dazzling inventions. He said, in his famous Wheeling, West Virginia, speech, that there were 205 Communists in the State Department and that he

had right there with him a list of them. He later claimed that he had been misunderstood, saying once that his figure was 81 and another time that it was 57, but these revisions are unimportant (except that they, too, got him in the papers) alongside the fact that he picked a *specific* number and a *large* one. Had he said, that day when he was an unknown and evidently uninteresting Senator, that there were three Communists in the State Department, or seven, or that he had reason to believe that there might be quite a lot of them, no one would have paid the slightest attention to him (SENATOR CHARGES COMMUNIST INFLUENCE IN STATE DEPARTMENT might have turned up over a two-inch story on page fifteen of your local newspaper). Many people, after all, were saying something of that sort. But when he said there were "205" or even "57" and that he had their names in his hand (naturally, he didn't have any names; all he had was a letter from James Byrnes to Adolph Sabath giving some figures, without a single name, on loyalty investigations), the press simply had to go wild.

The very sight of a newspaperman would set his mind going. Once he ran into a pair of them idling along in the Senate Office Building. "You two looking for a story?" he asked, knowing full well that their answer would be, "Sure, have you got one?" "Mmm," he said, "now let's see." The three walked along together, took an elevator to the basement and boarded the little subway that leads to the Capitol. McCarthy was thinking hard. Then he lighted up. "I'm going to subpoena Truman, that's what I'm going to do." He reached in his pocket where he always kept a wad of blank subpoenas, and began making one out for the ex-President. "You're not serious, Joe, you can't be," one of the reporters said. "What are you going to subpoena him for?" McCarthy tapped his big skull with his forefinger several times. "Oh, I'm calling him to testify about Harry Dexter White, that's what."

Publicity helps; indeed, without it all is lost. But McCarthy had far more than a flair for press-agentry. And he had more than the luck that presented him with the Communist issue in 1950. (It *was* largely accident. He had been casting about for speech material of any sort, and a friend tipped him off to some largely unused material on infiltration that had been gathered, filed and forgotten by an investigating committee a couple of years back. It had been forgotten because it wasn't very impressive—but there it was, unused. Now it belongs to the ages.) The issue was not to be scoffed at—certainly not in the aftermath of the Hiss case. McCarthy was not the first to pounce on it, but he was the first to build a large career on it. To it, he contributed his own personality, which was formidable. He was an authentic mob organizer and galvanizer. He may not have drawn out the affection and bonhomie that Huey Long could get; he may not have been able to reach into the dark places of the American soul as Hitler could reach into the dark places of the German soul. This may have been because there are too many American souls—no one man, of good or evil bent, can rally us all. But McCarthy had his own ways, and they were very

American and very effective and he rallied a large minority.

And then he ran into some heavy weather, gave up the struggle and shortly thereafter died. Why? The issue was still hot. There were other issues to be exploited. He was still a young man.

Civic virtue has proposed several answers, to wit:

—Truth crushed to earth does not burrow out of sight, but in happy reality rises again. The facts, in time, found McCarthy out, and after that his cause was hopeless.

—You can't fool even many of the people all the time. No sizable number will forever put up with a lout.

—He had only slime for mortar. Demagogues, to be truly successful, must hold up to their following some hope and plan—however malign in content—for making life better and more equitable. This McCarthy failed to do. He was a mischief-maker, a destroyer, a nihilist, and in the end he could not even satisfy himself.

No doubt each of these points has merit, but even if they explain McCarthy's defeats in 1954, they do not account for his acceptance of them. Normally, demagogues, like lovers and poets, simply do not recognize rejection and repudiation. Juan Perón, thrown out of his own country and subsequently a refugee from his place of refuge, continues to inflame his followers and to stir things up in half a dozen countries.

I believe that just as the sources of McCarthy's power were to be found in McCarthy's person, there, too, may be found the principal reasons for his easy capitulation in 1954.

McCarthy was a great demagogue, but he was, in my view, an essentially frivolous one. The world took him seriously, as indeed it should have, but he never really took himself seriously. He was the leader of a fanatical movement, and he gave his name to a fanatical doctrine, but he was no kind of fanatic himself. He was a hellraiser, a born troublemaker, a political racketeer, a con man who loved the game for its own sake. It is conceivable that in his later days he began to believe what he was saying and to imagine himself truly persecuted by his enemies; at times, during the Army-McCarthy hearings, he would fly into fits of what appeared to be genuine hysteria. He may by then have cast his spell over himself.

The cultivated tantrum

But even this is doubtful. Mostly his hysteria was for the birds. He was capable of going into a tantrum before the television cameras and screaming, "Mr. Chairman, Mr. Chairman, Point of Order, Point of Order," tearing passions to tatters, announcing that he could bear no more of "this farce" and would dignify it with his presence not a moment longer— and then making a beeline for the gents' room, the objective he had had in mind when he began the outburst. Why not put nature into politics? Sometimes he would "walk out" and get no further than a corner of the room that was out of the sweep of the

cameras, there to observe calmly and be amused by the commotion he had caused. He often timed his walkouts for the newspaper deadlines.

If he came to believe his own lies and to hate and fear his detractors as they hated and feared him, he did so only sporadically. If he fell under his own spell, the spell quickly passed. He was, to be sure, a prince of hatred. The haters rallied round him; at a word from him, their hate glands would puff and swell— fresh supplies of venom would flow into their venom sacs. But this most successful and menacing of all our apostles of hatred was himself as incapable of true rancor, spite, and animosity as a eunuch is of marriage. He just did not have the equipment for it. He faked it all and couldn't understand anyone who didn't. When he ran into Dean Acheson in a Senate elevator, he thought it cold and unfriendly of Acheson to respond to his "Hello, Dean," with clenched teeth and a crimson forehead. When, in the Army-McCarthy hearings, he sunk to what even Roy Cohn knew to be the very bottom of the pit of degradation —by trying to hurt Joseph Welch, the Army's attorney, with a wholly gratuitous smear on a young friend and associate of Welch's who had nothing whatever to do with the case—he was baffled by the way everyone shrank from him and cleared the path before him as before a leper (Unclean! Unclean!) when he left the Caucus Room. They had all been on Welch's side when he addressed McCarthy:

"Until this moment, Senator, I think I had never really gauged your cruelty or your recklessness. . . . If it were in my power to forgive you for your reckless cruelty, I would do so. I like to think that I am a gentle man, but your forgiveness will have to come from someone other than me."

When, later, McCarthy at last found someone who would speak to him, he held out his hands, palms upward, and said, "What did I *do*?" He knew what he had *said*, of course, but I believe he genuinely did not know what he had *done*. In his mind, there was a severance between words and their meanings. A year or so before he died, he met at a Washington party a former associate, a man he had publicly betrayed and ruined. He went up to this man and within the hearing of the astonished guests asked why they had not seen each other in months. "Jeanie was talking about you the other night," he said. "How come we never see you? What the hell are you trying to do— *avoid* us?"

I am trying to suggest—it is a perilous as well as a difficult undertaking—that there was to this ogreish creature a kind of innocence that may be one of the clues to his fate. The man was a moral vacuum. Somehow or other, he could simulate hatred and several other passions, but he was numb to the sensations they produced in others. Perhaps because of this, certainly in spite of it, he had—dare one say it now?—a certain personal charm. It must be said, for there were many people who loathed him and liked him. Among them were several of the reporters who were assigned to him regularly, who referred to themselves as the Goon Squad, and who put the Republic greatly in their debt by their scholarly and unrelenting pursuit of the truths he sought to bury with his Multiple Lies. Many of them were fond of him, as he was fond of many of them; they knifed him in their stories, they knew full well that his knife was always drawn for them, yet they could drink together and be, in a sense, friends.

There was the classic case of the celebrated English journalist, a man who had convinced himself at his desk in London that McCarthy was a great beast at large in the world—a monster that had to be destroyed, and right away, in the name of human decency. He appointed himself a St. George, grabbed up his typewriter, and boarded the first transatlantic plane he could make. He was to write a series of articles so powerful that McCarthy, exposed at last, would immediately be crushed. Naturally, he had to see the dragon. In Washington, he phoned McCarthy's office and asked for an appointment. He got one right away. Bracing himself, reminding himself that violence never solved anything, he went off to the appointment. He was shown in, and the opening conversation went something like this:

McCARTHY: They tell me you're a hell of a reporter. Have a drink?

CELEBRATED JOURNALIST: Senator McCarthy, I think you should know that I despise you and everything you stand for. I think you are the greatest force for evil in the world today.

McC: No kidding. How about the drink? What'll you have?

CJ: I have just told you, Senator McCarthy, that I loathe and detest you. I am here to expose you. It will get you nowhere to try to be kind to me.

McC: We can talk later. Now what. . . ?

CJ: I will start talking now. I wish only to warn you fairly that you can expect no quarter from me. In my opinion. . . .

McC: For chrissake, are you going to have a drink or aren't you? Let's settle that first.

CJ (nearly dehydrated): If it is clearly understood that I am under no obligations, that I am retracting not one word that I have said about you, that your hospitality will not gain you my good opinion, I will join you in a drink. I will, if you please, have some whiskey, with perhaps just a dash of soda.

McC: Good.

The interview then began and proceeded without interruption for an hour or so. The Londoner could not put a question without telling McCarthy what a foul and poisonous creature he was. McCarthy could not answer without offering some more whiskey with perhaps just a splash of soda. Both were loaded almost to the muzzle when McCarthy was reminded that he had a dentist's appointment. He invited St. George to come along, and the interview went on insofar as it was possible with McCarthy's great jaw clamped open and a dentist with trembling hands worked over McCarthy's cavities and tried to keep his head in an atmosphere blue with the talk and quavering with the fumes of the bourbon he had consented to allow his patient to use as a rinse. Back in McCarthy's office, and after that in McCarthy's apartment, the interview still continued, in a much degenerated form,

and carried over to the next morning. Finally it ended. The Englishman wrote his articles; they burned with moral outrage, but they were not quite so powerful an assault on McCarthy as he had hoped they would be. He was not destroyed.

The night McCarthy died, a friend of his, one with nothing but contempt for the role McCarthy had played, returned home late in the evening to find his wife sitting by the radio and weeping—not in pure grief, as it turned out, but in frustration. She had, she explained, listened to all the comments that had been made about McCarthy's death. "Everyone has said that same thing," she said through her tears, "and they have all been wrong, wrong, wrong! They have told exactly the opposite of the truth. They all hated him, but they had to find a saving grace for their obituaries, so what have they given him?—sincerity. Each one had said, 'At least he was sincere—he believed in what he was doing,' when that was the one goddamn thing you couldn't say of him." She went on in lachrymose eloquence. "He was a stinker, he was never sincere, he'd never thought of *believing* in what he was doing. There wasn't much good you could say of him, except that he was generous to his friends and a few of us couldn't *help* liking him. No one has said that, and no one will. Only this junk about his being 'sincere.'"

McCarthy simulated belief for the true believers. Among those who knew him, very few thought that he spoke from any kind of conviction. He was a political speculator, a wildcatter who drilled communism and saw it come up a gusher. He liked his gusher, but he would have liked any other just as well. He was an enormously skillful manipulator of political issues, but he was almost wholly indifferent to them. He had run for the Senate with valuable assistance from the Communists ("Communists have the same right to vote as anyone else, don't they," he had said when taxed with his left-wing support, and to get more of it, he had said, "Stalin's proposal for world disarmament is a great thing"), and he had spent four years in the Senate making scarcely a mention of communism. When he found there was something in it, he worked it, but he was a lazy as well as a frivolous demagogue, and he never really mastered it. He served up what Roy Cohn gave him to serve up; most of the time, he didn't know what he was talking about or even whom he was talking about. (The late Howard Rushmore, a real specialist, left McCarthy's employ because he couldn't stand the sloppiness of the organization. "Those files," Rushmore said with a shudder. "My God, what a mess.") McCarthy was singular. Only he could say, on a spring day in 1950, that the next morning he would name "the Number One Communist spy in the United States," when in fact he had not the slightest idea of whom he would name—and then deliver the next morning the name of a man of whose very existence he had been unaware the previous day. No one but McCarthy could hold up a scrap of paper that might have been a parking ticket or a laundry list, anything but a list of Communists in a government agency—and say it was a list of Communists in a government agency.

The demon was not possessed by one

McCarthy was a demon, but he was not, to our great good fortune, a man possessed by demons. His talents as a demagogue were great, but he lacked the most necessary and awesome of demagogic gifts—a belief in the sacredness of his own mission. To persevere in the face of adversity, a man needs the courage of his convictions, and if he has no convictions he can scarcely draw courage from them. It was the lack of conviction that made him at once a more vulnerable and interesting human being than any of his followers. The conviction he lacked was an absurd thing, and any man was the better for not having it. His friend and lawyer, Edward Bennett Williams, has always insisted that McCarthy's was a glory drive, not a power drive, and the distinction seems a valid one, in his case and in general.

The glory drive is always less dangerous because it is more easily frustrated. It is selfish, or self-seeking, in the narrowest sense, and it makes defeat and humiliation a more personal affair. "Faith in a holy cause," Eric Hoffer has written, "is to a considerable extent a substitute for the lost faith in ourselves." If McCarthy ever had faith in a holy cause he lost it early and reposed all his faith in himself. He was a cynic, a true one. Cynicism is never admirable, but it is better for the world when a man as gifted as McCarthy is contemptuous of morality than when he is aflame over a vicious and destructive one. McCarthy employed a vicious and destructive one, but it never set him afire, and he proved in the end unable to set even the United States Senate afire.

John Kenneth Galbraith (Mark Epernay):

The Fully Automated Foreign Policy

Welcome to the hog-wild machine

"This innovation in communications technique represents an important contribution to management effectiveness and will aid us in the achievement of our foreign-policy objectives."—Statement by Dean Rusk, Secretary of State, inaugurating the Automatic Data Exchange (ADX) developed by the International Telephone and Telegraph Corporation, as reported in the *Herald Tribune*, Paris Edition, September 20, 1962.

The big rectangular room was quiet, oppressively so. The Secretary drummed his fingers on the desk and let his eyes travel over the chairs, sofas, mahogany plywood paneling, the framed commission from the President of the United States. Once more he thought how the decorator had managed to make it hideous without looking expensive. He rose from his chair and looked down at the pickets making their endless rounds in the street below. His eye caught the gleam of the Potomac and the distant line of the Pentagon. He returned to his chair and rang for his secretary. Faintly, even through the soundproofed walls, he heard the buzz. When she came in, he said, "I suppose you notice it too?"

"It's very lonely but I think I'm getting accustomed."

A little awkwardly, conscious of the unnatural gesture, he reached over and patted her hand. "I think we both will. When does Dr. McLandress get here?"

"He should be here now. He wanted to get an early plane to Boston. Oh, here he is."

The door of the office framed a large, broad-shouldered man of around fifty in a well-cut suit of dark worsted. He gave the impression of dressing with taste but no particular care. Above the high cheekbones and deep angular lines of his face, his high bald head stood in sharp contrast with the heavy, grey eyebrows. The Secretary rose to greet his visitor.

The mysterious Mark Epernay contributed a series of satirical articles in 1963 (this one appeared in September); many readers wrote Esquire to lodge their guesses, but Professor Galbraith abandoned his cover only with the publication of his book The McLandress Dimension *in 1968.*

"Well, so from today I'm on my own?"

"Not exactly. You have an installation which will do everything your boys ever did and much faster."

"I know. It still seems so . . . impersonal."

"Let's run through the day. That's your best reassurance."

"All right," said the Secretary, "only I wish it hadn't left me with this big building. Sometimes it gives me the creeps."

As they started toward the door, the Secretary glanced down again at the picket line. A little cluster had gathered around Professor Rostow who was gesticulating vehemently. He noticed Averell Harriman, tall, handsome, patrician, leaning over to listen, and beside him the short, compact figure of former Undersecretary McGhee. Behind, also attentive as though waiting to speak, was Ambassador Chester Bowles. At a little distance, one of the policemen stood eyeing the group. Marching stolidly under their signs were Undersecretary Ball, U. Alexis Johnson, Mennen Williams, the Ambassador to the Court of St. James's, David Bruce—others. There was scarcely a man he did not recognize on sight.

"I wonder what Walt was saying," the Secretary mused as he followed Dr. McLandress into the great empty anteroom. "There must be some things that a machine can't. . . ." He suppressed the rest of the thought.

Moments later, under the eye of the great psychometrist, he was twirling the combination of a heavy steel door. It swung open, and the two men stepped inside. The Secretary looked at the neutral grey steel cabinets, the green-and-white console, the occasional flashing red buttons of light, the racks of coded punch cards, the high-speed printer, the rolls of printed tape. His mind started back again, this time to the morning staff meeting when each man in turn had told of the trouble in his part of the world and the policies under discussion. Again he suppressed a twinge of nostalgia. "What do we have first?" he asked.

"Nothing on Afghanistan or Albania," Dr. McLandress said. "Argentina, routine seizure of government by engineer regiment. Free elections promised. The first important thing in the alphabetic file is Berlin. Code Be. 1.046. Khrushchev in Sofia threatens to sign a peace treaty with East Germany."

"What is our reply?"

" 'We stand willing to negotiate but we cannot act under threat or pressure. We can make no concessions. The reunification of Germany remains our goal and we do not thereby concede the existence of East Germany. We support the brave people of West Berlin.' Teletyped all posts. Released A.P., U.P.I., all local Bureaus. Every hour on V.O.A. Fulbright to be informed at proper time."

"That's certainly according to policy," said the Secretary. "I'm glad it wasn't in the '0' series. Lyndon Johnson again. Or Clay? Good God. What's next?"

"This one is '0.' Brazil. Code Br. 0.464. 'Immediate threat of bankruptcy and economic collapse. $75,000,000.' "

"I'll call the Secretary of the Treasury."

"It now goes automatically, Mr. Secretary," McLandress said gently.

"Anything from China?"

"Yes. Ch. 2.00. 'Routine threat to invade mainland. Demand for American support.' "

"Same answer?"

"Yes, almost. 'Our deep sympathy for the suffering Chinese people needs no reiteration. We stand firmly by our policy of unleashment. However, the time may not yet be imminent. . . .' "

The men worked on through the tapes. At France, there was a crisis in the upper "0" series, a speech in Toulouse by General de Gaulle demanding that the United States abandon its independent nuclear deterrent, refrain from negotiations with the Soviets, confine its foreign policy to Cuba. American withdrawal from N.A.T.O. requested. The Secretary tucked in his pocket a copy of the press release that had already gone out.

":As between friends and partners, honest differences of opinion are occasionally inevitable. However, the nations of the North Atlantic Community have never been more united or stronger in their determination. . . ."

Many of the items were routine. At Iraq (Code Ir. 1.24.) came word of a coup. Seventy-six army officers executed on television. "The situation remains unclear. The Department is keeping in closest touch."

At the United States (Code U.S. 4.25.) was a speech by Dean Acheson. "Mr. Acheson was speaking only in his personal capacity as a member of the law firm of Covington & Burling and former Secretary of State."

The two men continued steadily and finally, a little after noon, Dr. McLandress handed the Secretary Yu. 10.050., an administrative message from Belgrade: "EMB AUTOMATION NOW COMPLETE. TAKING LEAVE TONIGHT. KENNAN."

Below was the answer: "CONGRATULATIONS. BEST OF LUCK WITH YOUR LECTURES."

The Secretary glanced through the White House tapes. The British Prime Minister would arrive on Thursday on his fortnightly visit. It was the one concession he would not make to automation. The President would use the occasion for pressing for the merger of BBC with French television. The gold outflow had come to an end although copper and zinc were still going in some quantity. The Secretary leafed through a speech which had been prepared for delivery at a meeting of the Foreign Service Institute, copies of which were neatly stacked by the printer.

"Most of all, we seek prompt decisions. . . . Timely action today may forestall grave crises tomorrow. . . . Press the search for new initiatives. . . . Break with routine. . . . Originality. . . ."

The speech had come from the machine as scheduled the day before, a harmless error in programming, Dr. McLandress had explained. The Secretary dropped the manuscript in the wastepaper basket. The morning's work was over.

The two men shook hands at the elevator. The Secretary looked again at his watch and thought of escaping to a companionable lunch at the Metropolitan Club. But he knew that the pickets would by now be stacking their signs outside the entrance and trooping in for a martini and discussion of the day's foreign-policy developments. He could not face them. He pressed the Up button, got off at the top floor and went along the hall to the Secretary's dining room. Dropping two quarters into the slot, he took out a plate of corned beef hash and then went to the dispenser for a glass of milk. Glancing out of the window, he noticed that one lone picket was keeping guard—he recognized the slightly stooped shoulders of Ambassador Charles Bohlen and his eye took in the meticulous wording of the sign. He wondered for a moment why he hadn't invited his secretary to join him. She would be eating alone in the cafeteria. Then he sat down at a table and was lost in thought.

II

"Some inventions," Dr. Herschel McLandress has written, "such as the sewing machine and the steam engine are like Athena in their origin. They spring full-blown from the head of the inventor; no one could predict their arrival or say why they arrived at a particular moment. But there are others—the automatic gearshift, the supersonic airplane, color television—which are predestined and predictable. Like a piece of coal on a conveyor belt, anyone could look and see them on the way. The automation of American foreign policy was of this sort. Few innovations were ever more predictable."[1]

The long-range cause of the automation of American foreign policy, in the view of Dr. McLandress, was automation in other industries. As labor was released by the automobile industry, the steel industry, by modern large-scale agriculture, it was increasingly absorbed into the administration of the Armed Forces and the making of foreign policy. There was nothing subtle about this. After earlier wars, officers, N.C.O.'s and enlisted men had bade farewell to their units and headed for a homestead, a job as a factory foreman or a place at the bench. Following World War II and the Korean War, these opportunities no longer existed. So men got a job in

1. Herschel McLandress, "The Automation of American Foreign Policy: A Retrospective View." Foreign Affairs, XCVII.

the Pentagon or went to the State Department. A generation ago, the boy from a farm in rural Michigan set off for Detroit and a job at Ford. As automation closed this door, he prepared himself for a life in diplomacy.

Throughout the country in the years following World War II, enlightened programs for the training of men for foreign policy were launched by the universities. If these programs were to succeed, there had to be employment for the people so trained. Congress and the Executive moved readily, far more readily than is commonly supposed, to provide the jobs.[2]

The immediate cause of foreign-policy automation, in Dr. McLandress' view, was the spread among foreign-policy administrators in the years after World War II of what, with a gift for homely illustration, he calls "the potato syllogism." As a potato farmer faces more complex and difficult harvesting conditions—a heavy crop, wet soil, imminent frost, an increasingly infirm market prospect—he adds to his harvesting crew. Following this simple pattern, as the problems of foreign policy became increasingly intricate, urgent and baffling after World War II, those in charge increased proportionately the number of men to handle them. Some of the problems being infinitely difficult, the possibility was not remote that the number working on them would be infinitely large.[3]

"In fact, the parallel between potato harvesting and the making of foreign policy is not exact. To increase the number of men working on a foreign-policy problem—Berlin, Castro, Vietnam—is to increase the number of men whose agreement must be obtained before action is taken. The more men whose agreement must be obtained, the more time required.

"If the number at work on a given job is large enough, action, it would seem to follow, will be indefinitely postponed. Although this tendency does exist, things work out somewhat differently in practice. In many foreign-policy situations, action is often unavoidable. Accordingly, while no new step can command agreement, something must still be done. So opinion will eventually coalesce on whatever has been done before. Those who aspire to a position of leadership will realize this and urge the existing or previous action. Others will fall in behind and so confirm the position of leadership of those who urge the status quo. Even a large group of men can reach agreement provided it is on positions previously taken."[4]

2. *The factors influencing the level of employment in the public services have only recently been clarified by a lengthy research project conducted by the Bureau of the Budget. This has culminated in what has come to be called the Dawes-Bell Law. The D.B.L., as it is known to public administrators and to which Dr. McLandress attaches high significance, states that whereas in many branches of economic activity employment depends on the number of job openings available, in the public service, as also in the advertising business, social-science investigation and university administration, the level of employment regularly depends on the number of men available and devoting their time to the creation of job opportunities.*
Thus, in the field of foreign policy, which is strongly subject to the D.B.L., the availability of a group of North Central Asian specialists will lead to speeches, panel discussions, monographs on foreign policy, thoughtful articles in The New York Times Magazine, *lectures at the National War College and Congressional testimony all stressing the importance and complexity of North Central Asian problems and the urgent need for strengthening research, intelligence, diplomatic representation and administrative and logistic support in the N.C.A. field. This discussion will continue until action taken in response thereto results in the employment of the available N.C.A. specialists.*
3. *Elsewhere Dr. McLandress notes that in 1940 the number of employees of State was 6222; in 1946 it was 20,015; by 1962, 23,937.*
4. *"The Automation of American Foreign Policy." Op. cit.*

III

There were many who suggested to Dr. McLandress that, in its bearing on American foreign policy, the potato syllogism was not adverse. They noted that the truly sophisticated man argues not for the wisdom or even the prudence of a foreign policy, but for its continuity. Few things more clearly mark the amateur in diplomacy than his inability to see that even the change from the wrong policy to the right policy involves the admission of previous error and hence is damaging to national prestige. As a built-in source of continuity, the potato syllogism was held to be admirable rather than otherwise.

Working on Dr. McLandress' side, however, were the very great delays inherent in the old system. All opinions, all research, all intelligence had necessarily to be heard, evaluated and then considered. Given the large number of policy makers produced by the potato syllogism, there would always be a number expressing themselves in favor of some change, however slight. Accordingly, even a simple affirmation of the existing policy might take weeks or even months. In a fast-moving world, this eventually became intolerable. In the Spring of 1962, it became known that the American Ambassador to the U.S.S.R. had to request Mr. Khrushchev to delay for several weeks a routine attack on the nuclear tests on Christmas Island because agreement had not been reached on repeating the previous replies to his last denunciation. The Policy Planning Council of the State Department then produced its fateful paper entitled, "Continuity in Foreign Policy as Modified by Discontinuity along the Time Parameter."

In recommending that Dr. McLandress be called in for study and to make recommendations for "an effective acceleration of the necessarily multivariate character of a sound decision-making process," there had been no thought that any action would result. As Dr. McLandress himself has said, "It is a well-understood principle in the administration of American foreign policy that study and recommendation do not lead to revision of policy. Rather, the continuity of American policy is partly protected by the practice of ordering a study when anyone proposes change."

But Dr. McLandress' recommendations *were* accepted. No one could make a dent in the logic of this quiet but unexpectedly forceful man. "The formulation of foreign policy is the reiteration of the previous position. That reiteration is now compromised by time-consuming discussion. So long as you have people, you will have discussion. But to get the previous decision, you do not need people. You need only to classify and code the various crises and program them into a computer along with the established response. For the given crisis, the machine will then produce the right response and do it instantaneously. BUT YOU MUST ELIMINATE THE PEOPLE."

On the last point, Dr. McLandress was uncompromising, obdurate, ruthless. As noted, logic was on his side. So were the men from I.B.M. So were many members of Congress who saw an arrangement which would insure continuity in the nation's Cuban policy.

The potato syllogism prevented the policy makers from reacting. Meetings were still in progress on the day that the machine ground out the rectangular cards with the cropped corner, the cabalistic holes and the neat message: "THE DEPARTMENT OF STATE THANKS YOU FOR YOUR - - - - YEARS AND - - - - MONTHS OF DEVOTED, LOYAL SERVICE AND WISHES YOU A REWARDING RETIREMENT. UNDER AMENDED RETIREMENT REGULATIONS, YOUR PENSION WILL BE $00,000.00 PER ANNUM. THANK YOU AGAIN."

McLandress had triumphed. The decision to engage in peaceful picketing at the token level was taken by officers as individuals.

IV

The Secretary was surprised to see that it was nearly half past two. He wondered if he had dozed off. Back in his office, he sent his secretary for the latest tapes of the day's business and then experienced the slightly annoying sense of uneasiness which he always felt when the white phone rang. It was only a White House secretary asking if he could run through the day's business at six-twenty. The Secretary noted that he had something over three hours ahead of him and took up the tapes.

At four-thirty, a semiliterate ambassador from a minor Latin American republic came in. The man was congenitally incapable of understanding the notes and demarches which came into his embassy on the teletype. The Secretary read him a protest in basic English against a decree making membership in opposition parties subject to a life sentence and reflected that the fellow probably didn't have any trouble deciphering a bank draft. A call came in from Stevenson in New York. His Security Council speech had come from the computer with an unpunctuated paragraph. They chatted companionably for twenty minutes and the Secretary authorized the Ambassador to exercise discretion. He wondered, for a moment, if McLandress would have approved. At six, his secretary brought in the afternoon tapes and he finished reading them in his car.

Things still went well.

Albania. Code Al. 4.44. "Diplomatic relations severed by both China and the Soviet Union. Asking recognition by West."

"No action. Await real evidence of abandonment of aggressive intentions and willingness to take wheat under Public Law 480."

Ecuador. Code Ec. 0.45. "Impending bankruptcy." "$10,000,000."

In Germany, there was a crisis in the "0" series. Code Ge. 0.898. Speech in Dinkelsbühl by Chancellor. "The United States must sever relations with Soviet Union and Rumania. Stop honoring East German postage stamps. Announcement of West German loan of D.M. 600,000,000 for financing necessary trade with East Germany."

"As between friends and partners, honest differences of opinion are occasionally inevitable. However, the nations of the North Atlantic Community have never...."

Geneva. Code UNRM 4.55. Speech by Soviet delegate calling for general and complete disarmament.

"The United States stands committed to the principle of complete and general disarmament. It will not compromise the safety of the free world."

Persepolis. Code Pe. 0.457. "Reported land fighting with small Greek forces. Naval reverse at Salamis."

"The Department is keeping in closest touch. The situation remains unclear."

India. Code In. 10.05. "Internal. Embassy asking clarification of instructions."

"Sympathize your problem. However, do not feel at this juncture any departure from existing policy necessary or desirable."

On several of the crises, the tapes showed no response. Dr. McLandress explained the need to avoid breaking too radically with established tradition.

The car pulled up at the West Basement of the White House and the Secretary nodded familiarly to the Secret Service man as he passed inside the door. As he climbed the stairs, he was struck by the warm and pleasant hum of offices that were filled with people. He went along the narrow corridor to the President's office.

The President was running through the tapes that had just come from the White House printer. "Glad to see you," he said briefly and motioned the Secretary to a chair. In a minute, he was finished.

"Do you really think this machine can handle every situation—everything?"

"I think so, Mr. President. You remember that home economist in Saigon last week. Caught doing the twist in her shower?"

"That was pretty impressive. But what about always basing our policy on what was done before? Aren't we ever moving forward?"

"You know, Mr. President. You once asked for some new policies yourself."

"Good God. The delay *that* caused. But one thing...."

"Yes, Mr. President."

"It is pretty inconvenient your having to come over here."

"Would you like me to move back into the old State Department building?"

"I wonder if it is really necessary. The Vice-President can do the embassy dinners. A lot of them are installing cafeterias anyhow, so that takes care of the entertaining."

The Secretary noticed for the first time that the President was holding one of the rectangular cards with the cropped corner.

The Secretary left his car and driver at the basement entrance and walked out on Pennsylvania Avenue. Three pickets were strolling back and forth in front of the White House. The Secret Service men watched from their box. The Secretary walked over to Ambassador W. Walton Butterworth and, with something akin to a feeling of pleasure, relieved him of his sign.

Saul Bellow:

Literary Notes on Khrushchev

Why the Soviet Premier used his shoe to make his point

Khrushchev, the heir of Lenin and Stalin, Malenkov's successor and the evident head of the Russian oligarchy, has stamped his image on the world and compels us to think about him. It is hard of course to believe that this bald, round, gesticulating, loud man may be capable of overcoming, of ruining, perhaps of destroying us.

"It's him, Khrushchev, dat nut," a garage attendant on Third Avenue said to me last September as the fleet of Russian Cadillacs rushed by. This time Khrushchev was a self-invited visitor. He did not arrive with our blessings, and he did not have our love, but that didn't seem to matter greatly to him. He was able, nevertheless, to dominate the headlines, the television screens, the U.N. Assembly and the midtown streets. An American in his position, feeling himself unwanted and, even worse, unloved, would have been self-effacing. Not Khrushchev. He poured it on, holding press conferences in the street and trading insults from his balcony with the crowd, singing snatches of the *Internationale*, giving a pantomime uppercut to an imaginary assassin. He played up to the crowd and luxuriated in its attention, behaving like a comic artist in a show written and directed by himself. And at the U.N., roaring with anger, interrupting Mr. Macmillan, landing his fists on the desk, waving a shoe in the air, hugging his allies and bugging his opponents, surging up from his seat to pump the hand of the elegant black Nkrumah in his gilt crimson toga or interrupting his own blasts at the West to plug Soviet mineral water, suddenly winsome, Khrushchev the charmer, not once did he give up the center of the stage. And no one seemed able to take it from him.

Balzac once described the statesman as a "monster of self-possession." He referred of course to the bourgeois statesman. Khrushchev is another sort of fish altogether. And since his debut on the world scene shortly after Stalin died and Malenkov "retired," Khrushchev—running always a little ahead of Bulganin—has astonished, perplexed, bamboozled

Early in the Sixties Esquire was in the middle of the discovery that a novelist can sometimes do a journalist's job better than a journalist can, and got Mr. Bellow to interrupt briefly his work on Herzog for a report on the rhetorical style of the number-one diplomatic orator of his time. The result was published in March, 1961.

and appalled the world. If the traditional statesman is a prodigy of self-possession, Khrushchev seems instead to give himself away. He seems to be a man of candor, just as Russia seems to be a union of socialist republics. Other statemen are satisfied to represent their countries. Not so Khrushchev. He wishes to personify Russia and the Communist cause.

Timidity will get us nowhere. If we want to understand him we must give the imagination its freedom and let it, in gambler's language, go for broke. Anyway, he compels us to think of him. We have him continually under our eyes. He is in China, he is in Paris and Berlin and San Francisco, and he performs everywhere. In Austria he inspects a piece of abstract sculpture and, with an astonished air, he asks the artist to tell him what the devil it stands for. Listening or pretending to listen, he observes that the sculptor will have to hang around forever to explain his incomprehensible work. He arrives in Finland in time to attend the birthday celebration of its president; he pushes the poor man aside and frolics before the cameras, eats, drinks, fulminates and lets himself be taken home. In America, on his first visit, his progress across the land was nothing less than spectacular. And no fifteenth-century king could have been more *himself*, whether with the press, with Mr. Garst on the farm, with dazzling dolls of Hollywood, or with the trade-union leaders in San Francisco. "You are like a nightingale," he said to Walter Reuther. "It closes its eyes when it sings, and sees nothing and hears nobody but itself." In Hollywood with Spyros Skouras, he matched success stories, each protagonist trying to prove that he rose from greater depths. "I was a poor immigrant." "I began working when I learned to walk—I was a shepherd boy, a factory laborer, I worked in the coal pits, and now I am Prime Minister of the great Soviet State." Neither of them mentioned the cost of his rise to the public-at-large: Skouras said nothing of the effects of Hollywood on the brains of Americans nor did Khrushchev mention deportations and purges. We who had this greatness thrust upon us had no spokesman in the debate. But then people in show business have always enjoyed a peculiar monopoly of patriotism. The mixture of ideology and entertainment on both sides brought about an emotional crisis on the West Coast, and it was here that Khrushchev was provoked into disclosing some of his deeper feelings. "When we were in Hollywood, they danced the cancan for us," he told the meeting of the trade-union leaders in San Francisco. "The girls who dance it have to pull up their skirts and show their backsides. They are good, honest actresses, but have to perform that dance. They are compelled to adapt themselves to the tastes of depraved people. People in your country will go to see it, but Soviet people would scorn such a spectacle. It is pornographic. It is the culture of surfeited and depraved people. Showing that sort of film is called freedom in this country. Such 'freedom' doesn't suit us. You seem to like the 'freedom' of looking at backsides. But we prefer freedom to think, to exercise our mental faculties, the freedom of creative progress." I take these words from a semiofficial Russian-sponsored publication. It does not add what some American reports added, namely, that the Premier here raised his coattails and exposed his rear to the entire gathering as he swooped into a parody of the cancan.

This, friends, is art. It is also an entirely new mode of historical interpretation by the world leader of Marxist thought who bodily, by the use of his own person, delivers a critique of Western civilization. It is, moreover, theatre. And we are its enthralled and partly captive audience. Khrushchev's performance is, in the term used by James Joyce, an epiphany, a manifestation which summarizes or expresses a whole universe of meanings. "We will bury you," Khrushchev has told the capitalist world, and though it has since been said over and over that this is merely a Ukrainian figure of speech meaning, "We will exceed you in production," I think that in watching this dance we might all feel the itching of the nose which, according to superstition, means that someone is walking on our graves. We would not be far out in seeing auguries of death in this cancan. The "culture of surfeited and depraved people" is doomed. That is the meaning of his brutal and angry comedy. It is also what he means when he plays villain and buffoon to the New York public. To him this is the slack, shallow, undisciplined and cultureless mob of a decadent capitalist city. Still, life is very complicated, for if the Hollywood cancan is poor stuff, what can we say of the products of Socialist realism with their pure and loyal worker-heroes and their sweet and hokey maidens? Khrushchev himself is far above such junk. It is possible to conclude from this that in a dictatorship the tyrant may suck into himself all the resources

of creativity and leave the art of his country impoverished.

It may, in fact, take not only Russia but the entire world to feed the needs of a single individual. For it can't be ideology alone that produces such outbursts; it must be character. "I have often thought," wrote William James, "that the best way to define a man's character would be to seek out the particular mental or moral attitude in which, when it came upon him, he felt himself most intensely active and alive. At such moments there is a voice inside which speaks and says: '*This* is the real me!'" So perhaps Khrushchev feels himself, or attempts to reach himself, in these outbursts. And perhaps it is when the entire world is watching him soar and he is touching the limits of control that he feels most alive. He does not exhibit a great range of feelings. When he takes off the rudimentary masks of bureaucratic composure or peasant dignity or affability, he is angry or jeering. But fear is not the best school for expressiveness, and no man could be an important party functionary under Stalin without the ability to live in fear. We cannot therefore expect him to be versatile. He had, however, what it took to finish the course, the nerves, the control, the patience, the piercing ambition, the strength to kill and to endure the threat of death. It would be premature to say that he has survived all that there is to survive in Russia, but it is a safe guess that in the relief of having reached first place he is whooping it up. Instead of having been punished for his crimes he has become a great leader, which persuades him that life is inherently dramatic. And in his joy at having reversed the moral-accounting system of bourgeois civilization he plays his role with ever greater spirit.

Our ablest political commentators have used theatrical metaphors to describe Khrushchev's behavior. Mr. Sulzberger in The New York *Times* speaks of the "fierce illogic of a Brendan Behan play." Others have been reminded of the Leningrad circus, and a British psychologist has suggested that Khrushchev may have made a study of Pavlov's conditioned reflex. After Pavlov had rewarded his dogs for responding to given signals, he scrambled the pattern and the animals suffered a hysterical breakdown. Our leaders, amid flowers, smiles and exchanges of charm, made appointments to meet Khrushchev at the Summit only to find he had turned into the Great Boyg of the northern snows who deafened them with snarls and stunned them with ice. If Khrushchev had needed instruction in the technique of blowing hot and cold he could have gotten it from Hitler, who made a great deal of noise in the world, rather than from Pavlov, who made very little. From Hitler he might have learned that angry demonstrations unnerve well-conducted people, and that in statesmanship the advantage always lies with the unprincipled, the brutal and the insane. Hitler could at will convulse himself with rage and, when he had gained his ends, be coolly correct to his staff, all in a matter of moments. Khrushchev does not seem to have this combination of derangement and cold political technique which threatens the end of the world in fire and ice. But does he need lessons from Professor Pavlov in psychological techniques? Teach your granny to suck an egg.

No, the dramatic metaphor is the best one, and in trying to place his style, even before I had seen Khrushchev in action during his recent American visit, a short, buoyant, ruddy, compact, gesturing, tough man—it struck me that Marcel Marceau, another mime appearing in *The Overcoat* at a New York theatre, and Khrushchev, at the other side of town, had both been inspired by the Russian comic tradition. The masterpiece of that tradition is Gogol's *Dead Souls*. From Gogol's landlords and peasants, grotesquely thickheaded or just as grotesquely shrewd, provincial autocrats, creeps, misers, officials, gluttons, gamblers and drunkards, Khrushchev seems to have taken many of the elements of his comic style. He is one of Gogol's stout men who "know better than thin men how to manage their affairs. The thin ones are more often employed on special missions, or are merely 'on the staff,' scurrying hither and thither; their existence is somehow too slight, airy and altogether insubstantial. The stout ones are never to be found filling ambiguous posts, but only straightforward ones; if they sit down anywhere, they do so solidly and firmly, so that, though their position may creak and bend beneath them, they never fall off."

When the occasion demands more earnestness he plays the Marxist. Speaking at the U.N. he made me think, when he called for colonial liberation, of Trotsky in the first years of the Russian Revolution and in particular of Trotsky's conduct during the signing of the Treaty of Brest-Litovsk. There to the amazement of the German generals, he delayed the negotiations in order to make speeches calling on the world proletariat to support and extend the revolution. Those days are gone forever, of course. They were gone even before Lenin died. And there is a great difference between the fresh revolutionary ardor of Trotsky and the stale agitational technique of an old party hack. Still, when it suits him, Khrushchev is a Marxist. Defending the poor working girls of Hollywood, he delivered the judgment of Marxian orthodoxy on their wriggling and kicking (more of the alienating labor imposed by capitalism on humanity).

There are certain similarities between Khrushchev's Marxism and the liberal ideology of Western businessmen. They make use of it at their convenience. Khrushchev, however, enjoys a considerable advantage in that the needs of Russian history and those of his own personality have coincided so that he is able at times to follow his instincts without restraint. He has besides a great contempt for the representatives of the West who are unable to do without the brittle, soiled and compromised conventions of civilized diplomacy. It is the great coma, the deep sleep, and he despises the sleepers and takes advantage of them. The pictures taken at the Summit reveal the extent of his success. General de Gaulle's mouth is drawn very small in a pucker of foreboding and distaste. Mr. Macmillan seems deeply hurt. Former President Eisenhower looks sad, but also opinionated. Things have gone wrong again, but it is certainly no fault of his. Together, they each must have seemed to Khrushchev like Keats's "still unravished bride of quietness." And it is not hard to guess what he, the descendant of serfs, risen to a position of such might, must have experienced. Confronting the leaders of the bourgeois West, so long feared and hated, Khrushchev saw himself to be tougher, deeper and more intelligent than any of them. And, in expressing his feelings, more free.

It's hard to know whether the Khrushchev we saw banging with his shoe at the U.N. Assembly is the "real" Khrushchev. But one of the privileges of power seems to be the privilege of direct emotional self-expression. It is not a privilege exercised by many people in the West, so far as I can see.

"Men who have arrived can do what they like," declared the *Daily News* recently in one of its snappy ads. "There was a guy who liked spaghetti and beer, but when he became a junior executive, he thought it more fitting to order steak and asparagus. It was only when he became president of his company that he felt assured enough to go back to spaghetti and beer."

Such are the privileges of power, but bafflingly enough, apart from artists and tyrants, few people, even among company presidents, feel strong enough to tell the world how they feel. New York's Police Commissioner Kennedy, a man who has apparently arrived, could not, some time ago, express his honest views as to the religious convictions of the Jewish members of the force. Everyone knows that the commissioner is not anti-Semitic. Yet the New York Rabbinate felt compelled, as did Mayor Wagner, for formal reasons, to ask for a retraction. So it's not easy to speak one's mind. Even the artists have taken cover, disguising themselves as bank clerks and veiling their sayings. That leaves us with the tyrants. (Is it only a coincidence that Emily Post died during Khrushchev's visit?)

Masked in smiles and peasant charm, or in anger, the Russian Premier releases his deepest feelings and if we are not shaken by them it is because we are not in close touch with reality. In the West the connections between opinion, feeling and bodily motion have been broken. We have lost the expressive power. It is in the use of such power, falsely exploiting his Russian and peasant background, that Khrushchev has shown himself to be an adept. He has a passion always ready to exploit and, though he lies, he has the advantage. The principles of Western liberalism seem no longer to lend themselves to effective action.

Deprived of the expressive power, we are awed by it, have a hunger for it and are afraid of it. Thus we praise the grey dignity of our soft-spoken leaders, but in our hearts we are suckers for passionate outbursts, even when those passionate outbursts are hypocritical and falsely motivated.

> *The best lack all conviction*
> *While the worst are full*
> *of passionate intensity.*

At times Khrushchev goes beyond Gogolian comedy; this is no longer the amiable chiseler who stuffs himself with fish or pancakes dipped in butter. Gogol's Chichikov, to congratulate himself when he has pulled a fast one, dances in the privacy of his room. But Khrushchev goes into his cancan before the world public with a deep and gnomish joy. Here is a man whom all the twisted currents of human purpose have brought within reach of world power. At a time when public figures show only secondary or tertiary personal characteristics, he appears to show only primary ones. He wears his instincts on his sleeve or like Dostoevski's Father Karamazov, that corrupt and deep old man, he feigns simplicity.

When the charm and irony wear thin, he shows himself to be a harsh, arbitrary and complicated man. It was a simple enough matter for him to have joked contemptuously with Spyros Skouras; in debate with well-informed men who press him closely he becomes abusive, showing that the habit of authority has made him inflexible. He seems unable to discuss any matter except on his own terms. Nature, history, Russian Marxism and, perhaps most of all, the fact that he has survived under Stalin make it impossible for him to entertain other views. What amounted in Paris to ex-President Eisenhower's admission of a blunder must have seemed to him incredible. He lives under an iron necessity to be right. What he perhaps remembers best about men who were not right is their funerals. For him the line between the impossible and the possible is drawn with blood, and foreigners who do not see the blood must be preposterous to him.

Tom Wicker:

Kennedy Without Tears

While it was still possible—before reality faded into myth
and the monuments obscured the man—
a last effort to see him as he was

Shortly after President Kennedy was shot, the following inscription appeared on a plaque in one of the private bedrooms of the White House: *In this room Abraham Lincoln slept during his occupancy of the White House as President of the United States, March 4, 1861-April 13, 1865.*

In this room lived John Fitzgerald Kennedy with his wife Jacqueline Kennedy during the two years, ten months and two days he was President of the United States, January 20, 1961-November 22, 1963.

Before many years pass, that deliberate linkage of two Presidents, that notice chiseled upon history by Jacqueline Kennedy, may seem as inevitable as the Washington Monument. Already, airports and spaceports and river bridges and a cultural center have been named for her husband. Books about him, even phonograph records, are at flood tide and *Profiles in Courage* has returned to the top of The New York *Times* best-seller list. It is almost as if he had never called businessmen sons of bitches, sent the troops to Ole Miss, the refugees to the Bay of Pigs, or kicked the budget sky-high.

Six months after his death, John F. Kennedy is certain to take his place in American lore as one of those sure-sell heroes out of whose face or words or monuments a souvenir dealer can turn a steady buck. There he soon will stand, perhaps in our lifetime— cold stone or heartless bronze, immortal as Jefferson, revered as Lincoln, bloodless as Washington. One can imagine the graven words on his pedestal:

Ask not what your country can do for you. Ask what you can do for your country.

What his country inevitably will do for John Kennedy seems a curious fate for the vitality and intensity, the wry and derisive style of the man who was the Thirty-fifth President of the United States. His wit surely would have seared the notion of John

Tom Wicker's brilliant (and heartbreaking) coverage of the assassination for The New York Times *moved Esquire to ask him to write this essay seven months later in June, 1964. Mr. Wicker went on to become chief of the Washington bureau and an associate editor of The* Times.

F. Kennedy International Airport, much less Cape Kennedy—for this was the man who once told the great-great-grandson of John Adams, "It is a pleasure to live in your family's old house, and we hope that you will come by and see us."

One suspects the Eternal Flame might have embarrassed him as much as the Navy did that brilliant Pacific day last June when the strutting admirals put him literally on a flag-draped pedestal aboard an aircraft carrier while the band played *Hail to the Chief* and the jets screamed overhead on taxpayers' money; one of his favorite quips, after all, was that he had gone from Lieutenant J.G. to Commander-in-Chief without any qualifications at all.

I can almost hear that amused Boston voice inquiring, as he once did after reading a favorable Gallup Poll, where all those people who admired him so much were when Congress turned down his school bill in 1961. Staring from Valhalla at himself cast in stone in the middle of some downtown Washington traffic circle, he might well whisper to earthly passers-by what he once told 12,000 Democrats in Harrisburg, Pennsylvania:

"I will introduce myself. I am Teddy Kennedy's brother."

And when children rise reverently in some future Fourth of July pageant to recite the chiastic prose of the Kennedy Inaugural Address—the stirring words that raced so many pulses among that "new generation of Americans" to which he appealed— some may recall instead the same rhythm, the same rhetoric, but different words and a more subtle imagination at work:

"We observe tonight not a celebration of freedom but a victory of party, for we have sworn to pay off the same party debt our forebears ran up nearly a year and three months ago. Our deficit will not be paid off in the next hundred days, nor will it be paid off in the first one thousand days, nor in the life of this Administration. Nor, perhaps, even in our lifetime on this planet. But let us begin—remembering that generosity is not a sign of weakness and that ambassadors are always subject to Senate confirma-

119

tion. For if the Democratic Party cannot be helped by the many who are poor, it cannot be saved by the few who are rich. So let us begin."

Now a politician who could laugh at a parody of his noblest speech—let alone make it himself, as Kennedy did the foregoing—obviously was something more intricate in life than the mere sum of the virtues symbolized by the Eternal Flame: purity, steadfastness, warmth, light. A President delighted by the political caricature of Everett McKinley Dirksen, but impatient with the solemn earnestness of Chester Bowles, obviously had a wide streak of Honey Fitz down his spine; yet that same President, confronted with an adulatory mob of hundreds of thousands of cheering Europeans, could not bring himself to respond with more than a halfhearted jab of the arm from the chest—something like a halfback straight-arming a tackler, apologetically. And lest it be imagined that he was merely unemotional, remember that it was the crowd's transmitted frenzy that led Kennedy to make the inspiring but not very wise cry: *Ich bin ein Berliner!*

In the early days of Kennedy's New Frontier (there was bound to be something roguish about a man who could bring the Ivy Leaguers—and himself—to Washington with a slogan that evoked echoes of the Wild West, which appalled most of them), I thought Richard Nixon was perhaps a more interesting *man* than Kennedy. I thought Nixon was, as Conrad wrote of Lord Jim, "one of us." But Kennedy, I thought then, for all his charm and fire and eloquence, was a straightforward political man, who listened to his own rhetoric, contrived his "image" in the comforting faith that a statesman had to get elected before he could do anyone any good, and believed sincerely that his causes were not only right but actually offered solutions to human problems. I thought Kennedy had what Senator Eugene McCarthy called the perfect political mentality—that of a football coach, combining the will to win with the belief that the game is important.

Now, I think that what Kennedy really had of that mentality was a rather peculiar form of the will to win. He wanted power, all right, but something more; "This ability," he once said, "to do things well, and to do them with precision and with modesty, attracts us all." It was a theme to which he often returned—the pursuit of excellence. And as the probability of his political canonization turns toward certainty, and the sad calcification of his humanity into stone and bronze continues, there is not much football coach in the man Kennedy who recalls himself to me most strongly.

If that human Kennedy still seems to me to have been altogether too detached and too controlled to have been, as were Nixon and Lord Jim, "one of us," with all those fascinating hesitancies and inadequacies and torments out of which literature is made, nevertheless he *was* a man "of few days and full of trouble," and for all I know he may even have played "such fantastic tricks before high heaven as to make the angels weep." But the statues will tell us nothing of that.

Not many of them, for instance, will bear inscriptions drawn from his wit—that derisive, barbed, spontaneous wit, just short of mordant, that played so steadily through his speeches and recurred in such stable patterns of wording and attitude that it strikes me in retrospect as the true expression of a point of view, of a way of thinking not subject to time or circumstance or conditions.

It is astonishing, in retrospect, how constantly and boldly this Irish Catholic President, this young man so publicly committed to things like patriotism and public affairs, lampooned politicians, politics, notions, men, systems, myths, himself, even his church. When *The Wall Street Journal* criticized Nixon, Kennedy said, it was like *"L'Osservatore Romano* criticizing the Pope." And Speaker John McCormack denies that Kennedy called him "Archbishop"; "He called me 'Cardinal,' " McCormack recalls.

When the Vatican implied some criticism of Kennedy's campaign efforts to prove himself free of papal influence, Kennedy said ruefully to a pair of reporters: "Now I understand why Henry the Eighth set up his own church."

He and McKinley were the only Presidents ever to address the National Association of Manufacturers, Kennedy told that august body, so "I suppose that President McKinley and I are the only two that are regarded as fiscally sound enough to be qualified." And to the $100-a-plate guests at a glittering political occasion, he confessed: "I could say I am deeply touched, but not as deeply touched as you have been in coming to this luncheon."

Not even the Kennedy family was spared its scion's irreverence. To a dinner of the Alfred E. Smith Foundation during the 1960 campaign, he remarked:

"I had announced earlier this year that if successful I would not consider campaign contributions as a substitute for experience in appointing ambassadors. Ever since I made that statement I have not received one single cent from my father."

Everyone remembers his remark, upon appointing Bob Kennedy Attorney General, that his brother might as well get a little experience before having to practice law; not so many heard him late one night at a Boston dinner last fall when he paid similar respects to the youthful Edward M. Kennedy:

"My last campaign may be coming up very shortly," he said, "but Teddy is around and, therefore, these dinners can go on indefinitely."

The Kennedy wit was so pronounced and so identifiable that it could be reproduced with near exactitude by Ted Sorensen, his speech writer. A deadly serious man, Sorensen's few recorded public jokes include one perfect specimen of Kennedy-style wit.

"There will be a meeting this afternoon of representatives from Baltimore, Atlantic City, San Francisco, Philadelphia, Chicago and other cities interested in holding the 1964 national convention," he said in a mock announcement to a Democratic Party gathering. "The meeting will be held in Mayor Daley's room."

In order to laugh—as the Democrats did—one

had to know of course that Richard Daley was mayor of Chicago and one of the most powerful figures in the Democratic Party—and that the competition for the convention was cutthroat. But Sorensen, as Kennedy always did, had tuned his derision precisely to his audience and the circumstances. The target was the situation—Daley's power, the party's foibles, the audience's pretensions. But whatever the situation, the *point of view* remained constant in Kennedy-style wit; it was the point of view that marked the man.

That point of view, as these few examples show, was a blending of amiable irreverence into a faintly resigned tolerance. It was a point of view that did not expect too much of human beings, even of its possessor; even less did it count heavily upon the wisdom or majesty of politicians; and often enough the political process itself was seen with frank disrespect. Perhaps a British M.P., but no American politician in memory except John Kennedy, would have been capable of the devastating "endorsement" of Senator George Smathers that the President delivered at a fund-raising dinner in Miami Beach:

"I actually came down here tonight to pay a debt of obligation to an old friend and faithful adviser. He and I came to the Eightieth Congress together and have been associated for many years, and I regard him as one of my most valuable counselors in moments of great personal and public difficulty.

"In 1952, when I was thinking about running for the United States Senate, I went to the then Senator Smathers and said, 'George, what do you think?'

"He said, 'Don't do it. Can't win. Bad year.'

"In 1956, I was at the Democratic Convention, and I said—I didn't know whether I would run for Vice-President or not, so I said, 'George, what do you think?'

"'This is it. They need a young man. It's your chance.' So I ran—and lost.

"And in 1960, I was wondering whether I ought to run in the West Virginia primary. 'Don't do it. That state you can't possibly carry.'

"And actually, the only time I really got nervous about the whole matter at the Democratic Convention of 1960 was just before the balloting and George came up and he said, 'I think it looks pretty good for you.'"

The audience was already in stitches, but Kennedy had saved the real barb of his wit to the last, for an astonishing punch line in which Smathers appears not only as a target but as part of an apparatus—the Presidency and its problems—that was in itself somewhat ridiculous in its pretensions:

"It will encourage you to know [Kennedy said] that every Tuesday morning . . . we have breakfast together and he advises with me—Cuba, anything else, Laos, Berlin, anything—George comes right out there and gives his views and I listen very carefully."

Nor did he stop with such small targets as Smathers. Composing a birthday telegram to his touchy Vice-President, Lyndon Johnson, he once told a reporter, was like "drafting a state document."

When Prime Minister Lester B. Pearson of Canada arrived at Hyannis Port in the Spring of 1963, his reputation as a baseball expert had preceded him. The resident White House baseball nut was Dave Powers, an Irishman of jovial mien who could sing *Bill Bailey Won't You Please Come Home* with marvelous vigah at the drop of a Scotch and soda. After a chilly Cape Cod dinner, Pearson followed Kennedy into seclusion, only to find it shattered by a summons to Powers.

"Dave," the President said, "test him out."

Whereupon Powers put the Prime Minister through an exhaustive baseball catechism, while the President rocked silently in his rocking chair, puffing on a cigar inscrutably, either measuring his man or enjoying the incongruous match—or both. Back and forth flowed the batting averages, managers' names, World Series statistics, and other diamond esoterica, until finally it was Dave Powers, not Mike Pearson, who tripped on some southpaw's 1926 earned run average.

"He'll do," Kennedy said then, with some satisfaction. After which he and Pearson hit it off famously and jointly equipped Canada with nuclear warheads.

Probably the finest piece of work Kennedy did in his eight generally lackluster years in the Senate was his leadership of the fight against reform of the electoral college in 1956. He argued brilliantly for the system as it was and still is. His side prevailed for a number of sound reasons, but not least because Kennedy succeeded in convincing enough Senators that, as he put it, "Falkland's definition of conservatism is quite appropriate—'When it is not necessary to change, it is necessary not to change.'"

That might almost have been Lord Melbourne speaking: *If it was not absolutely necessary, it was the foolishest thing ever done*, Melbourne said of a Parliamentary act. Indeed, Melbourne may have been in Kennedy's mind; for in the course of that brutal exposure of all his habits and persuasions to which Americans subject their President, it was to become known that his favorite book was David Cecil's *Melbourne*.

Probably no monument of the future will record that fact; yet it ought to give biographers pause. If the Kennedy campaign of 1960 meant anything, in terms of the man who waged it, it ought to have meant that Kennedy was a man who aimed to set the country right, who saw no reason it couldn't be done, who intended to let nothing stand in the way of doing it. The President who took office that cold day in January, 1961, saying, "let us begin," seemed to promise that the nation's problems could be solved if only enough brains and vigor and determination and money were applied to them.

Why would such a man enjoy reading of Melbourne, who believed government, in fact most human effort, was futile; who counseled, *When in doubt do nothing*; who said of a proposal to reform the English municipal councils, *We have got on tolerably well*

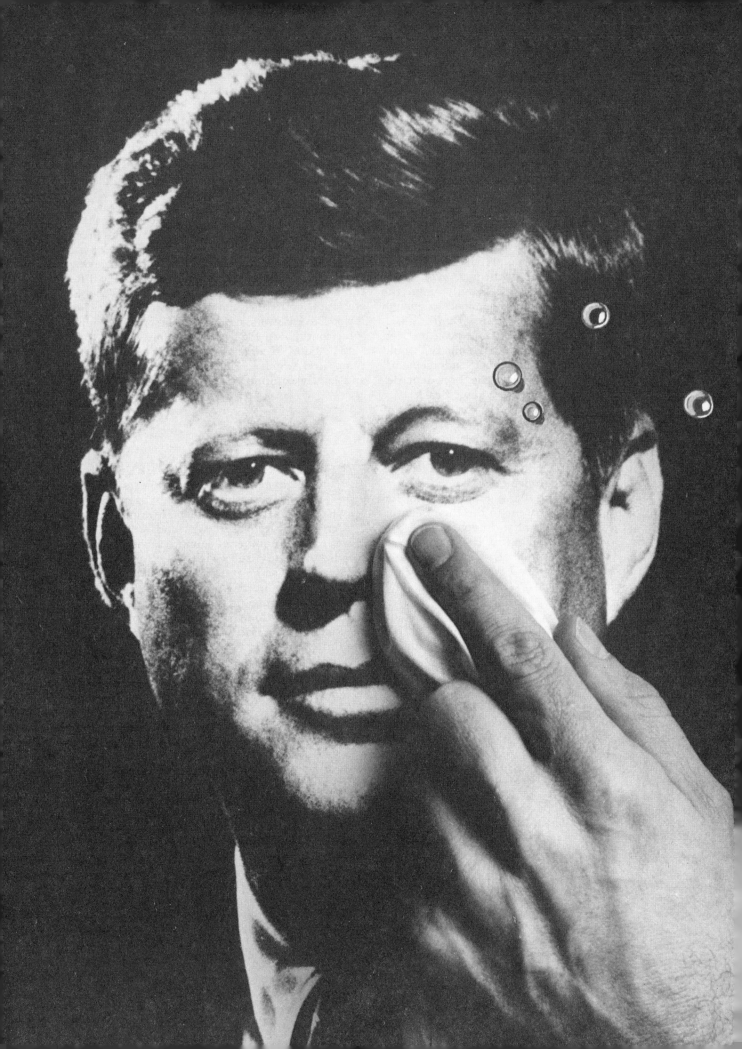

with the councils for five hundred years; we may contrive to go on with them for another few years or so; and who thought the most damaging part of reform was that it aroused extravagant hopes that government and society—even men—might actually be improved.

But perhaps Kennedy was never quite the man the 1960 campaign suggested—just as Melbourne was not quite the fogy a few random quotations might suggest. Melbourne, in fact, as his biographer pictures him, was a man of immense charm and wit, great learning, considerable understanding of human nature, and remarkable courage in going his way—attributes that might be aspired to by any man. Certainly Kennedy possessed some of them and there is evidence to suggest that he shared to some extent Melbourne's skepticism about political and other human efforts at improving the condition of man.

The Kennedy wit certainly implies that he did. So did his remarks on a famous television interview in December of 1962, when he reviewed his first two years in office.

"There is a limitation upon the ability of the United States to solve these problems," he said. ". . . there is a limitation, in other words, upon the power of the United States to bring about solutions. . . . The responsibilities placed on the United States are greater than I imagined them to be and there are greater limitations upon our ability to bring about a favorable result than I had imagined them to be. . . . It is much easier to make the speeches than it is finally to make the judgments. . . ."

And it might have been Melbourne speaking again when he said of his efforts to roll back steel prices: "There is no sense in raising hell and then not being successful. There is no sense in putting the office of the Presidency on the line on an issue and then being defeated."

A few months later, I asked Kennedy at a news conference if he would comment on what I said was a feeling in the country that his Administration seemed "to have lost its momentum and to be slowing down and to be moving on the defensive."

"*There is a rhythm to a personal and national and international life and it flows and ebbs,*" Kennedy replied. He even conceded—sounding not unlike Melbourne on the Reform Laws—that "Some of our difficulties in Europe have come because the military threat in Europe is less than it has been in the past. In other words, whatever successes we may have had in reducing that military threat to Europe brought with it in its wake other problems. . . ."

Later, Ted Sorensen was to publish a book that in its essence was a discussion of the limitations upon a President—the reasons why, as Kennedy wrote in a foreword, "Every President must endure a gap between *what he would like and what is possible*" (the italics are mine). Once again Sorensen had caught the spirit of his chief and reproduced it; politics was not after all simply a matter of brains and vigor and determination, or even money. Its events, life itself, flowed also from the contrary nature of men, the blind turns of chance, the inertia of custom. And in that

same foreword Kennedy quoted Franklin Roosevelt as saying:

Lincoln was a sad man because he couldn't get it all at once. And nobody can.

On a more personal level, some who knew Kennedy well sensed something deeper than skepticism in him, though he was a private man who did not much reveal himself even to men who worked with him for years. He was absolutely fearless about airplanes, for instance, flying anywhere, at any time, in any weather in which he could get aloft, sleeping through anything, scarcely seeming aware that he was off the ground. Yet four persons in his family—his brother, his sister, Ethel Kennedy's parents—had died in aircraft accidents.

Kennedy sometimes discussed the possibility that he would be assassinated with members of his staff. They would be anxious to explain the details of security precautions to him, to show him that it was unlikely it could happen. "If someone is going to kill me," he would say, "they're going to kill me."

And one of those who was close to him believes that Kennedy bothered little about what he was going to do with all those years that presumably would be on his hands when he emerged from the White House at age fifty-one (assuming he won two terms).

"It didn't really concern him," the aide recalls. "He never thought he was going to live to be an old man anyway."

Yet he had his imperatives. A man owed something to the public service. He had to be a patriot. He ought to be physically fit and courageous. (Good war records received special consideration on the New Frontier, and Dave Powers remembers that Kennedy once learned by heart the citation for a medal that had been awarded to General Douglas MacArthur.) A man's job was to act, not talk—to begin, to take the first step in a journey of a thousand miles.

Kennedy has been compared to Franklin Roosevelt and he liked to pose in front of an F.D.R. portrait. In fact, some of his qualities more nearly recall Theodore Roosevelt, the apostle of the big stick, the strenuous life and the bully pulpit. Like T.R., for instance, Kennedy fancied himself in the role of national taste maker—Roosevelt picked up Edward Arlington Robinson and Kennedy adopted Robert Frost. Roosevelt let his rather rigid literary ideas get about and the Kennedys thought they ought to provide White House examples—Casals, Shakespeare and opera in the East Room—for the cultural uplift of the nation. Yet, after an American opera group had sung a scene from *The Magic Flute* in English, after a dinner for the President of India, Kennedy could confess to a group of guests: "I think they ought to sing it in the original language. It doesn't sound right any other way."

There is not much doubt that Kennedy's publicized delight in Ian Fleming's spoof-spy novels doubled Fleming's sales, though there has been no big run on Cecil's *Melbourne*.

He kept green, graceful, Lafayette Square in Washington from disappearing into the capital's Great Stone Face. One of his last interests was in a plan to redeem Pennsylvania Avenue from army-surplus stores, cheap steak houses and bumbling federal architects. But it was as if art and culture were in the National Interest, like the test-ban treaty and Project Mercury; and if Kennedy was an avid reader of history, he did not seem to suffer from a great personal involvement in drama, music, art. The movies shown in the White House screening room were often the commonplace of Hollywood, and, except in the East Room, Kennedy's favorite music was more nearly Sinatra than Schönberg. As President, his first venture to Broadway took him to the slick musical, *How to Succeed in Business Without Really Trying*. Once, when he had a group of newspapermen in his house at Palm Beach, I stole a look at a stack of recordings; the one on top was a Chubby Checker twist collection.

But the imperatives of taking part, of public service, seemed, like those that moved Teddy Roosevelt, to be genuine and even profound. To the Touchdown Club of New York, he quoted with obvious approval the rather fervent view of T.R. on the matter:

"The credit belongs to the man who is actually in the arena—whose face is marred by dust and sweat and blood . . . a leader who knows the great enthusiasms, the great devotions—and spends himself in a worthy cause—who at best if he wins knows the thrills of high achievement—and if he fails at least fails while daring greatly—so that his place shall never be with those cold and timid souls who know neither victory nor defeat."

Many times, he voiced a similar sentiment in his own words. Oddly, the man of detachment, of cool wit and ironic view, preached the "long twilight struggle" in which the most certain thing was that there would be "neither victory nor defeat." Yet, the man of commitment, of action, rejected with robustious Teddy the "cold and timid souls" who had no blood and dust upon their faces. And another quotation he liked to throw at university audiences was the rhetorical question of George William Curtis of Massachusetts:

"Would you have counted him a friend of ancient Greece who quietly discussed the theory of patriotism on that hot summer day through whose hopeless and immortal hours Leonidas and the three hundred stood at Thermopylae for liberty? Was John Milton to conjugate Greek verbs in his library when the liberty of Englishmen was imperiled?"

To the students of George Washington University, Kennedy gave his own answer: "No, quite obviously, the duty of the educated man or woman, the duty of the scholar, is to give his objective sense, his sense of liberty to the maintenance of our society at the critical time."

But in the next breath he was telling the story of someone who went to Harvard years ago and "asked for President Lowell. They said, 'He's in Washington, seeing Mr. Taft.' I know that some other day, when they are asking for the President of your university, they will say that he is over at the White House seeing Mr. Kennedy. They understood at Harvard, and you understand here, the relative importance of a university president and a President of the United States."

If that was a joke, it did not come from one who often gave up "his objective sense, and his sense of liberty." Honey Fitz would sing *Sweet Adeline* until his tonsils gave out, but his grandson was never known to wear a funny hat in public. It may seem a small point, but John Kennedy maintained it literally to his dying day. On November 22, in Fort Worth, he went through the Texas ritual of being presented a cowboy hat—but steadfastly resisted the pleas of two thousand Texans that he put it on.

"Come to Washington Monday and I'll put it on for you in the White House," he joked. But even in that comparative privacy, had he reached it, he would not have worn that hat. The man of detachment had yielded himself enough; he would make his little pushing gesture at the crowds, but he would not wave his arms exuberantly above his head like Eisenhower, or thump his chest like Theodore Roosevelt.

So, despite their similarities, he was radically different from the ebullient T.R. Restraint was his style, not arm-waving. There was nothing detached, nothing ironic, about Roosevelt, who could say and believe it that in the White House "my teaching has been plain morality." Kennedy would never claim more than that he hoped he was a "responsible President"; he would not often speak on television because he believed people would tire of him and stop listening.

Sometimes, it seemed, he even thought of politics, the Presidency itself, as a sporting proposition. Kennedy never tired of exhorting college students to prepare themselves for the public service, but he was seldom stuffy about it. He did not propose, he told the University of North Carolina student body, to adopt "from the Belgian constitution a provision giving three votes instead of one to college graduates —at least not until more Democrats go to college."

As the campaign of 1960 wore on, the atmosphere around the candidate sometimes seemed almost like one of those parlor games the Kennedys played so often. "Tell me a delegate and I'll tell you who he's for," Kennedy would say to members of his staff, in his best Twenty Questions manner. "Give me a state and I'll give you the delegate breakdown."

The election was so close it inhibited Kennedy; he would point out how closely divided was the country at every opportunity. Yet, he could compare his own disputed election to the plight of a Notre Dame football team that had won a game by means some thought illegal. "And we're not going to give it back," he told the National Football Foundation.

Kennedy disliked the solemn ideologues and myopic Babbitts who crowd American political life—Senator Karl Mundt of South Dakota, for instance—but he delighted in the skillful shenanigans of some who took the game of politics less seriously—even, in some cases, when the voters and taxpayers were taken too. With obvious relish, he once described the operations of the raffish but highly effective Senator Warren Magnuson of Washington as follows:

"He speaks in the Senate so quietly that few can hear him. He looks down at his desk—he comes into the Senate late in the afternoon—he is very hesitant about interrupting other members of the Senate—when he rises to speak, most members of the Senate have left—he sends his messages up to the Senate and everyone says, 'What is it?' And Senator Magnuson says, 'It's nothing important.' And Grand Coulee Dam is built."

The night before he died, Kennedy spoke in tribute to Representative Albert Thomas in Houston, Texas. Not the least of Thomas' achievements over the years had been the enrichment of Houston with federal investments; his most recent coup had been the somewhat controversial establishment there of the Manned Spacecraft Center. Kennedy recounted a bit floridly how Thomas had helped put the United States in a position to fire into space the largest booster rocket bearing the largest "payroll" in history. As the audience laughed, Kennedy hastily corrected the word to "payload."

That slip might have embarrassed most politicians, but it obviously struck Kennedy as funny. "It will be the largest payroll, too," he added, grinning, "and who should know that better than Houston. We put a little of it right in here." Wasn't that what made the wheels go round?

Kennedy laughed out loud when he heard that Everett Dirksen had said that one of his early economic measures would have "all the impact of a snowflake on the bosom of the Potomac." He once carried a letter from de Gaulle around the White House, pointing out its elegances to his staff. It mattered not who won or lost, but how they played the game.

Even the selection of winners of the Medal of Freedom, a sort of royal honors list Mrs. Kennedy and the President invented, was not free in Kennedy's mind from the sporting balance of politics—you scratch mine and I'll scratch yours. When the painter Andrew Wyeth was selected, Kennedy—who had put up an early argument for Ben Shahn—decreed: "Next year, we'll have to go abstract."

One night on his plane, returning to Washington from a speech in Trenton, he talked about his love of boating with a group of us, and confided: "I'd really like to have that yacht Eisenhower laid up in Philadelphia [the old *Williamsburg*]. But he said he did it for economy reasons and if I took it out of mothballs now they'd never let me hear the end of it." That

was how the game was played; all you could do was grin and bear it, and play the game yourself.

Thus John Kennedy, in his pursuit of excellence, his commitment to active service, spent a great deal of his short life playing and thinking politics—running and angling for office, first; pushing political solutions to social and economic problems, second. But that is not necessarily the same thing as being profoundly involved in politics; it is not the same thing as a belief in solutions or the efficacy of politics. Kennedy seemed sometimes to think of himself as taking the first steps he so often urged upon the country and the world; he would use politics, he would propose a program, not with much hope for either, but to raise a question, to start someone thinking, to bring a matter into whatever light there was.

One Saturday morning in 1963 in Los Angeles he appeared at the Hollywood Palladium to address a Democratic women's breakfast; it was the only time I ever heard *Hail to the Chief* played with a twist beat. He was supposed to make "brief remarks"; instead, he plunged in his familiar machine-gun delivery into a half hour of Democratic Party evangelism so impassioned and so portentous of phrase that some of my colleagues wrote that he had "kicked off his 1964 campaign." I was so stirred by the speech that I phoned the *Times* to hold space for the full text of it. It was a "major address," I assured my editors.

When the transcript came spinning from the White House mimeograph an hour later, I thumbed through it in search of those memorable phrases, those ringing pledges, those grand calls to battle that had rung through the Palladium. I have that transcript before me now and it confirms my disillusionment; there was nothing there, nothing but rhetoric and delivery. We had seen a performance in which J.F.K. had been playing the game unusually well.

In 1962, Kennedy proposed a Cabinet-level Department of Urban Affairs. Robert C. Weaver, the Administration's housing chief, was to be its Secretary—the first Negro to sit in any President's Cabinet. The proposal was hailed as a political masterstroke. Who could vote, in effect, against Weaver except the Southerners? And who cared about them?

In any event a great many members of Congress voted against the proposal and it became one of Kennedy's most embarrassing defeats. Not long afterward, I asked him how it had happened.

He took a cigar out of his mouth and answered bluntly: "I played it too cute. It was so obvious it made them mad." In short, he had played the game poorly. I think he often did.

He could go before a captive audience of Democratic old people in Madison Square Garden and shed crocodile tears in behalf of his medical-care plan—and look as political and as uncomfortable as he was. Before an audience in Miami Beach from which he had little further to gain, the A.F.L.-C.I.O., he was so palpably bored, his speech was so blatantly routine and uninspired, that men of more objective political judgment might have booed him from the platform. He went into General Eisenhower's home county during the 1962 campaign and delivered a speech so demagogic and so extravagant in its claims for Democratic virtue and Republican sloth that even the General was enraged and promptly proceeded to emerge from retirement to campaign against him—a development that might have been politically important had not the Cuban crisis changed the whole picture in October. On his Western trip in the Fall of 1963—his last extended tour in the country—Kennedy looked and felt so out of place talking about conservation and nature and wildlife that the reporters following him gave him the nickname "Smokey the Bear"; it was reported by Pierre Salinger at Jackson Lake Lodge that the President actually had seen a moose from the window of his room.

Shortly after Kennedy's death, Carroll Kilpatrick and I visited J. Frank Dobie at the University of Texas and asked him what was the difference in Kennedy and Lyndon Johnson. Mr. Dobie knew Johnson well; he knew Kennedy only as most Americans knew him—as a voice on the radio, a face on the screen, a presence in the land. "Johnson is concerned with means," Mr. Dobie said at once, as if the contrast was obvious. "Kennedy was interested in ends."

A generality, perhaps, but near enough to truth to *ring* true. Kennedy played the game as a political man had to, sometimes brilliantly, often with boredom and ineptitude. But it was not then that he stirred us. Even his memorable campaign of 1960, the finest exercise of his strictly political life, was not politics-as-usual; it was outside the ordinary rules, for Kennedy was a Roman Catholic, an inexperienced younger man, something of an intellectual, who put little trust in traditional politicians, and relied instead upon his own men, his own techniques, his own personality.

Perhaps he had to move beyond the rules, get out of the game, before he really involved himself—and therefore involved other men. His trip to Europe in 1963 exhilarated him, for instance; he knew he had broken through the traditional wall of diplomatic niceties, spoken above the heads of politicians and governments, and he believed a new generation of Europeans had responded. At his death, his tax bill was mired in Congress, but its mere presentation may yet be the longest step toward lifting American economic policy out of the twin ruts of ignorance and cliché. His civil-rights bill was fumbled and botched, but he was the first American President to recognize in the outpouring of events a "moral crisis" in race relations. The long shadow of de Gaulle darkened his European policy, but he had proclaimed on both sides of the Atlantic a commitment to the interdependence of two continents. Nobody could say there would be no nuclear war, but he had taken the "first step" of the test-ban treaty.

That is what haunts me about Kennedy—not just that he was a man of certain admirable visions, but that he had the kind of mind that could entertain vision, the kind of outlook that could put in perspective the gambits and maneuvers of the moment, see truly the futility of most means, the uncertain glory of most ends. Surely he was one of those men "educated in the liberal traditions, willing to take the long look, undisturbed by prejudices and slogans of the moment, who attempt to make an honest judgment on difficult events"; surely he tried to be one of those, to borrow his words again, who could "distinguish the real from the illusory, the long-range from the temporary, the significant from the petty...."

And that is the real irony of John F. Kennedy's coming immortality. For when James Reston asked him in the Summer of 1961, during a long afternoon's talk at Hyannis Port, what kind of a world it was he had in mind, what vision he had of the future, John Kennedy—President of the United States for half a year, perpetrator of the Bay of Pigs, not long home from his "somber" meeting with Khrushchev in Vienna—could reply: "I haven't had time to think about that yet."

It is the classic story of the liberal man in politics. *I claim not to have controlled events*, Lincoln said, *but confess plainly that events have controlled me*. And perhaps it is symbolized in a compelling picture of Kennedy that comes to us from one of Washington's most imposing men.

It is a glimpse from the Cuban missile crisis of October, 1962, a period of great tension at the White House as throughout the world. The personage and the President were alone in Kennedy's oval office, discussing what in New Frontier jargon were known as "the options"; that month, the options were pretty grim.

Kennedy rose from his rocking chair, leaving his visitor seated on a sofa. The President went across his office to the French doors that opened on the terrace of the West Executive Wing. Beyond the terrace lay the famous Rose Garden, redesigned like almost everything else about the White House by the elegant stylists who had come to live there. But at its end still towered the famous magnolia planted by Andrew Jackson.

Kennedy stood for a long time, silent, gazing at the garden and the magnolia, his hands behind his back, the burden of decision almost visible on his shoulders. "Well," he said at last, "I guess this is the week I earn my salary."

The detached thinker had been brought to bay by the necessities of the moment. That questing mind with its sensitivity to the complexity of things, to the illusory nature of answers and solutions, had come to the moment of black vs. white. That derisive and worldly wit was stilled in the sheer responsibility of choice. Action and events had overtaken contemplation and vision, and Kennedy shared the plight of Melbourne: *I am afraid the question of the Irish Church can neither be avoided nor postponed. It must therefore be attempted to be solved*. And for Kennedy, that fall, humanity itself was the question.

So with his football coach's will to win, with his passion for "the ability to do things well," Kennedy had had his dreams and realized them. But I believe he stood on the sidelines, too, even while the game was going on, measuring his performance, wryly remarking upon it, not much impressed, not much deluded. Perhaps he knew all along that events would control, action overwhelm, means fail to reach ends. "There stands the decision," he wrote, "and there stands the President." Sooner or later, they would be as one.

The decisions he made, the slogans he spoke—let them be carved on the monuments. But for me his epitaph is inscribed on Dave Powers' silver beer mug, that John Kennedy gave him for his birthday last year. It reads:

There are three things which are real:
God, human folly and laughter.
The first two are beyond our
    comprehension
So we must do what we can with the
    third.

No one at the White House knew the source of those lines. I can find the words in no book of quotations. The Library of Congress has not been able to discover who wrote them. But I think I know.

John Sack:

When Demirgian Comes Marching Home Again (Hurrah? Hurrah?)

A tour of duty in Vietnam lasts one year.
The members
of M company have had it

Ninety-nine bottles of beer on the wall, ninety-nine bottles of beer. If one of those bottles should happen to fall, ninety-eight bottles of beer on the wall. Ninety-eight. . . .

On the bottom side of earth in that strange land of Vietnam, time is a row of old brown bottles that are toppling down, of concrete balls that are cracking apart—time, in Vietnam, is a great burlap bag of rocks, and each day a soldier's shoulders are lightened of one more pound. As the night disappears, as sun makes the metal mess kits shine and warms a boy's cheeks, as day breaks he tells himself words like "Ninety-nine days." The next day he tells himself "Ninety-eight. . . ."

Tonight is the last night of Demirgian's tour of duty. Demirgian, a boy with the rank of specialist, his specialty being the rifle, his duty being to kill communists with it—Demirgian, the three hundreds, two hundreds, one hundreds over, the days strewn in back of him like little worthless pieces of broken glass, a staleness issuing out of them, a sickening smell—Demirgian has just tonight left as a rifleman in Asia. And when those seemingly endless hours are safely behind him—hurrah! Demirgian comes marching home again, uninjured, undead! Everybody cross your fingers! Pray for Demirgian! Pray!

That night Demirgian lay in his combat clothes—his steel helmet, the damp fabric of his shirt and trousers, his canvas boots—and Demirgian had a wet black rifle on the soil beside him as with intricate fingers he made himself a glass of grape juice. Slower than a caterpillar chews on a maple leaf his fingers tore a small paper packet of Kool-Aid and quieter than a dandelion loses its fluff his hand shook the light purple powder into his Army canteen. The cold stars above, the cool earth below him kept their complete silence as Demirgian tilted his rubber canteen to its

left—right—left—right—with the slow periodicity of a pendulum. One long minute of this and Demirgian took a quiet sip. And ah! Demirgian had come alive! He's in the grape-juice generation! He buried the torn paper packet quietly in six inches of Vietnam's soil.

The time was about ten or ten-thirty at night. It shouldn't be thought that on ambush parties (for Demirgian's invisible squad had an ambush assignment tonight: to lie in the total darkness, if anyone comes it's a communist, shoot him)—it shouldn't be thought that soldiers on ambush parties lie like panthers ready to leap, their legs up under them, their eyes all alert: ridiculous. The essence of American ambush parties is that nothing—*nothing*—happens, nowhere but in the grave do the endless hours pass by a mass of human substance so stubbornly true to its configurations of one hour earlier, nobody in an American ambush party does a cotton-picking thing, the hours between sunset and sunrise hang as languidly as a hammock between two willow trees, one in a hundred times does a star-crossed communist happen by—a real event. Demirgian, a year of these uninteresting ambush parties and he still hadn't ambushed one living breathing soul. Demirgian had waited, he had scratched at where the mosquitoes bit, in his feet he had pins and needles, accordingly: he had wiggled his toes, he had given himself to little insidious itches, the nibbles of little millions of imaginary ants, he had *in—out—in—out—*he had carefully not neglected to breathe, the earth, like a big brown blotter, had sopped up his *élan vital*, his muscle tone, his temperature, his blood, he was pressed to these stretches of Asia hour after hour and hi-di-ho, I should have brought my yo-yo, at dawn he had lifted himself like a heavy canvas tarpaulin and carried himself back to the company camp. It was three meals a day, pink pills on Sunday, payday on the thirtieth—it was a living and it soon would be over, America hello!

And so Demirgian lay in a last night of lassitude. Elsewhere in this ambush party a pair of flat shadows coalesced and imperceptible whispers rose. "Sergeant?"

"Yes?"

"Sergeant. I have a headache."

"You have a headache?"

Private Demirgian entered Esquire as the hero, or anyway the focal point, of Mr. Sack's M (October, 1966); the author followed Demirgian, now a sergeant, all the way home for this article in January, 1968.

"Sergeant? You have an aspirin?"

"Yes."

Another boy in Demirgian's dull ambush party quietly snored. The sergeant in charge of this tableau said his bedtime prayers, he said to himself, "*Padre nuestro,*" bowing his dark-colored face to the earth, "*que estas en los cielos. . . .*" The sergeant prayed for a typical night: no communists.

A VISIT TO THE BULLET FACTORY. *Splash! At the factory where the bright bullets for Demirgian's rifle are made, Connecticut citizens in big iron shoes are carrying lead to the melting pot—splash! From out of the press comes the hot wet wire, the width of a bullet's width, the length of eternity, and Curtis, a colored man, a giant, the wire in his muscular hands, his body bowed over the floor like an ogre's over a steaming caldron, is coiling it—coiling it—oiling it, the machinery sends it along. The machinery is gargantuan, the gears are like wagon wheels, the con-rods are making the motions of steady animal love. And chop! And chop! The wire is cut into bullet sizes, the slippery bullets slide from the chopping block on a gangway of grease, they are slithering, skiddering, and slippering into one another—sleighs on a snowy hillside, jingle all the way!*

Careful of the powdery stuff, boys and girls. Like little chipped pieces of pencil lead, it comes to the bullet plant in cases, it gets itself on clothing like a city's soot, it makes the wooden floor of the factory like a ballroom floor, as though beneath the balls of the feet lay little ball bearings. Roll out the barrel! To Agnes, in her sensible shoes, the floor is like the floor of the Pleasure Beach Ballroom, in Bridgeport. We'll have a barrel of. . . . Agnes had met her husband there as the polka played. With her cardboard card and a brisk black brush, Agnes gets the powder up once every day, as David with his—bang—with his little leather—bang—with his little leather mallet—BANG, David hits the feeder lines to clean them, too. No smoking, please, as busy little birdlike ladies in glasses of plastic take the black powder, the bullets, the brass, as forty-nine at one time of these instrumentalities are made in the U.S.A. And a thousand wheels go round and round! And the air's on edge in the factory sound! And boxes of bullets abound on the ground! And—

Click. Clack. Mechanically, Demirgian puts one of Connecticut's bullets into his mean-looking rifle. A power uncalled upon, a lion asleep, here in its cave the bullets shall sit in steely silence all through an Asian night, an unnecessary accessory to American ambush parties with no one to set upon. But coming in in the morning—bang! and Demirgian will sometimes shoot at a C-ration can. And bang! and Demirgian shoots at a squealing pig. And bang! and Demirgian gets him a chicken with one of Connecticut's accurate bullets. Demirgian—

what a character, the other risible soldiers say, Demirgian king of the shooting gallery, give him a box of candy, give him a cuddly teddy bear! However, Demirgian has still never shot at a communist. And he has adequate reason. A year in the Vietnam bushes (the endless series of stops and starts, the waits at the ambush sites, the walks)—a year minus a day in Vietnam and Demirgian has still never seen a communist to shoot at. Typical.

The time was getting on past eleven. Demirgian still lay on his hard lumpy mattress of earth—the ambush area, as across from him in the bushes a little thickening of blackness seemed to have suddenly moved, like a fish in the Stygian deep. Old soldier Demirgian tiredly recognized it for what it was, a banana leaf in the evening breeze. If only it were a communist soldier—ah! *Charlie tries to creep up on me,* Demirgian said to himself wistfully—*Charlie ever tries that and I'm just going to lie here—yeah! Let him get ten meters from me, the stupid little son-of-a. Yeah, and I'll have my hand grenade and I'll pull the pin—Charlie you're about to have had it! k-k-k! And then I'll let the handle go and I'll one—! two—! and I'll throw it!* Thumb on the bottom, fingers on top, a lazy little catlike windup, the pitch—Demirgian could see himself throw the grenade like a baseball, a rock, Demirgian had had some practice at that in Newton, Massachusetts, the city where he had been drafted from and where he had been a schoolboy before. "*Foreigner,*" some of the other kids had cried at Demirgian, "*Camel chaser,*" some of the Irish would say, and Demirgian, age twelve, his body behind a cardboard carton with its color of dead lawns and a dry-spell smell, his eyes at two tiny fiber-filled holes—Demirgian had thrown lumps of pudding stone at the Irish children, that is how he would throw his grenade at that communist if the stars in their slowly maundering courses should offer him—*at last*—one of his unseen enemies. To kill himself a communist soldier: that was Demirgian's dream, the Irish had been the object of nothing like it, this was Demirgian's sacred quest. For a boy with no past history of animus to Asians of any political party, a year on that distant continent and Demirgian's wish to kill communists had gone beyond all expectations, it was something fierce, his bones had become like a thing turned black, a thin black liquid ran in his arteries, no other friends of his felt it that passionately, the reason—that was Demirgian's secret. A bullet, a piece of his bayonet, it didn't make a diff to Demirgian *how,* a tent peg if it's sharp enough, a shovel, a can of kerosene, a kitchen match and—*bastard, die!* Demirgian's imagination knew no mercy—kick him in the genitals, finger in his eyeballs, stick him in the ashcan, ha-ha-ha! *Yeah,* Demirgian thought in his wait at this ambush area, it might be the night tonight—a toss of a hand grenade, success! An explosion, *and I'll look at him lying there dead and I'll think to myself*—Demirgian thought of a pale yellow face, the mouth like a broken bottle, the starlight on crooked teeth—*I think I'll be sorry about him—*

yeah, Demirgian thought. *I'll say to him poor bastard! You're fighting for a losing cause!* If there was a watch or something upon him, Demirgian thought he might take it, a souvenir.

It wouldn't be easy. It's a practical fact of Vietnam that the airplane pilots and artillerymen kill the communists while the riflemen like Demirgian kill themselves—one doesn't have to say: by accident—and Demirgian would have to throw himself over the odds if his heart's desire was to be gratified tonight. Still, there had been soldiers in Demirgian's own squad who had killed themselves communists, it had been known to happen sometimes in spite of Charlie's invisible, really, ways. A boy in Demirgian's squad who once killed a real communist in a pineapple patch had been written about in *Newsweek* for that unusual deed. *Our forearms*, a senior editor of *Newsweek* had written—*our forearms [were being] slashed by thorns and our fatigues drenched with sweat. Suddenly*—suddenly a pal of Demirgian's had seen a real enemy soldier—*the bullet ripped through the Vietcong's head.* Though his name had been spelled wrong in *Newsweek*, the commie-killing infantryman had been given a hero's due by Demirgian's proud battalion commander, a trip via cargo plane to the China Sea, a holiday spree at the beaches—time out, a Coppertone tan, a blanket, sand, a date in a blue bikini, only the brave deserve the fair! Another day, a Red had been made dead by the steady machine gun of Demirgian's best friend—his buddy. His holiday over, Demirgian's friend had returned to the envious squad with his China Sea suntan to learn that he had been recommended for a medal—a Bronze Star and a "V" for valor—in addition, in recognition of that extraordinary act. It wasn't unheard of, Demirgian knew!

RECOMMENDED AWARD OF THE BRONZE STAR MEDAL. *"With complete disregard for his own personal safety and well-being —— moved the machine gun to the forward position of the platoon and began placing accurate fire on enemy positions. His actions are in keeping with the highest traditions of the military service, and. . . ."*

Obligatory words. Kill every communist in China and still you'll get no medal to wear if your company commander's letter of recommendation doesn't say that you've done it with a certain very specific élan. It is Army tradition —if a man's to have a Medal of Honor bestowed upon him a letter of recommendation has to follow form in saying verbatim, "He never relented from his determined effort to destroy the enemy," and Demirgian's best friend is certain to be laughed out of court if the letter in which he has been recommended for a Bronze Star and a "V" for valor leaves it unsaid that he killed his communist in a way that evinced the virtues of aggressiveness, devotion to duty, and bravery, and if it doesn't say, "His actions are in keeping with the highest traditions." All these amenities observed, the letter of recommendation has been given to a clerk with the order to send it speedily through the Army's bureaucratic channels— someone has killed a communist, hurrah!

AWARD OF THE BRONZE STAR MEDAL. *"By direction of the President, under the provisions of the executive order 11046, the Bronze Star Medal is awarded to —— for outstanding meritorious service as a company clerk in. . . ."*

Fie on that clerk—he has thrown the letter of recommendation away and given the Bronze Star to himself, the stinker! A very latent heterosexual, the clerk has a way of walking in the company camp and throwing his soft weight around as though he were keeping a hula-hoop up—a typical Army clerk, and he isn't about to let medals be bestowed on those awful-awful boys in Demirgian's squad who always make fun of his mannerisms by crying at him in the shower tent, "Gentlemen only," or calling to him at bedtime, "Tuck me in?" The clerk has become so wrought up ("Careful," the boys in Demirgian's squad say, "careful, he'll hit you with his purse")—so angry that not in a zillion years will he see a Bronze Star and a "V" for valor hung on any friend of Demirgian's. Instead, the clerk, who every morning, afternoon, and evening has discharged his responsibilities in spite of his having a typewriter with a raggedy old typewriter ribbon and a filing cabinet with an army of—eek—insects inside, who sometimes even has gone around back of the orderly room to identify a dead soldier's bloody body—ugh, the clerk has simply given a Bronze Star to himself lest the Army let these meritorious achievements go unrecognized. He has written himself a letter of recommendation, none of the Army's high-sounding words has he left unsaid, he has signed it with his commander's scratchy signature, and he has wished it Godspeed on the winding road to higher headquarters. One month later the very handsome medal is his.

". . . Through his untiring efforts and professional ability, he constantly obtained outstanding results. He was quick to grasp the implications of new problems with which he was faced as a result of the ever-changing situation inherent in a counterinsurgency operation and to find ways and means to solve these problems. The energetic application of his extensive knowledge has materially contributed to the efforts of the United States Mission to the Republic of Vietnam to assist that country in ridding itself of the communist threat to its freedom. His initiative, zeal, sound judgment, and devotion to duty have been in the highest traditions of. . . ."

Eleven-thirty. Midnight almost, and Demirgian still hadn't met a communist, a passerby at whom he could fire his bright golden bullet or throw his grenade at and kill.

One click—one kilometer—from the area where the passing hours went by Demirgian's ambush party like a trickle of lukewarm water was Demirgian's company camp, a tight little triangular area of huts and holes in the starlight, a Kipling place. Just outside of these earthworks, the Coke stand, as the soldiers called it, was deserted, of course, it was closed until six o'clock, but that afternoon as Vietnamese small businessmen stood at its shaky wooden tables to give soldiers beer and Coke, to busily pop bottle tops off with rusty openers, to grow a garden of bottle tops in their fatherland's soil, to overcharge, and to shout at their weary customers not to walk off with the empties— that afternoon at the Coke stand something very strange had happened. Sitting drinking a bottle of Vietnamese formaldehydic beer, a soldier in this company had sought to fill up the empty interstices of time by saying one of those two or three formula phrases whose endless iteration passes for conversation at the Coke stand, "Hey mamasan, VC come tonight?" A catechism, but that after-noon instead of her cackling laugh and inveterate answer, "VC no come tonight," the Vietnamese in her clothes of black wrinkled rayon had looked at that soldier scaredly and quietly said, "Yes."

Now, it must be under-stood that the loud little people who worked at the Coke stand, dirt in each crease of their bodies, teeth the color of cockroaches, the words in their skinny mouths a caterwaul of ugly *ow* sounds—that the Vietnamese were a people whom the cus-tomers at the Coke stand had very little respect for, Demirgian, in fact, had even wanted to murder them, at times. Once in his early days in Vietnam he had bought himself an orange pop, he had given the lady a fifty-piastre bill, the Vietnamese had pushed it into the dirty seam of her dress—Demirgian had said quite politely, "Change?" At that, the lady had started to shriek—to *shriek* in the half-hysterical *ow*'s of a dog when there's somebody on its tail, to shriek at Demirgian and the echoing acres that fifty piastres—half an American dollar—was a fair market price for a bottle of pop in Asia. It was seven o'clock in the morning, and Demirgian's ears had become used to the unbroken silence of the ambush party that he had been lying in all that night to guarantee the right of this shrieking lady to engage in private enter-prise. It rankled Demirgian to think he had risked life and limb for a race of such ungrateful people as to challenge—in *shrieks*—even his right to refresh himself afterward with a bottle of soda without paying them ten times the wholesale price. He believed that if it was necessary—and it *was*—to twist the Viet-namese lady's arm, to give her a karate chop at the base of her cervical spine, or simply to shoot her in that goddamn shrieking skull in order to get change, that

he was just angry enough to do this. But he didn't— Demirgian was very tired, anyhow he had left his rifle up against a palm tree ten or fifteen yards away. He didn't murder the Vietnamese lady.

Still, the customers at the Coke stand had precious little use for the counterwomen there. It was "Mama-san, give me Coke" and "Mamasan, you VC?" and "*Di di!*" to the little children who simply crawled in their ears as they crowded around them for C-ration chewing gum or candy—"Go!" the only word of Vietnamese that all American soldiers knew by heart, just as the Coke-stand crowd and prostitutes were the only citizens of Vietnam that any soldier knew on sight. Among the American soldiers it was an article of faith that the longer the Vietnamese war would last the happier the Vietnamese people would be— war to them meant money, even the salmon-size cans of C-rations that the soldiers gave to those screaming chil-dren went to their mamasans the same afternoon to sell on the Vietnamese black mar-ket ("Or give to the VC," Demirgian used to say). Our allies, our friends in arms— the boys in Demirgian's com-pany didn't think of the Vietnamese people as that, enemies, in fact, is closer to what soldiers thought of the native people, in fact their word for things sold at those rickety tables was "VC beer" or "VC orange pop" or "VC Coke." And these were the boys whose predispositions the mamasan's answer of that strange afternoon had fallen upon: "Hey mamasan, VC come tonight?" "Yes."

No one at the Coke stand had believed her. Someone had wanted to notify the Captain—no! a sergeant had argued, the Captain he hears about this, he gets nervous in the service, he calls a hundred percent alert and who of us here's going to get to sleep? So forget it! And this explains why at eleven-thirty most of those in the dark company camp or Demirgian's little typical ambush party were sound asleep in their camouflage-colored blankets and unaware that a full battalion of communists lay in the blackness in range of Demirgian's peaceful rifle. Any minute now, they would attack.

WHAT DID YOU DO IN THE WAR, DADDY-O? *Five seconds. Four seconds. Three seconds. Two seconds. One—*

A soldier in a lightly starched tan uniform is keeping a close eye on a wall clock that is some-where about as large as the harvest moon. For a minute now, he hasn't taken a puff on the cigarette that he grips in his motionless fingers, he hasn't spoken a word since he whispered, "Out—out," to a boy so innocent of the circumstances that he had just walked into the quiet electronic-looking room.

At zero the soldier's impatient finger taps on a button of green—go! A circle of grey steel rotates, acetate issues, it interrupts the quanta discriminately, electrons are correspondingly let loose, a shower of electromagnetism falls on Vietnam as thoroughly as the monsoon rain—not a blade of grass escapes it. On earth, at a thousand electrical receptors all is reconstituted instantly into the luminous images of Batman and Robin. Holy von Clausewitz, it's the Armed Forces Television Network! Zow!

Nobody had a television set at Demirgian's dark ambush area, and Demirgian was bored—bored. To be sure, the past ten or a dozen minutes had given Demirgian some sounds that he could attend to—*o-o-o-o-o*, artillery in the black atmosphere, *crump*, when it hits the ground, *ta-ta-ta-ta*, machine guns, the *bang* and *bang* of distant rifles, Demirgian also could look at things—the yellow sky, yellow because of the falling flares, the yellow sky shrinking in and around like a tired tent, a tracer bullet's long arc of red, another. Demirgian sat through this *son et lumière* with no great intellectual curiosity, things in the night were no great surprise to Demirgian, he had become used to them in Vietnam, war is war. He didn't guess that his company camp was under attack by two or three running hundreds of real actual communists, one kilometer away.

This startling news, the sergeant who prayed in Spanish had just heard in soft crackling sentences on the warm rubbery "telephone" receiver of an Army field radio. To this smart soldier, his elbows in the stony soil, the receiver tight to his attentive ear—to this experienced leader of the ambush party the news translated itself into an order of the highest urgency—*nobody should fire!* "Look," he said in a whisper to his radio operator, a PFC, a shadowy mass at his side—"look, we all been cut off. Charlie got the trails going to the company block now. Is no way that we can penetrate back to the company. We—"

"How about the company?" the radio operator asked him. He knew if the company fell the squad wouldn't have a prayer.

"They are still fighting like good ones. We going to have to stay sweat 'im out. So it will be no fire," the sergeant said—"*it will be no fire unless they attack us.*" One little rifle sound, one little ray of red-orange light, one little grenade explosion and it was clear to this squad leader that the many companies of Charlies in the dark middle distance, advancing, retreating, giving themselves their pep talks, go give 'em hell, comrade, the Charlies would know of their whereabouts at once, not a boy on this lonely detachment would be left alive. A matter of their life and death, and to impress everyone on this perilous ambush party with the strategy of *don't shoot*, the sergeant said to the radio operator that he would crawl on the dark ground ten, twenty, thirty meters to the invisible figures on their left, the radio operator was to crawl to the right—to Demirgian.

Thus at about midnight, the radio operator, a good-looking guy, a Negro with light skin, thick hair, was doing what was without precedent in his many quiet nights on ambush parties: he was moving. His chest in the cold earth, his knees and elbows going like the claws of crabs, the pebbles going by beneath his stomach, the *o-o-o-o-o*'s going over, the *crump*'s, as the radio operator crawled by the strange shapes of night he was asking himself, *what am I doing this for?*

He was on a madman's errand, that was a fact. To tell Demirgian that he must abandon his heart's desire, arrest his every instinct, keep his itchy finger from the trigger of his rifle or the cotter pin of his little grenade no matter how many black presences passed him in the night—this was an act of saintly restraint that a whole heavenly choir of angels couldn't easily urge on that hellcat, easier that a rattlesnake be told to ignore a rat! Moreover, the order of *don't shoot at the enemy* couldn't even be offered for Demirgian's consideration until the Negro radio operator had come within earshot—and rifle shot, it couldn't be delivered to Demirgian until the quietly crawling soldier had made himself a target to Demirgian's wide-awake eyes. *What's with Demirgian?* often the radio operator had asked himself that, any other infantryman could fire a gun at communist areas, pick up the brass, give me a piece of your fruitcake, thanks—a job is a job, didn't have to get *ferocious* about it! But Demirgian! What was Demirgian after, get a holiday at the China Sea? Get a medal for killing a communist? Get a souvenir—a Russian watch or some raggedy wet piastres to buy himself orange pop at the Coke stand with? Demirgian was a real spitfire, the radio operator knew—was it something psychological, perhaps? Had the Irish kids who called him a camel chaser now become sublimated into Asian revolutionaries? Or did Demirgian suffer inferiority feelings, a year in Vietnam in the wilds and woollies and he still hadn't proved himself, he didn't have a scalp to show although other boys did? Or simply, did Demirgian want to get written about in *Newsweek*, that's all? *His forearms were being slashed by thorns, his fatigues were....* Many times the radio operator had asked himself the question: what is Demirgian bugged by, never, though, had he guessed at Demirgian's real secret, he hadn't come close. He had satisfied himself by thinking, *well—Demirgian's an Armenian, that is the answer.* He had seen a show on television about the Gurkhas once, the Gurkhas all swinging a sword and taking a slice at a living breathing ox, a splash, a bucket of blood, an ox head lay on the ground like a rotten melon—a fierce race of people, obviously enough, and Demirgian had Armenian ancestors, Demirgian's family traced itself to the Gurkha part of the world. *That is the answer*, the radio operator had told himself—mistakenly.

He had crawled over the stones to five or ten yards from Demirgian's position—close enough, and he whispered a word in the darkness that he knew would identify him to Demirgian as a bona fide friend from the Army, no communist. The radio operator whispered, "Demirgian!"

He heard Demirgian answer, "Yeah?"

The radio operator whispered to him, "Don't fire no matter what," and turning a hundred and eighty degrees he quickly crawled back to the dark patch of earth he had started at, where he opened a cold can of C rations. His favorite kind of C-rats was turkey loaf—it was everybody's, it disappeared from the boxes quickly and tonight he was making do with boneless chicken, at least it wasn't the Spam ham and lima beans: *ugh!* a little wet pillar of salt, a cattle lick. With his G.I. opener in between his thumb and index finger he went to work experiencedly on that chicken can, the opener going as silently and as surely as a knitting needle, the tracer bullets making a *slap—slap*—as they passed above him. The skies were as yellow as Mars's, in the distances yellow smoke rose, at every horizon the heavens and earth seemed to have jarred apart, the yellow bowl of heaven rocked on the dark brown earth and—*boom! boom!* the universe, it seemed, had gone against the rocks, it was breaking up.

The radio operator heard a man whisper, "*What are you doing?*"

He answered truthfully, "Sergeant, when I'm hungry I eat." He buried his empty chicken can in cold earth, and with his little knitting-needle tool he quietly split the circumferences of a pound cake and a fruit cocktail, thinking, *all I need now is vanilla ice cream—mm,* exactly as mother used to make it! The noises continued, *o-o-o-o-o! crump!* For his midnight crawl the radio operator was to get other desserts than C-rats, the Army commendation medal with a "V" for valor ("His actions are in keeping with the finest traditions of the military service . . .").

Demirgian. As for Demirgian, the infantryman *terrible* had given a good minute's thought to the portent of those whispered words, "Don't fire no matter what." He had asked himself, *what is there to fire at? Why are they suddenly telling me this?* Nothing in the night's sound and fury seemed to this veteran of three-hundred-and-something similar ones to be anything other than the usual mutual harassments of Vietnam's hours of darkness, Vietnam was a shooting gallery after dark, it wasn't a place for women or children but it wasn't anything new to Demirgian's ears and eyes. Old soldier Demirgian let himself forget it. Twelve o'clock his long boring hours of being on guard duty had ended, and rolling over in the damp earth he whispered to a sleeping sergeant, "Hey. Wake up," for staying awake was that man's responsibility now. Then as the skies issued sounds like a house of a thousand shutters in a September storm, Demirgian rolled over on his shoulder blades and closing his tired eyes he fell asleep.

MEANWHILE, BACK AT THE CAMP. . . . *Back at Demirgian's triangular camp the Captain is shouting things to his company with his shotgun in one hand and flip-flops on his feet—Vietnamese rubber shower shoes, he hadn't time to dress, a lieutenant is thinking worriedly what's with the mortars? Why don't the company mortars fire? The first sergeant is lying wounded, the enemy is fifty—forty—thirty yards away and coming closer. Running to where the mortars are, crying why aren't they being fired, told we are waiting for data, sir, we need to be given our azimuth data, our elevation data, our increment data, our—hearing this, the lieutenant cries one of the inspired cries of the twentieth century, let history record that the lieutenant cried, "The hell with data!" And seizing the mortar tube in his sweating hands he says to start dropping the mortar rounds in—and crump! crump! he levels them on the charging communists. From out of the west come the hoofbeats of water buffalo, the lone lieutenant cries again, the lieutenant says, "The buffalo are coming! And they—" the lieutenant means the enemy soldiers, "they are right behind them," the mortars turn to the water buffalo, the buffalo are turning back! The communists are being buffalo-bumped! But now there is one more mortar round left in that beleaguered camp—no more. The mortarmen kiss it, caress it, slip it into their mortar tube, it exits, the mortar round falls in the midst of America's enemy with a bump, it doesn't go crump! All is quiet on the mortar front! Boo to American industry!*

The communists still keep coming—damn. The camp is frightfully shy of rifle soldiers, some are in Army hospitals, irregular holes in their arms or legs, malaria, gonorrhea, some are on pacification work and Demirgian is fast asleep, the artillery officer is a playboy in Tokyo on a rest and recreation leave, a terror-stricken lieutenant is still in his little cotton tent, his shoes shined, his belt buckle bright with metal polish. Outside of the company camp the barbed wire is absent—orders, we've got to show the Vietnamese we're not a bunch of scaredies, damn! On one whole side of the triangle not a rifle is functioning, double damn—the bullets are stuck inside of them and of the machine guns, too! Boo to Connecticut! Nuts to the Nutmeg State! The communists are coming over the earthen walls now! Are we downhearted? YES! As soon as they've taken the company camp the little abandoned ambush party is next!

And meanwhile Demirgian sleeps through it all (When the bough breaks, the cradle will fall).

The sergeant whose turn at guard duty was from midnight to two o'clock in the morning had been lying flat on his back almost sleeping when Demirgian's tiny whisper of "Hey. Wake up" advanced him to the state of being almost awake. Nor did the Negro sergeant roll to the prone position, to his stomach. The silhouette of a hip, a shoulder going over, an arm—anything, the sergeant had told himself, would be just enough to notify whoever was making all those shooting sounds in the night, the *o-o-o-o-o*'s and the *crump*'s, the *ta-ta-ta-ta*'s like a cold motor, the rifle shots, of his presence on this lonely square yard of earth, and he had stayed flat on his back during his whole tour of guard duty. Inconspicuousness—the secret of one's survival.

He could look at the stars. Years ago, he had become aware that as stars go across the Carolina night they aren't like the wild ducks, the stars aren't shoving themselves one ahead of the other or slipping behind, the star patterns that he thought he saw in the Carolina sky didn't change for hours—for years, and when he had come to Vietnam he was pleased to see that these special relationships one to the other held for that alien land, as well. He looked at these familiar faces now in his motionless hours of standing guard—of his lying on guard, the rocking chair, the cup and the saucer, these are what the sergeant had called his precious constellations. Low in that friendly sky was the "V" shape of Taurus the bull, to the sergeant this was a part of a spaceship, the nose cone. Orion at this season lay on its side horizontally, its belt became a bandleader's hat to the sergeant's nostalgic eyes, its sword was a celluloid visor—the sergeant remembered the golden braid in its broad figure eights, the sergeant could even see it! The little silver whistle, the hand on that shiny scepter, a downbeat flat as a fist on a wooden table, *be kind to your web-footed friends!* The sergeant had been a bandleader once—at a high school for Negroes he had played on the drums, the clarinet, the bass and baritone tubas, he hadn't cared to play on the trombone, it didn't ever get to solo, still he liked the guitar the best, really and truly. Tonight while he lay on his back on sentry duty he sang to himself sentimentally, *He took a hundred pounds of clay and He said, Hey listen! I'm goin' to fix this world today because I know what's missin'!* A pretty song—it reminded him of his wife in Scotland Neck, N.C.

Being in Vietnam made the sergeant want to sing, a melody held the minutes together in a way that simply twiddling his fingers didn't, time was as thin as skimmed milk if the sergeant didn't fill it with remembered songs. Demirgian he didn't understand at *all*, Demirgian for whom every second patch of elephant grass was enough to make the senses quicken, the eyes become as lively as a chirping bird's, the life forces start to flow, Demirgian who looked for a destructible enemy in every second cranny of every paddy even as the sergeant tried to keep acedia away by singing to himself, *can't get no . . . satisfaction.* "Demirgian. Now take it easy," often the sergeant had to preach patience to Demirgian when the disappointed soldier shot at the pigeons and people's chickens after yet another day of not shooting communists. Demirgian's mysterious vendetta wasn't—well, it wasn't a vendetta even, the sergeant knew. Not a boy in Demirgian's whole platoon had been killed or wounded by *communists* since the first days of Demirgian's tour of duty. Accidents do happen and Demirgian had many friends who weren't alive any longer, still he couldn't fault the communists for something as American in its origins as "I didn't know it was loaded" ways of behavior, this the sergeant appreciated. One of Demir-

gian's late lamented friends had been scratching his head using a 45 when he had idiotically pulled the trigger, one soldier who didn't have a "church key" to open a can of orange soda at the Coke stand had tried unintelligently with a 50-caliber bullet instead, another had tried to use gasoline to burn up the stuff underneath the latrines and *poof!* he had been burned to death like a Buddhist monk, it wasn't the fault of the Bolsheviks any of those. Seven whole boys (a lieutenant, even) had shot themselves in this or that organ in the course of one particularly ridiculous week, the fault was in themselves and Demirgian wasn't out to get revenge, obviously enough —his ferocity wasn't due to this. *Must be, Demirgian had a brother killed*, the sergeant had told himself: untrue. Demirgian the fire-eating soldier, a mystery to that sergeant lying beside him.

"*I love you*," the sergeant was thinking now.

"*No, no!*"

"*Yes, I love you. You are more to me than anything in the whole world,*" the line was Lord Darlington's in *Lady Windermere's Fan*, by Oscar Wilde. Who would have guessed as that sergeant lay in his dirty combat clothes on sentry duty, as the *o-o-o-o-o*'s and the *crump*'s reverberated, and as time itself seemed to condense from the night air to settle all around him as damp as a heavy dew—that the Negro sergeant had once played the Darlington part in his segregated high school's big auditorium, an ascot around his neck, in its center a pearl stickpin, the hints of his acting teacher firm in his senses: say *rawther* instead of *rather*, cup in the right hand and saucer in the left. The line of Wilde's that he remembered most was "Excuse me, you fellows. I have to write a few letters," the sergeant had given it many earnest reprises, the teacher had been in the wings with a copy, whenever the sergeant's half-open mouth had failed to entice one of Darlington's speeches to fill it with apropos sounds he had simply said, "Excuse me, you fellows. . . ."

Uh-oh. A squad of little communists was quietly coming along the trail—the sergeant didn't see it since he hadn't eyes on top of his head, and Demirgian the wistful communist-killer was fast asleep.

A TRAGIC HAPPENING. *Bang! Bang! At the company camp the enemy has broken through, a corner of that black triangle is communist-held—a bunker, inside it a couple of Coke bottles, bottle caps, the colorful crumbs of fruitcake, pound cake in a C-ration can, a can that is empty, lids, a couple of comic books, ten or a dozen Playmates, mosquito lotion, the empty brass of Connecticut's bullets—that, and some communist soldiers too. American boys are throwing the last of the hand grenades with a Batman abandon, one soldier not even pausing to pull out the cotter pin. But there come the reinforcements—hurrah! The resupply of ammunition, the high-explosive rounds, the phosphorus, the bullets made in Connecticut by sweet old ladies in steel shoes—the ammo is coming along the trail in a steel tank and bang! it suddenly explodes, the tank, the mighty ammunition too. The communists on their ambush party are luckier on this awful night than Demirgian on his.*

From out of the smoking top of the tank wreck a tank soldier crawls. An officer, his clothes are in terrible shreds, one of his legs is missing, he hasn't one of his arms, instead of his genital organs there is a bleeding hole, the phosphorus has gone through his eyeballs, they are like glowing charcoals—they are like orange "exit" bulbs. From now until dawn he will crawl on the scorching steel, then he will fly to Washington for medical treatment.

Visions of sugarplums danced in the head of Demirgian, the sleeping soldier. Months ago he had taken a week's leave in Bangkok and there wasn't a night that he still didn't think or dream of his respite from war in that fabulous city—Bangkok, a beautiful story. Three hours out of Saigon's ridiculous airport, ten thousand planes, the planes in the treetops almost, the planes sitting one on the other like the grey arrays at automobile graveyards, the noise, the inconsiderateness, the Vietnamese people—three hours after this and Demirgian had been dining in quiet luxury in the land of the white elephants, the setting immaculate, a candle, a low teak table reposing like a tamed lion on a purple rug, a picture window, a curtain made of tissue-paper flowers as delicate as moths, and seen through it a garden, the wind was in the palm trees, a star. Everything in that restaurant in Bangkok had shone, and music as soft as water running over a bed of pebbles had quietly come to Demirgian from—where? it had seemed to Demirgian that molecule on molecule of air just tapped onto one another like little tinkling cat bells, Bangkok! It had been a real revelation, he had never guessed that the Orient offered things to the senses other than the sight of running noses, the smell of the sewage in streets. In this first delightful hour in Bangkok, girls in purple silk hostess gowns had come to Demirgian smiling adoringly, crawling to him on their reverential knees with a pitcher of water or wine, apologizing to Demirgian for entering upon his serenity uninvited, *forgive me for saying so except* . . . the flowers, the petals of these flowers are meant to delight the palate as well as the wondering eyes, the petals are a finely carved chestnut. Crawling to Demirgian, one of these orchid girls had given him a silver silk bag of Bangkok's perfume, the girl herself whispering thank you—thank you! Never before in Asia had Demirgian heard the words thank you, even the loud little children that he had left chewing gum in the grabby little hands of had never said *cam on* in Vietnamese, they had simply shoved out their other hand. Bangkok had been enchanting, it didn't smell of deteriorating fish, it had traffic lights, lines in the center of its wide streets, it seemed that the people of Bangkok *cared*, the barbers—even the barbers had worn a white doctor's robe and had shaved off the fluff on Demirgian's eyelids and inside of his ear canals, sending a small squirt of water in afterward, what a wonderful country! Demirgian said to some friends of his, "If they had a war here, I'd reenlist if I could go to Thailand, wouldn't you?"

His friends had said yes. Demirgian had taken this leave (the Army called it a rest and recreation leave, and every boy in Vietnam whether he kills an enemy soldier or doesn't has a week of it in his year's tour of duty)—Demirgian had come to Bangkok with two good friends, the first was Demirgian's most immediate sergeant, a Botticelli angel boy, a sergeant with a sweet almost watery smile, eyes of calamine blue, the other was Demirgian's friendly lieutenant, the leader of his platoon. A real source of humor this—if Demirgian asked him, "Do you have a match," the lieutenant would say something like, "I don't light a cigarette for a private, *private*," the lieutenant lighting it anyhow, the three of them laughing, friends in Bermudas and sports shirts. After the wine, the chestnut carved like a frangipani flower, the Thai girls with fingers like cattails doing a delicate dance, the music of gentle stringed instruments—after the candlelit dinner the three boys had gone to a nightclub, the sergeant had fallen in love: Keri, the young girl's name. The rest of that wonderful week the three had become a foursome as Keri showed them the bright shining temples of her beloved city, Keri, the friendly lieutenant, Keri's friend the sweet-smiling sergeant, and Demirgian, Demirgian wittily imitating her at every tenth item of interest, "Now this temple is built of marble. It was started in the year a hundred and it took a thousand years to finish. There is a legend . . . ," the three of them laughing and Keri laughing too, Keri biting her lower lip so her laughter wouldn't go beyond the bounds of her people's sense of etiquette.

On the seventh day they had visited the zoo, the monkeys swinging there like indian clubs, a black arm, a leg, a tail of each spider monkey twisted around the steel trapezes, the graceful, surprisingly, giraffes, the elephants like an Egyptian relief, a row of them standing all looking left, a rope on their enormous legs to orient them in that direction, the elephants rocking side to side as slowly as heavy punkahs on hot afternoons, the trunks of these elephants swinging, the ears slowly moving like old shredded regimental flags—it seemed that these monumental elephants had been standing there through all of Asia's history, swaying side to side. Above the center elephant was a high golden roof—a temple roof, its millions of little sequins the color of old mustard shone in the Bangkok sun, and Keri had said almost reverentially, "This is the King's elephant."

Demirgian had asked her cheerfully, "Which is the Queen's elephant?" and Keri had suddenly turned away looking hurt. "Aw," Demirgian said in embarrassment. "Doesn't the Queen have an elephant?" and Keri got rigidly silent.

"You shouldn't make fun of their king and queen," the soft-spoken sergeant told him.

"I'm not making fun," Demirgian answered honestly. "Which is the King's giraffe?" But every lighthearted thing that Demirgian thought of saying to Keri so she would smile again, Keri just got angrier at, her lips got tighter together, the sergeant got quite apprehensive. "I wish I were a king so I could have an elephant," Demirgian tried—it didn't work, to a Thai there is little one should say of their benevolent king and queen except perhaps hosanna. "Hey," Demirgian said in some despair. "Let's do the dodger cars," and he ran from those difficult elephants to a nearby kind of Playland park—he was already in a miniature blue car, he was driving it every which way, he was—*crash*—he was crashing it into the native people by the time the surprised others had come walking up. "Everyone let's do *this*," Demirgian drove up shouting to them.

The lieutenant wasn't too terribly sure. "I don't think the Thais are as barbaric as we are, Demirgian," the lieutenant said, the Thais in the other dodger cars had been driving them, in fact, as gingerly as A&P shopping carts, the Thais had been smiling to one another, tipping their hats, in effect, and acting as though they had only learner's permits till Demirgian had charged at them, Demirgian who—*zzzzz*—was suddenly off again in a cloud of concrete dust, the terror of the Thai five hundred, the wheels rising, the tires crying, the side of his steel sports car was *crash! crash!* was crashing on everyone else's, the metal getting dented, the shower of sparks, the Thais in their battered chariots all laughing happily and Keri, at last, laughing, too, Keri having to sit on a bench because of her laughing so hard, the sergeant laughing, the lieutenant laughing and crying, "Go gettem, cat! Go gettem," Demirgian laughing triumphantly, the Grand Prix of Bangkok his.

In the evening they ate at the river, the sunset lay on the temple tops and slivers of orange sunset fell in the silver river and drifted by like goldfish. Keri said to the real catfish, "Here, baby. Here," giving the fish little bits of bread to nibble on. That night Keri slept at the sergeant's hotel, washing him, bringing his towel to him, crying in the morning when he said good-bye, when he promised her, "I will be back," sincerely. At the Saigon airport a little later, the Vietnamese people pushing, the porters not getting the change right, the dirt, the speaker making its static and saying, "*Attention all military personnel . . . ,*" the holiday plane from Bangkok had scarcely landed when the three soldiers met a Guamanian friend from their own platoon, the lieutenant naturally asking him, "What's new?" Well, in Vietnam it had been another of those stupid weeks, the Guamanian said— Demirgian's best friend, the medal-less communist-killer, had been lying on ambush when he was taken for Charlie and accidently shot in the head by a squad sergeant and, well, the platoon sergeant had been killed one morning at reveille by American artillery, idiotically one of our howitzers had been aimed at his sleeping tent, so it's hi-dee-hee in the field artillery and, of course, the first sergeant, he had been telling guys to police up this, police up that, exactly as some clumsy son-of-a-dumbbell stepped on a detonator and *bang!* as *police up* died on the first sergeant's lips the first sergeant himself had died and also, a company next to theirs, unintentionally it had been bombed by American airplanes, twenty or thirty soldiers had gone to the hospital for napalm burns, another

twenty or thirty boys had died and—anyhow, it had been a bad week, the Guamanian had stated, you couldn't really deny it. Demirgian went to buy a hot dog saying to Keri's sergeant, "Vietnam! The cesspool of the universe!"

"The cesspool of the universe," the sergeant repeated—he was shaking uncontrollably now, he had started doing this as the Guamanian gave his report. He was still acting strange the next afternoon ("He looked like he was under water," a boy remembered) —the next afternoon when he got to his quarters: the company camp, a dark canvas tent, a long row of cots, a couple of Vietnamese laundry boys on one of them, sitting, looking at dirty photographs of ways of making love, and saying things in English like "Fucky-fucky," laughing, showing their wide red mouths. Putting one of Connecticut's bright bullets in his rifle chamber, *click! clack!* The sergeant said, "I'm going to do some hunting."

"I hope you'll do your hunting out yonder," the soldier who owned the photographs said to him uneasily.

"I can do my hunting right here," the sergeant replied. Once he had killed the Vietnamese laundry boys he was taken away in handcuffs and court-martialed. Now the sergeant is serving a life sentence at Leavenworth, the Negro who looked at constellations and sang *can't get no . . . satisfaction* taking his place as Demirgian's sergeant.

A QUESTION FROM THE COURT. "*Were these dirty pictures of American women?*"

"*They were just some old dirty pictures you buy around.*" The witness is the soldier who owned them.

"*Were there oriental women in them? Or were they caucasian—white—women?*"

"*Oriental.*"

"*Pictures of oriental women?*"

"*Yes sir.*"

"*Were there dirty pictures of oriental men or caucasian men?*"

"*Oriental men. They had masks on, some of them.*"

"*The dirty pictures consisted of both oriental men and oriental women?*"

"*Yes sir.*"

"*There were no white women in those pictures?*"

"*No sir.*"

A CROSS-EXAMINATION BY THE DEFENSE: "*You say that these pictures were of oriental women—right?*"

"*Yes sir.*"

"*Now here you say that the men had on masks?*"

"*Yes sir.*"

"*How do you know whether they were oriental or caucasian?*"

"*They all looked like the same man, sir.*"

"*But if a man had on a mask, how would you know?*"

"*Well, he didn't look American, sir.*"

"*What didn't look American?*"

"*The man. There was something about him that was oriental.*"

"*I repeat my question. What didn't look American?*"

"The whole bunch! The pictures! They weren't American."

A PART OF THE DEFENSE'S SUMMATION. *"He goes to his tent to get ready to go to the field—to pick up his equipment. After entering he sees the two Vietnamese for whom he has no love or trust, sitting on the bunks, talking, laughing, and enjoying themselves. He explains to himself, why should he fight in their country on their behalf and risk his life for these people while they perform menial tasks at the base camp in the relative safety of the base camp. As he gathers his equipment perhaps he thinks about this. Maybe he becomes angry...."*

A PART OF THE PROSECUTION'S SUMMATION. *"... Well, okay, he disliked the Vietnamese, fine. That's up to an individual. If he wants to hate the Vietnamese, fine! But putting his hatred in action by killing is not quite correct."*

"Huh?" Demirgian said.

The other boys in the ambush party had waked up Demirgian an hour before dawn and related to him what great alarms and excursions there had been while God had His guardian angels over him—the company camp had been attacked, a corner taken, a tank carrying ammo had been blown to kingdom come, a second tank had gotten into the triangle, *tarantara,* the tide of war turning, communists withdrawing, company enduring, hurrah! Not a boy in Demirgian's sturdy army had been killed by those two or three or four hundred communists (one had been killed by accident by a friend of his, nothing more)—a very great victory for America. By the wet yellow light of the flares, Demirgian could now glimpse some of the forty or fifty communist dead, the easy victims of American artillery and of six-barreled machine guns on American planes, fat fire-breathing planes that the soldiers had given the sobriquet of Puff the magic dragon (... *lived by the sea,* the Negro sergeant had sung to himself at one o'clock in the morning, the magic dragon's rain of red tracer bullets lighting the night with a pillar of fire—*lived by the sea, and frolicked in the autumn mist in a land of Honah Lee*).

Good soldiers all, nobody in the ambush party had shot at that communist squad when it innocently went by, the silver starlight above it, behind it, the final score had been nothing to nothing, the ambush party the communists. Demirgian got to his heavy feet, the bullet still in Demirgian's dew-dappled rifle like a disappointed suitor, the hand grenades still on Demirgian's belt, mud in the crack of their cotter pins, dew. *Damn, but I would have fired at them,* Demirgian said to himself angrily while he walked back to camp, while he passed the dead communist soldiers who were lying simply everywhere, kicking them—*damn, I'd have thrown a grenade, at LEAST!* At times in the humdrum months of his tour, Demirgian had walked by the Coke stand waiting until—waiting until—the moment that he felt a little hand at his wallet pocket he had whirled around and given the thievish child the kicking that he well deserved, now he was kicking the communist soldiers every bit

as hard and shouting at their unlistening ears, "Wake up, you sorry bastard—you stupid bastard—you goddamn bastard! Wake up!"

"Hey, Demirgian," somebody said to him, laughing. "They're already dead."

"Wake up, you silly bastard," Demirgian said to a dead communist, kicking.

"Demirgian," the Negro radio operator said to him softly. "Don't do that."

"What do you mean don't do that?" Demirgian asked.

"Don't do that," the Negro radio operator said. He didn't like to see brutality, the radio operator—once he had been in a street gang, he was twelve years old, at a gas station he had gotten himself in a fight with the white-colored kids. It had been simply sticks till a two-tone automobile had driven by, a Negro, he was a boy of twenty, perhaps, had gotten out of that great automobile, he had squatted on the chest of one white boy, he had raised up a concrete block and—*down,* the boy's white face had broken apart like a bag of blood, the fight had stopped immediately. Running, everyone running, the Negro radio operator running, a fruit cart had toppled over, the grapes had rolled after him like little bloodshot eyeballs, running, falling, the dirty red blood on his elbows, after the Negro child reached home he had prayed all night, "Oh, Lord! Don't let him die!" Since then the Negro radio operator had disliked to see brutality—yet, he thought, how could there be brutality if the communists felt no pain, if the sufferers were already dead, if the bodies lay every random way as though they had fallen from airplanes, Demirgian kicking, calling them dirty bastards, mud of his boots spattering on the yellow faces, the skin of the faces shivering like raindrops on mud—uncomfortably, the radio operator walking away as Demirgian still kicked at them and called to them, "Wake up!" But none of the communist soldiers woke up.

One of the communist soldiers woke up! He looked at Demirgian slowly through one of his eyes, an eye like a twist of lemon rind, an oily eye! He moved one of his bloody arms! A living breathing communist, a boy of about eighteen, a Vietnamese in black, Demirgian brought down his foot on his face and *crunch,* Demirgian felt his little nose go like a macaroon, he said to the communist, "Bastard—well, was it worth it," kicking him in his eyeballs. "Stupid bastard—what did it get you," kicking him on his Adam's apple. "Goddamn bastard...."

DEMIRGIAN'S SECRET. *Demirgian hates the Vietnamese people—well, so does every soldier, but Demirgian hates and hates! The goddamn bastards! Goddamn people! Come to help their miserable country and what? Anyone get a word of thanks? Dead or alive—crippled, I could be blind, a basket case and they wouldn't care, not if they'd had my damn piastres first! Money is all they'd care, the crooked bastards! Give me—give me—that's the extent of it, give 'em a stick of soap, though, do you suppose they'd use it, the filthy people? No—they'd sell it, the filthy bastards! Nya nya nasal language, they sound like* they've got their tongue up their nose, the ugly bastards! Faces like wet brown prunes, teeth the color of coffee grounds, mouths like a hole in the kitchen sink —the breath of a garbage bag, I bet, I expect to see ants start crawling out! They're ignorant people— dumb! A lady I saw took a bottle of metal polish what do you think for? It says on the label "fatal" and I don't really recommend it for teeth—but I should give a good goddamn! Let her kill herself, I should care! They're worthless people!

A really and truly detestable race of people. Demirgian's year of duty among the Vietnamese had taught him to loathe them, the earth and Demirgian would be better rid of them, Vietnamese go to your damnable ancestors, die! Demirgian wants to kill communists because they're the only native people the Army's regulations allow him to kill.

". . . Goddamn bastard, stupid bastard, dumb bastard, thought you were better than us Americans, didn't you? Ignorant bastard," Demirgian said and he kicked at that black bag of bones until it had given a consummation to Demirgian's tour of duty and a success to Demirgian's quest by quietly becoming dead. Congratulations, Demirgian's foot! For it hadn't been by Connecticut's fancily manufactured bullets that he had achieved his heart's desire, Demirgian had become a communist-killer by force of foot alone —Agnes' dustpan hadn't been necessary, David's leather mallet neither, America could have saved itself money, each of those bullets was costing it ten cents.

"Sorry about that," Demirgian said to the lifeless body, and he continued on toward camp by the dawn's early light, a Russian watch in his pants pocket—a souvenir.

Like a great headache going, a pressure on the ears relieved, the black of night receded into the skies and a pink sunrise came to that company camp, the tents became green, not grey, the brass of Connecticut's bullets lay on the earth like little bright buttercups. A couple of tired soldiers went to police the bodies up, another was at the washbasin brushing his teeth, spitting the pink water into the Vietnamese mud, a toe slowly turning it under and stirring the liquidy pink and brown, washing, drying himself, his olive-colored towel wet with the morning dew, another was having coffee from a grey aluminum cup, the gritty metallic taste of aluminum oxide on his tongue, nails in a carpenter's mouth. It was morning and each soldier said to himself so-and-so-many days, each was a day nearer to getting out of that abominated country. Six o'clock at the Coke stand it was business as usual, the Vietnamese women with their betel-black teeth, the raggedy tan piastre notes, the sticky yellow dribbles of paint on the soda bottles so soldiers wouldn't want to take the empties away, the price of four times the wholesale price, the heat, the children on the tired soldiers saying give me—give me—and saying dirty words if they didn't get given, a Vietnamese shouting at the tired soldiers, "Ong da ban chet . . . ," the mortar rounds had wounded one of his water buffalo, he wanted compensation. "Well," Demirgian said to another soldier, "I finally killed me a gook," and Demirgian smiled satisfiedly, Demirgian's soul was at peace, Demirgian, a little later, had started back to the country in whose interests he had been posted to Asia, to his green gabled home in Newton, to the sign in the living room welcome home in red, white, and blue! Safe and sound, Demirgian came marching home again! Let's give him a hearty welcome then! Hurrah! Hurrah!

ROLL CALL

PFC Barry *Abrams*, Amarillo, Tex, "Out—out." S/Sgt Doroteo Q *Aguigui*, Agat, Guam, who is the Guamanian. S/Sgt. Lonnie *Brown* Jr, Killeen, Tex, "What are you doing?" Capt Terry W *Brown*, New Orleans, La, "I repeat my question. What didn't look American?" Sp/4 Donald A *Carlisle*, Concord, Cal, Demirgian told him, "I finally killed me a gook." Sgt Patrick *Condron*, Lakewood, NJ, "I'm going to do some hunting." Sp/4 Varoujan *Demirgian*, Newton, Mass, "Wake up!" Sgt James A *Dickens*, Scotland Neck, NC, "Can't get no . . . satisfaction." F/Sgt Oliver D *Dumas*, Atlanta, Ga, "Police up." Col Paul J *Durbin*, Washington, DC, "Were these dirty pictures of American women?" PFC George W *Garrison* Jr, Owensboro, Ky, who quietly snored. S/Sgt Donald L *Heaston*, Columbus, Ga, the howitzers had been aimed at his sleeping tent. Sp/4 Billy L *Johns*, St Cloud, Fla, whose name was spelled wrong in *Newsweek*. PFC Billie A *Judah*, Pensacola, Fla, "I hope you do your hunting out yonder." S/Sgt Miguel A *Julia-Vasquez*, Caguas, PR, "Padre nuestro." Sp/4 Claude G *Lumbeck*, Richmond Heights, Mo, "I have a headache." Capt Edward S *Molnar*, Cleveland, Ohio, "If he wants to hate the Vietnamese, fine." F/Sgt Julius M *Panikowski*, Cheektowaga, NY, who was lying wounded. Sp/4 John G *Patten*, Shadyside, Md, "He looked like he was underwater." Capt Gary L *Race*, Orlando, Fla, who was the captain. Sgt Raymond *Robinson*, Ogden, Utah, "You have a headache?" 1/Lt David E *Sullivan*, Sheffield, Iowa, "I don't light a cigarette for a private, *private*." Sp/4 Gerald F *Sullivan*, Auburndale, Mass, who was Demirgian's best friend. Sp/4 Lenard Q *Stevens*, Bronx, NY, "Don't fire no matter what." 1/Lt Jerald L *Thompson*, San Jose, Cal, "The hell with data!"

TWO TOM WOLFES

"I am inevitable," wrote Thomas Wolfe. "The only thing that can stop me is insanity, disease or death." Death stopped him in September, 1938, but not before he had completed five books and, as his editor described it, "the breast-high stack of manuscript pages" which was to yield four more posthumously.

During his brief life, Esquire in June, 1935, presented his short story, "Arnold Pentland," which, while it belonged naturally within *Of Time and the River*, did not appear in book form until the publication of *The Hills Beyond* in 1943.

Later we published the story that follows and in October, 1957, when Wolfe's final editor, Edward C. Aswell, made it available for publication, Esquire presented the author's early, full-length play, *Welcome To Our City*. The play was curiously prophetic, for Wolfe chose to set it within the tensions of Southern segregation and the resulting chaos. The setting, ironically enough, was the fictitious city of "Altamont."

Tom Wolfe (the younger) is still very much with us. His first article for the magazine, in November, 1963, was called *There Goes (Varoom! Varoom!) That Kandy Kolored Tangerine-Flake Baby*, which is a moving headline no matter how you look at it. With slight variations, it became the title piece in a collection issued later. Wolfe's report on "Junior" Johnson which follows is one of ten major pieces under his by-line that have appeared in these pages. It was Byron Dobell, then Esquire's managing editor, who helped Wolfe perfect his now-famous style which became linked to the "New Journalism," a movement for which Wolfe has been a prominent standard-bearer.

Thomas Wolfe:

THE HOLLOW MEN

How one dweller in mean city streets,
just a grey-faced, grey-hatted cipher, made
the news by jumping out a window

How often have we read the paper in America! How often have we seen it *blocked* against our doors! Little route-boys fold and block it, so to throw it—and so we find it and unfold it, crackling and ink-laden, at our doors. Sometimes we find it tossed there lightly with flat *plop*; sometimes we find it thrown with solid, whizzing *whack* against the clapboards (clapboards here, most often, in America); sometimes servants find just freshly folded sheets laid neatly down in doorways, and take them to the table for their masters. No matter how it got there, we always find it.

How we do love the paper in America! How we do love the paper, all!

Why do we love the paper in America? Why do we love the paper, all?

Mad masters, I will tell ye why.

Because the paper is "the news" here in America, and we love the *smell* of news. We love the smell of news that's "fit to print." We also love the smell of news *not* fit to print. We love, besides, the smell of *facts* that news is made of. Therefore we love the paper because the news is so fit-printable—so unprintable—and so fact-printable.

Is the news, then, like America? No, it's not—

The news is *not* America, nor is America the *news* —the news is *in* America. It is a kind of light at morning, and at evening, and at midnight in America. It is a kind of growth and record and excrescence of our life. It is not good enough—it does not tell our story— yet it is the news!

Take the following, for instance:

An unidentified man fell or jumped yesterday at noon from the twelfth story of the Admiral Francis Drake Hotel in Brooklyn. The man, who was about thirty-five years old, registered at the hotel about a week ago, according to the police, as C. Green. Police are of the opinion that this was an assumed name. Pending identification, the body is being held at the King's County Morgue.

This, then, is news. Is it also the whole story, Admiral Drake? No! Yet we do not supply the whole story—we who have known all the lights and weathers of America.

This story appeared in October, 1940, two years after Wolfe's death. It is a major part of Chapter 29 of You Can't Go Home Again, *the last of his posthumous novels, published that same year.*

Well, then, it's news, and it happened in your own hotel, brave Admiral Drake, so, of course, you'll want to know what happened.

"An unidentified man"—well, then, this man was an American. "About thirty-five years old" with "an assumed name"—well, then, call him C. Green as he called himself ironically in the hotel register. C. Green, the unidentified American, "fell or jumped," then, "yesterday at noon . . . in Brooklyn"—worth six lines of print in today's *Times*—one of seven thousand who died yesterday upon this continent—one of three hundred and fifty who died yesterday in this very city (see dense, close columns of obituaries, page 15: begin with "Aaronson," so through the alphabet to "Zorn"). C. Green came here "a week ago"—

And came from where? From the deep South, or the Mississippi Valley, or the Middle West? From Minneapolis, Bridgeport, Boston, or a little town in Old Catawba? From Scranton, Toledo, St. Louis, or the desert whiteness of Los Angeles? From the pine barrens of the Atlantic coastal plain, or from the Pacific shore?

And so—was *what*, brave Admiral Drake? In what way an American? In what way different from the men *you* knew, old Drake?

When the ships bore home again and Cape St. Vincent blazed in Spaniard's eye—or when old Drake was returning with his men, beating coastwise from strange seas abreast, past the Scilly Isles toward the slant of evening fields, chalk cliffs, the harbor's arms, the town's sweet cluster and the spire—where was Green?

When, in red-oak thickets at the break of day, coon-skinned, the huntsmen of the wilderness lay for bear, heard arrows rattling in the laurel leaves, the bullets' whining *plunk*, and waited with cocked musket by the tree—where was Green?

Or when, with strong faces turning toward the setting sun, hawk-eyed and Indian-visaged men bore gunstocks on the western trails and sternly heard the fierce war-whoops around the Painted Buttes—where, then, was Green?

Was never there with Drake's men in the evening when the sails stood in from the Americas! Was never there beneath the Spaniard's swarthy eye at Vincent's Cape! Was never there in the red-oak thicket in the morning! Was never there to hear the war-cries round the Painted Buttes!

No, no. He was no voyager of unknown seas, no pioneer of western trails. He was life's little man, life's nameless cipher, life's manswarm atom, life's American—and now he lies disjected and exploded on a street in Brooklyn!

He was a dweller in mean streets, was Green, a man-mote in the jungle of the city, a resident of grimy steel and stone, a stunned spectator of enormous salmon-colored towers, hued palely with the morning. He was a waker in bleak streets at morning, an alarm-clock watcher, saying, "Jesus, I'll be late!"—a fellow who took shortcuts through the corner lot, behind the advertising signs; a fellow used to concrete horrors of hot day and blazing noon; a man accustomed to the tormented hodgepodge of our architectures, used to broken pavements, ash cans, shabby store fronts, dull green paint, the elevated structure, grinding traffic, noise, and streets betortured with a thousand bleak and dismal signs. He was accustomed to the gas tanks going out of town, he was an atom of machinery in an endless flow, going, stopping, going to the winking of the lights; he tore down concrete roads on Sundays, past the hot-dog stands and filling stations; he would return at darkness; hunger lured him to the winking splendor of chop-suey signs; and midnight found him in The Coffee Pot, to prowl above a mug of coffee, tear a coffee cake in fragments, and wear away the slow grey ash of time and boredom with other men in grey hats and with skins of tallow-grey, at Joe the Greek's.

C. Green could read (which Drake could not), but not too accurately; could write, too (which the Spaniard couldn't), but not too well. C. Green had trouble over certain words, spelled them out above the coffee mug at midnight, with a furrowed brow, slow-shaping lips, and "Jesus!" when news stunned him—for he read the news. Preferred the news "hot," straight from the shoulder—socko!—biff!—straight off the griddle, with lots of mustard, shapely legs, roadside wrecks and mutilated bodies, gangsters' molls and gunmen's hide-outs, tallow faces of the night that bluntly stare at flashlight lenses—this and talk of "heart-balm," "love-thief," "sex-hijacker"—all of this liked Green.

Yes, Green liked the news —and now, a bit of news himself (six lines of print in *Times*), has been disjected and exploded on a Brooklyn pavement!

Behold him, Admiral Drake! Observe the scene now! Listen to the people! Here's something strange as the Armadas, the gold-laden

cargoes of the bearded Spaniards, the vision of unfound Americas!

What do you see here, Admiral Drake?

Well, first, a building—your own hotel—a great block of masonry, grimy-white, fourteen stories tall, stamped in an unvarying pattern with many windows. Sheeted glass below, the store front piled with medicines and toilet articles, perfumes, cosmetics, health contrivances. Within, a soda fountain, Admiral Drake. The men in white with monkey caps, soda jerkers sullen with perpetual overdriven irritation. Beneath the counter, pools of sloppy water, filth, and unwashed dishes. Across the counter, women with fat, rouged lips consuming ice cream sodas and pimento sandwiches.

Outside upon the concrete sidewalk lies the form of our exploded friend, C. Green. A crowd has gathered round—taxi drivers, passersby, hangers-on about the subway station, people working in the neighborhood, and the police. No one has dared to touch exploded Green as yet—they stand there in a rapt and fascinated circle, looking at him.

Not much to look at either, Admiral Drake; not even those who trod your gory decks would call the sight a pretty one. Our friend has landed on his head— "taken a nose dive," as we say—and smashed his brains out at the iron base of the second lamp post from the corner.

So here Green lies, on the concrete sidewalk all disjected. No head is left, the head is gone now, head's exploded; only brains are left. The brains are pink, and almost bloodless, Admiral Drake. (There's not much blood here—we shall tell you why.) But brains exploded are somewhat like pale sausage meat, fresh-ground. Brains are stuck hard to the lamp post, too; there is a certain driven emphasis about them, as if they had been shot hydraulically out of a force-hose against the post.

The head, as we have said, is gone completely; a few fragments of the skull are scattered round—but of the face, the features, forehead—nothing! They have all been blown *out*, as by some inner explosion. Nothing is left but the back of the skull, which curiously remains, completely hollowed out and vacant, and curved over, like the rounded handle of a walking stick.

The body, five feet eight or nine of it, of middling weight, is lying—we were going to say "face downward"; had we not better say "stomach downward"? —on the sidewalk. And save for a certain indefinable and curiously "disjected" quality, one could scarcely tell that every bone in it is broken. The hands are still spread out, half-folded and half-clenched, with a still-warm and startling eloquence of recent life. (It happened just four minutes ago!)

Well, where's the blood, then, Drake? You're used to blood; you'd like to know. Well, you've heard of casting bread upon the waters, Drake, and having it return—but never yet, I'll vow, of casting blood upon the streets—and having it run away—and then come back to you! But here it comes now, down the street now toward C. Green, the lamp post, and the crowd!— a young Italian youth, his black eyes blank with horror, tongue mumbling thickly, arm held firmly by a policeman, suit and shirt all drenched with blood, and face bespattered with it! A stir of sudden interest in the crowd, sharp nudges, low-toned voices whispering:

"Here he is! Th' guy that 'got it'! . . . He was standin' *deh* beside the post! Sure, *that's* the guy!— talkin' to anotheh guy—he got it all! *That's* the reason you didn't see more blood—*this* guy got it!— Sure! The guy just missed him by six inches!—Sure! I'm tellin' you I *saw* it, ain't I! I looked up an' saw him in the air! He'd a hit this guy, but when he saw that he was goin' to hit the lamp post, he put out his hands an' tried to keep away! *That's* the reason that he didn't hit this guy! . . . But this guy heard him when he hit, an' turned around—and zowie!—he got all of it right in his face!"

And another, whispering and nudging, nodding toward the horror-blank, thick-mumbling Italian boy: "Jesus! Look at th' guy, will yuh! . . . He don't know what he's doing! . . . He don't know yet what happened to him! . . . Sure! He got it *all*. I tell yuh! An' when it happened—when he got it—he just stahted runnin'. . . . He don't know yet what happened! . . . That's what I'm tellin' yuh—th' guy just stahted runnin' when he got it."

And the Italian youth, thick-mumbling: ". . . Jeez! W'at happened? . . . Jeez! . . . I was standin' talkin' to a guy—I heard it hit . . . Jeez! . . . W'at happened, anyway? . . . I got it all oveh me! . . . Jeez! . . . I just stahted runnin' . . . Jeez! I'm sick!"

Voices: "Here, take 'im into the drugstore! . . . Wash 'im off! . . . That guy needs a shot of liquor! . . . Sure! Take him into the drugstoeh *deh!* . . . *They'll* fix him up!"

The plump young man who runs the newsstand in the corridor, talking to everyone around him, excitedly and indignantly: ". . . Did I *see* it? Listen! I saw *everything!* I was coming across the street, looked up, and saw him in the air! . . . See it? . . . *Listen!* If someone had taken a big ripe watermelon and dropped it on the street from the fourteenth floor you'd have some idea what it was like! . . . See it! *I'll* tell the world I saw it! I don't want to see anything like *that* again!" Then excitedly, with a kind of hysterical indignation: "Shows no consideration for other people, that's all *I've* got to say! If a man is going to do a thing like that, why does he pick a place like *this*— one of the busiest corners in Brooklyn? . . . How did *he* know he wouldn't hit someone? Why, if that boy had been standing six inches nearer to the post, he'd have

killed him, as sure as you live! . . . And here he does it right in front of all these people who have to look at it! It shows he had no consideration for other people! A man who'd do a thing like that. . . ."

(Alas, poor youth! As if C. Green, now past considering, had considered nice "considerations.")

A taxi driver, impatiently: "That's what I'm tellin' yuh! . . . I watched him for five minutes before he jumped. He crawled out on the window sill an' stood there for *five* minutes, makin' up his mind! . . . Sure, I saw him! Lots of people saw him!" Impatiently, irritably: "Why didn't we *do* somethin' to stop him? F'r Chri' sake, what was there to do? A guy who'd do a thing like that is nuts to start with! You don't think he'd listen to anything *we* had to say, do you? . . . Sure, we *did* yell at him! . . . Jesus! . . . We was almost *afraid* to yell at him—we made motions to him to get back—tried to hold his attention while the cops sneaked round the corner into the hotel. . . . Sure, the cops got there just a second after he jumped—I don't know if he jumped when he heard 'em comin', or what happened, but Christ!— he stood there gettin' ready for five minutes while we watched!"

Observe now, Admiral, with what hypnotic concentration the people are examining the grimy-white facade of your hotel. Watch their faces and expressions. Their eyes go traveling upward slowly—up—up—up until they finally arrive and come to rest with focal concentration on that single open window twelve floors up. It is no jot different from all the other windows, but now the vision of the crowd is fastened on it with a fatal and united interest. And after staring at it fixedly, the eyes come traveling slowly down again— down—down—down—the faces strained a little, mouths all slightly puckered as if something set the teeth on edge—and slowly, with fascinated measurement—down—down—down—until the eyes reach sidewalk, lamp post, and—the Thing again.

The pavement finally halts all, stops all, answers all. It is the American pavement, Admiral Drake, our universal city sidewalk, a wide, hard stripe of grey-white cement, blocked accurately with dividing lines. It is the hardest, coldest, cruellest, most impersonal pavement in the world: all of the indifference, the atomic desolation, the exploded nothingness of one hundred million nameless "Greens" is in it.

It came from the same place where all our sidewalks come from—from Standard Concentrated Production Units of America, No. 1. This is where all our streets and lamp posts (like the one on which Green's brains are spattered) come from, where all our white-grimy bricks (like those of which your hotel is constructed) come from, where the red facades of our standard-unit tobacco stores (like the one across the street) come from, where our motor cars come from, where our drugstores and our drugstore windows and displays come from, where our soda fountains (complete, with soda jerkers attached) come from, where our cosmetics, toilet articles, and the fat, rouged lips of our women come from, where our soda water, slops and syrups, steamed spaghetti, ice cream, and pimento sandwiches come from, where our clothes, our hats (neat, standard stamps of grey), our faces (also stamps of grey, not always neat), our language, conversation, sentiments, feelings, and opinions come from. All these things are made for us by Standard Concentrated Production Units of America, No. 1.

So here we are, then, Admiral Drake. You see the street, the sidewalk, the front of your hotel, the constant stream of motor cars, the cops in uniform, the people streaming in and out of the subway, the rusty, pale-hued jungle of the buildings, old and new, high and low. There is no better place to see it, Drake. For this is Brooklyn—which means ten thousand streets and blocks like this one. Brooklyn, Admiral Drake, is the Standard Concentrated Chaos No. 1 of the Whole Universe. That is to say, it has no size, no shape, no heart, no joy, no hope, no aspiration, no center, no eyes, no soul, no purpose, no direction, and no anything—just Standard Concentrated Units everywhere—exploding in all directions for an unknown number of square miles like a completely triumphant Standard Concentrated Blot upon the Face of the Earth. And here, right in the middle, upon a minute portion of this magnificent Standard Concentrated Blot, where all the Standard Concentrated Blotters can stare at him, and with the brains completely out of him—

—Lies Green!

And this is bad—most bad—oh, very bad—and should not be allowed! For, as our young news-vendor friend has just indignantly proclaimed, it "shows no consideration for other people"—which means, for other Standard Concentrated Blotters. Green has no right to go falling in this fashion in a public place. He has no business *being* where he is at all. A Standard Concentrated Blotter is not supposed to *be* places, but to *go* places.

You see, dear Admiral, this sidewalk, this Standard Concentrated Mobway, is not a place to walk on, really. It is a place to swarm on, to weave on, to thrust and dodge on, to scurry past on, to crowd by on. One of the earliest precepts in a Concentrated Blotter's life is: "Move on there! Where th' hell d'you think you are, anyway—in a cow pasture?"

And, most certainly, it is not a place to lie on, to sprawl out on.

But look at Green! Just *look* at him! No wonder the plump youth is angry with him!

Green has willfully and deliberately violated every Standard Concentrated Principle of Blotterdom. He has not only gone and dashed his brains out, but he has done it in a public place—upon a piece of Standard Concentrated Mobway. He has messed up the sidewalk, messed up another Standard Concentrated Blotter, stopped traffic, taken people from their business, upset the nerves of his fellow Blotters—and now *lies* there, all *sprawled* out, in a place where he has no right to *be*. And, to make his crime unpardonable, C. Green has—

—Come to Life!

What's that, Admiral? You do not understand it? Small wonder, though it's really very simple:

For just ten minutes since, C. Green was a Concentrated Blotter like the rest of us, a nameless atom, swarming with the rest of us, just another "guy" like a hundred million other "guys." But now, observe him! No longer is he just "another guy"—already he has become a "special guy"—he has become "*The* Guy." C. Green at last has turned into a—*Man!*

The Last American Hero Is Junior Johnson. Yes!

He is a coon hunter, a rich man, an ex-whiskey runner,
a good old boy who hard-charges stock cars 175 m.p.h. Mother dog!
He is the lead-footed chicken farmer from Ronda,
the true vision of the New South

Ten o'clock Sunday morning in the hills of North Carolina. Cars, miles of cars, in every direction, millions of cars, pastel cars, aqua green, aqua blue, aqua beige, aqua buff, aqua dawn, aqua dusk, aqua aqua, aqua Malacca, Malacca lacquer, Cloud lavender, Assassin pink, Rake-a-cheek raspberry, Nude Strand coral, Honest Thrill orange, and Baby Fawn Lust cream-colored cars are all going to the stock-car races, and that old mothering North Carolina sun keeps exploding off the windshields. Mother dog!

Seventeen thousand people, me included, all of us driving out Route 421, out to the stock-car races at the North Wilkesboro Speedway, 17,000 going out to a five-eighths-mile stock-car track with a Coca-Cola sign out front. This is not to say there is no preaching and shouting in the South this morning. There is preaching and shouting. Any of us can turn on the old automobile transistor radio and get all we want:

"They are greedy dogs. Yeah! They ride around in big cars. Unnh-hunh! And chase women. Yeah! And drink liquor. Unnh-hunh! And smoke cigars. Oh yes! And they are greedy dogs. Yeah! Unh-hunh! Oh yes! Amen!"

There are also some commercials on the radio for Aunt Jemima grits, which cost ten cents a pound. There are also the Gospel Harmonettes, singing: "If you dig a ditch, you better dig two. . . ."

There are also three fools in a panel discussion on the New South, which they seem to conceive of as General Lee running the new Dulcidreme Labial Cream factory down at Griffin, Georgia.

And suddenly my car is stopped still on Sunday morning in the middle of the biggest traffic jam in the history of the world. It goes for ten miles in every direction from the North Wilkesboro Speedway. And right there it dawns on me that as far as this situation is concerned, anyway, all the conventional notions about the South are confined to . . . the Sunday radio. The South has preaching and shouting, the South has grits, the South has country songs, old mimosa traditions, clay dust, Old Bigots, New Liberals—and all of it, all of that old mental cholesterol, is confined to the Sunday radio. What I was in the middle of—well, it wasn't anything one hears about in panels about the South today. Miles and miles of eye-busting pastel cars on the expressway, which roar right up into the hills, going to the stock-car races. In ten years baseball—and the state of North Carolina alone used to have forty-four professional baseball teams—baseball is all over with in the South. We were all in the middle of a wild new thing, the Southern car world, and heading down the road on my way to see a breed such as sports never saw before, Southern stock-car drivers, all lined up in these two-ton mothers that go over 175 m.p.h., Fireball Roberts, Freddie Lorenzen, Ned Jarrett, Richard Petty, and—the hardest of all the hard chargers, one of the fastest automobile racing drivers in history—yes! Junior Johnson.

The legend of Junior Johnson! In this legend, here is a country boy, Junior Johnson, who learns to drive by running whiskey for his father, Johnson, Senior, one of the biggest copper-still operators of all times, up in Ingle Hollow, near North Wilkesboro, in northwestern North Carolina, and grows up to be a famous stock-car racing driver, rich, grossing $100,000 in 1963, for example, respected, solid, idolized in his hometown and throughout the rural South, for that matter. There is all this about how good old boys would wake up in the middle of the night in the apple shacks and hear a supercharged Oldsmobile engine roaring over Brushy Mountain and say, "Listen at him—there he goes!", although that part is doubtful, since some nights there were so many good old boys taking off down the road in supercharged automobiles out of Wilkes County, and running loads to Charlotte, Salisbury, Greensboro, Winston-Salem, High Point, or wherever, it would be pretty hard to pick out one.

After the initial confusion of his name with that of his illustrious predecessor, Tom (Thomas K.) Wolfe found his own voice within the techniques of what was hurriedly called "New Journalism." Whether that label is accurate or not, this piece, published in March, 1965, represents an early full flowering of that school of reporting.

It was Junior Johnson specifically, however, who was famous for the "bootleg turn" or "about-face," in which, if the Alcohol Tax agents had a roadblock up for you or were too close behind, you threw the car up into second gear, cocked the wheel, stepped on the accelerator and made the car's rear end skid around in a complete 180-degree arc, a complete about-face, and tore on back up the road exactly the way you came from. God! The Alcohol Tax agents used to burn over Junior Johnson. Practically every good old boy in town in Wilkesboro, the county seat, got to know the agents by sight in a very short time. They would rag them practically to their faces on the subject of Junior Johnson, so that it got to be an obsession. Finally, one night they had Junior trapped on the road up toward the bridge around Millersville, there's no way out of there, they had the barricades up and they could hear this souped-up car roaring around the bend, and here it comes—but suddenly they can hear a siren and see a red light flashing in the grille, so they think it's another agent, and boy, they run out like ants and pull those barrels and boards and sawhorses out of the way, and then—Ggghhzzzzzzzzhhhhhhggggggzzzzzzzeeeeeong! —gawdam! there he goes again, it was him, Junior Johnson!, with a gawdam agent's si-reen and a red light in his grille!

I wasn't in the South five minutes before people started making oaths, having visions, telling these hulking great stories, and so forth, all on the subject of Junior Johnson. At the Greensboro, North Carolina, Airport there was one good old boy who vowed he would have eaten "a bucket of it" if that would have kept Junior Johnson from switching from a Dodge racer to a Ford. Hell yes, and after that—God-almighty, remember that 1963 Chevrolet of Junior's? Whatever happened to that car? A couple of more good old boys join in. A good old boy, I ought to explain, is a generic term in the rural South referring to a man, of any age, but more often young than not, who fits in with the status system of the region. It usually means he has a good sense of humor and enjoys ironic jokes, is tolerant and easygoing enough to get along in long conversations at places like on the corner, and has a reasonable amount of physical courage. The term is usually heard in some such form as: "Lud? He's a good old boy from over at Crozet." These good old boys in the airport, by the way, were in their twenties, except for one fellow who was a cabdriver and was about forty-five, I would say. Except for the cabdriver, they all wore neo-Brummellian wardrobing such as Lacoste tennis shirts, Slim Jim pants, windbreakers with the collars turned up, "fast" shoes of the winkle-picker genre, and so on. I mention these details just by way of pointing out that very few grits, Iron Boy overalls, clodhoppers or hats with ventilation holes up near the crown enter into this story. Anyway, these good old boys are talking about Junior Johnson and how he has switched to Ford. This they unanimously regard as some kind of betrayal on Johnson's part. Ford, it seems, they regard as the car symbolizing the established power structure. Dodge is kind of a middle ground. Dodge is at least a challenger, not a ruler. But the Junior Johnson they

like to remember is the Junior Johnson of 1963, who took on the whole field of NASCAR (National Association For Stock Car Auto Racing) Grand National racing with a Chevrolet. All the other drivers, the drivers driving Fords, Mercurys, Plymouths, Dodges, had millions, literally millions when it is all added up, millions of dollars in backing from the Ford and Chrysler Corporations. Junior Johnson took them all on in a Chevrolet without one cent of backing from Detroit. Chevrolet had pulled out of stock-car racing. Yet every race it was the same. It was never a question of whether anybody was going to *outrun* Junior Johnson. It was just a question of whether he was going to win or his car was going to break down, since, for one thing, half the time he had to make his own racing parts. God! Junior Johnson was like Robin Hood or Jesse James or Little David or something. Every time that Chevrolet, No. 3, appeared on the track, these wild curdled yells, "Rebel" yells, they still have those, would rise up. At Daytona, at Atlanta, at Charlotte, at Darlington, South Carolina; Bristol, Tennessee; Martinsville, Virginia—Junior Johnson!

And then the good old boys get to talking about whatever happened to that Chevrolet of Junior's, and the cabdriver says he knows. He says Junior Johnson is using that car to run liquor out of Wilkes County. What does he mean? For Junior Johnson ever to go near another load of bootleg whiskey again—he would have to be insane. He has this huge racing income. He has two other businesses, a whole automated chicken farm with 42,000 chickens, a road-grading business—but cabdriver says he has this dream Junior is still roaring down from Wilkes County, down through the clay cuts, with the Atlas Arc Lip jars full in the back of that Chevrolet. It is in Junior's blood— and then at this point he puts his right hand up in front of him as if he is groping through fog, and his eyeballs glaze over and he looks out in the distance and he describes Junior Johnson roaring over the ridges of Wilkes County as if it is the ghost of Zapata he is describing, bounding over the Sierras on a white horse to rouse the peasants.

A stubborn notion! A crazy notion! Yet Junior Johnson has followers who need to keep him, symbolically, riding through nighttime like a demon. Madness! But Junior Johnson is one of the last of those sports stars who is not just an ace at the game itself, but a hero a whole people or class of people can identify with. Other, older examples are the way Jack Dempsey stirred up the Irish or the way Joe Louis stirred up the Negroes. Junior Johnson is a modern figure. He is only thirty-three years old and still racing. He should be compared to two other sports heroes whose cultural impact is not too well known. One is Antonino Rocca, the professional wrestler, whose triumphs mean so much to New York City's Puerto Ricans that he can fill Madison Square Garden, despite the fact that everybody, the Puerto Ricans included, knows that wrestling is nothing but a crude form of folk theatre. The other is Ingemar Johansson, who had a tremendous meaning to the Swedish masses —they were tired of that old king who played tennis all the time and all his friends who kept on drinking

Cointreau behind the screen of socialism. Junior Johnson is a modern hero, all involved with car culture and car symbolism in the South. A wild new thing—

Wild—gone wild, Fireball Roberts' Ford spins out on the first turn at the North Wilkesboro Speedway, spinning, spinning, the spin seems almost like slow motion—and then it smashes into the wooden guardrail. It lies up there with the frame bent. Roberts is all right. There is a new layer of asphalt on the track, it is like glass, the cars keep spinning off the first turn. Ned Jarrett spins, smashes through the wood. "Now, boys, this ice ain't gonna get one goddamn bit better, so you can either line up and qualify or pack up and go home—"

I had driven from the Greensboro Airport up to Wilkes County to see Junior Johnson on the occasion of one of the two yearly NASCAR Grand National stock-car races at the North Wilkesboro Speedway.

It is a long, very gradual climb from Greensboro to Wilkes County. Wilkes County is all hills, ridges, woods and underbrush, full of pin oaks, sweet-gum, maples, ash, birch, apple trees, rhododendron, rocks, vines, tin roofs, little clapboard places like the Mount Olive Baptist Church, signs for things like Double Cola, Sherrill's Ice Cream, Eckard's Grocery, Dr. Pepper, Diel's Apples, Google's Place, Suddith's Place and—yes!—cars. Up onto the highway, out of a side road from a hollow, here comes a 1947 Hudson. To almost anybody it would look like just some old piece of junk left over from God knows when, rolling down a country road . . . the 1947 Hudson was one of the first real "hot" cars made after the war. Some of the others were the 1946 Chrysler, which had a "kickdown" gear for sudden bursts of speed, the 1955 Pontiac and a lot of the Fords. To a great many good old boys a hot car was a symbol of heating up life itself. The war! Money even for country boys! And the money bought cars. In California they suddenly found kids of all sorts involved in vast drag-racing orgies and so forth and couldn't figure out what was going on. But in the South the mania for cars was even more intense, although much less publicized. To millions of good old boys, and girls, the automobile represented not only liberation from what was still pretty much a land-bound form of social organization but also a great leap forward into twentieth-century glamour, an idea that was being dinned in on the South like everywhere else. It got so that one of the typical rural sights, in addition to the red rooster, the grey split-rail fence, the Edgeworth Tobacco sign and the rusted-out harrow, one of the typical rural sights would be . . . you would be driving along the dirt roads and there beside the house would be an automobile up on blocks or something, with a rope over the tree for hoisting up the motor or some other heavy part, and a couple of good old boys would be practically disappearing into its innards, from below and from above, draped over the side under the hood. It got so that on Sundays there wouldn't be a safe straight stretch of road in the county, because so many wild country boys would be out racing or just raising hell on the roads. A lot of other kids, who weren't basically wild, would be driving like hell every morning and every night, driving to jobs perhaps thirty or forty miles away, jobs that were available only because of automobiles. In the morning they would be driving through the dapple shadows like madmen. In the hollows, sometimes one would come upon the most incredible tar-paper hovels, down near the stream, and out front would be an incredible automobile creation, a late-model car with aerials, continental kit overhangs in the back, mudguards studded with reflectors, fender skirts, spotlights, God knows what all, with a girl and perhaps a couple of good old boys communing over it and giving you rotten looks as you drive by. On Saturday night everybody would drive into town and park under the lights on the main street and neck. Yes! There was something about being right in there in town underneath the lights and having them reflecting off the baked enamel on the hood. Then if a good old boy insinuated his hands here and there on the front seat with a girl and began . . . necking . . . somehow it was all more *complete.* After the war there was a great deal of stout-burgher talk about people who lived in hovels and bought big-yacht cars to park out front. This was one of the symbols of a new, spendthrift age. But there was a great deal of unconscious resentment buried in the talk. It was resentment against (a) the fact that the good old boy had his money at all and (b) the fact that the car symbolized freedom, a slightly wild, careening emancipation from the old social order. Stock-car racing got started about this time, right after the war, and it was immediately regarded as some kind of manifestation of the animal irresponsibility of the lower orders. It had a truly terrible reputation. It was—well, it looked *rowdy* or something. The cars were likely to be used cars, the tracks were dirt, the stands were rickety wood, the drivers were country boys, and they had regular feuds out there, putting each other "up against the wall" and "cutting tires" and everything else. Those country boys would drive into the curves full tilt, then slide maniacally, sometimes coming around the curve sideways, with red dirt showering up. Sometimes they would race at night, under those weak-eyed yellow-ochre lights they have at small tracks and baseball fields, and the clay dust would start showering up in the air, where the evening dew would catch it, and all evening long you would be sitting in the stands or standing out in the infield with a fine clay-mud drizzle coming down on you, not that anybody gave a damn—except for the Southern upper and middle classes, who never attended in those days, but spoke of the "rowdiness."

But mainly it was the fact that stock-car racing was something that was welling up out of the lower orders. From somewhere these country boys and urban proles were getting the money and starting this sport.

Stock-car racing was beginning all over the country, at places like Allentown, Langhorne and Lancaster, Pennsylvania, and out in California and even out on Long Island, but wherever it cropped up, the Establishment tried to wish it away, largely, and stock-car racing went on in a kind of underground world of tracks built on cheap stretches of land well out from the town or the city, a world of diners, drive-ins, motels, gasoline stations, and the good burghers might drive by from time to time, happen by on a Sunday or something, and see the crowd gathered from out of nowhere, the cars coming in, crowding up the highway a little, but Monday morning they would be all gone.

Stock-car racing was building up a terrific following in the South during the early Fifties. Here was a sport not using any abstract devices, any *bat* and *ball*, but the same automobile that was changing a man's own life, his own symbol of liberation, and it didn't require size, strength and all that, all it required was a taste for speed, and the guts. The newspapers in the South didn't seem to catch onto what was happening until late in the game. Of course, newspapers all over the country have looked backward over the tremendous rise in automobile sports, now the second-biggest type of sport in the country in terms of attendance. The sports pages generally have an inexorable lower-middle-class outlook. The sportswriter's "zest for life" usually amounts, in the end, to some sort of gruff Mom's Pie sentimentality at a hideously cozy bar somewhere. The sportswriters caught onto Grand Prix racing first because it had "tone," a touch of de-frocked European nobility about it, what with a few counts racing here and there, although, in fact, it is the least popular form of racing in the United States. What finally put stock-car racing onto the sports pages in the South was the intervention of the Detroit automobile firms. Detroit began putting so much money into the sport that it took on a kind of massive economic respectability and thereby, in the lower-middle-class brain, status.

What Detroit discovered was that thousands of good old boys in the South were starting to form allegiances to brands of automobiles, according to which were hottest on the stock-car circuits, the way they used to have them for the hometown baseball team. The South was one of the hottest car-buying areas in the country. Cars like Hudsons, Oldsmobiles and Lincolns, not the cheapest automobiles by any means, were selling in disproportionate numbers in the South, and a lot of young good old boys were buying them. In 1955, Pontiac started easing into stock-car racing, and suddenly the big surge was on. Everybody jumped into the sport to grab for themselves The Speed Image. Suddenly, where a good old boy used to have to bring his gasoline to the track in old filling-station pails and pour it into the tank through a funnel when he made a pit stop, and change his tires with a hand wrench, suddenly, now, he had these "gravity" tanks of gasoline that you just jam into the gas pipe, and air wrenches to take the wheels off, and whole crews of men in white coveralls to leap all over a car when it came rolling into the pit, just like they do at Indianapolis, as if they are mechanical apparati *merging* with the machine as it rolls in, forcing water into the radiator, jacking up the car, taking off wheels, wiping off the windshield, handing the driver a cup of orange juice, all in one synchronized operation. And now, today, the *big money* starts descending on this little place, the North Wilkesboro, North Carolina,

Speedway, a five-eighths-of-a-mile stock-car track with a Coca-Cola sign by the highway where the road in starts.

The private planes start landing out at the Wilkesboro Airport. Freddie Lorenzen, the driver, the biggest money winner last year in stock-car racing, comes sailing in out of the sky in a twin-engine Aero Commander, and there are a few good old boys out there in the tall grass by the runway already with their heads sticking up watching this hero of the modern age come in and taxi up and get out of that twin-engine airplane with his blond hair swept back as if by the mother internal-combustion engine of them all. And then Paul Goldsmith, the driver, comes in in a 310 Cessna, and *he* gets out, all these tall, lanky, hard-boned Americans in their thirties with these great profiles like a comic-strip hero or something, and then Glenn (Fireball) Roberts—Fireball Roberts!—Fireball is *hard* —he comes in in a Comanche 250, like a flying yacht, and then Ray Nichels and Ray Fox, the chief mechanics, who run big racing crews for the Chrysler Corporation, this being Fox's last race for Junior as his mechanic, before Junior switches over to Ford, they come in in two-engine planes. And even old Buck Baker—hell, Buck Baker is a middling driver for Dodge, but even he comes rolling in down the landing strip at two hundred miles an hour with his Southern-hero face at the window of the cockpit of a twin-engine Apache, traveling first class in the big status boat that has replaced the yacht in America, the private plane.

And then the Firestone and Goodyear vans pull in, huge mothers, bringing in these huge stacks of racing tires for the race, big wide ones, 8.20's, with special treads, which are like a lot of bumps on the tire instead of grooves. They even have special tires for qualifying, soft tires, called "gumballs," they wouldn't last more than ten times around the track in a race, but for qualifying, which is generally three laps, one to pick up speed and two to race against the clock, they are great, because they hold tight on the corners. And on a hot day, when somebody like Junior Johnson, one of the fastest qualifying runners in the history of the sport, 170.777 m.p.h. in a one-hundred-mile qualifying race at Daytona in 1964, when somebody like Junior Johnson really pushes it on a qualifying run, there will be a ring of blue smoke up over the whole goddamned track, the whole thing, a ring like an oval halo over the whole thing from the gumballs burning, and some good old boy will say, "Great smokin' blue gumballs god almighty dog! There goes Junior Johnson!"

The thing is, each one of these tires costs fifty-five to sixty dollars, and on a track that is fast and hard on tires, like Atlanta, one car might go through ten complete tire changes, easily, forty tires, or almost $2,500 worth of tires just for one race. And he may even be out of the money. And then the Ford van and the Dodge van and the Mercury van and the Plymouth van roll in with new motors, a whole new motor every few races, a 427-cubic-inch stock-car-racing motor, 600 horsepower, the largest and most powerful allowed on the track, that probably costs the company $1,000 or more, when you consider that they are not mass

Tom Wolfe

produced. And still the advertising appeal. You can buy the very same car that these fabulous wild men drive every week at these fabulous wild speeds, and some of their power and charisma is yours. After every NASCAR Grand National stock-car race, whichever company has the car that wins, this company will put big ads in the Southern papers, and papers all over the country if it is a very big race, like the Daytona 500, the Daytona Firecracker 400 or the Atlanta and Charlotte races. They sell a certain number of these 427-cubic-inch cars to the general public, a couple of hundred a year, perhaps, at eight or nine thousand dollars apiece, but it is no secret that these motors are specially reworked just for stock-car racing. Down at Charlotte there is a company called Holman & Moody that is supposed to be the "garage" or "automotive-engineering" concern that prepares automobiles for Freddie Lorenzen and some of the other Ford drivers. But if you go by Holman & Moody out by the airport and Charlotte, suddenly you come upon a huge place that is a *factory*, for God's sake, a big long thing, devoted mainly to the business of turning out stock-car racers. A whole lot of other parts in stock-car racers are heavier than the same parts on a street automobile, although they are made to the same scale. The shock absorbers are bigger, the wheels are wider and bulkier, the swaybars and steering mechanisms are heavier, the axles are much heavier, they have double sets of wheel bearings, and so forth and so on. The bodies of the cars are pretty much the same, except that they use lighter sheet metal, practically tinfoil. Inside, there is only the driver's seat and a heavy set of roll bars and diagonal struts that turn the inside of the car into a rigid cage, actually. That is why the drivers can walk away unhurt—most of the time—from the most spectacular crackups. The gearshift is the floor kind, although it doesn't make much difference, as there is almost no shifting gears in stock-car racing. You just get into high gear and go. The dashboard has no speedometer, the main thing being the dial for engine revolutions per minute. So, anyway, it costs about $15,000 to prepare a stock-car racer in the first place and another three or four thousand for each new race and this does not even count the costs of mechanics' work and transportation. All in all, Detroit will throw around a quarter of a million dollars into it every week while the season is on, and the season runs, roughly, from February to October, with a few big races after that. And all this turns up even out at the North Wilkesboro Speedway, with the Coca-Cola sign out front, out in the up-country of Wilkes County, North Carolina.

Sunday! Racing day! Sunday is no longer a big church day in the South. A man can't very well go to eleven o'clock service and still expect to get to a two o'clock stock-car race, unless he wants to get into the biggest traffic jam in the history of creation, and that goes for North Wilkesboro, North Carolina, same as Atlanta and Charlotte.

There is the Coca-Cola sign out where the road leads in from the highway, and hills and trees, but here are long concrete grandstands for about 17,000 and a paved five-eighths-mile oval. Practically all the drivers are out there with their cars and their crews, a lot of guys in white coveralls. The cars look huge . . . and curiously nude and blind. All the chrome is stripped off, except for the grilles. The headlights are blanked out. Most of the cars are in the pits. The so-called "pit" is a paved cutoff on the edge of the infield. It cuts off from the track itself like a service road off an expressway at the old shopping center. Every now and then a car splutters, hacks, coughs, hocks a lunga, rumbles out onto the track itself for a practice run. There is a lot of esoteric conversation going on, speculation, worries, memoirs:

"What happened?"

"Mother—condensed on me. Al brought it up here with him. Water in the line."

"Better keep Al away from a stable, he'll fill you up with horse manure."

". . . they told me to give him one, a cream puff, so I give him one, a cream puff. One goddamn race and the son of a bitch, he *melted* it. . . ."

". . . he's down there right now pettin' and rubbin' and huggin' that car just like those guys do a horse at the Kentucky Derby. . . ."

". . . They'll blow you right out of the tub. . . ."

". . . No, the quarter inch, and go on over and see if you can get Ned's blowtorch. . . ."

". . . Rear end's loose. . . ."

". . . I don't reckon this right here's got nothing to do with it, do you? . . ."

". . . Aw, I don't know, about yea big. . . ."

". . . Who the hell stacked them gumballs on the bottom? . . ."

". . . th'ow in rocks. . . ."

". . . won't turn seven thousand. . . ."

". . . strokin' it. . . ."

". . . blistered. . . ."

". . . spun out. . . ."

". . . muvva. . . ."

Then, finally, here comes Junior Johnson. How he does come on. He comes tooling across the infield in a big white dreamboat, a brand-new white Pontiac Catalina four-door hardtop sedan. He pulls up and as he gets out he seems to get more and more huge. First his crew-cut head and then a big jaw and then a bigger neck and then a huge torso, like a wrestler's, all done up rather modish and California modern, with a red-and-white candy-striped sport shirt, white ducks and loafers.

"How you doing?" says Junior Johnson, shaking hands, and then he says, "Hot enough for ye'uns?"

Junior is in an amiable mood. Like most up-hollow people, it turns out, Junior is reserved. His face seldom shows an emotion. He has three basic looks: amiable, amiable and a little shy, and dead serious. To a lot of people, apparently, Junior's dead-serious look seems menacing. There are no cowards left in stock-car racing, but a couple of drivers tell me that one of the things that can shake you up is to look into your rearview mirror going around a curve and see Junior Johnson's car on your tail trying to "root you out of the groove," and then get a glimpse of Junior's dead-serious look. I think some of the sportswriters are afraid of him. One of them tells me Junior is strong, silent—and explosive. Junior will only give you three answers, "Uh-huh," "Uh-unh," and "I don' know," and so forth and so on. Actually, I find he handles questions easily. He has a great technical knowledge of automobiles and the physics of speed, including things he never fools with, such as Offenhauser engines. What he never does offer, however, is small talk. This gives him a built-in poise, since it deprives him of the chance to say anything asinine. "Ye'uns," "we'uns," "h'it" for "it," "growed" for "grew" and a lot of other unusual past participles—Junior uses certain older forms of English, not exactly "Elizabethan," as they are sometimes called, but older forms of English preserved up-country in his territory, Ingle Hollow.

Kids keep coming up for Junior's autograph and others are just hanging around and one little old boy comes up, he is about thirteen, and Junior says: "This boy here goes coon hunting with me."

One of the sportswriters is standing around, saying: "What do you shoot a coon with?"

"Don't shoot 'em. The dogs tree 'em and then you flush 'em out and the dogs fight 'em."

"Flush 'em out?"

"Yeah. This boy right here can flush 'em out better than anybody you ever did see. You go out at night with the dogs, and soon as they get the scent, they start barking. They go on out ahead of you and when they tree a coon, you can tell it, by the way they sound. They all start baying up at that coon—h'it sounds like, I don't know, you hear it once and you not likely to forget it. Then you send a little old boy up to flush him out and he jumps down and the dogs fight him."

"How does a boy flush him out?"

"Aw, he just climbs up there to the limb he's on and starts shaking h'it and the coon'll jump."

"What happens if the coon decides he'd rather come back after the boy instead of jumping down to a bunch of dogs?"

"He won't do that. A coon's afraid of a person, but he can kill a dog. A coon can take any dog you set against him if they's just the two of them fighting. The coon jumps down on the ground and he rolls right over on his back with his feet up, and he's *got* claws about like this. All he has to do is get a dog once in the throat or in the belly, and he can kill him, cut him wide open just like you took a knife and did it. Won't any dog even fight a coon except a coon dog."

"What kind of dogs are they?"

"*Coon* dogs, I guess. Black and tans they call 'em sometimes. They's bred for it. If his mammy and pappy wasn't coon dogs, he ain't likely to be one either. After you got one, you got to train him. You trap a coon, live, and then you put him in a pen and tie him to a post with a rope on him and then you put your dog in there and he has to fight him. Sometimes you get a dog just don't have any fight in him and he ain't no good to you."

Junior is in the pit area, standing around with his brother Fred, who is part of his crew, and Ray Fox and some other good old boys, in a general atmosphere of big stock-car money, a big ramp truck for his car, a white Dodge, number 3, a big crew in white coveralls, huge stacks of racing tires, a Dodge p.r. man, big portable cans of gasoline, compressed air hoses, compressed water hoses, the whole business. Herb Nab, Freddie Lorenzen's chief mechanic, comes over and sits down on his haunches and Junior sits down on his haunches and Nab says:

"So Junior Johnson's going to drive a Ford."

Junior is switching from Dodge to Ford mainly because he hasn't been winning with the Dodge. Lorenzen drives a Ford, too, and the last year, when Junior was driving the Chevrolet, their duels were the biggest excitement in stock-car racing.

"Well," says Nab, "I'll tell you, Junior. My ambition is going to be to outrun your ass every goddamned time we go out."

"That was your ambition last year," says Junior.

"I know it was," says Nab, "and you took all the money, didn't you? You know what my strategy was. I was going to outrun everybody else and outlast Junior, that was my strategy."

Setting off his California modern sport shirt and white ducks, Junior has on a pair of twenty-dollar rimless sunglasses and a big gold Timex watch, and Flossie, his fiancée, is out there in the infield somewhere with the white Pontiac, and the white Dodge that Dodge gave Junior is parked up near the pit area—and then a little thing happens that brings the whole thing right back there to Wilkes County, North Carolina, to Ingle Hollow and to hard muscle in the clay gulches. A couple of good old boys come down to the front of the stands with the screen and the width of the track between them and Junior, and one of the good old boys comes down and yells out in the age-old baritone raw-curdle yell of the Southern hills:

"Hey! Hog jaw!"

Everybody gets quiet. They know he's yelling at Junior, but nobody says a thing. Junior doesn't even turn around.

"Hey, hog jaw! . . ."

Junior, he does nothing.

"Hey, hog jaw, I'm gonna get me one of them fastback roosters, too, and come down there and get you!"

Fastback rooster refers to the Ford—it has a "fastback" design—Junior is switching to.

"Hey, hog jaw, I'm gonna get me one of them fastback roosters and run you right out of here, you hear me, hog jaw!"

One of the good old boys alongside Junior says, "Junior, go on up there and clear out those stands."

Then everybody stares at Junior to see what he's gonna do. Junior, he don't even look around. He just looks a bit dead serious.

"Hey, hog jaw, you got six cases of whiskey in the back of that car you want to let me have?"

"What you hauling in that car, hog jaw!"

"Tell him you're out of that business, Junior," one of the good old boys says.

"Go on up there and clean house, Junior," says another good old boy.

Then Junior looks up, without looking at the stands, and smiles a little and says, "You flush him down here out of that tree—and I'll take keer of him."

Such a howl goes up from the good old boys! It is almost a blood curdle--

"Goddamn, he *will*, too!"

"Lord, he better know how to do an *about-face* hissef if he comes down here!"

"Goddamn, get him, Junior!"

"Whooeeee!"

"Mother dog!"

A kind of orgy of reminiscence of the old Junior before the Detroit money started flowing, wild combats *d'honneur* up-hollow—and, suddenly, when he heard that unearthly baying coming up from the good old boys in the pits, the good old boy retreated from the edge of the stands and never came back.

Later on Junior told me, sort of apologetically, "H'it used to be, if a fellow crowded me just a little bit, I was ready to crawl him. I reckon that was one good thing about Chillicothe.

"I don't want to pull any more time," Junior tells me, "but I wouldn't take anything in the world for the experience I had in prison. If a man needed to change, that was the place to change. H'it's not a waste of time there, h'it's good experience.

"H'it's that they's so many people in the world that feel that nobody is going to tell them what to do. I had quite a temper, I reckon. I always had the idea that I had as much sense as the other person and I didn't want them to tell me what to do. In the penitentiary there I found out that I could listen to another fellow and be told what to do and h'it wouldn't kill me."

Starting time! Linda Vaughn, with the big blonde hair and blossomy breasts, puts down her Coca-Cola and the potato chips and slips off her red stretch pants and her white blouse and walks out of the officials' booth in her Rake-a-cheek red show girl's costume with her long honeydew legs in net stockings and climbs up on the red Firebird float. The Life Symbol of stock-car racing! Yes! Linda, every luscious morsel of Linda, is a good old girl from Atlanta who was made Miss Atlanta International Raceway one year and was paraded around the track on a float and she liked it so much and all the good old boys liked it so much, Linda's flowing hair and blossomy breasts and honeydew legs, that she became the permanent glamour symbol of stock-car racing, and never mind this other modeling she was doing . . . this, she liked it. Right before practically every race on the Grand National circuit Linda Vaughn puts down her Coca-Cola and potato chips. Her momma is there, she generally comes around to see Linda go around the track on the float, it's such a nice spectacle seeing Linda looking so lovely, and the applause and all. "Linda, I'm thirstin', would you bring me a Coca-Cola?" "A lot of them think I'm Freddie Lorenzen's girl friend, but I'm not any of 'em's girl friend, I'm real good friends with 'em all, even Wen-dell," he being Wendell Scott, the only Negro in big-league stock-car racing. Linda gets up on the Firebird float. This is an extraordinary object, made of wood, about twenty feet tall, in the shape of a huge bird, an eagle or something, blazing red, and Linda, with her red show girl's suit on, gets up on the seat, which is up between the wings, like a saddle, high enough so her long honeydew legs stretch down, and

a new car pulls her—Miss Firebird!—slowly once around the track just before the race. It is more of a ceremony by now than the national anthem. Miss Firebird sails slowly in front of the stands and the good old boys let out some real curdle Rebel yells, "Yaaaaa-aaaaaaaaghhhhoooooo! Let me at that car!" "Honey, you sure do start my motor, I swear to God!" "Great God and Poonadingdong, I mean!"

And suddenly there's a big roar from behind, down in the infield, and then I see one of the great sights in stock-car racing. That infield! The cars have been piling into the infield by the hundreds, parking in there on the clay and the grass, every whichway, angled down and angled up, this way and that, where the ground is uneven, these beautiful blazing brand-new cars with the sun exploding off the windshields and the baked enamel and the glassy lacquer, hundreds, thousands of cars stacked this way and that in the infield with the sun bolting down and no shade, none at all, just a couple of Coca-Cola stands out there. And already the good old boys and girls are out beside the cars, with all these beautiful little buds in short shorts already spread-eagled out on top of the car roofs, pressing down on good hard slick automobile sheet metal, their little cupcake bottoms aimed up at the sun. The good old boys are lollygagging around with their shirts off and straw hats on that have miniature beer cans on the brims and buttons that read, "Girls Wanted—No Experience Required." And everybody, good old boys and girls of all ages, are out there with portable charcoal barbecue ovens set up, and folding tubular-steel terrace furniture, deck chairs and things, and Thermos jugs and coolers full of beer —and suddenly it is not the up-country South at all but a concentration of the modern suburbs, all jammed into that one space, from all over America, with blazing cars and instant goodies, all cooking under the bare blaze—inside a strange bowl. The infield is like the bottom of a bowl. The track around it is banked so steeply at the corners and even on the straightaways, it is like . . . the steep sides of a bowl. The wall around the track, and the stands and the bleachers are like . . . the rim of a bowl. And from the infield, in this great incredible press of blazing new cars, there is no horizon but the bowl, up above only that cobalt-blue North Carolina sky. And then suddenly, on a signal, thirty stock-car engines start up where they are lined up in front of the stands. The roar of these engines is impossible to describe. They have a simultaneous rasp, thunder and rumble that goes right through a body and fills the whole bowl with a noise of internal combustion. Then they start around on two build-up runs, just to build up speed, and then they come around the fourth turn and onto the straightaway in front of the stands at—here, 130 miles an hour, in Atlanta, 160 miles an hour, at Daytona, 180 miles an hour—and the flag goes down and everybody in the infield and in the stands is up on their feet going mad, and suddenly here is a bowl that is one great orgy of everything in the way of excitement and liberation the automobile has meant to Americans. An orgy!

The first lap of a stock-car race is a horrendous, a wildly horrendous spectacle such as no other sport approaches. Twenty, thirty, forty automobiles, each of them weighing almost two tons, 3700 pounds, with 427-cubic-inch engines, 600 horsepower, are practically locked together, side to side and tail to nose, on a narrow band of asphalt at 130, 160, 180 miles an hour, hitting the curves so hard the rubber burns off the tires in front of your eyes. To the driver, it is like being inside a car going down the West Side Highway in New York City at rush hour, only with everybody going literally three to four times as fast, at speeds a man who has gone eighty-five miles an hour down a highway cannot conceive of, and with every other driver an enemy who is willing to cut inside of you, around you or in front of you, or ricochet off your side in the battle to get into a curve first.

The speeds are faster than those in the Indianapolis 500 race, the cars are more powerful, much heavier, and the drivers have more courage, more daring, more ruthlessness than Indianapolis or Grand Prix drivers. The prize money in Southern stock-car racing is far greater than that in Indianapolis-style or European Grand Prix racing, but few Indianapolis or Grand Prix drivers have the raw nerve required to succeed at it.

Although they will deny it, it is still true that stock-car drivers will put each other "up against the wall" —cut inside on the left of another car and ram it into a spin—if they get mad enough. Crashes are not the only danger, however. The cars are now literally too fast for their own parts, especially the tires. Firestone and Goodyear have poured millions into stock-car racing, but neither they nor anybody so far has been able to come up with a tire for this kind of racing at the current speeds. Three well-known stock-car drivers were killed last year, two of them champion drivers, Joe Weatherly and Fireball Roberts, and another, one of the best new drivers, Jimmy Pardue, from Junior Johnson's own home territory, Wilkes County, North Carolina. Roberts was the only one killed in a crash. Junior Johnson was in the crash but was not injured. Weatherly and Pardue both lost control on curves. Pardue's death came during a tire test. In a tire test, engineers, from Firestone or Goodyear, try out various tires on a car, and the driver, always one of the top competitors, tests them at top speed, usually on the Atlanta track. The drivers are paid three dollars a mile and may drive as much as five or six hundred miles in a single day. At 145 miles an hour average that does not take very long. Anyway, these drivers are going at speeds that, on curves, can tear tires off their casings or break axles. They practically run off from over their own automobiles.

J unior Johnson was over in the garden by the house some years ago, plowing the garden barefooted, behind a mule, just wearing an old pair of overalls, when a couple of good old boys drove up and told him to come on up to the speedway and get in a stock-car race. They wanted some local boys to race, as a preliminary to the main race, "as a kind of sideshow," as Junior remembers it.

"So I just put the reins down," Junior is telling me, "and rode on over 'ere with them. They didn't give us seat belts or nothing, they just roped us in. H'it was a dirt track then. I come in second."

Junior was a sensation in dirt-track racing right from the start. Instead of going into the curves and just sliding and holding on for dear life like the other drivers, Junior developed the technique of throwing himself into a slide about seventy-five feet before the curve by cocking the wheel to the left slightly and gunning it, using the slide, not the brake, to slow down, so that he could pick up speed again halfway through the curve and come out of it like a shot. This was known as his "power slide," and—yes! of course! —every good old boy in North Carolina started saying Junior Johnson had learned that stunt doing those goddamned *about-faces* running away from the Alcohol Tax agents. Junior put on such a show one night on a dirt track in Charlotte that he broke two axles, and he thought he was out of the race because he didn't have any more axles, when a good old boy came running up out of the infield and said, "Goddamn it, Junior Johnson, you take the axle off my car here, I got a Pontiac just like yours," and Junior took it off and put it on his and went out and broke *it* too. Mother dog! To this day Junior Johnson loves dirt-track racing like nothing else in this world, even though there is not much money in it. Every year he sets new dirt-track speed records, such as at Hickory, North Carolina, one of the most popular dirt tracks, last spring. As far as Junior is concerned, dirt-track racing is not so much of a mechanical test for the car as those long five- and six-hundred-mile races on asphalt are. Gasoline, tire and engine wear aren't so much of a problem. It is all the driver, his skill, his courage—his willingness to mix it up with the other cars, smash and carom off of them at a hundred miles an hour or so to get into the curves first. Junior has a lot of fond recollections of mixing it up at places like Bowman Gray Stadium in Winston-Salem, one of the minor-league tracks, a very narrow track, hardly wide enough for two cars. "You could always figure Bowman Gray was gonna cost you two fenders, two doors and two quarter panels," Junior tells me with nostalgia.

Anyway, at Hickory, which was a Saturday-night race, all the good old boys started pouring into the stands before sundown, so they wouldn't miss anything, the practice runs or the qualifying or anything. And pretty soon, the dew hasn't even started falling before Junior Johnson and David Pearson, one of Dodge's best drivers, are out there on practice runs, just warming up, and they happen to come up alongside each other on the second curve, and—the thing is, here are two men, each of them driving $15,000 automobiles, each of them standing to make $50,000 to $100,000 for the season if they don't get themselves killed, and they meet on a curve on a goddamned practice run on a dirt track, and neither of them can resist it. Coming out of the turn they go into a wild-ass race down the backstretch, both of them trying to get into the third turn first, and all the way across the infield you can hear them ricocheting off each other and bouncing at a hundred miles an hour on loose dirt, and then they go into ferocious power slides, red dust all over the goddamned place, and then out of this goddamned red-dust cloud, out of the fourth turn, here comes Junior Johnson first, like a shot, with Pearson right on his tail, and the good old boys in the stands going wild, and the *qualifying* runs haven't started yet, let alone the race.

Junior worked his way up through the minor leagues, the Sportsman and Modified classifications, as they are called, winning championships in both, and won his first Grand National race, the big leagues, in 1955 at Hickory, on dirt. He was becoming known as "the hardest of the hard-chargers," power sliding, rooting them out of the groove, raising hell, and already the Junior Johnson legend was beginning.

He kept hard-charging, power sliding, going after other drivers as though there wasn't room on the track but for one, and became the most popular driver in stock-car racing by 1959. The automobile companies had suddenly dropped out of stock-car racing in 1957, making a devout covenant never again to try to capitalize on speed as a selling point, the Government was getting stuffy about it, but already the presence of Detroit and Detroit's big money had begun to calm the drivers down a little. Detroit was concerned about Image. The last great duel of the dying dog-eat-dog era of stock-car racing came in 1959, when Junior and Lee Petty, who was then leading the league in points, had it out on the Charlotte raceway. Junior was in the lead, and Petty was right on his tail, but couldn't get by Junior. Junior kept coming out of the curves faster. So every chance he got, Petty would get up right on Junior's rear bumper and start banging it, gradually forcing the fender in to where the metal would cut Junior's rear tire. With only a few laps to go, Junior had a blowout and spun out up against the guardrail. That is Junior's version. Petty claimed Junior hit a pop bottle and spun out. The fans in Charlotte were always throwing pop bottles and other stuff onto the track late in the race, looking for blood. In any case, Junior eased back into the pits, had the tire changed, and charged out after Petty. He caught him on a curve and—well, whatever really happened, Petty was suddenly "up against the wall" and out of the race, and Junior Johnson won.

What a howl went up. The Charlotte chief of police charged out onto the track after the race, according to Petty, and offered to have Junior arrested for "assault with a dangerous weapon," the hassling went on for weeks—

"Back then," Junior tells me, "when you got into a guy and racked him up, you might as well get ready, because he's coming back for you. H'it was dog eat dog. That straightened Lee Petty out right smart. They don't do stuff like that anymore, though, because the guys don't stand for it."

Anyway, the Junior Johnson legend kept building up and building up, and in 1960 it got hotter than ever when Junior won the biggest race of the year, the Daytona 500, by "discovering" a new technique called "drafting." That year stock-car racing was full of big powerful Pontiacs manned by top drivers, and they would go like nothing else anybody ever saw. Junior went down to Daytona with a Chevrolet.

"My car was about ten miles an hour slower than the rest of the cars, the Pontiacs," Junior tells me.

"In the preliminary races, the warmups and stuff like that, they was smoking me off the track. Then I remember once I went out for a practice run, and Fireball Roberts was out there in a Pontiac and I got in right behind him on a curve, right on his bumper. I knew I couldn't stay with him on the straightaway, but I came out of the curve fast, right in behind him, running flat out, and then I noticed a funny thing. As long as I stayed right in behind him, I noticed I picked up speed and stayed right with him and my car was going faster than it had ever gone before. I could tell on the tachometer. My car wasn't turning no more than 6000 before, but when I got into this drafting position, I was turning 6800 to 7000. H'it felt like the car was plumb off the ground, floating along."

"Drafting," it was discovered at Daytona, created a vacuum behind the lead car and both cars would go faster than they normally would. Junior "hitched rides" on the Pontiacs most of the afternoon, but was still second to Bobby Johns, the lead Pontiac. Then, late in the race, Johns got into a drafting position with a fellow Pontiac that was actually one lap behind him and the vacuum got so intense that the rear window blew out of Johns' car and he spun out and crashed and Junior won.

This made Junior the Lion Killer, the Little David of stock-car racing, and his performance in the 1963 season made him even more so.

Junior raced for Chevrolet at Daytona in February, 1963, and set the all-time stock-car speed record in a hundred-mile qualifying race, 164.083 miles an hour, twenty-one miles an hour faster than Parnelli Jones's winning time at Indianapolis that year. Junior topped that at Daytona in July of 1963, qualifying at 166.005 miles per hour in a five-mile run, the fastest that anyone had ever averaged that distance in a racing car of any type. Junior's Chevrolet lasted only twenty-six laps in the Daytona 500 in 1963, however. He went out with a broken push rod. Although Chevrolet announced they were pulling out of racing at this time, Junior took his car and started out on the wildest performance in the history of stock-car racing. Chevrolet wouldn't give him a cent of backing. They wouldn't even speak to him on the telephone. Half the time he had to have his own parts made. Plymouth, Mercury, Dodge and Ford, meantime, were pouring more money than ever into stock-car racing. Yet Junior won seven Grand National races out of the thirty-three he entered and led most others before mechanical trouble forced him out.

All the while, Junior was making record qualifying runs, year after year. In the usual type of qualifying run, a driver has the track to himself and makes two circuits, with the driver with the fastest average time getting the "pole" position for the start of the race. In a way this presents stock-car danger in its purest form. Driving a stock car does not require much handling ability, at least not as compared to Grand Prix racing, because the tracks are simple banked ovals and there is almost no shifting of gears. So qualifying becomes a test of raw nerve—of how fast a man is willing to take a curve. Many of the top drivers in competition are poor at qualifying. In effect, they are willing to calculate their risks only against the risks the other drivers are taking. Junior takes the pure risk as no other driver has ever taken it.

"Pure" risk or total risk, whichever, Indianapolis and Grand Prix drivers have seldom been willing to face the challenge of the Southern stock-car driver. A. J. Foyt, last year's winner at Indianapolis, is one exception. He has raced against the Southerners and beaten them. Parnelli Jones has tried and fared badly. Driving "Southern style" has a quality that shakes a man up. The Southerners went on a tour of Northern tracks last fall. They raced at Bridgehampton, New York, and went into the corners so hard the marshals stationed at each corner kept radioing frantically to the control booth: "They're going off the track. They're all going off the track!"

But this, Junior Johnson's last race in a Dodge, was not his day, neither for qualifying nor racing. Lorenzen took the lead early and won the 250-mile race a lap ahead of the field. Junior finished third, but was never in contention for the lead.

"Come on, Junior, do my hand—"

Two or three hundred people come out of the stands and up out of the infield and onto the track to be around Junior Johnson. Junior is signing autographs in a neat left-handed script he has. It looks like it came right out of the Locker book. The girls! Levis, stretch pants, sneaky shorts, stretch jeans, they press into the crowd with lively narbs and try to get their hands up in front of Junior and say:

"Come on, Junior, do my hand!"

In order to do a hand, Junior has to hold the girl's hand in his right hand and then sign his name with a ball-point on the back of her hand.

"Junior, you got to do mine, too!"

"Put it on up here."

All the girls break into . . . smiles. Junior Johnson does a hand. Ah, sweet little cigarette-ad blonde! She says:

"Junior, why don't you ever call me up?"

"I 'spect you get plenty of calls 'thout me."

"Oh, Junior! You call me up, you hear now?"

But also a great many older people crowd in, and they say:

"Junior, you're doing a real good job out there, you're driving real good."

"Junior, when you get in that Ford, I want to see you pass that Freddie Lorenzen, you hear now?"

"Junior, you like that Ford better than that Dodge?"

And: "Junior, here's a young man that's been waiting some time and wanting to see you—" and the man lifts up his little boy in the middle of the crowd and says: "I told you you'd see Junior Johnson. This here's Junior Johnson!"

The boy has a souvenir racing helmet on his head. He stares at Junior through a buttery face. Junior signs the program he has in his hand, and then the boy's mother says:

"Junior, I tell you right now, he's beside you all the way. He can't be moved."

And then: "Junior, I want you to meet the meanest little girl in Wilkes County."

"She don't look mean to me."

Junior keeps signing autographs and over by the pits the other kids are all over his car, the Dodge. They start pulling off the decals, the ones saying Holly Farms Poultry and Autolite and God knows whatall. They fight over the strips, the shreds of decal, as if they were totems.

All this homage to Junior Johnson lasts about forty minutes. He must be signing about 250 autographs, but he is not a happy man. By and by the crowd is thinning out, the sun is going down, wind is blowing the Coca-Cola cups around, all one can hear, mostly, is a stock-car engine starting up every now and then as somebody drives it up onto a truck or something, and Junior looks around and says:

"I'd rather lead one lap and fall out of the race than stroke it and finish in the money."

"Stroking it" is driving carefully in hopes of outlasting faster and more reckless cars. The opposite of stroking it is "hard-charging." Then Junior says:

"I hate to get whipped up here in Wilkes County."

Wilkes County, North Carolina! Who was it tried to pin the name on Wilkes County, "The bootleg capital of America"? This fellow Vance Packard. But just a minute. . . .

The night after the race Junior and his fiancée, Flossie Clark, and myself went into North Wilkesboro to have dinner. Junior and Flossie came by Lowes Motel and picked me up in the dreamboat white Pontiac. Flossie is a bright, attractive woman, *saftig*, well-organized. She and Junior have been going together since they were in high school. They are going to get married as soon as Junior gets his new house built. Flossie has been doing the decor. Junior Johnson, in the second-highest income bracket in the United States for the past five years, is moving out of his father's white frame house in Ingle Hollow at last. About three hundred yards down the road. Overlooking a lot of good green land and Anderson's Store. Junior shows me through the house, it is almost finished, and when we get to the front door, I ask him, "How much of this land is yours?"

Junior looks around for a minute, and then backs up the hill, up past his three automated chicken houses, and then down into the hollow over the pasture where his $3,100 Santa Gertrudis bull is grazing, and then he says:

"Everything that's green is mine."

Junior Johnson's house is going to be one of the handsomest homes in Wilkes County. Yes. And—such complicated problems of class and status. Junior is not only a legendary figure as a backwoods boy with guts who made good, he is also popular personally, he is still a good old boy, rich as he is. He is also respected for the sound and sober way he has invested his money. He also has one of the best business connections in town, Holly Farms Poultry. What complicates it is that half the county, anyway, reveres him as the greatest, most fabled night-road driver in the history of Southern bootlegging. There is hardly a living soul in the hollows who can conjure up two seconds' honest moral indignation over "the whiskey business." That is what they call it, "the whiskey business." The fact is, it has some positive political overtones, sort of like the I.R.A. in Ireland. The other half of the county—well, North Wilkesboro itself is a prosperous, good-looking town of 5000, where a lot of hearty modern business burghers are making money the modern way, like everywhere else in the U.S.A., in things like banking, poultry processing, furniture, mirror and carpet manufacture, apple growing, and so forth and so on. And one thing these men are tired of is Wilkes County's reputation as a center of moonshining. The U.S. Alcohol and Tobacco Tax agents sit over there in Wilkesboro, right next to North Wilkesboro, year in and year out, and they have been there since God knows when, like an Institution in the land, and every day that they are there, it is like a sign saying, Moonshine County. And even that is not so *bad*—it has nothing to do with it being immoral and only a little to do with it being illegal. The real thing is, it is—raw and hillbilly. And one thing thriving modern Industry is not is hillbilly. And one thing the burghers of North Wilkesboro are not about to be is hillbilly. They have split-level homes that would knock your eyes out. Also swimming pools, white Buick Snatchwagons, flagstone *terrasse*-porches enclosed with louvered glass that opens wide in the summertime, and built-in brick barbecue pits and they give parties where they wear Bermuda shorts and Jax stretch pants and serve rum collins and play twist and bossa-nova records on the hi-fi and tell Shaggy Dog jokes about strange people ordering Martinis. Moonshining . . . just a minute—the truth is, North Wilkesboro. . . .

So we are all having dinner at one of the fine new restaurants in North Wilkesboro, a place of suburban plate-glass elegance. The manager knows Junior and gives us the best table in the place and comes over and talks to Junior a while about the race. A couple of men get up and come over and get Junior's autograph to take home to their sons and so forth. Then toward the end of the meal a couple of North Wilkesboro businessmen come over ("Junior, how are you, Junior. You think you're going to like that fast-backed Ford?") and Junior introduces them to me, from Esquire Magazine.

"Esquire," one of them says. "You're not going to do like that fellow Vance Packard did, are you?"

"Vance Packard?"

"Yeah, I think it was Vance Packard wrote it. He wrote an article and called Wilkes County the bootleg capital of America. Don't pull any of that stuff. I think it was in *American* Magazine. The bootleg capital of America. Don't pull any of that stuff on us."

I looked over at Junior and Flossie. Neither one of them said anything. They didn't even change their expressions.

Ingle Hollow! The next morning I met Junior down in Ingle Hollow at Anderson's Store. That's about fifteen miles out of North Wilkesboro on County Road No. 2400. Junior is known in a lot of Southern newspapers as "the wild man from Ronda" or "the lead-footed chicken farmer from Ronda," but Ronda is only his post-office-box address. His telephone exchange, with the Wilkes Telephone Membership Corporation, is Clingman,

North Carolina, and that isn't really where he lives either. Where he lives is just Ingle Hollow, and one of the communal centers of Ingle Hollow is Anderson's Store. Anderson's is not exactly a grocery store. Out front there are two gasoline pumps under an overhanging roof. Inside there are a lot of things like a soda-pop cooler filled with ice, Coca-Colas, Nehi drinks, Dr. Pepper, Double Cola, and a gumball machine, a lot of racks of Red Man chewing tobacco, Price's potato chips, OKay peanuts, cloth hats for working outdoors in, dried sausages, cigarettes, canned goods, a little bit of meal and flour, fly swatters, and I don't know what all. Inside and outside of Anderson's there are good old boys. The young ones tend to be inside, talking, and the old ones tend to be outside, sitting under the roof by the gasoline pumps, talking. And on both sides, cars; most of them new and pastel.

Junior drives up and gets out and looks up over the door where there is a row of twelve coon tails. Junior says:

"Two of them gone, ain't they?"

One of the good old boys says, "Yeah," and sighs.

A pause, and the other one says, "Somebody stole 'em."

Then the first one says, "Junior, that dog of yours ever come back?"

Junior says, "Not yet."

The second good old boy says, "You looking for her to come back?"

Junior says, "I reckon she'll come back."

The good old boy says, "I had a coon dog went off like that. They don't ever come back. I went out 'ere one day, back over yonder, and there he was, cut right from here to here. I swear if it didn't look like a coon got him. Something. H'it must of turned him every way but loose."

Junior goes inside and gets a Coca-Cola and rings up the till himself, like everybody who goes into Anderson's does, it seems like. It is dead quiet in the hollow except for every now and then a car grinds over the dirt road and down the way. One coon dog missing. But he still has a lot of the black and tans, named Rock. . . .

Rock, Whitey, Red, Buster are in the pen out back of the Johnson house, the old frame house. They have scars all over their faces from fighting coons. Gypsy has one huge gash in her back from fighting something. A red rooster crosses the lawn. That's a big rooster. Shirley, one of Junior's two younger sisters, pretty girls, is out by the fence in shorts, pulling weeds. Annie May is inside the house with Mrs. Johnson. Shirley has the radio outside on the porch aimed at her, The Four Seasons! "Dawn!—ahhhh, ahhhhhh, ahhhhhhhhh!" Then a lot of electronic wheeps and lulus and a screaming disc jockey, yessss! WTOB, the Vibrant Voice of Winston-Salem, North Carolina. It sounds like station WABC in New York. Junior's mother, Mrs. Johnson, is a big, good-natured woman. She comes out and says, "Did you ever see anything like that in your life? Pullin' weeds listenin' to the radio." Junior's father, Robert Glenn Johnson Sr.—he built this frame house about thirty-five years ago, up here where the gravel road ends and the woods start. The road just peters out into the woods up a hill. The house has a living room, four bedrooms and a big kitchen. The living room is full of Junior's racing trophies, and so is the piano in Shirley's room. Junior was born and raised here with his older brothers, L.P., the oldest, and Fred, and his older sister, Ruth. Over yonder, up by that house, there's a man with a mule and a little plow. That's L.P. The Johnsons still keep that old mule around to plow the vegetable gardens. And all around, on all sides like a rim, are the ridges and the woods.

Well, what about those woods, where Vance Packard said the agents come stealing over the ridges and good old boys go crashing through the underbrush to get away from the still and the women start "calling the cows" up and down the hollows as the signal *they* were coming....

Junior motions his hand out toward the hills and says, "I'd say nearly everybody in a fifty-mile radius of here was in the whiskey business at one time or another. When we growed up here, everybody seemed to be more or less messing with whiskey, and myself and my two brothers did quite a bit of transporting. H'it was just a business, like any other business, far as we was concerned. H'it was a matter of survival. During the Depression here, people either had to do that or starve to death. H'it wasn't no gangster type of business or nothing. They's nobody that ever messed with it here that was ever out to hurt anybody. Even if they got caught, they never tried to shoot anybody or anything like that. Getting caught and pulling time, that was just part of it. H'it was just a business, like any other business. Me and my brothers, when we went out on the road at night, h'it was just like a milk run, far as we was concerned. They was certain deliveries to be made and...."

A milk run—yes! Well, it was a business, all right. In fact, it was a regional industry, all up and down the Appalachian slopes. But never mind the Depression. It goes back a long way before that. The Scotch-Irish settled the mountains from Pennsylvania down to Alabama, and they have been making whiskey out there as long as anybody can remember. At first it was a simple matter of economics. The land had a low crop yield, compared to the lowlands, and even after a man struggled to grow his corn, or whatever, the cost of transporting it to the markets from down out of the hills was so great, it wasn't worth it. It was much more profitable to convert the corn into whiskey and sell that. The trouble started with the Federal Government on that score almost the moment the Republic was founded. Alexander Hamilton put a high excise tax on whiskey in 1791, almost as soon as the Constitution was ratified. The "Whiskey Rebellion" broke out in the mountains of western Pennsylvania in 1794. The farmers were mad as hell over the tax. Fifteen thousand Federal troops marched out to the mountains and suppressed them. Almost at once, however, the trouble over the whiskey tax became a symbol of something bigger. This was a general enmity between the western and eastern sections of practically every seaboard state. Part of it was politi-

cal. The eastern sections tended to control the legislatures, the economy and the law courts, and the western sections felt shortchanged. Part of it was cultural. Life in the western sections was rougher. Religions, codes and styles of life were sterner. Life in the eastern capitals seemed to give off the odor of Europe and decadence. Shays' Rebellion broke out in the Berkshire hills of western Massachusetts in 1786 in an attempt to shake off the yoke of Boston, which seemed as bad as George III's. To this day people in western Massachusetts make proposals, earnestly or with down-in-the-mouth humor, that they all ought to split off from "Boston." Whiskey—the mountain people went right on making it. Whole sections of the Appalachians were a whiskey belt, just as sections of Georgia, Alabama and Mississippi were a cotton belt. Nobody on either side ever had any moral delusions about why the Federal Government was against it. It was always the tax, pure and simple. Today the price of liquor is sixty-percent tax. Today, of course, with everybody gone wild over the subject of science and health, it has been much easier for the Federals to persuade people that they crack down on moonshine whiskey because it is dangerous, it poisons, kills and blinds people. The statistics are usually specious.

Moonshining was *illegal*, however, that was also the unvarnished truth. And that had a side effect in the whiskey belt. The people there were already isolated, geographically, by the mountains and had strong clan ties because they were all from the same stock, Scotch-Irish. Moonshining isolated them even more. They always had to be careful who came up there. There are plenty of hollows to this day where if you drive in and ask some good old boy where so-and-so is, he'll tell you he never heard of the fellow. Then the next minute, if you identify yourself and give some idea of why you want to see him, and he believes you, he'll suddenly say, "Aw, you're talking about *so-and-so*. I thought you said—" With all this isolation, the mountain people began to take on certain characteristics normally associated, by the diffident civilizations of today, with tribes. There was a strong sense of family, clan and honor. People would cut and shoot each other up over honor. And physical courage! They were almost like Turks that way.

In the Korean War, not a very heroic performance by American soldiers generally, there were seventy-eight Medal of Honor winners. Thirty-nine of them were from the South, and practically all of the thirty-nine were from small towns in or near the Appalachians. The New York metropolitan area, which has more people than all these towns put together, had three Medal of Honor winners, and one of them had just moved to New York from the Appalachian region of West Virginia. Three of the Medal of Honor winners came from within fifty miles of Junior Johnson's side porch.

Detroit has discovered these pockets of courage almost like a natural resource, in the form of Junior Johnson and about twenty other drivers. There is something exquisitely ironic about it. Detroit is now engaged in the highly sophisticated business of offering the illusion of Speed for Everyman—making their cars go 175 miles an hour on racetracks—by discovering and putting behind the wheel a breed of mountain men who are living vestiges of a degree of physical courage that became extinct in most other sections of the country by 1900. Of course, very few stock-car drivers have ever had anything to do with the whiskey business. A great many always lead quiet lives off the track. But it is the same strong people among whom the whiskey business developed who produced the kind of men who could drive the stock cars. There are a few exceptions, Freddie Lorenzen, from Elmhurst, Illinois, being the most notable. But, by and large, it is the rural Southern code of honor and courage that has produced these, the most daring men in sports.

Cars and bravery! The mountain-still operators had been running white liquor with hopped-up automobiles all during the Thirties. But it was during the war that the business was so hot out of Wilkes County, down to Charlotte, High Point, Greensboro, Winston-Salem, Salisbury, places like that; a night's run, by one car, would bring anywhere from $500 to $1,000. People had money all of a sudden. One car could carry twenty-two to twenty-five cases of white liquor. There were twelve half-gallon fruit jars full per case, so each load would have 132 gallons or more. It would sell to the distributor in the city for about ten dollars a gallon, when the market was good, of which the driver would get two dollars, as much as $300 for the night's work.

The usual arrangement in the white-liquor industry was for the elders to design the distillery, supervise the formulas and the whole distilling process and take care of the business end of the operation. The young men did the heavy work, carrying the copper and other heavy goods out into the woods, building the still, hauling in fuel—and driving. Junior and his older brothers, L.P. and Fred, worked that way with their father, Robert Glenn Johnson Sr.

Johnson Senior was one of the biggest individual copper-still operators in the area. The fourth time he was arrested, the agents found a small fortune in working corn mash bubbling in the vats.

"My Daddy was always a hard worker," Junior is telling me. "He always wanted something a little bit better. A lot of people resented that and held that against him, but what he got, he always got h'it by hard work. There ain't no harder work in the world than making whiskey. I don't know of any other business that compels you to get up at all times of night and go outdoors in the snow and everything else and work. It's the hardest way in the world to make a living, and I don't think anybody'd do it unless they had to."

Working mash wouldn't wait for a man. It started coming to a head when it got ready to and a man had to be there to take it off, out there in the woods, in the brush, in the brambles, in the muck, in the snow. Wouldn't it have been something if you could have just set it all up inside a good old shed with a corrugated metal roof and order those parts like you want them and not have to smuggle all that copper and all that sugar and all that everything out here in the woods and be a coppersmith and a plumber and a cooper and a carpenter and a packhorse and every other goddamned thing God ever saw in this world, all at once.

And live decent hours—Junior and his brothers, about two o'clock in the morning they'd head out to the stash, the place where the liquor was hidden after it was made. Sometimes it would be somebody's house or an old shed or someplace just out in the woods, and they'd make their arrangements out there, what the route was and who was getting how much liquor. There wasn't anything ever written down. Everything was cash on the spot. Different drivers like to make the run at different times, but Junior and his brothers always liked to start out from three to four a.m. But it got so no matter when you started out you didn't have those roads to yourself.

"Some guys liked one time and some guys liked another time," Junior is saying, "but starting about midnight they'd be coming out of the woods from every direction. Some nights the whole road was full of bootleggers. It got so some nights they'd be somebody following you going just as fast as you were and you didn't know who h'it was, the law or somebody else hauling whiskey."

And it was just a business, like any other business, just like a milk route—but this funny thing was happening. In those wild-ass times, with the money flush and good old boys from all over the county running that white liquor down the road ninety miles an hour and more than that if you try to crowd them a little bit—well, the funny thing was, it got to be competitive in an almost aesthetic, a pure sporting way. The way the good old boys got to hopping up their automobiles—it got to be a science practically. Everybody was looking to build a car faster than anybody ever had before. They practically got into industrial espionage over it. They'd come up behind one another on those wild-ass nights on the highway, roaring through the black gulches between the clay cuts and the trees, pretending like they were officers, just to challenge them, test them out, race . . . *pour le sport,* careening through the darkness, old Carolina moon. All these cars were registered in phony names. If a man had to abandon one, they would find license plates that traced back to . . . nobody at all. It wasn't anything, particularly, to go down to the Motor Vehicle Bureau and get some license plates, as long as you paid your money. Of course, it's rougher now, with compulsory insurance. You have to have your insurance before you can get your license plates, and that leads to a lot of complications. Junior doesn't know what they do about that now. Anyway, all these cars with the magnificent engines were plain on the outside, so they wouldn't attract attention, but they couldn't disguise them altogether. They were jacked up a little in the back and had 8.00 or 8.20 tires, for the heavy loads, and the sound—

"They wasn't no way you could make it sound like an ordinary car," says Junior.

God-almighty, that sound in the middle of the night, groaning, roaring, humming down into the hollows, through the clay gulches—yes! And all over the rural South, hell, all over the South, the legends of wild-driving whiskey running got started. And it wasn't just the plain excitement of it. It was something deeper, the symbolism. It brought into a modern focus the whole business, one and a half centuries old, of the country people's rebellion against the Federals, against the seaboard establishment, their independence, their defiance of the outside world. And it was like a mythology for that and for something else that was happening, the whole wild thing of the car as the symbol of liberation in the postwar South.

"They was out about every night, patroling, the agents and the state police was," Junior is saying, "but they seldom caught anybody. H'it was like the dogs chasing the fox. The dogs can't catch a fox, he'll just take 'em around in a circle all night long. I was never caught for transporting. We never lost but one car and the axle broke on h'it."

The fox and the dogs! Whiskey running certainly had a crazy game-like quality about it, considering that a boy might be sent up for two years or more if he were caught transporting. But these boys were just wild enough for that. There got to be a code about the chase. In Wilkes County nobody, neither the good old boys nor the agents, ever did anything that was going to hurt the other side physically. There were supposed to be some parts of the South where the boys used smoke screens and tack buckets. They had attachments in the rear of the cars, and if the agents got too close they would let loose a smoke screen to blind them or a slew of tacks to make them blow a tire. But nobody in Wilkes County ever did that because that was a good way for somebody to get killed. Part of it was that whenever an agent did get killed in the South, whole hordes of agents would come in from Washington and pretty soon they would be tramping along the ridges practically inch by inch, smoking out the stills. But mainly it was— well, the code. If you got caught, you went along peaceably, and the agents never used their guns. There were some tense times. Once was when the agents started using tack belts in Ardell County. This was a long strip of leather studded with nails that the agents would lay across the road in the dark. A man couldn't see it until it was too late and he stood a good chance of getting killed if it got his tires and spun him out. The other was the time the State Police put a roadblock down there at that damned bridge at Millersville to catch a couple of escaped convicts. Well, a couple of good old boys rode up with a load, and there was the roadblock and they were already on the bridge, so they jumped out and dove into the water. The police saw two men jump out of their car and dive in the water, so they opened fire and they shot one good old boy in the backside. As they pulled him out, he kept saying:

"What did you have to shoot at me for? What did you have to shoot at me for?"

It wasn't pain, it wasn't anguish, it wasn't anger. It was consternation. The bastards had broken the code.

Then the Federals started getting radio cars.

"The radios didn't do them any good," Junior says. "As soon as the officers got radios, then *they* got radios. They'd go out and get the same radio. It was an awful hard thing for them to radio them down. They'd just listen in on the radio and see where they're setting up the roadblocks and go a different way."

And such different ways. The good old boys knew back roads, dirt roads, up people's back lanes and every whichway, and an agent would have to live in the North Carolina hills a lifetime to get to know them. There wasn't hardly a stretch of road on any of the routes where a good old boy couldn't duck off the road and into the backcountry if he had to. They had wild detours around practically every town and every intersection in the region. And for tight spots— the legendary devices, the "bootleg slide," the siren and the red light. . . .

"Yeah, we used to do that turnabout," Junior says. "H'it wasn't hard. You just cock the wheel and sling the rear end around."

And the siren and the red light—don't you see, it was just a matter of keeping up with the competition. You always have to have the latest equipment. It was a business thing, like any other business, you have to stay on top—"They was some guys who was more dependable, they done a better job"—and it may have been business to Junior, but it wasn't business to a generation of good old boys growing up all over the South. The Wilkes County bootleg cars started picking up popular names in a kind of folk hero worship —"The Black Ghost," "The Grey Ghost," which were two of Junior's, "Old Mother Goose," "The Midnight Traveler," "Old Faithful."

And then one day in 1955 some agents snuck over the ridges and caught Junior Johnson at his daddy's still. Junior Johnson, the man couldn't *any*body catch!

The arrest caught Junior just as he was ready to really take off in his career as a stock-car driver. Junior says he hadn't been in the whiskey business in any shape or form, hadn't run a load of whiskey for two or three years, when he was arrested. He says he didn't need to fool around with running whiskey after he got into stock-car racing, he was making enough money at that. He was just out there at the still helping his daddy with some of the heavy labor, there wasn't a good old boy in Ingle Hollow who wouldn't help his daddy lug those big old cords of ash wood, it doesn't give off much smoke, out in the woods. Junior was sentenced to two years in the Federal reformatory in Chillicothe, Ohio.

"If the law felt I should have gone to jail, that's fine and dandy," Junior tells me. "But I don't think the true facts of the case justified the sentence I got. I never had been arrested in my life. I think they was punishing me for the past. People get a kick out of it because the officers can't catch somebody, and this angers them. Soon as I started getting publicity for racing, they started making it real hot for my family. I was out of the whiskey business, and they knew that, but they was just waiting to catch me on something. I got out after serving ten months and three days of the sentence, but h'it was two or three years I was set back, about half of '56 and every bit of '57. H'it takes a year to really get back into h'it after something like that. I think I lost the prime of my racing career. I feel that if I had been given the chance I feel I was due, rather than the sentence I got, my life would have got a real boost."

But, if anything, the arrest only made the Junior Johnson legend hotter.

And all the while Detroit kept edging the speeds up, from 150 m.p.h. in 1960 to 155 to 165 to 175 to 180 flat out on the longest straightaway, and the good old boys of Southern stock-car racing stuck right with it. Any speed Detroit would give them they would take right with them into the curve, hard-charging even though they began to feel strange things such as the rubber starting to pull right off the tire casing. And God! Good old boys from all over the South roared together after the Stanchion—Speed! Guts!—pouring into Birmingham, Daytona Beach, Randleman, North Carolina; Spartanburg, South Carolina; Weaverville, Hillsboro, North Carolina; Atlanta, Hickory, Bristol, Tennessee; Augusta, Georgia; Richmond, Virginia; Asheville, North Carolina; Charlotte, Myrtle Beach—tens of thousands of them. And still upper- and middle-class America, even in the South, keeps its eyes averted. Who cares! They kept on heading out where we all live, after all . . . even outside a town like Darlington, a town of 10,000 souls, God, here they come, down route 52, up 401 on 340, 151 and 34, on through the South Carolina mesas. By Friday night already the good old boys are pulling into the infield of the Darlington raceway with those blazing pastel dreamboats stacked this way and that on the clay flat and the Thermos jugs and the brown whiskey bottles coming on out. By Sunday—the race! —there are 65,000 piled into the racetrack at Darlington. The sheriff, as always, sets up the jail right there in the infield. No use trying to haul them out of there. And now—the *sound* rises up inside the raceway, and a good old boy named Ralph goes mad and starts selling chances on his Dodge. Twenty-five cents and you can take the sledge he has and smash his car anywhere you want. How they roar when the windshield breaks! The police could interfere, you know, but they are busy chasing a good old girl who is playing Lady Godiva on a hog-backed motorcycle, naked as sin, hauling around and in and out of the clay ruts.

Eyes averted, happy burghers. On Monday the ads start appearing—for Ford, for Plymouth, for Dodge—announcing that we gave it to you, speed such as you never saw. There it was! At Darlington, Daytona, Atlanta—and not merely in the Southern papers but in the albino pages of the suburban women's magazines, such as *The New Yorker,* in color—the Ford winners, such as Fireball Roberts, grinning with a cigar in his mouth in *The New Yorker* Magazine. And somewhere, some Monday morning, Jim Paschal of High Point, Ned Jarrett of Boykin, Cale Yarborough of Timmonsville and Curtis Crider from Charlotte, Bobby Isaac of Catawba, E. J. Trivette of Deep Gap, Richard Petty of Randleman, Tiny Lund of Cross, South Carolina; Stick Elliott of Shelby—and from out of Ingle Hollow.

And all the while, standing by in full Shy, in Alumicron suits—there is Detroit, hardly able to believe itself, what it has discovered, a breed of good old boys from the fastnesses of the Appalachian hills and flats—a handful from this rare breed—who has given Detroit . . . speed . . . and the industry can present it to a whole generation as . . . yours. And the Detroit p.r. men themselves come to the tracks like folk worshippers and the millions go giddy with the thrill of speed. Only Junior Johnson goes about it as if it were . . . the usual. Junior goes on down to Atlanta for the Dixie 400 and drops by the Federal penitentiary to see his daddy. His daddy is in on his fifth illegal-distillery conviction; in the whiskey business that's just part of it; an able craftsman, an able businessman, and the law kept hounding him, that was all. So Junior drops by and then goes on out to the track and gets in his new Ford and sets the qualifying speed record for the Atlanta Dixie 400, 146.301 m.p.h.; later on he tools on back up the road to Ingle Hollow to tend to the automatic chicken houses and the road-grading operation. Yes.

Yet how can you tell that to . . . anybody . . . out on the bottom of that bowl as the motor thunder begins to lift up through him like a sigh and his eyeballs glaze over and his hands reach up and there, riding the rim of the bowl, soaring over the ridges, is Junior's yellow Ford . . . which is his white Chevrolet . . . which is a White Ghost, forever rousing the good old boys . . . hard-charging! . . . up with the automobile into their America, and the hell with arteriosclerotic old boys trying to hold onto the whole pot with arms of cotton seersucker. Junior!

A QUESTION OF LEGALITY

Esquire's perennial concern with matters of law has ranged from Richard Rovere on Ezra Pound's indictment for treason to John Sack on the court-martial of Lieutenant Calley, from Dean Acheson on the sophistication of law to Dwight Macdonald on revising the Constitution. Just the names of those who have been featured in Esquire articles summon up a legal history of our times: Sacco and Vanzetti, Alger Hiss and Whittaker Chambers, even Dr. Stephen Ward and Mickey Jelke. In American advocacy, no name looms larger than that of Clarence Darrow, who wrote the article on the following page long after his defense of Eugene Debs, the Loeb-Leopold case and the Scopes trial had made him a legend. Darrow once said of the great Governor Altgeld of Illinois what might have been said of himself: "Even admirers have seldom understood the real character of this great human man. It was not a callous heart that so often led him to brave the most violent and malicious hate; it was not a callous heart, it was a devoted soul . . . that spoke for the poor, the oppressed, the captive and the weak."

No litigation has had greater significance for literary freedom than the 1960 English trial which finally revoked the obscenity ban on Lady Chatterley's Lover. Although an unabridged edition of Lawrence's book appeared in Paris in 1929, it was not until 1959 that an unexpurgated version was published in the United States. It was immediately banned by the U.S. Post Office, but Judge Frederick van Pelt Bryan ruled the ban unconstitutional. The following year, the book faced its final challenge in a London courtroom, and novelist and reporter Sybille Bedford was there to cover the trial for Esquire.

In the late Fifties, when John Steinbeck hailed Arthur Miller's defiance of the House Committee on Un-American Activities in the article which concludes this section, such dissent was a test of faith. And, as Arthur Miller later wrote in After the Fall, "If everyone broke faith, there would be no civilization. That is why the Committee is the face of the Philistine. And it astounds me that you can speak of truth and justice in relation to that gang of cheap publicity hounds!"

160

Clarence Darrow:

Attorney for the Defense

The laughing man and the poor man are best in the jury,
as they understand life's values

The audience that storms the box office of the theatre to gain entrance to a sensational show is small and sleepy compared with the throng that crashes the courthouse door when something concerning real life and death is to be laid bare to the public.

Everyone knows that the best portrayals of life are tame and sickly when matched with the realities. For this reason, the sophisticated Romans were wont to gather at the Colosseum to feast their eyes and other senses on fountains of real blood and await breathlessly the final thrust. The courtroom is a modern arena in which the greatest thrills follow closely on each other. If the combat concerns human life it presents an atmosphere and setting not unlike those cruel and bloody scenes of ancient Rome. The judge wears the same flowing robe with all of the dignity and superiority he can command. This sets him apart from his fellowmen and is designed to awe and intimidate and to impress the audience with seeming wisdom oftener than with kindliness and compassion.

One cannot help wondering what happens to the pomp and pretense of the wearer while the cloak is in the wash, or while changing into a maturer, more monarchical mantle, as his bench becomes a throne, or when he strolls along the street in file with the "plain clothes" people.

When court opens, the bailiff intones some voodoo singsong words in ominous voice that carries fear and respect at the opening of the rite. The courtroom is full of staring men and women shut within closed doors, guarded by officials wearing uniforms to confound the simple inside the sacred precinct. This dispels all hope of mercy to the unlettered, the poor and helpless, who scarcely dare express themselves above a whisper in any such forbidding place.

The stage, the arena, the court are alike in that each has its audience thirsting to drink deeply of the passing show. Those playing the parts vie for success and use whatever skill and talent they possess. An actor may fumble his lines, but a lawyer needs to be

Darrow was seventy-nine when Esquire asked him to write on the art of picking a jury. Darrow's response, published in May, 1936, went beyond the assignment to include his summation of a lifetime spent asking, "What is Justice?" He died two years later on March 13, 1938.

letter-perfect, at least, he has to use his wits, and he may forget himself, and often does, but never for a moment can he lose sight of his client.

Small wonder that ambitious, imaginative youths crowd the profession of law. Here, they feel, they, themselves, will find the opportunity to play a real part in the comedies as well as the tragedies of life. Everyone, no matter how small his chance may be, tries to hold the center of some stage where the multitude will scan his every move. To most lads it seems as though the courts were organized to furnish them a chance to bask in the public eye. In this field the adventure of life will never pall, but prove interesting, exciting and changeful to the end. Not only will he have the destinies of men to protect and preserve, but his own standing and success to create.

Chancery cases are not especially interesting or exciting, however. These are supposed to be heard by a judge. He listens long enough to feel satisfied that the case promises to consume considerable time and work and interfere with many hours of leisure, so he refers it to a "Master in Chancery," a lawyer-friend of his own appointment, who is paid by fees that come directly from the litigants; the Master in Chancery employs a court reporter who takes the evidence in shorthand while the Master may take a nap in an adjoining office. After the clients' resources are exhausted by the court reporters and Masters in Chancery, the documents are locked up in a safe to await the blowing of Gabriel's horn.

If it is a real case, criminal or civil, it usually is tried by a jury with the assistance and direction of the judge. In that event, every moment counts, and neither the lawyers nor the audience, or even the court, goes to sleep. If it is a criminal case, or even a civil one, it is not the law alone or the facts themselves that determine the result. Always the element of luck and chance looms large. A jury of twelve men is watching not only the evidence but the attitude of each lawyer, and the parties involved, in all their moves. Every step is fraught with doubt, if not mystery.

Selecting a jury is of the utmost importance. So far as possible, the lawyer should know both sides of the case. If the client is a landlord, a banker, or a manufacturer, or one of that type, then jurors sympathetic

161

to that class will be wanted in the box; a man who looks neat and trim and smug. He will be sure to guard your interests as he would his own. His entire environment has taught him that all real values are measured in cash, and he knows no other worth. Every knowing lawyer seeks for a jury of the same sort of men as his client; men who will be able to imagine themselves in the same situation and realize what verdict the client wants.

Lawyers are just as carefully concerned about the likes and dislikes, the opinions and fads of judges as of jurors. All property rights are much safer in the hands of courts than of jurors. Every lawyer who represents the poor avoids a trial by the court.

Choosing jurors is always a delicate task. The more a lawyer knows of life, human nature, psychology, and the reactions of the human emotions, the better he is equipped for the subtle selection of his so-called "twelve men, good and true." In this undertaking, everything pertaining to the prospective juror needs be questioned and weighed; his nationality, his business, religion, politics, social standing, family ties, friends, habits of life and thought; the books and newspapers he likes and reads, and many more matters that combine to make a man; all of these qualities and experiences have left their effect on ideas, beliefs and fancies that inhabit his mind. Understanding of all this cannot be obtained too bluntly. It usually requires finesse, subtlety and guesswork. Involved in it all is the juror's method of speech, the kind of clothes he wears, the style of haircut, and, above all, his business associates, residence and origin.

To the ordinary observer, a man is just a man. To the student of life and human beings, every pose and movement is a part of the personality and the man. There is no sure rule by which one can gauge any person. A man may seem to be of a certain mold, but a wife, a friend, or an enemy, entering into his life, may change his most vital views, desires and attitudes, so that he will hardly recognize himself as the man he once seemed to be.

It is obvious that if a litigant discovered one of his dearest friends in the jury panel he could make a close guess as to how certain facts, surrounding circumstances, and suppositions would affect his mind and action; but as he has no such acquaintance with the stranger before him, he must weigh the prospective juror's words, manner of speech and, in fact, hastily and cautiously "size him up" as best he can. The litigants and their lawyers are supposed to want justice, but, in reality, there is no such thing as justice, either in or out of court. In fact, the word cannot be defined. So, for lack of proof, let us assume that the word "justice" has a meaning, and that the common idea of the definition is correct, without even seeking to find out what is the common meaning. Then, how do we reach justice through the courts? The lawyer's idea of justice is a verdict for his client, and really this is the sole end for which he aims.

In spite of the power that the courts exercise over the verdict of a jury, still the finding of the twelve men is very important, sometimes conclusive. It goes without saying that lawyers always do their utmost to get men on the jury who are apt to decide in favor of their clients. It is not the experience of jurors, neither is it their brainpower, that is the potent influence in their decisions. A skillful lawyer does not tire himself hunting for learning or intelligence in the box; if he knows much about man and his making, he knows that all beings act from emotions and instincts, and that reason is not a motive factor. If deliberation counts for anything, it is to retard decision. The nature of the man himself is the element that determines the juror's bias for or against his fellowman. Assuming that a juror is not a half-wit, his intellect can always furnish fairly good reasons for following his instincts and emotions. Many irrelevant issues in choosing jurors are not so silly as they seem. Matters that apparently have nothing to do with the discussion of a case often are of the greatest significance.

In the last analysis, most jury trials are contests between the rich and poor. If the case concerns money, it is apt to be a case of damages for injuries of some sort claimed to have been inflicted by someone. These cases are usually defended by insurance companies, railroads, or factories. If a criminal case, it is practically always the poor who are on trial.

The most important point to learn is whether the prospective juror is humane. This must be discovered in more or less devious ways. As soon as "the court" sees what you want, he almost always blocks the game. Next to this, in having more or less bearing on the question, is the nationality, politics, and religion of the person examined for the jury. If you do not discover this, all your plans may go awry. Whether you are handling a damage suit, or your client is charged with the violation of law, his attorney will try to get the same sort of juror.

Let us assume that we represent one of "the underdogs" because of injuries received, or because of an indictment brought by what the prosecutors name themselves—"the state." Then what sort of men will we seek? An Irishman is called into the box for examination. There is no reason for asking about his religion; he is Irish; that is enough. We may not agree with his religion, but it matters not; his feelings go deeper than any religion. You should be aware that he is emotional, kindly and sympathetic. If he is chosen as a juror, his imagination will place him in the dock; really, he is trying himself. You would be guilty of malpractice if you got rid of him, except for the strongest reasons.

An Englishman is not so good as an Irishman, but still, he has come through a long tradition of individual rights, and is not afraid to stand alone; in fact, he is never sure that he is right unless the great majority is against him. The German is not so keen about individual rights except where they concern his own way of life; liberty is not a theory, it is a way of living. Still, he wants to do what is right, and he is not afraid. He has not been among us long, his ways are fixed by

his race, his habits are still in the making. We need inquire no further. If he is a Catholic, then he loves music and art; he must be emotional, and will want to help you; give him a chance.

If a Presbyterian enters the jury box, carefully rolls up his umbrella, and calmly and critically sits down, let him go. He is cold as the grave; he knows right from wrong, although he seldom finds anything right. He believes in John Calvin and eternal punishment. Get rid of him with the fewest possible words before he contaminates the others; unless you and your clients are Presbyterians you probably are a bad lot, and even though you may be a Presbyterian, your client most likely is guilty.

If possible, the Baptists are more hopeless than the Presbyterians. They, too, are apt to think that the real home of all outsiders is Sheol, and you do not want them on the jury, and the sooner they leave the better.

The Methodists are worth considering; they are nearer the soil. Their religious emotions can be transmuted into love and charity. They are not half bad, even though they will not take a drink; they really do not need it so much as some of their competitors for the seat next to the throne. If chance sets you down between a Methodist and a Baptist, you will move toward the Methodist to keep warm.

Beware of the Lutherans, especially the Scandinavians; they are almost always sure to convict. Either a Lutheran or Scandinavian is unsafe, but if both-in-one, plead your client guilty and go down the docket. He learns about sinning and punishing from the preacher, and dares not doubt. A person who disobeys must be sent to Hell; he has God's word for that.

As to Unitarians, Universalists, Congregationalists, Jews and other agnostics, don't ask them too many questions; keep them anyhow; especially Jews and agnostics. It is best to inspect a Unitarian, or a Universalist, or a Congregationalist, with some care, for they may be prohibitionists; but never the Jews and the real agnostics! And, do not, please, accept a prohibitionist: he is too solemn and holy and dyspeptic. He knows your client would not have been indicted unless he were a drinking man, and anyone who drinks is guilty of something, probably much worse than he is charged with, although it is not set out in the indictment. Neither would he have employed *you* as his lawyer had he not been guilty.

I have never experimented much with Christian Scientists; they are too serious for me. Somehow, solemn people seem to think that pleasure is wicked. Only the gloomy and dyspeptic can be trusted to convict. Shakespeare knew: "Yond' Cassius has a lean and hungry look; he thinks too much; such men are dangerous." You may defy all the rest of the rules if you can get a man who laughs. Few things in this world are of enough importance to warrant considering them seriously. So, by all means, choose a man who laughs. A juror who laughs hates to find anyone guilty.

Never take a wealthy man on a jury. He will convict, unless the defendant is accused of violating the anti-trust law, selling worthless stocks or bonds, or something of that kind. Next to the Board of Trade, for him, the Penitentiary is the most important of all public buildings. These imposing structures stand for Capitalism. Civilization could not possibly exist without them. Don't take a man because he is a "good" man; this means nothing. You should find out what he is good *for*. Neither should a man be accepted because he is a bad sort. There are too many ways of being good or bad. If you are defending, you want imaginative individuals. You are not interested in the morals of the juror. If a man is instinctively kind and sympathetic, take him.

Then, too, there are the women. These are now in the jury box. A new broom sweeps clean. It leaves no speck on the floor or under the bed, or in the darkest corners of life. To these new jurors, the welfare of the state depends on the verdict. It will be so for many years to come. The chances are that it would not have made the slightest difference to the state if all cases had been decided the other way. It might, however, make a vast difference to the unfortunates facing cruel, narrow-minded jurors who pass judgment on their fellowmen. To the defendants it might have meant the fate of life rather than death.

But, what is one life more or less in the general spawning? It may float away on the tide, or drop to the depths of oblivion, broken, crushed and dead. The great sea is full of embryo lives ready to take the places of those who have gone before. One more unfortunate lives and dies as the endless stream flows on, and little it matters to the wise judges who coldly pronounce long strings of words in droning cadence: the victims are removed, they come and go and the judges keep on chanting senseless phrases laden with doom upon the bowed heads of those before them. The judge is as unconcerned about the actual meaning of it all as the soughing wind rustling the leaves of a tree just outside the courthouse door.

Women still take their new privilege seriously. They are all puffed up with the importance of the part they feel they play, and are sure they represent a great step forward in the world. They believe that the sex is cooperating in a great cause. Like the rest of us, they do not know which way is forward and which is backward, or whether either one is any way at all. Luckily, as I feel, my services were almost over when women invaded the jury box.

A few years ago I became interested in a man charged with selling some brand of intoxicant in a denatured land that needed cheering. I do not know whether he sold it or not. I forgot to ask him. I viewed the case with mixed feelings of pity and contempt, for, as Omar philosophized, "I wonder often what the vintners buy one half so precious as the stuff they sell?" When I arrived on the scene, the courtroom looked ominous with women jurors. I managed to get rid of all but two, while the dismissed women lingered around in the big room waiting for the victory, wearing solemn faces and white ribbons. The jury disagreed. In the second trial there were four women who would not budge from their seats, or their verdict. Once more I went back to the case with distrust and apprehension. The number of women in the jury box had grown to six. All of them were unprejudiced. They said so. But everyone connected with the case was growing tired and skeptical, so we concluded to call it a draw. This was my last experience with women jurors. I formed a fixed opinion that they were absolutely dependable, but I did not want them.

Whether a jury is a good one or a bad one depends on the point of view. I have always been an attorney for the defense. I can think of nothing, not even war, that has brought so much misery to the human race as prisons. And all of it is so futile!

I once spent a winter on the shores of the Mediterranean Sea. In front of my windows, four fishermen were often wearily trudging back and forth, and slowly dragging a long net across the sand. When it was safely landed, a few small, flopping fish disclosed the results of their labors. These were scattered dying on the beach, while the really worthwhile fishes were left in the sea, which somehow reminded me of our courts and juries, and other aims and efforts of optimistic men and their idle undertakings, and disheartening results.

Judges and jurors are like the rest of humans. Now and then some outstanding figures will roll up their sleeves, as it were, and vigorously set to work to reform the courts and get an efficient administration of justice. This will be ably seconded by the newspapers, lashing courts and jurors, past, present and prospective, into a spasm of virtue that brings down the innocent and guilty together, assuming always that there are innocent and guilty. Then, for a time, every defendant is convicted; and soon the campaign reaches the courts; after ruining a few lives and reputations, the frenzy is over, and life goes on smoothly and tranquilly as before.

When I was a boy in the country, one of the standard occupations was whittling. It became as mechanical as breathing. Since then I have decided that this is as good a way to live as any other. Life depends on the automatic taking in and letting out of breath, but in no way is it lengthened or made happier by deep thinking or wise acting. The one big word that stands over courts and other human activities is Futility.

The courts may be unavailing, lawyers stupid, and both as dry as dust, but the combination makes for something interesting and exciting, and it opens avenues that seem to lead somewhere. Liberty, lives, fortunes often are at stake, and appeals for assistance and mercy rend the air for those who care to hear. In an effort to help, often a casual remark may determine a seemingly vital situation, when perhaps the remark, of all the palaver, was the least important one breathed forth. In all questions men are fre-

quently influenced by some statement which, spoken at the eventful time, determines fate. The most unforeseen, accidental meetings sometimes result in seemingly new and strangely fateful family lines. In fact, all that occurs in life is an endless sequence of events resulting from the wildest chance.

Amongst the twelve in a jury box are all degrees of alertness, all sorts of ideas, and a variety of emotions; and the lawyers, too, are important factors in the outcome. They are closely observed by the jurors. They are liked, or disliked. Mayhap because of what they say, or how they speak, or pronounce their words, or part their hair. It may be that a lawyer is disliked because he talks too little, or too much; more often the latter. But a lawyer of subtlety should know when to stop, and when to go on, and how far to go. As a rule, he must not seem to be above the juror, nor below him. He must not too obviously strive for effect. He often meets baffling situations not easily explained. Sometimes it is better for him to talk of something else. Explanations must not be too fantastic, or ridiculous. It does no harm to admit the difficulty of the situation, to acknowledge that this circumstance or that seems against him. Many facts point to guilt, but in another light these facts may appear harmless.

Lawyers are apt to interpret deeds and motives as they wish them to appear. As a matter of fact, most actions are subject to various inferences, sometimes quite improbable, but nonetheless true. Identifications show common examples of mistakes. Many men are in prison and some are sent to death through mistaken identifications. One needs but recall the countless errors he himself has made. How many have met some person whom they believed to be an old-time friend, and have found themselves greeting a total stranger? This is a common mistake made in restaurants and other public places. Many identifications in court are made from having seen a person but once, and under conditions not critical. Many are made from descriptions and photographs, and urged on by detectives, lawyers, and others vitally interested in the results. From all of this it is easy to see that many are convicted who are guiltless of crime. In situations of strong agitation, acquittals are rare, and sentences made long and barbarous and inhuman.

The judge is, of course, an important part of the machinery and administration of the court. Like carpenters, and lawyers, bricklayers, and saloonkeepers, they are not all alike. No two of them have the same fitness for their positions. No two have the same education; no two have the same natural understanding of themselves and their fellowman, or are gifted with the same discernment and balance. Not that judges are lacking in knowledge of law. The ordinary rules for the administration of law are rather simple and not difficult to follow. But judges should be students of life, even more than of law. Biology and psychology, which form the basis of understanding human conduct, should be taken into account. Without a fair knowledge of the mechanism of man, and the motives and urges that govern his life, it is idle to venture to fathom a situation; but, with some knowledge, officers and the public can be most useful in preserving and protecting those who most need such help. The life of almost any unfortunate, if rightly understood, can be readjusted to some plan of order and system, instead of left to drift on to ruin, the victim of ignorance, hatred and chance.

If the physician so completely ignored natural causes as the lawyers and judges, the treatment of disease would be relegated to witchcraft and magic, and the dungeon and rack would once more hold high carnival in driving devils out of the sick and afflicted. Many of the incurable victims of crime are like those who once were incurable victims of disease; they are the product of vicious and incompetent soothsayers who control their destinies. Every human being, whether parent, teacher, physician, or prosecutor, should make the comfort and happiness of their dependents their first concern. Now and then some learned courts take a big view of life, but scarcely do they make an impression until some public brainstorm drives them back in their treatment of crime to the methods of sorcery and conjury.

No scientific attitude toward crime can be adopted until lawyers, like physicians and scientists, recognize that cause and effect determine the conduct of men.

When lawyers and courts, and laymen accept the scientific theory which the physicians forced upon the world long years ago, then men will examine each so-called delinquency until they discover its cause, and then learn how to remove the cause. This requires sympathy, humanity, love of one's fellowman, and a strong faith in the power of knowledge and experience to conquer the maladies of men. The forum of the lawyers may then grow smaller, the courthouse may lose its spell, but the world will profit a thousandfold by a kindlier and more understanding relation toward all humankind.

Sybille Bedford:

The Last Trial of Lady Chatterley

A novelist's account of the
most recent tribulations and the ultimate
victory of Mr. D. H. Lawrence

*Lawyers have been known to wrest from reluc-
tant juries triumphant verdicts of acquittal for
their clients even when those clients were
clearly and unmistakably innocent.*
—OSCAR WILDE

*How beastly the bourgeois is
    especially the male of the species . . .
Let him meet a new emotion, let him be faced
    with another man's need.
Let him come home to a bit of moral difficulty.
Let life face him with a new demand on his
    understanding
And then watch him go soggy, like a wet
    meringue.
Watch him turn into a mess, either a fool or a
    bully.
Just watch the display of him, confronted with a
    new demand on his intelligence,
A new life-demand.*   —D. H. LAWRENCE

The CROWN v. Penguin Books Limited Before Mr.
Justice Byrne And A Jury At The Central Criminal
Court London October 20-November 2, 1960.

L et there be no mistake: this was a criminal prosecution. It was entirely unlike the action on the
same book between Grove Press Inc. and the
Postmaster General that was heard before a
judge in the United States District Court in
1959. Publication of an obscene article is a criminal
offense in Britain, and before the new Act of Parliament was passed in July, 1959, there was no defense
against it—other than a factual denial of having published; the author had no right to be heard in defense
of his own book, nor had publishers, booksellers,
critics or members of the general or specialized public.
The penalty could be a prison sentence, and there was

*Bedford has kept Esquire readers abreast of the foreign judicial scene
with articles on English murder trials, Her Majesty's judges, summary justice in Paris and this account of England's most famous
obscenity trial. It was published in April, 1961.*

no maximum limit as to the number of years. The
book did not have to be judged as a whole. The practice was to give juries passages marked by the prosecution or the police on which they had to decide whether
the book was obscene or not, and that was that.

The new Act was designed to protect bona fide
literature, and it took five years of devoted effort to
get it passed. It tightened the powers against pornography, Judge Woolsey's dirt-for-dirt's-sake. It did
not put through all that the reformers could have
wished, but the best, in the circumstances, they could
get. The most important new provisions of the Act are
that the book must now be judged as a whole; that
literary merit is a justification; and that the defense
may call expert evidence.

Almost exactly one year afterward, two things happened. Nineteen Sixty was the year of the seventy-fifth
anniversary of D. H. Lawrence's birth and the
thirtieth anniversary of his death; it was also the year
of Penguin Books' twenty-fifth jubilee. They decided
to round off their edition of Lawrence's works by
publishing the unexpurgated version of *Lady Chatterley's Lover*. The authorities decided to prosecute.
Penguin voluntarily delayed distribution and, not
wishing to involve a bookseller, provided evidence of
publication by handing over some copies to a police
inspector by arrangement, and so offered themselves
up as subjects of a test case.

The reaction of one section of the public was that
this was plain incredible; had not the new Act been
created to protect precisely this kind of book by this
kind of author? They began to read or reread *Lady
Chatterley's Lover* (the American edition was circulating in the country) and, reading, became aware
that indeed a grave injustice was about to be committed. It seemed a monstrous irony that the authorities—who surely must have *some* duty to the
public—should have acted against one of the very few
writers of our time who bitterly protested against
prostitution and perversion. Scores of eminent people
wrote to Penguin, offering their testimony, and so began the mounting of the first full-scale literary trial in
our legal history.

The authorities prepared by sending down to the Old
Bailey Mr. Justice Byrne—since retired—considered

167

by the profession one of the best criminal judges in England (he tried Lord Haw-Haw), an Irishman and seemingly a man with little taste for fiction. The prosecution was entrusted to Mr. Mervyn Griffith-Jones, Second Senior Counsel to the Crown at the Central Criminal Court, Eton, Cambridge, Coldstream Guards, and a veteran of many previous obscenity cases. What one could see of his face in court was framed by the wig: high cheekbones, a florid color, a strong jaw and a thin mouth—the head of a conventionally handsome man. He neither stooped nor lounged.

The trial, like every major trial for a century, took place in Number 1 Court at the Old Bailey. (And as if to nudge, as it were, the historical undertones, Oscar Wilde's son, Mr. Vyvyan Holland, was present the first day.) Number 1 is the largest courtroom in the building, which does not mean that it is not fairly cramped and small. It uncomfortably holds two hundred people, most of whom are unable to see *and* hear justice being done. The acoustics are wretched. The huge dock, solidly planted in the center, successfully shuts off vision and sound.

The first move was the calling of the jury. Now, in the case of United States *v.* One Book Called *Ulysses*, the parties waived their right to a trial by jury, and Judge Woolsey commented on this as "highly appropriate in a case involving books . . . a jury trial would have been extremely unsatisfactory, in fact an almost impossible way to deal with it. . . ." And, as it is ironical to remember in the light of what did happen, the defense in the present case is said to have shared that view; given the choice, counsel would have chosen trial by a judge. But in English law there is no actual choice; the magistrate must make the final decision; in the case of Penguin it was trial by jury.

An English jury is a permanent unknown quantity, a number of men and women chosen at random and finally by lot, about whom nothing is known, or allowed to be known, by anyone concerned. They are—forever—so many names and faces. (There is an unwritten law that a jury cannot be spoken to afterward, and even if somebody did try to speak to them—as some of the press did in this case—the jury would not answer, and if it did answer nobody would dare to print it.) The fine art of weeding out a jury, as is done in the United States, is no longer practiced in England. The defense has still the right to object to up to seven jurors without giving a reason, the peremptory challenge as it is called. But it is an obsolescent right, very rarely used nowadays.

Here it *was* used. Counsel made some slight sign and the Clerk said to the man who had just been marched into the jury box, "Will you step down, please," and the man did. He left the box. We all looked at him. Why? He had been the fourth or fifth man called; the box went on filling up; the twelfth and last juror was already halfway through his oath when there was another last-instant rejection. Amen said, and it would have been too late. That last man had been making a hash of trying to read his printed formula.

Now, the woman who was drawn in the last man's stead, and who was to become the twelfth acting juror in this trial, was a most educated-looking woman, with an alive and responsive face, and she may well have been the kingpin in the decision of that jury. Of course we shall never know. . . .

Mr. Griffith-Jones, opening for the Crown, addressed them. His evidence, he said, would be this book: *Lady Chatterley's Lover*. Penguin proposed to publish it at the price of 3/6 (fifty cents), and indeed had printed 200,000 copies of it for sale. His voice was thin, clear and slow, and at this state neutral, level. He explained the law as it stood now.

" 'An article shall be deemed obscene if its effect, taken as a whole, is such as to tend to deprave and corrupt persons who are likely, having regard to all relevant circumstances, to read the matter contained in it.' " There was, however, another Section of the Act which said that it was not an offense to publish " 'If it is proved that the article is for the public good, on the ground that it is in the interest of science, literature, art or learning or other objects of general concern.' "

The jury would have to give one verdict, but they would really have two questions to decide. One, whether the book was obscene; two, if so, whether its publication was justified as being for the public good. "If you find the book is not obscene, that is an end of this matter and you must acquit. But if you find that it *is* obscene, then you have to go on to consider—is it proved that publication is in the interest of literature, art and so forth. . . .

"A point you have to consider is how freely the book is going to be distributed. Is it a book published at £5 a copy as a historical volume, or is it a book widely distributed at a price the merest infant can afford?

"When you have read this book, you may think that it sets upon a pedestal promiscuous and adulterous intercourse, commends sensuality almost as a virtue, and encourages and advocates vulgarity of thought and language."

Mr. Griffith-Jones went on more emotionally: "You may think one of the ways you can test this book is to ask yourself the question: would you approve of your own son and daughter—because girls can read as well as boys—reading this book? Is it a book you would have lying in your own house? Is it a book you would wish your wife or your servant to read?

"Members of the jury, you may think that the book is a picture of little else than vicious indulgence in sex and sensuality. I wish to concede that D. H. Lawrence is a world-recognized writer; I also concede, though not to such a great extent, that there may be some literary merit in this book, not to put it any higher.

"The book is about a young woman whose husband was wounded in the First World War so that he was paralyzed from the waist downwards and unable to have sexual intercourse. I invite you to say that in effect the book is a description of how that woman, deprived of sex from her husband, satisfied her sexual desires—a sex-starved girl and how she satisfied that starvation with a particularly sensual man who happened to be her husband's gamekeeper."

In a voice quivering with thin-lipped scorn, Mr. Griffith-Jones went on:

"There are thirteen passages of sexual intercourse in this book. The curtain is never drawn. One follows them not only into the bedroom, but into bed, and one remains with them there. The only variation between all thirteen occasions is the time and the place where it happens. So one starts in my lady's boudoir; one goes to a hut in the forest with a blanket laid down on the floor. We see them doing it again in the undergrowth, in the forest amongst the shrubbery, and again in the undergrowth in the pouring rain, both of them stark naked and dripping with raindrops. One sees them in the keeper's cottage: first in the evening on the hearthrug; then we have to wait until dawn to see them doing it again in bed. Finally we move the site to Bloomsbury, and we have it all over again in a Bloomsbury boardinghouse.

"That is the variation—the time and the place where it happens with. the emphasis always on the *pleasure*, the *satisfaction*, the *sensuality*. . . .

"Sex, members of the jury, is dragged in at every opportunity, even the girl's father, a Royal Academician, introduces a description of his legs and loins. The book says little about the character of any of these people; they are little more than bodies which continuously have sexual intercourse with one another. The plot, you may find, is little more than padding, until we reach the hut again, the cottage or the undergrowth in the forest. . . ."

The jury sat through this blank-faced as juries are apt to sit. Then came the shock tactics: the passage in the prosecution speech which is by now well-known, the four-letter-word count.

"The word such-and-such," said Mr. Griffith-Jones, "appears thirty times. The word so-and-so fourteen times. The word balls thirteen times; shit six times; arse and piss three times apiece."

This was flung across the court with deliberate brutality. And we were shocked. Not because of the words—the words, paradoxically enough, are commonplace in an English court of law; we are much less mealymouthed in that than many of the Continental courts—but shocked by the staggering insensitiveness of this approach, the bookkeeper's approach, the line of attack. So this was to be the quality of the stand against a work by D. H. Lawrence.

An American writer, who was next to me, said, "Why this is going to be the upper-middle-class English version of our Tennessee Monkey Trial."

The prosecution speech ended by pointing out that Penguin stated it had taken thirty years for it to be possible to publish the unmutilated version of *Lady Chatterley's Lover* in this country. "You, members of the jury," Mr. Griffith-Jones said in a tone both ominous and smug, "will have to say whether it *has* taken thirty years, or whether it will take still longer."

Then the prosecution called their one and only witness, a policeman. Yes, he said, he had been given a dozen copies of the book in the Penguin offices. (This was formal evidence of publication.)

The chief witness, the book itself, was still unread; and before reading it the jury had to hear the opening speech by the defense. Penguin had briefed a dazzling team of counsel. The leader was Mr. Gerald Gardiner Q.C., one of the great silks of the London Bar, making one of the largest, perhaps the largest, income that it is possible to make there these days. Mr. Gardiner is a Quaker, a law reformer and a man recognized for his high principles. His court style is unemotional, cool, undramatic; he's the man who appeals to reason. His juniors were Mr. Jeremy Hutchinson and Mr. Richard Du Cann, two distinguished barristers in their own right. Mr. Hutchinson was himself brought up within an inner circle of the English world of letters, his father and mother having been patrons of the arts and friends of the writers of their time, George Moore, the Woolfs, Aldous Huxley, D. H. Lawrence. . . .

This is how Gerald Gardiner began. He spoke gently, one might say compassionately. "You have been told that this book is full of descriptions of sexual intercourse—and so it is. That it is full of four-letter words—and so there are.

"You may ask yourself at once: How comes it that reputable publishers, apparently after considerable thought and quite deliberately, are publishing an appalling book of the nature which has been described to us? . . . Penguin Books began in 1935 under a man called Lane, a man who thought that people like himself who were not very rich should be able to buy books. They started with a novel and some detective stories, then came classics and translations of masterpieces of literature, all costing sixpence [ten cents]. Twenty-five years later they had sold 250,000,000 books; they had published the whole of Shakespeare, most of Shaw; they had published fourteen books by D. H. Lawrence, and now they intended to publish the rest, including *Lady Chatterley's Lover*. This book has had unfortunately a checkered history. . . ." It was written in 1928; it had not been possible to publish it at that time. "There are many books circulating in London now which nobody would have thought ought to have been printed even twenty years ago." There had been expurgated editions of *Lady Chatterley*, and there would have been nothing to stop Penguin years ago from publishing one, but they had always refused to publish a mutilated book. The expurgated edition was not the book Lawrence wrote. One could have expurgated editions of *Hamlet* and of the *Canterbury Tales*, but they would not be the books Shakespeare or Chaucer wrote.

The dock in this trial, said Mr. Gardiner, was empty. The Crown had decided to prosecute Penguin merely as a company, and not the individual directors responsible. "But there is nothing to stop them from what they frequently have done before. Possibly the prosecution thought that a jury might come to a verdict of Guilty rather more readily if the dock were empty than if they had someone sitting there."

He then read dictionary definitions of To Deprave and To Corrupt. " 'To make morally bad; to pervert; to deteriorate; to make rotten; to infect, taint; to render unsound, to debase, to defile. . . .' " Strong words, and, as Mr. Gardiner at once pointed out, "So for a book to be obscene within the meaning of the law, it must obviously effect a change of character, a leading on of the reader to do something wrong which he would not otherwise have done.

"When you have read the book you will see certain things which the author was aiming at. . . . Mr. Griffith-Jones has suggested that this was a book which contained thirteen descriptions of physical intercourse, and the only variation between them was the time and place. I would suggest that you will find exactly the opposite. Here is a book about England of the Twenties. . . . Lawrence's message is that the society of his day was sick, the result of the machine age and the importance which everybody attached to money, and to the extent to which mind had been stressed at the expense of the body, and that what we ought to do was to reestablish the personal relationships. And one of the greatest things, the author thought, was the relationship of a man and a woman in love, and their physical union formed an essential part of a relation which was normal and wholesome and not something to be ashamed of, but something to be discussed openly and frankly. . . . Now if a man is going to write a book of that kind, and deal with the physical relation between the sexes, it is necessary to describe what he means.

"I submit that the descriptions of physical union were necessary for what Lawrence was trying to say.

"It is quite true that the book includes what is called four-letter words, and it is quite plain that what the author intended was to drag these words out of the rather shameful connotation which they had achieved since Victorian times. The attitude of shame with which large numbers of people have always viewed sex in any form has reduced us to the position where it is not at all easy for fathers and mothers to find words to describe to their children the physical union. The author thought that if he used what had been part of our spoken speech for about six hundred years, he could purify it. . . . Whether he succeeded or not in his attempt to purify these words by dragging them into the light of day, there is nothing in the words themselves which can deprave or corrupt. If these words can deprave or corrupt, then ninety-five percent of the Army, Navy and Air Force are past redemption.

"Whole parts of the book may (and I do not doubt will) shock you; but there is nothing in the book which will in fact do anybody any harm. No one would suggest that the Director of Public Prosecutions would become depraved by reading the book, nor counsel, nor witnesses; no one would suggest that the judge and jury would become corrupted; it is always someone else, it is never ourselves!"

When Mr. Gardiner had done, it was really afternoon, and the Judge said that the question now was how the reading was to be arranged. Mr. Gardiner stepped forward, and so did Mr. Griffith-Jones, and the following exchange took place.

Mr. Gardiner: "I understand the usual practice has been for the jury to take the book home."

The Judge: "I don't think I'm in agreement with that."

The Judge looked an elderly gentleman, with a polite, dry voice; a wizened bit of face looked out from the full wig. Upright, he gave the impression old judges sometimes give, of a husk light as kindling under the scarlet robes.

Mr. Gardiner: "The jury rooms are jolly uncomfortable. There are hard wooden chairs, and anything more unnatural than twelve men and women sitting on hard chairs around a table reading cheek by jowl in one another's presence is hard to imagine."

The Judge tilted his head.

Mr. Gardiner stood hunched up and tall. His face looked flexible, yet expressionless, and quite grey.

Mr. Griffith-Jones: "I have no wish to cause the jury any discomfort, but, in my submission, for them to read the book in the jury room is the proper way."

Mr. Gardiner: "When you read, what you read is private to the author and you. Besides some people read more slowly than others—"

The Judge (quietly): "In my experience, books are read in court." Here the Clerk put his head above the dais. Confabulations. "The Clerk does not agree that the jury rooms are uncomfortable." Pause. "I have never been in a jury room myself."

Mr. Gardiner: "The average rate of reading is about two hundred words a minute. . . . What would happen when one member of the jury has finished reading and others have not?"

The Judge (to the jury box): "I am very sorry, I don't want to put you to any kind of discomfort, but if you were to take this book home you might have distractions."

So the jury was directed to present themselves next morning, and the case was adjourned.

When the case resumed one week later on Day Two, as they call it, the place was filled with men and women who looked each more like themselves than it is customary for any multitude to do: the expert witnesses. Rumors as to who was going to appear had been circulating for some months. In the press, names were piled on speculative names. In fact, the actual list was unknown, and, what's more, remained so until the last witness had showed up on the last day. The solicitors responsible for organizing the defense had kept it absolutely quiet. One popular paper spread the startling news that a fleet of London taxis was standing by to convey the poets of England from where they might lurk to the Old Bailey. As it turned out, the actual selections were much more subtle, much more effective and much more *terre à terre*.

The day began with Mr. Griffith-Jones asking for the witnesses to be out of court during each other's testimony. Mr. Gardiner objected that this was not the custom as far as experts were concerned. Mr. Justice Byrne ruled that if there was no agreement on this point by the two sides, the custom was for the witnesses to stay out. A number of men and women thereupon withdrew.

How does one give evidence as to literary merit in a

BEFORE THE BENCH

"Scores of eminent people wrote to Penguin, offering their testimony,
and so began the mounting of the first full-scale literary trial in our legal history."

Gerald Gardiner
Defense Counsel

Central Criminal Court
(Old Bailey)

Mervyn Griffith-Jones
Prosecutor

Dame Rebecca West
Journalist

Helen Gardner
Oxford Scholar

E. M. Forster
Novelist

Stephen Potter
Literary Critic

John Arthur Thomas Robinson
The Bishop of Woolwich

Sarah Beryl Jones
Schoolmistress

court of law? We were soon to hear. The first witness called was Mr. Graham Hough, the literary critic and D. H. Lawrence specialist, Lecturer in English and Fellow of Christ College, Cambridge.

Mr. Gardiner: "When did you first read the unexpurgated edition of *Lady Chatterley's Lover?*"

Mr. Hough: "In about 1940." (This question was put to everyone, and all, whatever their upbringing or generation, had at one time or another read an underground copy.)

Mr. Gardiner: "Will you tell us something about Lawrence's place in English literature?"

Mr. Hough: "He is generally recognized as being one of the most important novelists of this century. I should put him with Hardy and with Conrad and George Eliot. I do not think that is seriously disputed."

"How many books have been written about D.H.L.?"

"About eight hundred published."

"How do you rank *Lady Chatterley?*"

"I don't think it's the best of Lawrence's novels, but not the least good either. About fifth place. He wrote nine."

"Will you tell us what is the theme or meaning of this book?"

". . . an attempt to give a sympathetic understanding to a very painful, intricate human situation. The book is in fact concerned with the relationships between men and women, with their sexual relations, and with the nature of marriage—all matters of great importance to us all."

Mr. Gardiner: "It has been claimed that sex is dragged in at every opportunity and the plot is little more than padding."

"I totally disagree. If true, this would be an attack on the integrity and honesty of the author. But it is quite false. In the first place, it is a matter of simple numerical proportion—the sexual passages occupy no more than about thirty pages of the whole book, a book of some three hundred pages. No man in his senses is going to write a book of three hundred pages as mere padding. . . . And then the literary merit of the nonsexual passages is very high."

Mr. Gardiner: "It has been suggested that the book puts upon a pedestal promiscuous and adulterous intercourse."

Mr. Hough: "Promiscuity hardly comes into it. It is very much condemned by Lawrence. It is true that at the center of the book there is an adulterous situation—that is true of a great deal of the literature of Europe."

"It has been said that the only variation in the scenes of intercourse is in the places they take place. Do you agree?"

"No, I don't! They show the development of Connie Chatterley's awareness of her nature. They are not repetitive. They are different and necessary to the author's purpose."

Mr. Gardiner: "How far are the descriptions of intercourse relevant or necessary?"

"They are extremely necessary. Lawrence was trying to show sexual relationships more clearly than is usually done in fiction. Lawrence was making a bold experiment."

"A what?" said the Judge.

"A bold experiment."

"A bold experiment," repeated the Judge as he wrote it down.

Mr. Gardiner: "How far are the four-letter words relevant or necessary?"

Mr. Hough: "May I answer that by explaining why they are in? In Lawrence's view, there is no proper language to talk about sexual matters. They are either discussed in clinical terms, which deprive them of all emotional content, or they are described in words that are usually thought to be coarse or obscene. He wished to find a language in which sex could be discussed plainly and not irreverently, and to do this he tried to redeem the normally obscene words by using them in a context that is entirely serious. I don't myself think that this is successful, but that is what he was trying to do. In trying to treat sex in this way, Lawrence had few precedents before him. He had to try to find a way through."

Mr. Gardiner: "Do you spend a great deal of your time teaching young people?"

Mr. Hough: "I do."

"And have you a daughter of eighteen and a son of twelve?"

"I have."

So far, so good. Mr. Hough had given his answers with thoughtful care. The jury had been sitting through their course in literary criticism with noncommittal attention. Now came the first crossexamination.

Mr. Griffith-Jones: "Do you know a lady called Esther Forbes?"

Mr. Hough: "No. I'm afraid not."

"Do you know a lady called Katherine Anne Porter?"

"A writer of short stories. American. . . . Very distinguished."

"Are you familiar with a magazine called *Encounter?*"

"*Encounter?* Yes, I am."

"Is *Encounter* a serious publication?"

Mr. Hough: "Reasonably so." (Laughter, instantly suppressed, in one section of the court; stony faces in the rest.)

Mr. Griffith-Jones: "Would you agree with this American lady writing in *Encounter* that this novel is 'a dreary, sad performance, with some passages of unintentionally hilarious low comedy,' and 'written with much inflamed apostolic solemnity'?"

Mr. Hough: "I think that is an eccentric opinion."

Mr. G.-J. (quickly): "Because you do not agree with it? Do you agree with this view of Lady Chatterley, '. . . she is merely a moral imbecile . . . she is stupid'?"

"Connie is not stupid; she is an emancipated young woman of the period, friendly, warmhearted, patient—"

"What do you mean warmhearted—*filled with sex?*"

"No—this is not what *I* mean."

Mr. G.-J.: "Miss Porter says the book is 'a blood-chilling anatomy of the activities of the rutting season between two rather dull persons.' Do you think that is a view one is entitled to hold?"

Mr. Hough: "Oh, anyone is entitled to hold any view. This one disposes of the argument that the book excites the sexual passions."

(Again there is a slight ripple of laughter. Did the jury stir uneasily at academic levity?)

Mr. G.-J.: "Is this book 'the feeble daydream of a dying man sitting under the umbrella pines indulging his sexual fantasies'?" (He puts the magazine down and looks at the witness.) *Is this novel the feeble daydream of a dying man?*"

Mr. Hough (very coldly): "Lawrence died two years after publication."

Mr. Griffith-Jones dropped it, and started on another tack. "Should a good book by a good writer repeat things again and again? This is a tiresome habit, is it not?"

"I don't agree with that. It is a technique frequently employed. . . . There is a great deal of repetition in the Bible—"

"Never mind the Bible. We are concerned with *this* book. Listen to this [reading]: 'Connie went slowly home. . . . Another self was alive in her, burning and molten and soft in her womb and bowels and with this self she adored him. She adored him till her knees were weak as she walked. In her womb and bowels she was flowing and alive now and vulnerable and helpless in adoration. . . .' *Womb and bowels, womb and bowels*—" said Mr. Griffith-Jones. "Is that good writing? Or is it ludicrous?"

"Not to me."

"We have two parts of her anatomy coupled together twice in three lines. Is *that expert* and *artistic* writing?"

"He is describing a woman in a highly emotional condition."

The Judge joined in: "Is it a piece of good English?"

Mr. Hough: "In context it is."

Mr. G.-J.: "And in the last line of that page there is the phrase 'bowels and womb' again. Is that writing of high *literary* merit?" And the prosecution pressed on, with hard persistence, pressed on and the scene took much longer, more beyond endurance than one could make it last with words on paper. It was a scene of willful bullying, and like such scenes it was embarrassing to watch.

"I am asking you whether a work of high literary merit has that kind of repetition?"

Mr. Hough: "Knowing Lawrence, yes. It was his method. He was trying to describe—"

"Never mind what he was trying to describe. Is it good writing to repeat again and again 'womb and bowels'?"

"Yes. It was his method."

"It may well be his method. But has this kind of repetition any literary merit?"

"I would say so."

Mr. Griffith-Jones now read aloud another passage (pages 233-234 of the Grove paperback edition). "We have had two four-letter words appear repeatedly in twelve lines—is that a realistic conversation between a gamekeeper and a baronet's wife?"

"I don't think so," said Mr. Hough. "I think as a passage this is a failure."

Mr. G.-J. (heavily): "You grant me this much? In this book which is of such merit there is at least one passage which is a failure?"

"There are several," said Mr. Hough.

Mr. G.-J. (reading a paragraph, Grove, p. 266): "As a *literary critic* and an *expert*, do you regard this as good writing to repeat that offensive word three times?"

"I think in this case it is."

Mr. Griffith-Jones read the letter which is the finale of the novel. He read the passage of it that begins, "So I love chastity now. . . ." He read it very badly, not on purpose, but like a man who reads a foreign language, a man who cannot see. The effect was unexpected. The power and beauty of Lawrence's writing carried. Up in the gallery, on the court benches, in the jury box, people were sitting absolutely quiet, listening, their hands still, listening deeply moved.

Unaware, isolated, prosecuting counsel read on. He read the after-dinner conversation at Wragby (Grove, p. 77). "Does that conversation present an accurate picture of the way gentlemen of that class talk together on that kind of occasion with their hostess present?"

Mr. Hough: "I think it is quite convincing."

Mr. G.-J.: "And the entire rest of the book, let's face it, is about sex? Even the old nurse—Mrs. Bolton—is dragged in without any point at all so that Sir Clifford may feel her breasts?"

"There is very much point. This is most relevant. . . . The decay of Clifford. Clifford is shown to have become like an unpleasant child."

Mr. G.-J.: "Is there any particular literary or sociological advantage in having this described?"

"Yes, I think there is. These are representations of false and wrong sexual attitudes, and this is an important part of the book."

"Where do the good attitudes come in?"

"Well, in the relationship between Connie and Mellors, who really loved one another."

The Judge raised an eyebrow. Mr. Hough repeated his answer.

Mr. G.-J.: "Are you an expert on good sexual relationships?"

Mr. Hough (calmly): "I do not share the sexual ethics of D.H.L., I was never a disciple of his doctrine, but I think it is important and should be clearly stated."

"Listen to this," said Mr. Griffith-Jones, " 'Lift up your heads O ye gates, that the King of glory may come in.' [Grove, p. 270.] We have looked up the correct quotation which is, 'Lift up your heads O ye gates; and be ye lift up, ye ever-lasting doors; *and* the King of glory *shall* come in.' Do you not think that if—in a book of literary merit—he is quoting from the Twenty-fourth Psalm, he might look it up?"

Mr. Hough: "Oh, no. Writers often misquote. And in this case it is the gamekeeper who is speaking—"

"Do you think that the inclusion of the words from the Scriptures adds literary merit to the book?"

Here Mr. Hough allowed himself once more to be flippant. "I think it is the only sentence of this passage that *has* any literary merit."

The second witness called turned out to be one of the most effective and impressive witnesses of the whole case. One saw climbing onto the witness stand a woman of homely appearance with a pleasant, open face, the kind of person one is apt to think jury members would welcome as a forthright and respected aunt; and indeed some of them were lifting trusting faces at her entrance. She was Helen Gardner.

"And are you," said Mr. Gardiner Q.C., "the Reader of Renaissance English Literature at Oxford University? The author of books on T. S. Eliot, John Donne, and the Metaphysical Poets? A member of the Radio Critic's Panel?"

Miss Gardner said she was all these things.

"It has been said," Mr. Gardiner asked her, "that the four-letter words form the whole subject matter of the prosecution, and that one word occurred thirty times?"

Miss Gardner stood up there unruffled. It is not at all easy to come out well in that witness box. It is very hard to lie successfully about a point of fact; it is impossible to get away with an opinion not sincerely held. You stand up there, very much exposed, all the eyes are on you; the jury, the bench, the two counsels are ready to pounce, to twist, to fling your words back at you. And at the end it all depends not on what you know and the ability to express it, not on courage and unflappability—though they all count—but on *what you are*. It shows. And that was why in this case nearly all those witnesses scored so heavily. They had come (at their own expense and risk) because they felt it their duty to do so; they were people of patent honesty and honor, men of splendid goodwill . . . and, of course, considerable abilities.

So Miss Gardner stood there and shone with goodness and integrity. She captured the hearts of the public gallery (many hardened murder-trial queuers among them), she may have captured the jury. . . . "I do not think words are brutal or disgusting in themselves," she said; "they are brutal if used in such a sense or context. The very fact that this word is used so frequently in this book means that with every use the original shock is diminished. By the time one had read the last page one feels that Lawrence has gone far to redeem this word."

Mr. Gardiner: "What do you gather was Lawrence's original intention?"

"To make us feel that the sexual act is not shameful and the word used in its original sense is not shameful either," she said with complete simplicity. "Those passages succeed in doing something extraordinarily difficult, and very few writers have attempted with such courage and vision to put into verbal media experiences that are difficult to verbalize."

"Do you feel any embarrassment in discussing this book in a mixed class?"

"Good gracious, no," said Miss Gardner.

"What, in your view, is the theme?"

"I think Lawrence felt very deeply the degrading conditions in which many people lived without beauty or joy and in slavery to what he calls, from William James, the Bitch Goddess Success, and he thought the most fundamental wrong was in the relationship between men and women—in sex; he thought through a better relationship there the whole of society might be revivified. Padding? *Oh, no!* It is a remarkable though not wholly successful novel, and though it doesn't rank with the greatest of Lawrence's work, I think certain passages are amongst his greatest. The ride through Derbyshire—the narrative of Mrs. Bolton—Oh, Mrs. Bolton—a character worthy of Dickens."

Mr. Griffith-Jones had no questions. The prosecution did not choose to cross-examine.

The next witness was Joan Bennett, the Cambridge Don and critic (*George Eliot, The Victorian Novel,* etc.). She looked like a distinguished intellectual, in fact rather like Janet Flanner. She had a tendency to answer quickly, and then to qualify. Mr. Griffith-Jones kept his eye on her.

Lawrence's view, she said, was that the physical life was of great importance; many people lived poor emasculated lives, they only lived with one half of themselves; Lawrence dealt with sex seriously, very seriously. . . . Promiscuous intercourse was shown as unsatisfactory, giving no fulfillment or joy, as being rather disgusting. . . . He thought that marriage was a complete relationship, marriage, not quite in the legal sense, but a union between two people for a lifetime was of the highest importance, of almost sacred importance—

"What did you say?" said the Judge. "*Of almost sacred importance*." He wrote it down.

Mr. Gardiner: "And have you got one son, three daughters and eight grandchildren?"

"I have," said Mrs. Bennett.

Mr. Griffith-Jones was ready for her. "Does not this book show a picture of a woman who has sexual relationships with people who are not her husband?"

"Yes."

"Does this adulterous intercourse show a regard for marriage as it is generally understood by the average reader?"

"What average reader?" asked Mrs. Bennett, faithful to precision. "If you mean an intelligent child—"

Mr. G.-J.: "If you *can* come down to our humbler level from your academic heights will you answer my question—does this book show regard for marriage?"

"In what sense do you mean marriage?"

The Judge leaned toward her: "Lawful wedlock, madam!"

Mrs. Bennett said bravely, though in not too sure a voice, "Lawrence believed it can be—as I think the law allows—broken in certain conditions."

Down swooped Mr. Griffith-Jones: "Is not that precisely what Lawrence himself did? He ran off with somebody else's wife, did he not? Did he not?"

Mr. Gardiner's reexamination consisted of one question. "Did D. H. Lawrence's one and only marriage last his lifetime?"

"It did," said Mrs. Bennett.

"I call," said Mr. Gardiner, "Dame Rebecca West."

Dame Rebecca went into that box and said her say. There was no prodding *her* into the question-and-answer shafts. She made the points she found necessary to make, she made them in her own way and she made them well, and that was that.

The story of Lady Chatterley, she said, was designed as an allegory; the baronet and his impotence were a symbol of the impotent culture of our time which had become sterile and unhelpful to man's deepest needs, and the love affair with the gamekeeper was a return of the soul to a more intense life. Lawrence was not a fanciful writer; he knew he was writing about something *quite real*—he saw that in every country in the world there were populations who had lost touch with life and who could be exploited. All the time he was governed by this fear that something was going to happen—fascism, nazism—something that did happen in the shape of the war. . . .

Of course one could find individual passages which appeared to have no literary merit. By this time Dame Rebecca was addressing the court and jury as she might some fairly alert committee. "But the same is true of Shakespeare and Wordsworth, they all have some terrible lines. *Lady Chatterley* is full of sentences any child could make a fool of. You see, Lawrence was a man without a background of formal education and he also had one great defect which impairs this book, he had absolutely no sense of humor. And a lot of the scenes are, I think, ludicrous. But in spite of the ugly things, the ugly words, it is still a good book."

Witnesses of sufficient eminence, or who have shown a deal of character, were not likely to be cross-examined. They might boomerang. Dame Rebecca was not questioned; the prosecution left well enough alone.

Mr. Gardiner said, "I am calling the Bishop of Woolwich!"

This was the moment of thrill for the regular crime reporters, who now made a dash for their telephones. The Bishop looked delightful, like a well-groomed and angelic poet, and he wore his pectoral cross and violet silk cloth with a romantic air. He admitted to being the Dr. John Arthur Thomas Robinson, the father of four children, the author of several works on the New Testament, and to having long experience in teaching and ministering to university students. He had read *Lady Chatterley's Lover* in the summer.

He was cut short by Mr. Griffith-Jones: "I submit that the Bishop cannot be heard—his qualifications do not entitle him to give evidence about the book's literary merit."

Mr. Gardiner said the Bishop had come to give evidence on its ethical merits.

Mr. G.-J.: "Ethical merits are not mentioned in the Obscene Publications Act."

Mr. Gardiner: "My Lord, the Act mentions art or learning or other objects of general concern."

The Judge: "I agree with you, ethics must be considered an object of general concern."

So the Bishop was allowed to proceed. "Clearly," he said, "Lawrence did not have a Christian valuation of sex, and the kind of relationships depicted in the book are not necessarily of the kind I should regard as ideal. But what Lawrence is trying to do, I think, is to portray the sex relationship as something sacred. . . . I might quote Archbishop Temple, 'Christians do not make jokes about sex for the same reason they do not makes jokes about Holy Communion, not because it is sordid but because it is sacred.' I think Lawrence tried to portray this relation in the real sense as an act of Holy Communion, in a lower case. For him flesh was sacramental. . . ."

The Judge took it down ostentatiously.

"Lawrence's descriptions of sexual relationships cannot be taken out of the context of his whole quite astonishing sensitivity to the beauty and value of all organic relationships. Some of the descriptions of nature in the book seem to me extraordinarily beautiful, and to portray an attitude to the whole organic world in which he saw sex as the culmination."

Mr. Gardiner: "Can you make a distinction between the book as it is, and as it would be with the sexual passages left out?"

The Bishop: "I think the effect of that would be to suggest that what Lawrence was doing was something sordid and could be put before the public only if the passages about sex were eliminated. I think that is a false view. I think neither in intention nor in effect is this book depraving."

"It had been said that it puts promiscuous and adulterous intercourse on a pedestal."

"That seems a distorted view. In the last pages there is a tremendous and most moving advocacy of chastity: 'How can men want wearisomely to philander?' "

The Bishop's cross-examination took place after the luncheon adjournment. By that time on that day one of the unusual features of this trial had become more distinct, and that was the invasion of the professional sanctity of the court by the outer world. The Old Bailey is very much a place of its own, a highly specialized place where (apart from the occasional sensational trial) humdrum, brutal, shabby crime is dealt with day after day in a steady, drab, conscientious grind. The prisoner sits in the dock, the contests are fought between teams of professionals and their attendants. Of course, there are other people in court, but they don't count. They are there because they must: if the accused has partisans they are helpless people, frightened, involved; his wretched wife perhaps in a back row, a humbled father; or they are there out of some unengaged curiosity, or to do a job, law pupils, the regular crime reporters, a pack of Pavlov dogs sitting in their pew waiting for their cues of sex and violence. This, then, was one of the rare occasions when the court was packed with outside people of conscience, heart and mind, people who were passionately concerned about the outcome, and who were not wholly—at least outside the actual court— mute and powerless: writers, poets, educators, Lawrence enthusiasts, literary journalists, English, American, Canadian. . . . The French, or members of other Latin nations, did not participate.

Mr. Griffith-Jones started with this question to the Bishop.

"Do you tell us that this book is a valuable work on ethics?"

The Bishop answered that it had positive value from an ethical point of view. "It is not a treatise on marriage, but Lawrence made it clear that he was not against marriage relationships—"

Mr. G.-J.: "I don't want to be offensive to you, but you are not here to make speeches. Just answer my questions. Are you asking the jury to accept this book as a valuable work on ethics?"

"I would not say it had an *instructional* value—"

"Is it a book Christians ought to read?"

The Judge: "Does it portray the love of an immoral woman?"

The Bishop: "It portrays the love of a woman in an immoral relationship, so far as adultery is an immoral relationship."

By now Bench and prosecution were seen to have spun themselves into the old fallacy: a book dealing with immorality is an immoral book. It is neither law nor logic, but it is an easy web for juries to get lost in, and the Churchman at any rate was being shown as having tied himself into apparent knots.

"*Is* this a book Christians ought to read?" asked Mr. Griffith-Jones.

"Yes, I think it is. And because—" But the Bishop was not allowed to explain; the prosecution stopped him in his tracks. And by evening the headlines proclaimed: Bishop's Defense of Lady C—Book All Christians Ought To Read.

"Sir William Emrys Williams!" A director of Penguin Books, Secretary-General of the Arts Council, knighted in 1955.

"Will you explain why you printed 200,000 copies of this book?"

"That is nothing out of the ordinary. An average first printing of a Penguin would be 40,000 to 50,000 copies, but for some books we print as many as 250,000."

"Why did you not think of putting in rows of asterisks?"

Sir William: "That would make it a dirty book."

"What about dashes for the four-letter words?"

"That would make for unwholesomeness."

"Do you think you could have sold a large number of copies of an *expurgated* edition?"

"Quite the same number." (There is in fact such an expurgated edition published in Britain, and it sold nearly a quarter million copies in nine months last year.)

"Professor Vivian de Sola Pinto!" Professor of English at Nottingham University; perhaps one of the greatest D. H. Lawrence authorities living today.

Mr. Griffith-Jones (cross-examining): "Professor, just let me make sure what your ideas of beauty are?" He reads from page 234.

Professor Pinto: "An able piece of realism."

Mr. Griffith-Jones (furiously): "C! C! C! C! F! F! F! F!"

"The Reverend A. S. Hopkinson!" Vicar of St. Catherine Cree, London; General Director of Industrial Christian Fellowship; Anglican Adviser to Associated Television.

". . . A study in compassion. . . . A book of moral purpose." ("A book of?" said the Judge.) ". . . All comes from God, thus sex comes from God; it is utterly wrong to link sex with sin. The words? The words are about activities that are an essential part of human life; it would be a mistake to replace them with blanks. . . . Yes, I would like my children to read it, I should like them to discuss it with me and their mother."

The Judge asked: "You have no objection to your children reading this book?"

"Only one of them has, to my knowledge," said the clergyman, "and he found it rather dull."

Mr. Griffith-Jones: "As a minister of the Church, you would have the highest opinion of the marriage vows?"

"Yes."

"Would you not agree that this was a book about a man and a woman who have little regard for the marriage vow at all?"

"No."

Mr. G.-J.: "I am sure you do not hold the view that we can throw our marriage bond overboard?"

"No, I do not."

"That is what this woman is doing! That is what this whole book is about—she throws her marriage bond overboard in order to get sexual satisfaction. That is what this book teaches."

"With respect, I should say that the marriage goes wrong, and afterwards she takes the wrong course."

Mr. G.-J.: "None of you experts in this case is able to say Yes or No to any question! Listen to this, 'Lift up your heads O ye gates. . . .' " He read the whole Psalm passage again. "Is that shocking? Blasphemous?"

"That was not the author's intention."

"We are not concerned with the author's intention. Answer my question, will you? Were you shocked to find a Psalm in such a passage?"

"I did not recognize the Psalm."

"Mr. St. John-Stevas!" M.A. Oxford and Cambridge; Ph.D. Columbia; LL.D. Yale; Academic Lawyer and Qualified Barrister; author of *Obscenity and the Law*; legal adviser to the Committee which sponsored the Obscene Publications Bill; a Roman Catholic; student of Moral Theology; and still a very young man.

He said he would put Lawrence among the great literary moralists of our literature. "Lawrence was essentially concerned to purge, cleanse, reform. I have been horrified by the representation of him in some newspapers, in papers which I think he wouldn't have deigned to read!

"I have had the misfortune to have to read through a vast number of books of a pornographic and obscene nature, and I find it difficult to make comparisons with *Lady Chatterley*, so great is the gulf between them."

Mr. Hutchinson asked him if he found the book consistent with the tenets of his own faith.

Mr. St. John-Stevas said: Quite consistent. Of course Lawrence was neither a Christian nor a Catholic, but one could say he was a writer essentially in the Catholic tradition. "I mean by that the tradition that the sex instinct is good in itself, is implanted in man by God, is one of his greatest gifts. This tradition was opposed by the movement which started at the Reformation and has grown in Protestant minds that sex is something 'which is wrong,' which is essentially evil."

"I call the Headmaster of Alleyns!" D.S.O.; former Military Governor of Berlin (not cross-examined).

"I call the Master of the Temple!" Canon of Lincoln Cathedral (not cross-examined).

"Mr. Roy Jenkins, M.P.!" (Not cross-examined.)

All that day, and the next day, and the next, that procession of defense witnesses went on, professors, editors, schoolmasters, critics, poets, clergymen of the Church of England, psychologists....

There came to many of us a most moving moment, when counsel called:

"Edward Morgan Forster!" And in came Mr. E. M. Forster—alone—he had been sitting waiting on a bench in the hall the best part of the morning, waiting to be called. Now here he was, in a mackintosh, old only in years, looking very firm and calm.

The greatest living writer perhaps in the English language had come into this court, and of course there was no sign of recognition; that is not within the rules or spirit of the place. But Mr. Jeremy Hutchinson, very likely seized by a desire to do something, chose the one gesture of favor or respect that can be made in a courtroom—he asked the judge if Mr. E. M. Forster might be given a chair. His Lordship said: Certainly. But Mr. Forster said, no, no, he didn't want one, he didn't want a chair. Then he spoke.

"I knew Lawrence quite well. In nineteen hundred and fifteen...." And there came a sense of the past, and the years.

How would he place him in English literature, asked Mr. Hutchinson.

"I would place him enormously high. The greatest imaginative writer of his generation.... He is part of the great Puritan stream of writers, Bunyan, Blake.... Though that may seem a bit paradoxical at first sight. A preacher...."

But Mr. Forster's passage was all too brief. Mr. Griffith-Jones said he had no question, and Mr. Forster was gone.

"I call Sir Stanley Unwin!"

"Miss C. V. Wedgwood!"

"Mr. Walter Allen!" Novelist and literary critic.

"In your professional capacity, how many novels do you read a year?"

"Up to two hundred."

"How would you describe *Lady Chatterley's Lover?*"

Walter Allen: "A tract and the work of a genius."

"Miss Sarah Beryl Jones!" Classic Mistress and Senior Librarian at Keighley Grammar School. A little grey-haired woman, who speaks her own form of oath.

The Judge: "What did you say?"

Miss Jones (bright and fussy): "The whole truth as far as I am able to speak it." She is made to eat those words.

Mr. Gardiner: "Do girls grow up earlier now than they used to?"

Miss Jones: "In my experience, yes."

"Is there a good deal of literature available to them on sexual matters?"

"There are technical works, and there are what you might call dirty books."

"How far do girls understand the four-letter words?"

Miss Jones: "I have inquired of a number of girls—after they left school—and most of them have been acquainted with them since the age of ten."

"Has *Lady Chatterley's Lover* any educational value?"

"Considerable value, if taken at the right age, which is normally after seventeen, because it deals honestly and openly with problems of sex which are very real to the girls themselves. Girls are very good at knowing what is good for them. Girls read what they want to read and they don't read what they don't want to read."

"Miss Ann Scott-James!" A most smartly dressed young woman.

Mr. Griffith-Jones rises at once to object. "I understand you are the editor of a Ladies' Page?"

Miss Scott-James: "Not a Ladies' Page. It hasn't been called that since 1912. A Woman's Page."

"Do you claim any particular qualification to be a literary expert?"

"Of a popular kind. And I was a classical scholar at Oxford." She adds disarmingly, "It's not a negligible qualification."

Mr. G.-J.: "Does that make you a literary expert?"

"I was brought up in a very literary family. My father—" But Miss Scott-James is whisked out of the box.

"Mr. Stephen Potter!" "When I read the book again, I was surprised by its power! ... And the words only shock the eye, and that soon goes because they do not shock the brain. I think what D. H. L. was trying to do was something very difficult and courageous, he was trying to take these words out of the context of the lavatory wall."

"Dr. Clifford James Hemming!" Writer, lecturer, educational psychologist.

"Young people," he said, "reading *Lady Chatterley* might find themselves for the first time confronted with a concept of sex which includes compassion and tenderness.

"Young people nowadays are subject to constant insinuation of shallow and corrupting values.... Books and papers tell the young girl that if she has the right proportions, wears the right clothes, uses the right cosmetics, she will become irresistible to men, and that this is the supreme achievement of women, to become irresistible to men. And as far as the men are concerned, it is suggested that to have a pretty woman in your arms is the supreme thrill of life, and to seduce a woman is manful in yourself and something to envy in others. The contents of *Lady Chatterley* are an antidote. They show all that makes sex human. . . ."

Mr. Gardiner: "Are the detailed descriptions justified? Are they of any sociological value?"

"Oh, yes," said Dr. Hemming. "It is now recognized that for young people to grow up and marry with brutish and ashamed attitudes is most harmful. The rejection of our bodies can lead to mental ill health. This book would act as a positive antidote to those promiscuous and dehumanizing influences."

There was no doubt that the prosecution and the Bench were flabbergasted to be hearing what they heard. The views of apparently respectable professional men and women. . . . Chaos, it must have seemed to Mr. Justice Byrne, had come again.

Mr. Griffith-Jones, in cross-examination, asked, not unexpectedly: "Let us see what amounts to an antidote." And he began his now-familiar tone-deaf reading (Grove, p. 284). "Is *that* an antidote to promiscuous sex among young people?"

Dr. Hemming: "Yes."

"That was a description of what was happening just before the act of intercourse?"

"Yes."

"That was promiscuous intercourse by Lady Chatterley?"

Dr. Hemming: "Yes, but it is quite different from the street-corner promiscuity which is one of our problems today."

Mr. G.-J.: "I was not limiting my meaning to street corners. Is there anything to suggest that *she* wouldn't have gone on and on, from man to man, until she found someone who satisfied her?"

Dr. Hemming: "That is a conjectural question. I do not believe she would have led that kind of life."

As one can see, Constance Chatterley had ceased to be a character of fiction. To the defense she was poor Connie; to the other side, Lady Chatterley, a traitor to her class, a shocking example, and the guilty party to a divorce action of the most undesirable nature.

Mr. G.-J.: "Here we have another one of the bouts. Listen" (reading:) "does that strengthen the antidote much, does it?"

Dr. Hemming: "I don't see why not."

"'As he found her,' what do you think these words mean?"

"Getting into closer intimacy."

Mr. G.-J.: "What do you mean?"

"What Lawrence means."

"What do *you* mean by that?"

"A continuation of the physical act of love."

Mr. G.-J.: "What do you mean by that? I shall go on asking you until you tell us in plain good English words what you think that means!"

Dr. Hemming: "He was caressing her."

"Where?"

"It doesn't say."

"Where do you think?"

No answer.

"Where?"

And so it went on.

Sometime later, a witness, an Oxford Don, read D. H. L.'s own comment. "'It's the one thing they won't let you be, straight and open in your sex. You can be as dirty as you like. In fact, the more dirt you do on sex the better they like it. But if you believe in your own sex and won't have it done dirt to, they down you. It's the one insane taboo left—sex as a natural and vital thing.'"

To understand the conduct of the prosecution case, it may perhaps be well to bear several rather contradictory things in mind. One: prosecuting counsel acts as an advocate; it is his job to present one side, and to present it strongly, to the best of his abilities. This, however, is somewhat weakened by the contemporary principle by which the prosecution is held to present all the facts fairly and not to press for a conviction *per se*; and so it can be said that counsel's job is not to press a case beyond its merits.

Two: a criminal trial is the trial of an issue of fact; was this act committed, and was it committed in such and such a way, yes or no? Did this man stab his wife, did that man steal a load of cheeses? It is not a matter of opinion, it is a matter of facts—the knife, the prints, the eyewitness, the alibi. And this is where the prosecution here, and the whole legal machinery, ran into trouble. They were dealing with something pressed into a Procrustean framework devised for something else; they were dealing with what was in reality an issue of judgment or opinion by a procedure created for the pinning down of fact.

Obscenity, unlike murder and theft, is not self-evident fact; it involves, in (U.S.) Judge Bryan's words, "questions of constitutional judgment of the most sensitive and delicate kind"; it involves definitions, definitions depending on—relative and changeable—community standards, on private feelings, on opinions. And below the standards, the feelings and opinions, lie the powers of what are perhaps our deepest and most irrational taboos. In regard to sex, and even more so in regard to certain words, England is still Disraeli's Two Nations, and the thought barrier between them is complete.

And so, three: in a true issue of fact, counsel's feelings or opinions are of no account and must never be expressed. In this case counsel did express feelings and opinions. For one thing, because he could hardly help doing so in the context. But they also were, and this was crystal clear to everyone present, his own feelings and opinions, and he believed in them to the exclusion of anybody else's. He, like the witnesses, was the man he was, and that comprised, evidently, that he had never in his life been conditioned to regard with respect any modern classic in the realm of purely imaginative writing. Confronted with a very difficult one, he displayed his natural reactions.

And it must be for something of all these three considerations that the cross-examinations were so indignant, so ineffective and so very much beside the point.

"The Dean of the Faculty of Arts at Liverpool University!"

"The Editor of the *Manchester Guardian*!"

"The Provost of King's!"

"Sir Allen Lane!" Founder of Penguin Books.

"Mr. C. Day Lewis!"

"The Former Precentor of Birmingham Cathedral!" and Director of Religious Education.

". . . By reading it, young people will be helped to grow up as mature and responsible people. . . ."

The prosecution made a point of cross-examining nearly all the clergy. Their position was most vulnerable. (In fact, the Bishop of Woolwich was rebuked by the Archbishop of Canterbury after the trial.)

Mr. Griffith-Jones: "Is there anything to suggest that marriage is sacred and inviolable?"

"It is a novel."

Mr. Griffith-Jones repeats the question.

"I think it is taken for granted."

"Let us see. Mellors, the gamekeeper, did not regard marriage as sacred and inviolable?"

"He was very much attracted by Lady Chatterley."

"Of course he was. Everybody who commits adultery is very much attracted by the man or woman with whom he does it. Just answer my question please."

The Judge: "Does the book really deal with anything other than adultery?"

"Mr. John Connell!" the writer and critic. "I disagree utterly and totally about all those suggestions about indulgence and promiscuity and padding. The book is concerned with two intertwined themes in human life and English society—sex and class. And it deals with a tragic situation."

Mr. Hutchinson: "What about an expurgated edition?"

Mr. Connell: "I was unfortunate enough to be sent one for review the other day. I found it: a) trivial, b) furtive, c) obscene."

A reader, having reached this stage, may well feel that the portents now were for acquittal. All those witnesses, the sheer weight of numbers must have left their mark. Had they? We were far from certain. The lawyers and defendants were only faintly hopeful. A hung jury, perhaps. The American journalists present looked at us with pity. The more enlightened court decision of their country had not been allowed to be heard in evidence.

"Do you know," Mr. Gardiner had asked, "of any civilized country where this book cannot be bought except in Lawrence's own Commonwealth?" Mr. Griffith-Jones had objected. "What happens in other countries is not relevant," he said. Mr. Gardiner put forward that it would be evidence of literary value. "I'm against that," had said Mr. Justice Byrne.

The regular reporters told one with satisfied cynicism, "They won't get away with it—no British jury will swallow those words." So one went on staring at this British jury. Most of them looked like pleasant people. The women seemed at their ease. There were two of them besides the twelfth juror; one very pretty young woman with a gentle face—ought one to pin hopes on her?—and one middle-aged, more of the housewife type. The second day she had appeared without a hat. A favorable sign? One man often dozed. Another looked worried. Another sullen. The foreman, the twelfth juror and one or two of the men laughed and talked as they walked through the vestibule, a most unprecedented thing.

If the case had any turning point at all, it must have been the exchange with the most quietly and fervently assured (as well as one of the most brilliantly intelligent) of the witnesses, Richard Hoggart, on Day Three. Mr. Hoggart, Senior Lecturer of English at Leicester University, is a young man from the Midlands, dark and short, born, like Lawrence himself, into the coal-mining working class. He started his education at an elementary school.

He had called *Lady Chatterley* a highly virtuous, if not a puritanical book, and Mr. Hutchinson had invited him to enlarge on that. "I was thinking of the whole movement of the book, of Lawrence's enormous insistence on arriving at relationships of integrity. I was struck on rereading it to realize how much of it is contemporary; it tells us a great deal about our society at a level which we do not usually probe, and with an insight which we do not usually attain. . . . It makes you consider your relationship to society, it teaches you to question your place and your being. . . ."

Mr. Hutchinson: "It has been suggested that the only variations in the sexual descriptions lay in where they took place."

"A gross misreading," said Mr. Hoggart firmly. "I don't mean highbrow reading. I mean an honest reading."

Mr. Hutchinson asked him about repetition of words.

"Indeed, yes. It's one of Lawrence's characteristics, and one he uses to great effect. He hammered home and almost recreated words. Shakespeare repeated 'nothing' five times in one passage."

Mr. Hutchinson asked if the four-letter words were genuine and necessary.

No one who saw him on that morning will ever forget Richard Hoggart, how he stood up there talking in his serious, clear-minded, communicating way. And now he uttered the words we had so far only heard from the lips of the prosecution. "They are totally characteristic of many people," he said, "and I would like to say not only working-class people, because that would be wrong. They are used very freely indeed, far more freely than many of us know. Fifty yards from this court this morning, I heard a man say that word three times as I passed him, one, two, three, I heard him. He must have been very angry.

"These are common words; if you work on a building site, as I have done, you will hear them frequently. But the man I heard this morning and the men on the building site use this word as a word of contempt, and one of the most horrifying things to Lawrence was that the word used for sex has become a term of violent abuse, and has totally lost its meaning. He wanted to reestablish the proper meaning of it.

"When I first read it, the first effect was one of some shock, obviously because it is not used in polite literature. But as one read, one found the word losing that shock. We have no word in English which is not either an abstraction or has become an evasive euphemism for this act; we are constantly running away from it or dissolving into dots. I realized that it is we who are wrong. Lawrence was wanting to show what one does in the most simple, neutral way. . . . Just like that, with no snigger or dirt. That is what one does."

Mr. Griffith-Jones rose to cross-examine. And he underestimated Mr. Hoggart's effectiveness, virtue and strength; the passage that followed was the prosecution's biggest moral defeat in the case.

Mr. Griffith-Jones: "You described this as a puritanical book. Is that your genuine and considered view?"

"Yes."

Mr. G.-J. (with gentlemanly superiority): "I think I must have lived my life under a misapprehension of the word 'puritanical.' Will you help me?"

Mr. Hoggart (earnest and friendly): "Yes, I will. Many people do live their lives under a misapprehension of the meaning of puritanical. In Britain, and for a long time, the word has pretended to mean somebody who is against anything which is pleasurable, particularly sex, but the proper meaning of it to an historian is somebody who belongs to the tradition of British puritanism, and the main weight of that is an intense sense of responsibility for one's conscience. In that sense the book is puritanical."

Mr. Griffith-Jones said: "I am obliged to you for the lecture." (Reading a sexual passage:) "Is that puritanical?"

Mr. Hoggart: "Yes. Heavy with conscience."

"I am not asking you if it is heavy with conscience. I am asking you if it is puritanical?"

"Yes. It is one of the side issues of puritanism."

Mr. G.-J. (reading a passage from the Michaelis episode, Grove, p. 65): "Puritanical?"

"Yes—puritanical, poignant, tender, moving, and about two people who have no proper relationship."

Mr. G.-J.: "I should have thought that could be answered without a lecture. This is the Old Bailey, and not [with thin distaste] *Leicester* University."

A further passage.

Mr. G.-J.: "That is about all there is to keep those two connected? It was done purely for the satisfaction of her sexual lust, wasn't it?"

Mr. Hoggart: "No, it was done because she is lonely and lost, and she feels through the sexual act she may feel less lonely and lost."

Mr. Justice Byrne: "It is just an immoral relationship between a man and a woman?"

Mr. Hoggart: "Yes." (Suddenly, eagerly:) "In Milton, in *Paradise Lost* there is a great passage in which Adam and Eve come together in this way. . . . Highly sensual. . . ."

Mr. Griffith-Jones then read that extraordinary page about the source of life (Grove, p. 230). Again he read as though it were some foreign text; again the court sat rapt. "'The weight of a man's balls'— puritanical?"

"Yes, it is puritanical in its reverence."

"Reverence for what?" screamed Mr. Griffith-Jones. "*The balls?*"

"Indeed, yes," said Mr. Hoggart gently.

At the end of Day Four, Mr. Gardiner said that, although they still had thirty-six witnesses in reserve, of "the same sort of character and standing," the defense would call only one more. The prosecution now had the right to call witnesses in rebuttal, but Mr. Griffith-Jones said he did not propose to call any evidence. And so the case had reached the stage of the final speeches. The speech for the defense and the speech for the prosecution were two speeches made from two different levels, addressed to two kinds of people. Only one question remained: Which kind was the jury?

Mr. Gardiner rose to speak the next morning. His manner was quiet though firm, and he anticipated a good many prosecution points.

"It might be suggested," he told the jury, "that you should ignore the evidence given by the witnesses on the ground that it was given by professors of literature, by people who are living rarefied lives and are not really in touch with ordinary people. And indeed, no higher class of experts could have been called on any similar occasion." Now the most important single fact here was that Parliament had expressly provided that evidence may be called both by the Defense and by the Prosecution; yet when the prosecution's turn came to call evidence, they called none at all. "Not one single witness has been found to say anything against Lawrence or this book; we have only got to go by what Mr. Griffith-Jones said himself when opening the case.

". . . Hardly any question has been put to witnesses (by the prosecution) about the book as a whole. The technique has been that used before the new Act: to read out a particular passage and to say, is that moral?

". . . This is a book about human beings, about real people, and I protest at the statements that have been made about the characters, about Constance, as though she were a sort of nymphomaniac. When it is said that this is just a book about adultery, one wonders how there can be things which people cannot see? I suppose somewhere there may be a mind which would describe *Antony and Cleopatra* as a play about adultery, the story of a sex-starved Roman soldier copulating with an Egyptian queen.

"As a book published at 3/6, *Lady Chatterley* will be available to the general public and it may well be said that everyone will rush to buy it. This is always the effect of a wrong prosecution.

"Witnesses have been asked if it was a book they would like their wife or servant to read. This may have been consciously or unconsciously an echo of the Bench of years ago: 'It would never do to let the members of the working class read this.' I don't want to upset the prosecution by suggesting there are a certain number of people who do not have servants. This whole attitude is one Penguin Books was formed to fight against. It is the attitude that it is all right to publish a special edition at five or ten guineas, but quite wrong to let people who are less well-off read what those other people read. Is not everyone, whether their income is ten pounds or twenty pounds a week, equally interested in the society in which we live? In the problems of our relationships, including sexual relationships?

"... It would be very easy to say to you for counsel for the prosecution, 'You and I are ordinary chaps, don't you bother about those experts—they don't really know what goes on in the world at all.' Lawrence, members of the jury, was a man of the people. There are students of literature in all walks of life. ... If it is right that the book should be read, it should be available to the man working in a factory as it is to the teacher working in a school.

"... In England we have before banned books by Hardy, G. B. Shaw, Ibsen, Wilde, Joyce, and even Epstein's statues. But is Lawrence to be always confined to dirty bookshops? This would be the greatest irony in literary history.

"... A book is not obscene merely because part of its subject matter is a relationship between people who are not married, or who are married to someone else. If that were so, ninety percent of English literature is obscene.

"... Can it be seriously suggested that anyone's character will be changed by reading words that they already know?

"I submit that the defense has shown on balance of probabilities that it is for the public good that this book should be generally available. ... If this is not a book to which the Section of the new Act applies, then it is difficult to conceive of any book by such an author to which it can apply.

"We are a country known throughout the world for our literature and our democratic institutions. It is strange indeed that this is the only country where this Englishman's work cannot be read. Lawrence lived and died suffering from the public opinion, caused by the banning of this book, that he had written a piece of pure pornography. For the first time this case has enabled the book to be dragged out into the light of day. The slur was never justified. All the time the book was a passionate and sincere work of a moralist who believed he had a message for us in the society in which we live. Whether we agree with what he had in view or not, is it not time we rescued Lawrence's name from the quite unjust reputation and allowed our people—his people—to judge for themselves? I leave Lawrence's reputation and the reputation of Penguin Books with confidence in your hands."

Mr. Griffith-Jones's speech followed.

"This is a case of immense importance, and its effects will go far beyond the actual question which the jury has to decide.

"... It has been emphasized that you have heard no witnesses called by the prosecution. It may sound a good point to reiterate again and again, but it is an empty point, and not the kind of argument on which you are to decide the case. The law restricts me to calling evidence only as to literary, artistic and other merits of the book. As to the merits of the book as literature, I have from the first conceded that Lawrence was a great writer. These are matters upon which the prosecution never sought to argue, and upon which it would have been wholly irrelevant and redundant for me to call evidence. On whether the book is of educational or sociological merit, I am happy to leave that aspect to the book itself. I cannot believe that you, or any other jury, would wish evidence to be called simply to hear these words: This book is not a great educational document, nor is it of great sociological value.

"Members of the jury, there are standards, are there not? There must be standards which we are to maintain, standards of morality, language and conduct, which are essential to the well-being of our society. They must be instilled in all of us, and at the earliest possible age, standards of respect for the conventions, for the kind of conduct society approves, for other people's feelings, and there must be instilled in all of us standards of restraint.

"You have only to read your papers and see day by day the results of unbridled sex. ... It is all for lack of standards, lack of restraint, lack of mental and moral discipline. ...

"... It is true, as Mr. Gardiner has anticipated, that I would urge upon you that you alone will have to decide, and not the various witnesses whose views you have heard. You will not be browbeaten by these witnesses, you will judge the case as ordinary men and women, with your feet firmly planted on the ground. Were the views you have heard from those most eminent and academic ladies and gentlemen really of so much value as the views which *you*—without perhaps the eminence and the academic learning—possess yourselves? I do not question the integrity and sincerity of those witnesses, but suggest that they all have got a bee in their bonnet about this book. ...

"When one sees some of them launching themselves at the first opportunity, at the first question, into a sermon or a lecture—according to their vocation—one cannot help feeling that sincerely and honestly as they feel, they feel in such a way that common sense perhaps has gone by the board.

"One witness said that sex was treated 'on a holy basis.' Can that be a realistic view? Is that a way a boy leaving school would read it? The Bishop of

Woolwich went one better and called it something sacred as an Act of Holy Communion. Do you think that is the way girls working in a factory will read the book in their luncheon break? Or does it put the Lord Bishop wholly out of touch with the large percentage of the people who will buy this book at 3/6?

"A book of moral purpose, the Reverend Hopkinson has said. *What* moral purpose do *you* read into the book?

"I suggest that Miss [sic] Rebecca West is capable of reading what she said into the book, but is that typical of the effect that book will have on the average reader? Are they going to see an allegory in it? Is the baronet and his impotence going to be read by them as a symbol? One wonders whether one is talking in the same language. . . .

"Members of the jury, is there any moral teaching in the book at all? How can there be when right until the end, when they decide to get their respective divorces, not a single word is spoken between them during their thirteen bouts, other than sex. All they have done before they decide to run away with each other is to copulate thirteen times. . . .

"It has been suggested that the shock of using the foul words wore off as one got used to it. Is that not a terrible thing if we forget the shock of using this language?"

And here Mr. Griffith-Jones took up the book once more. Once more he read. He read the Psalm passage again. "Do you know *who* the king of glory is? Do you?" He read another. "Here we come to a little striptease. . . ." He read again the last letter; he read, for the first time, two pages of Connie's last night with Mellors before she leaves for Venice.

He shut the book. "You will have to go some way in the Charing Cross Road, in the back streets of Paris, or even Port Saïd, to find a description that is as lurid as that one.

"It is for the jury to decide this case, and not for the so-called experts. This book has to be read not as bishops and lecturers read it, but as ordinary men and women read it, people without any literary or academic qualifications. Do you think, as I submit, that its effect on the average person must be to deprave, to lead them into false conceptions, to lower their general standard of thought, conduct and decency, and must be the opposite of encouraging that restraint in sexual matters which is so all-important in present times? This is what you must ask yourselves. And if you decide that it has a tendency to deprave, then you have to ask yourselves what public good is being done by this book to outweigh the harm? Is there such a public need in the interest of public good for the publication of this document?

"There can be but one answer."

There was still the Judge's charge. Juries are apt to look up to the judge, and to look at him to clarify their minds. Mr. Justice Byrne began his summing up on the afternoon of Day Five and continued on Day Six. He began:

"In these days the world seems to be full of experts. There is no subject you can think of where there is not to be found an expert who will be able to deal, or says he will be able to deal, with the situation. But the criminal law is based on a view that a jury is responsible for the facts and not the experts."

The Judge's voice was discreet in tone, polite and quietly persuasive. He spoke for two and a half hours all in all, and here are some extracts from what he said.

"There is no intent to deprave necessary to be proved in order that this offense should be committed. The intention is quite irrelevant.

". . . This book is to be put upon the market at 3/6 a copy, which is by no means an excessive price in these days when there are not only high wages, but high pocket money. . . . Once a book gets into circulation, it does not spend its time in the rarefied atmosphere of some academic institutions; it finds its way into the bookshops and onto the bookstalls and into the public libraries where it is available to all and sundry to read.

". . . The book has been said to be a moral tract, a virtuous and puritanical production, and a book that Christians ought to read. What do *you* think about that?

"Is it right to say that the story is one of a woman who first of all before she was married had sexual intercourse, and then after marriage when her husband had met with disaster in the war, and became confined to a wheelchair, she was living with her husband in this dreary place, Wragby, and committed adultery on two occasions with somebody called Michaelis, while her husband was downstairs in the same house. After that she proceeded to have adulterous intercourse with her husband's gamekeeper. And that is described, you may think—is it or is it not?—in the most lurid way, and the whole sensuality and passion of the various occasions is fully and completely described.

". . . You will have to consider the tendency that this book will have on the moral outlook of people who buy it, people possibly without any knowledge of Lawrence, or of literature, and people perhaps quite young, the youth of the country. . . .

". . . If you are satisfied that the book is obscene, you must go on to the further question: are the merits of the book as a novel *so high* that they outbalance the obscenity so its publication is *for the public good*? . . . I would repeat the observation made by Mr. Griffith-Jones who said, 'Keep your feet on the ground.' In other words, do not allow yourselves to get lost in the higher realms of literature, education, sociology and ethics.

"One witness, Mrs. Bennett, said, 'A reader who is capable of understanding Lawrence could get much of what his view is.' Who, members of the jury, are the people capable of understanding Lawrence? You have to think of people with no literary background, with little or no learning. . . .

"It has been said that the book does not deal simply and solely with sexual relationships, but that it deals with other matters, such as the industrial state of the country and the hard lives people are living. Whether you find there is very much in the book about that or not is for you to say. . . . You may ask yourselves whether, unless a person is an authority on literature, he would be able to read into the book the many different things the many witnesses said he intended to be in the book. . . .

"Mrs. Bennett said that Lawrence believed that marriage, not in the legal sense, but the union of two people for a lifetime was of the highest importance. Members of the jury, what is marriage if it is not in the legal sense? What are they talking about? This is a Christian country, and right through Christianity there has been lawful marriage, even if it is only before a registrar.

"The Bishop of Woolwich said Lawrence was trying to portray the sex relationship as something sacramental." The Judge looked up. *"Where are we getting?"* Do *you* find that the author was trying to portray sex as something sacramental? Then we had the Master of the Temple, and he was full of praise for the book. Then we had Professor Pinto who said that in some measure it was a moral tract—does *that* coincide with *your* view? Do you find that the relationship between Lady Chatterley and the game-keeper was really moral? Did you find one spark of affection between these two? Or were they merely having sexual intercourse and enjoying it?

"You heard one witness say that it is possible to feel 'reverence for a man's balls'; what do you make of that? Does it coincide with your view of the matter? Well, members of the jury, there it is, there it is. . . . You must ask yourselves whether as you *read* the book, you find you can agree with all the things the witnesses said Lawrence was trying to say. . . . You are not bound by the evidence—you have to make up your own minds."

Well, and so they did.

The world now knows that verdict, but for us, who waited on that day, it was a long three hours before we heard—still incredulous in relief—those words: Not Guilty. A ripple of applause broke out, stentoriously suppressed; there was no other comment. It is customary for the Judge to express thanks to the jury; Mr. Justice Byrne did not do so, and the words were spoken by the Clerk.

John Steinbeck:

The Trial of Arthur Miller

A clear and present danger

The trial of Arthur Miller for contempt of Congress brings close to all of us one of the strangest and most frightening dilemmas that a people and a government have ever faced. It is not the first trial of its kind, nor will it in all probability be the last. But Arthur Miller is a writer—one of our very best. What has happened to him could happen to any writer; could happen to me. We are face to face with a problem by no means easy of solution. "Is a puzzlement!"

No man knows what he might do in a given situation, and surely many men must wonder how they would act if they were in Arthur Miller's shoes. I wonder what I would do.

Let me suppose that I were going to trial for contempt of Congress as he is. I might be thinking somewhat as follows:

There is no doubt that Congress has the right, under the law, to ask me any question it wishes and to punish my refusal to answer with a contempt charge. The Congress has the right to do nearly anything conceivable. It has only to define a situation or an action as a "clear and present danger" to public safety, public morals, or public health. The selling or eating of mince pie could be made a crime if Congress determined that mince pie was a danger to public health—which it probably is. Since many parents raise their children badly, mother love could be defined as a danger to the general welfare.

Surely, Congress has this right to ask me anything on any subject. The question is: Should the Congress take advantage of that right?

Let us say that the Congressional Committee feels that the Communist Party and many groups which have been linked with it—sometimes arbitrarily—constitute a clear and present danger to the nation. Now actually it is neither virtue nor good judgment on my part that has kept me from joining things. I am simply not a joiner by nature. Outside of the Boy Scouts and the Episcopal choir, I have never had an impulse to belong to things. But suppose I had. And suppose I have admitted my association with one or more of these groups posted as dangerous. As a writer,

After Arthur Miller was cited for contempt of Congress, Steinbeck was aroused to write this piece in Miller's defense. Esquire published it in June, 1957. In 1958, Miller was acquitted on appeal.

I must have been interested in everything, have felt it part of my profession to know and understand all kinds of people and groups. Having admitted these associations, I am now asked by the Committee to name individuals I have seen at meetings of such groups. I hope my reasoning then would go as follows:

The people I knew were not and are not, in my estimation, traitors to the nation. If they were, I would turn them in instantly. If I give names, it is reasonably certain that the persons named will be called up and questioned. In some cases they will lose their jobs, and in any case their reputations and standing in the community will suffer. And remember that these are persons who I honestly believe are innocent of any wrongdoing. Perhaps I do not feel that I have that right; that to name them would not only be disloyal but actually immoral. The Committee then is asking me to commit an immorality in the name of public virtue.

If I agree, I have outraged one of our basic codes of conduct, and if I refuse I am guilty of contempt of Congress, sentenced to prison and fined. One way outrages my sense of decency and the other brands me as a felon. And this brand does not fade out.

Now suppose I have children, a little property, a stake in the community. The threat of the contempt charge jeopardizes everything I love. Suppose, from worry or cowardice, I agree to what is asked. My deep and wounding shame will be with me always.

I cannot be reassured by the past performance of the Committee. I have read daily for a number of years the testimony of admitted liars and perjurers whose charges have been used to destroy the peace and happiness of people I do not know, and many of whom were destroyed without being tried.

Which path am I to choose? Either way I am caught. It may occur to me that a man who is disloyal to his friends could not be expected to be loyal to his country. You can't slice up morals. Our virtues begin at home. They do not change in a courtroom unless the pressure of fear is put upon us.

But if I am caught between two horrors, so is the Congress caught. Law, to survive, must be moral. To force personal immorality on a man, to wound his private virtue, undermines his public virtue. If the Committee frightens me enough, it is even possible that I may make up things to satisfy the questioners. This has been known to happen. A law which is immoral does not survive and a government which condones or fosters immorality is truly in clear and present danger. The Congress had a perfect right to pass the Alien and Sedition Act. This law was repealed because of public revulsion. The Escaped Slave laws had to be removed because the people of free states found them immoral. The Prohibition laws were so flouted that all law suffered as a consequence.

We have seen and been revolted by the Soviet Union's encouragement of spying and telling, children reporting their parents, wives informing on their husbands. In Hitler's Germany, it was considered patriotic to report your friends and relations to the authorities. And we in America have felt safe from and superior to these things. But are we so safe or superior?

The men in Congress must be conscious of their terrible choice. Their legal right is clearly established, but should they not think of their moral responsibility also? In their attempts to save the nation from attack, they could well undermine the deep personal morality which is the nation's final defense. The Congress is truly on trial along with Arthur Miller.

Again let me change places with Arthur Miller. I have refused to name people. I am indicted, convicted, sent to prison. If the charge were murder or theft or extortion I would be subject to punishment, because I and all men know that these things are wrong. But if I am imprisoned for something I have been taught from birth is a good thing, then I go to jail with a deep sense of injustice and the rings of that injustice are bound to spread out like an infection. If I am brave enough to suffer for my principle, rather than to save myself by hurting other people I believe to be innocent, it seems to me that the law suffers more than I, and that contempt of the law and of the Congress is a real contempt rather than a legalistic one.

Under the law, Arthur Miller is guilty. But he seems also to be brave. Congress feels that it must press the charge against him, to keep its prerogative alive. But can we not hope that our representatives will inspect their dilemma? Respect for law can be kept high only if the law is respectable. There is a clear and present danger here, not to Arthur Miller, but to our changing and evolving way of life. If I were in Arthur Miller's shoes, I do not know what I would do, but I could wish, for myself and for my children, that I would be brave enough to fortify and defend my private morality as he has. I feel profoundly that our country is better served by individual courage and morals than by the safe and public patriotism which Dr. Johnson called "the last refuge of scoundrels."

My father was a great man, as any lucky man's father must be. He taught me rules I do not think are abrogated by our nervous and hysterical times. These laws have not been annulled; these rules or attitudes. He taught me—glory to God, honor to my family, loyalty to my friends, respect for the law, love of country and instant and open revolt against tyranny, whether it come from the bully in the schoolyard, the foreign dictator, or the local demagogue.

And if this be treason, gentlemen, make the most of it.

COPING WITH THE ISSUES

Esquire has never turned its back on important social matters, as the following articles show. They concern, in these instances, the questions of Utopian order (Aldous Huxley); politics, friendship and self-definition (Allen, Trumbo, Schlesinger); and woman, sex and liberation (Sally Kempton). Huxley, whether writing about Freudian theory (often) or canned fish (Esquire, December, 1955), was always original and witty. Perhaps more than any other writer he personified what Publisher Arnold Gingrich meant when in November, 1955, he warned the magazine's audience that Esquire "stands for anything that will afford amusement to men of intelligence." He went on to qualify his use of the word "amusement," saying that "we aim to keep our readers' mind 'amused,' thoughtfully, intelligently and on a high intellectual level, much as that most civilized of modern men, Henry Adams, was 'amused' in *The Education of Henry Adams*, by the multiplicity of life around him." The essay included here has been selected from among some thirty pieces Huxley contributed to Esquire.

The Happy Jack Fish Hatchery Papers found their way into Esquire (January, 1970) in an unusual way. The original letters were sent to writer Tom Coffey (*Agony at Easter*) by a friend in California who wasn't quite sure where she, herself, had got them. Mr. Coffey found them interesting and showed them to his book editor, James Wade, who, because he too found them interesting, passed them on to Esquire's (then) Fiction Editor, Rust Hills. Mr. Hills passed them to (then) Managing Editor, Don Erickson, who got in touch with Dalton Trumbo, and then we passed them on to our readers.

Mr. Trumbo, a noted screenwriter, novelist and man-of-all-letters, returned later that year, July, 1970, with more of the same, *En Garde, Foolish World*, gleaned from a collection of his letters later published in book form as *Additional Dialogue* (M. Evans Co., New York, 1970). Mr. Allen had appeared in our pages a good deal earlier, as part of a humor panel, and with a long short story entitled *The Girls on the Tenth Floor* in November, 1956. Mr. Schlesinger's essays on social and historical issues have often appeared in Esquire.

Born in 1943, Sally Kempton traveled a different road to a position of individualized feminine dissent: "My sexual rage," she wrote, "was the most powerful single emotion of my life, and the feminist analysis has become for me, as I think it will for most women of my generation, as significant an intellectual tool as Marxism was for generations of radicals." *Cutting Loose* appeared in July, 1970, together with a profile of Dustin Hoffman also by Sally Kempton.

Aldous Huxley:

Brave New World Revisited

Proleptic meditations on Mother's Day,
euphoria and Pavlov's pooch

The most distressing thing that can happen to a prophet is to be proved wrong; the next most distressing thing is to be proved right. In the twenty-five years that have elapsed since *Brave New World* was written, I have undergone both these experiences. Events have proved me distressingly wrong; and events have proved me distressingly right.

Here are some of the points on which I was wrong. By the early Thirties Einstein had equated mass and energy, and there was already talk of chain reactions; but the Brave New Worlders knew nothing of nuclear fission. In the early Thirties, too, we knew all about conservation and irreplaceable resources; but their supply of metals and mineral fuel was just as copious in the seventh century After Ford as ours is today. In actual fact the raw-material situation will already be subcritical by A.F. 600 and the atom will be the principal source of industrial power. Again, the Brave New Worlders had solved the population problem and knew how to maintain a permanently favorable relationship between human numbers and natural resources. In actual fact, will our descendants achieve this happy consummation within the next six centuries? And if they *do* achieve it, will it be by dint of rational planning, or through the immemorial agencies of pestilence, famine and internecine warfare? It is, of course, impossible to say. The only thing we can predict with a fair measure of certainty is that humanity (if its rulers decide to refrain from collective suicide) will be traveling at vertiginous speed along one of the most dangerous and congested stretches of its history.

The Brave New Worlders produced their children in biochemical factories. But though bottled babies are not completely out of the question, it is virtually certain that our descendants will in fact remain viviparous. Mother's Day is in no danger of being replaced by Bottle Day. My prediction was made for strictly literary purposes, and not as a reasoned forecast of future history. In this matter I knew in advance that I should be proved wrong.

This essay from the July, 1956, issue was the most controversial of the series that appeared between August, 1955, and April, 1957, under the heading "From the Study of Aldous Huxley." It bears no relation to Huxley's more recently published discussion of modern liberty, also entitled Brave New World Revisited *(1958).*

From biology we now pass to politics. The dictatorship described in *Brave New World* was global and, in its own peculiar way, benevolent. In the light of current events and developing tendencies, I sadly suspect that in this forecast, too, I may have been wrong. True, the seventh century After Ford is still a long way off, and it is possible that, by then, hard economic necessity, or the social chaos resulting from nuclear warfare, or military conquest by one Great Power, or some grisly combination of all three will have bludgeoned our descendants into doing what we ought to be doing now, from motives of enlightened self-interest and common humanity—namely, to collaborate for the common good. In time of peace, and when things are going tolerably well, people cannot be expected to vote for measures which, though ultimately beneficial, may be expected to have certain disagreeable consequences in the short run. Divisive forces are more powerful than those which make for union. Vested interests in languages, philosophies of life, table manners, sexual habits, political, ecclesiastical and economic organizations are sufficiently powerful to block all attempts, by rational and peaceful methods, to unite mankind for its own good. And then there is nationalism. With its Fifty-Seven Varieties of tribal gods, nationalism is the religion of the twentieth century. We may be Christians, Jews, Moslems, Hindus, Buddhists, Confucians or Atheists; but the fact remains that there is only one faith for which large masses of us are prepared to die and kill, and that faith is nationalism. That nationalism will remain the dominant religion of the human race for the next two or three centuries at the very least seems all too probable. If total, nuclear war should be avoided, we may expect to see, not the rise of a single world state, but the continuance, in worsening conditions, of the present system, under which national states compete for markets and raw materials and prepare for partial wars. Most of these states will probably be dictatorships. Inevitably so; for the increasing pressure of population upon resources will make domestic conditions more difficult and international competition more intense. To prevent economic breakdown and to repress popular discontent, the governments of hungry countries will be tempted to enforce ever-stricter controls. Furthermore, chronic undernourishment reduces physical energy and disturbs the mind. Hunger and self-government are incompatible. Even where the average diet provides three thousand calories a day, it is hard enough to make democracy work. In a society in which most members are living on seventeen hundred to two thousand calories a day, it is simply impossible. The undernourished majority will always be ruled, from above, by the well-fed few. As population increases (twenty-seven hundred millions of us are now adding to our numbers at the rate of forty millions a year, and this increase is increasing according to the rules of compound interest); as geometrically increasing demands press more and more heavily on static or, at best, arithmetically increasing supplies; as standards of living are forced down and popular discontent is forced up; as the general scramble for diminishing resources becomes ever fiercer, these national dictatorships will tend to become more oppressive at home, more ruthlessly competitive abroad. "Government," says one of the Brave New Worlders, "is an affair of sitting, not hitting. You rule with the brains and the buttocks, not the fists." But where there are many competing national dictatorships, each in trouble at home and each preparing for total or partial war against its neighbors, hitting tends to be preferred to sitting, fists, as an instrument of policy, to brains and the "masterly inactivity" (to cite Lord Salisbury's immortal phrase) of the hindquarters. In politics, the near future is likely to be closer to George Orwell's *1984* than to *Brave New World*.

Let me now consider a few of the points on which, I fear, I may have been right. The Brave New Worlders were the heirs and exploiters of a new kind of revolution, and this revolution was, in effect, the theme of my fable. Past revolutions have all been in fields external to the individual as a psychophysical organism—in the field, for example, of ecclesiastical organization and religious dogma, in the field of economics, in the field of political organization, in the field of technology. The coming revolution—the revolution whose consequences are described in *Brave New World*—will affect men and women, not peripherally, but at the very core of their organic being. The older revolutionaries sought to change the social environment in the hope (if they were idealists and not mere power seekers) of changing human nature. The coming revolutionaries will make their assault directly on human nature as they find it, in the minds and bodies of their victims or, if you prefer, their beneficiaries.

Among the Brave New Worlders, the control of human nature was achieved by eugenic and dysgenic breeding, by systematic conditioning during infancy and, later on, by "hypnopaedia," or instruction during sleep. Infant conditioning is as old as Pavlov and hypnopaedia, though rudimentary, is already a well-established technique. Phonographs with built-in clocks, which turn them on and off at regular intervals during the night, are already on the market and are being used by students of foreign languages, by actors in a hurry to memorize their parts, by parents desirous of curing their children of bed-wetting and other troublesome habits, by self-helpers seeking moral and physical improvement through autosuggestion and "affirmations of positive thought." That the principles of selective breeding, infant conditioning and hypnopaedia have not yet been applied by governments is due, in the democratic countries, to the lingering, liberal conviction that persons do not exist for the state, but that the state exists for the good of persons; and in the totalitarian countries to what may be called revolutionary conservatism—attachment to yesterday's revolution instead of the revolution of tomorrow. There is, however, no reason for complacently believing that this revolutionary conservatism will persist indefinitely. In totalitarian hands, applied psychology is already achieving notable results. One third of all the American prisoners captured in Korea succumbed, at least partially, to Chinese brainwashing, which broke down the convictions, installed by their education and childhood conditioning, and replaced these comforting axioms by doubt, anxiety and a chronic sense of guilt. This was achieved by thoroughly old-fashioned procedures, which combined straightforward instruction with what may be called conventional psychotherapy in reverse, and made no use of hypnosis, hypnopaedia or mind-modifying drugs. If all or even some of these more powerful methods had been employed, brainwashing would probably have been successful with all the prisoners, and not with a mere thirty percent of them. In their vague, rhetorical way, speech-making politicians and sermon-preaching clergymen like to say that the current struggle is not material, but spiritual—an affair not of machines, but of ideas. They forget to add that the effectiveness of ideas depends very largely on the way in which they are inculcated. A true and beneficent idea may be so ineptly taught as to be without effect on the lives of individuals and societies. Conversely, grotesque and harmful notions may be so skillfully drummed into people's heads that, filled with faith, they will rush out and move mountains—to the glory of the devil and their own destruction. At the present time the dynamism of totalitarian ideas is greater than the dynamism of liberal, democratic ideas. This is not due, of course, to the intrinsic superiority of totalitarian ideas. It is due partly to the fact that, in a world where population is fast outrunning resources, ever larger measures of governmental control become necessary—and it is easier to exercise centralized control by totalitarian than by democratic methods. Partly, too, it is due to the fact that the means employed for the dissemination of totalitarian ideas are more effective, and are used more systematically, than the means employed for disseminating democratic and liberal ideas. These more effective methods of totalitarian propaganda, education and brainwashing are, as we have seen, pretty old-fashioned. Sooner or later, however, the dictators will abandon their revolutionary conservatism and, along with it, the old-world procedures inherited from the pre-psychological and palaeo-pharmacological past. After which, heaven help us all!

Among the legacies of the proto-pharmacological past must be numbered our habit, when we feel in need of a lift, a release from tension, a mental vacation from unpleasant reality, of drinking alcohol or, if we happen to belong to a non-Western culture, of smoking hashish or opium, of chewing coca leaves or betel or any one of scores of intoxicants. The Brave New Worlders did none of these things; they merely swallowed a tablet or two of a substance called Soma. This, needless to say, was not the same as the Soma mentioned in the ancient Hindu scriptures—a rather dangerous drug derived from some as yet unidentified plant native to South Central Asia—but a synthetic, possessing "all the virtues of alcohol and Christianity, none of their defects." In small doses the Soma of the Brave New Worlders was a relaxant, an inducer of euphoria, a fosterer of friendliness and social solidarity. In medium doses it transfigured the external world and acted as a mild hallucinant; and in large doses it was a narcotic. Virtually all the Brave New Worlders thought themselves happy. This was due in part to the fact that they had been bred and conditioned to take the place assigned to them in the social hierarchy, in part to the sleep-teaching which had made them content with their lot and in part to Soma and their ability, by its means, to take holidays from unpleasant circumstances and their unpleasant selves.

All the natural narcotics, stimulants, relaxants and hallucinants known to the modern botanist and pharmacologist were discovered by primitive man and have been in use from time immemorial. One of the first things that Homo sapiens did with his newly developed rationality and self-consciousness was to set them to work finding out ways to bypass analytical thinking and to transcend or, in extreme cases, temporarily obliterate the isolating awareness of the self. Trying all things that grew in field or forest, they held fast to that which, in this context, seemed good—everything, that is to say, that would change

the quality of consciousness, would make it different, no matter how, from everyday feeling, perceiving and thinking. Among the Hindus, rhythmic breathing and mental concentration have, to some extent, taken the place of the mind-transforming drugs used elsewhere. But even in the land of yoga, even among the religious and even for specifically religious purposes, cannabis indica has been freely used to supplement the effects of spiritual exercises. The habit of taking vacations from the more-or-less purgatorial world, which we have created for ourselves, is universal. Moralists may denounce it; but, in the teeth of disapproving talk and repressive legislation, the habit persists, and mind-transforming drugs are everywhere available. The Marxian formula, "Religion is the opium of the people," is reversible, and one can say, with even more truth, that "Opium is the religion of the people." In other words, mind-transformation, however induced (whether by devotional or ascetic or psycho-gymnastic or chemical means), has always been felt to be one of the highest, perhaps the very highest, of all attainable goods. Up to the present, governments have thought about the problem of mind-transforming chemicals only in terms of prohibition or, a little more realistically, of control and taxation. None, so far, has considered it in its relation to individual well-being and social stability; and very few (thank heaven!) have considered it in terms of Machiavellian statecraft. Because of vested interests and mental inertia, we persist in using alcohol as our main mind-transformer—just as our neolithic ancestors did. We know that alcohol is responsible for a high proportion of our traffic accidents, our crimes of violence, our domestic miseries; and yet we make no effort to replace this old-fashioned and extremely unsatisfactory drug by some new, less harmful and more enlightening mind-transformer. Among the Brave New Worlders, Noah's prehistoric invention of fermented liquor has been made obsolete by a modern synthetic, specifically designed to contribute to social order and the happiness of the individual, and to do so at the minimum physiological cost.

In the society described in my fable, Soma was used as an instrument of statecraft. The tyrants were benevolent, but they were still tyrants. Their subjects were not bludgeoned into obedience; they were chemically coerced to love their servitude, to cooperate willingly and even enthusiastically in the preservation of the social hierarchy. By the malignant or the ignorant, anything and everything can be used badly. Alcohol, for example, has been used, in small doses, to facilitate the exchange of thought in a symposium (literally, a drinking party) of philosophers. It has also been used, as the slave traders used it, to facilitate kidnapping. Scopolamine may be used to induce "twilight sleep"; it may also be used to increase suggestibility and soften up political prisoners. Heroin may be used to control pain; it may also be used (as it is said to have been used by the Japanese during their occupation of China) to produce an incapacitating addiction in a dangerous adversary. Directed by the wrong people, the coming revolution could be as disastrous, in its own way, as a nuclear and bacteriological war. By systematically using the psychological, chemical and electronic instruments already in existence (not to mention those new and better devices which the future holds in store), a tyrannical oligarchy could keep the majority in permanent and willing subjection. This is the prophecy I made in *Brave New World*. I hope I may be proved wrong, but am sorely afraid that I may be proved right.

Meanwhile it should be pointed out that Soma is not intrinsically evil. On the contrary, a harmless but effective mind-transforming drug might prove a major blessing. And anyhow (as history makes abundantly clear) there will never be any question of getting rid of chemical mind-transformers altogether. The choice confronting us is not a choice between Soma and nothing; it is a choice between Soma and alcohol, Soma and opium, Soma and hashish, ololiuqui, peyote, datura, agaric and all the rest of the natural mind-transformers; between Soma and such products of scientific chemistry and pharmacology as ether, chloral, veronal, benzedrine and the barbiturates. In a word, we have to choose between a more-or-less harmless all-round drug and a wide variety of more-or-less harmful and only partially effective drugs. And this choice will not be delayed until the seventh century After Ford. Pharmacology is on the march. The Soma of *Brave New World* is no longer a distant dream. Indeed, something possessing many of the characteristics of Soma is already with us. I refer to the most recent of the tranquilizing agents—the Happiness Pill, as its users affectionately call it, known in America under the trade names of Miltown and Equinel. These Happiness Pills exert a double action; they relax the tension in striped muscle and so relax the associated tensions in the mind. At the same time they act on the enzyme system of the brain in such a way as to prevent disturbances arising in the hypothalamus from interfering with the workings of the cortex. On the mental level, the effect is a blessed release from anxiety and self-regarding emotivity.

In my fable the savage expresses his belief that the advantages of Soma must be paid for by losses on the highest human levels. Perhaps he was right. The universe is not in the habit of giving us something for nothing. And yet there is a great deal to be said for a pill which enables us to assume an attitude toward circumstances of detachment, ataraxia, "holy indifference." The moral worth of an action cannot be measured exclusively in terms of intention. Hell is paved with good intentions, and we have to take some account of results. Rational and kindly behavior tends to produce good results, and these results remain good even when the behavior which produced them was itself produced by a pill. On the other hand, can we with impunity replace systematic self-discipline by a chemical? It remains to be seen.

Of all the consciousness-transforming drugs the most interesting, if not the most immediately useful, are those which, like lysergic acid and mescaline, open the door to what may be called the Other World of the mind. Many workers are already exploring the effects of these drugs, and we may be sure that other mind-transformers, with even more remarkable properties, will be produced in the near future. What man will ultimately do with these extraordinary elixirs, it is impossible to say. My own guess is that they are destined to play a part in human life at least as great as the part played, up till now, by alcohol, and incomparably more beneficent.

THE HAPPY JACK FISH HATCHERY PAPERS

In which the Messrs. Steve Allen, Dalton Trumbo and Arthur Schlesinger Jr. debate the true meaning of liberalism

Mrs. Beata Inaya   February 26, 1969
Los Angeles, California

Dear Mrs. Inaya:

Thank you for your letter of February 25th which I am answering five minutes after reading.

I'm sorry to report that I'm already committed for the evening of Friday, March 14th, and will therefore not be able to have the pleasure of attending the party that evening in honor of Mr. Bradley. As I believe you know, I *am* participating in another affair in his honor on March 1st.

It is absolutely none of my business that the March 14th affair is being held at the home of Mr. Dalton Trumbo, but I am assuming that those of you who are working so hard on Tom Bradley's behalf must know that Mr. Bradley's reactionary opponents will certainly make capital of the fact that Mr. Trumbo's home is the setting for this particular occasion.

I know absolutely nothing of Mr. Trumbo's present political convictions, nor have I any particular interest in what his political affiliation might have been, say, a quarter of a century ago. I *assume*, however, that at one time he was indeed a Communist. I have also been told he is a very likable individual personally and his position as one of our most talented screenwriters is widely acknowledged. It would in no way affect my own admiration for Mr. Bradley that Mr. Trumbo might be one of his supporters but—to go over the ground again—*if* (a) Mr. Trumbo is today of the Communist persuasion (something he has every legal right to be), and *if* (b) this fact is publicized by Mr. Bradley's rightist political opposition, then (c) the March 14th affair will almost certainly be used in such a way as to cost Mr. Bradley a perhaps significant number of votes in this not-always-politically-enlightened city. I am perfectly willing to have you show this letter to Mr. Bradley, or to Mr. Trumbo for that matter, should you feel so inclined.

If Mr. Bradley's present campaign is, let us say, similar to William Buckley's in New York, in that winning is out of the question, but the race is run

These letters were published in January, 1970, to demonstrate that stimulating correspondence was alive and well in Hollywood. The title for this exchange was a perplexing problem, one finally solved by a close inspection of Mr. Trumbo's flamboyant cc:s.

merely as a public profession of political principle, then, of course, my observations here will be irrelevant. But they do indeed have a relevance if Tom Bradley and his supporters are interested in winning the political contest.

Cordially yours, Steve Allen

                                 [Undated]
Mr. Dalton Trumbo
Los Angeles, California

Dear Mr. Trumbo:

The Arts Division of the American Civil Liberties Union inaugurated its first Annual Playwriting Contest open to all students in any college or university in Southern California. The response was overwhelming and enthusiastic, and we now have the two award-winning student plays. They will be presented at the Stage Society Theatre in Los Angeles for four performances only, on Sunday afternoon, June 8 (preview performance for students), and on Monday, Tuesday, and Wednesday evenings, June 9, 10, and 11.

It is because I am certain that you share my interests in both encouraging young, fresh talent and the free expression of ideas that I am asking you to participate as a sponsor in this unique project with me. Only $25 from you not only helps to underwrite the cost of these productions, but it will also make it possible to invite two students to the preview performance on Sunday.

Furthermore, your name will be listed on the program as a sponsor and you will receive two tickets for whichever evening performance you prefer. Please indicate your preference when you send your check made payable to the Arts Division, ACLU—which I hope you will do now.

Thanks so much for your support.

Cordially, Arts Division

Arts Division   May 7, 1969
American Civil Liberties Union
Los Angeles, California

Gentlemen:

Not so long ago, Mrs. Trumbo and I gave our names as sponsors for a liberal cause which I shall not

191

mention here, and somewhat reluctantly agreed to throw our house open in its behalf to a fund-raising party for 150 persons.

Unknown to us, Mr. Steve Allen, who appears to be the doyen of the Hollywood liberal community, wrote a letter to the organization charging that the use of my name would provide rightists and reactionaries with an opportunity to defeat their organization and the cause for which it stood.

Although no one had mentioned the matter to Mrs. Trumbo or me, and the invitations were already at the printers, the party was canceled forthwith, and we, quite after the fact, were notified of our undesirability. I did not like it, and I am resolved it shall not happen a second time.

I shall be glad to sponsor the Arts Division, ACLU Playwriting Contest provided you can secure Mr. Allen's written consent for my name to appear on your list. I know this seems odd, but it's the only way I can think of to avoid another spasm of nastiness and, perhaps, disavowel.

I enclose my check for $25 as a straight non-sponsoring contribution.

Cordially, Dalton Trumbo

cc: Mr. Steve Allen

Arts Division,   May 13, 1969
American Civil Liberties Union

Gentlemen:

Mr. Dalton Trumbo was kind enough to provide me with a copy of his letter of May 7th to you. I shall naturally accord him the same favor in attempting to clarify the misunderstanding to which an earlier letter of mine has apparently given rise. I can quite understand Mr. Trumbo's personal displeasure at the cancellation of a party for which, in the first place, he had agreed to serve as a somewhat reluctant host.

Secondly, I concede that he is correct in placing on my shoulders the primary blame for the cancellation of the party, although in referring to me as "the doyen of the Hollywood liberal community" he greatly exaggerates my influence upon liberal affairs in our community. Nevertheless, my letter of February 26th did indeed recommend against the holding of the fund-raising party in Mr. and Mrs. Trumbo's home.

To make my motives in this instance perfectly clear, I quote here the relevant portions of the letter to which Mr. Trumbo objects:

"It is absolutely none of my business that the March 14th affair is being held at the home of Mr. Dalton Trumbo, but I am assuming that those of you who are working so hard on Tom Bradley's behalf must know that Mr. Bradley's reactionary opponents will certainly make capital of the fact that Mr. Trumbo's home is the setting for this particular function.

"I know nothing of Mr. Trumbo's present political convictions, nor have I any particular interest in what his political affiliation might have been, say, a quarter of a century ago. I *assume*, however, that at one time he was indeed a Communist. I have also been told he is a very likable individual personally, and his

position as one of our most talented screenwriters is widely acknowledged. It would in no way affect my own admiration for Mr. Bradley that Mr. Trumbo might be one of his supporters but—to go over the ground again—*if* (a) Mr. Trumbo is today of the Communist persuasion (something he has every legal right to be), and *if* (b) this fact is publicized by Mr. Bradley's rightist political opposition, then (c) the March 14th affair will almost certainly be used in such a way as to cost Mr. Bradley a perhaps significant number of votes in this not-always-politically-enlightened city. I am perfectly willing to have you show this letter to Mr. Bradley, or to Mr. Trumbo for that matter, should you feel inclined to do so.

"If Mr. Bradley's present campaign is, let us say, similar to William Buckley's in New York, in that winning is out of the question, but the race is run merely as a public profession of political principle, then, of course, my observations here will be irrelevant. But they do indeed have relevance if Tom Bradley and his supporters are interested in winning the political contest."

Now may I draw your attention to something in Mr. Trumbo's letter of May 7th which is possibly crucially significant in this context. In his first paragraph he chooses not to identify Mr. Bradley's campaign but refers only to "a liberal cause which I shall not mention here. . . ." While it is conceivable that Mr. Trumbo omits Mr. Bradley's name because he has decided to base his argument on principle rather than on specifics, it seems to me more probable that he is motivated by a generous reluctance to draw Mr. Bradley's name into this discussion at a moment in the mayoralty race when it is unwise to rock boats. If the latter hypothesis is the valid one then perhaps, in choosing not now to link his name with that of Mr. Bradley, Mr. Trumbo may be motivated by precisely those considerations which dictated the writing of my letter of February 26th.

Mr. Trumbo seems to feel that the party at his house was canceled on my *instructions*. Such was not the case. I simply brought certain considerations of political expediency to the attention of one of Mr. Bradley's campaign workers. Apparently my letter was forwarded to higher-placed members of Mr. Bradley's staff; presumably it was these workers who issued the cancellation order. It is clear, I would think, that only someone more formally associated with Mr. Bradley's campaign would have the authority to dictate such a cancellation. I have no such authority. It is unfortunate that the reasons for the party's cancellation were not explained to Mr. Trumbo before rather than after the fact, and again I say that his emotional response to the manner in which the situation was handled is quite understandable.

Mr. Trumbo is a witty and trenchant writer and I stand properly amused by the irony of his suggestion that he will sponsor the ACLU-Arts Division's Playwriting Contest provided only that the organization can secure my written consent for his name to appear on its list of sponsors. I have, of course, no more authority to prevent his association with the Arts Division-ACLU in this instance than I had to prevent his public association with Mr. Bradley's campaign in the other. To this point my comments will probably have seemed unexceptionable to you, but concerning what I have now to say a raised eyebrow or two would be understandable. Can it indeed be the case that I have the temerity to recommend Mr. Trumbo's rejection a *second* time, to rub salt in his wounds, to attempt, in my capacity as doyen, to banish him into that exterior darkness into which, from time to time, in recent history, various representatives of the non-Communist left in America have attempted to push their pro-Soviet or pro-Marxist associates?

The question is, alas, impossible to answer for the reason that I haven't the slightest idea as to what Mr. Trumbo's present position on the political spectrum might be.

At which you should pin me to the wall and demand to know, in certain terms, what my recommendation in this matter would be if it could be absolutely certified—or even assumed for purposes of debate—that Mr. Trumbo is today a Communist and proud of it.

In which case I concede my strong anti-Communist bias. Since there are those seriously afflicted by the Either-or disease—a malady apparently as common on the political Left as it is on the Right—I am therefore obliged to state that my opposition to political tyranny does indeed take in all 360 degrees of the circle that stretches to the political horizon, which is to say that I am also revolted by Nazism, Fascism and McCarthyism. It is all very well for Communists to resent the criticisms of Liberals and Democratic Socialists; the hard fact remains that Liberals and Democratic Socialists in power do *not* send Communists to execution chambers and political prisons; whereas Communists in power—in country after country—do indeed exercise a barbarous vengeance against those members of the non-Communist Left whom the Communists correctly identify as their true rivals for the political affections of the masses.

It would be to a degree irrelevant and presumptuous here to review the political history of the last half-century but I cannot conceive how any true Liberal, being familiar with that history, could be anything but anti-Communist. As a Liberal, I am in favor of freedom of the press, freedom of speech, and of freedom of assemblage. But I know of no Communist society in which such freedoms exist. I am also opposed to the death penalty, as are most Liberals, but it is clear that Communist societies cannot function without the threat, and frequently the reality, of state murder. As a Liberal I am suspicious of official censorship, but I observe that it is harshly dominant in all Communist cultures. As a Liberal I do not think a college student should automatically be considered a criminal if a marijuana cigarette is found in his possession, but we know of the utter ruthlessness with which Communist societies stamp out such instances of bourgeois decadence. The civil liberties the ACLU so courageously defends are not the foundation-stones of any existing Marxist society. The litany of specifics need not be continued; certainly the point is clear enough.

I concede—indeed, I fervently hope—that all of this may be utterly irrelevant in Mr. Trumbo's case. If it is, I would be greatly relieved and—assuming the man has not forsaken one tyranny for another—would therefore be as willing to be associated with him in a worthwhile social endeavor as I would with any other law-abiding citizen.

I have frequently been a stern critic of American society and expect to function as such in the future, but for years I have consistently maintained the position that it does not profit the non-Communist political Left to be formally allied with those who will endorse a Liberal cause only when to do so coincides with the purposes of Moscow or Peking. In Vietnam, for example, what I hope for is *peace*; therefore I cannot cooperate with those who are motivated primarily by hopes of victory for Ho Chi Minh.

I leave it to you gentlemen to determine the relevance, if any, of these observations to the case which Mr. Trumbo's letter has brought to your attention.

Most cordially yours, Steve Allen
cc: Mr. Dalton Trumbo, Mr. Eason Monroe, Mr. Tom Bradley, Mr. Burt Lancaster

Mr. Steve Allen   May 19, 1969
Encino, California

My dear Stern-Critic of American Society Who Expects-to-Function-as-Such-in-the-Future:

Thanks for the copy of your May 13th Epistle to the Thespians. It soars. One must stand back to gain perspective. After just two readings I am a much better citizen than I really wanted to be.

Beyond adding three splendid new names to our circle of readers, you have also cast a dazzling light on that gritty little canceled campaign party by placing it in bold juxtaposition with the political history of the last half-century, the non-Communist left, pro-Soviet or pro-Marxist associates, Communism, anti-Communist bias, the Left, the Right, political tyranny, Nazism, Fascism, McCarthyism, Liberals, Democratic Socialists, execution chambers, political prisons, vengeance, the masses, the true Liberal, freedom of the press, freedom of speech, freedom of assemblage, the death penalty, state murder, official censorship, the marijuana laws, ruthlessness, bourgeois decadence, civil liberties, Marxist society, American society, Moscow, Peking, peace, Vietnam and Ho Chi Minh. Unhappily my fuller comment must be deferred because of a pledge I made to refrain from using certain names connected with the matter under discussion until after the election. Pending that time, however, allow me to toss a few of my own hang-ups into the pot which you have so generously provided, to wit:

The French withdrawal from NATO, British entry into the Common Market, abolition of the statute of limitations in West Germany, the prevalence of Huntington's chorea in the Sultanate of Muscat and Oman, equal access to the southern fishing banks of Iceland, the plight of West Irianese refugees and the Free Papua Liberation Command, the population explosion among North European elvers, the theft of four paintings from the collection of the Ninth Earl of Linster at Rudford Castle near Cockermouth, the demotion of Sophronia as patron saint of toothaches, the effect of the Spitz-Holter valve on hydrocephalic children, Portnoy's Complaint, the Schism of Photius, the Black Panther Party, tax relief, treasury notes, family foundations, tapped telephones, pornographic pictures, mandragora, nerve gas, vervain, air pollution, euthanasia, law and order, academic freedom, mace, the pill, yohimbe root, penis envy, stainless stealing, fire-buggery, Aristotle Onassis, Eldridge Cleaver, Abe Fortas, Patricia Nixon, Prince Abdul Rahman, Cesar Chavez, Andy Warhol, and Brenda Holton, 23, who died two weeks ago in Canterbury, England, of a diet restricted to honey, cereals and dandelion coffee.

I am passionately concerned with every one of these issues, some of which are more sinister than they sound, and confident that our forthcoming discussion of them, and those which you have introduced, cannot fail to provide our accumulated pen pals with much nourishment.

Sincerely yours, Dalton Trumbo
cc: Mr. Steve Allen, Mr. Eason Monroe, Mr. Tom Bradley, Mr. Burt Lancaster, Mr. George Plimpton, The Hon. Mr. Lyndon Baines Johnson, The Ninth Earl of Linster, Estate of Mr. Harold Bell Wright

Mr. Steve Allen   May 21, 1969

Dear Mr. Allen:

In my note of May 7 to the Arts Division, ACLU, the word disavowal was spelled *disavowel.* My secretary's mistake. In my letter to you of May 19 I identified St. Sophronia as the dethroned patroness of toothaches. The personage referred to was actually St. Apollonia (her day is February 9). My mistake.

In your May 13 Epistle to the Thespians the following line was quoted from your February 26 letter to Mrs. Beata Inaya: "I know nothing of Mr. Trumbo's present political convictions. . . ." The original letter, of which you forgot to send me a copy, reads: "I know *absolutely* (my italics) nothing of Mr. Trumbo's" etc. Your mistake.

History is watching us, Mr. Allen. We serve larger purposes than our own. Let's show our best profiles by keeping the record straight.

Faithfully yours, Dalton Trumbo
P.S. I discover in this morning's mail that Senator Cranston and Congressmen Bell and Rees are bugging me for a contribution to you-know-who's campaign. My name on a check? Don't they *know,* for God sake?
cc: Mr. Eason Monroe, Mr. Tom Bradley, Mr. Burt Lancaster, Mr. George Plimpton, The Hon. Mr. Lyndon Baines Johnson, The Ninth Earl of Linster, Estate of Mr. Harold Bell Wright, Mr. Haroldson Lafayette Hunt, Mr. Gus Hall

Mr. Steve Allen   May 22, 1969

Dear Mr. Allen:

I hate to interrupt your meditations at a moment when the campaign approaches its climax, but my

God, Mr. Allen, I've got another crisis. Before I tell you exactly what it is, I think I owe you an explanation of what led up to it.

Some time ago, when your concern for America and me was less apparent than today, I chaired a public dinner which sported, in addition to a congressman or two, more municipal and superior court judges than I'm really comfortable with. I thought the thing went off rather well: the only guest (an assemblyman) who put his feet on the table had clean shoes, nobody hoicked on the chicken *suprême,* nobody snerched too loud, and everything seemed real nice.

For some reason I'm not quite sure of (perhaps because my presence in the chair drew no attacks from right-wing reactionaries and the rest of that scum) somebody must have spread the word that I was a hell of a chairman, because not long afterward I was asked to chair another dinner in honor of somebody else, and I've got to confess that but for a previously scheduled pilgrimage to various shrines and cadavers of the sonofabitch side of the Iron Curtain, I'd have accepted. That I did not is probably the finest thing which ever happened to that particular honoree, although he himself has never acknowledged my part in his good fortune or even thanked me for it. On the other hand, how can you expect a man to be grateful for escaping an accident he wasn't in and never heard of? You can't. You just have to forget the whole thing and keep on living, which is exactly what I did and still am.

And then this thing happened that I've got to tell you about: last evening, in that hour which finds all high-strung chaps awash with pick-me-up, I was requested by telephone to chair a dinner honoring Mr. Julian Bond. The request was almost as importunate as that of Miss Beata Inaya to grab our house in behalf of you-know-who, and I, perhaps because of pick-me-up, perhaps because of that restless, feckless, reckless streak which keeps running down the middle of my back to dilute my character and befog the luster of my name, accepted.

However, on awakening this morning to the full glow of sunlight and sobriety, I fell at once into a kind of intellectual sweating fit, or whatever it is you call that particular condition which is induced by the collision of a bad conscience with a faulty nervous system. I said to myself, you fool, I said, Mr. Allen is every bit as interested in the triumph of Mr. Bond's cause as he is of you-know-who's, and when Mr. Allen is interested in something, he doesn't just sit around like some crumbum the way you do, he *acts;* things *happen.* Sooner or later he'll find out about what you did last night, compute the evil that's bound to flow from it, and five minutes later—bang!—another torpedo zoops off the old launching pad.

And as if that weren't enough, *you,* poor fool, will know nothing about what's zeroing in until that penultimate moment when (loins neuterized with dusty philters, armpits sweetened, black tie only slightly askew, spirits already afloat on wings of imaginary applause) you find yourself diving through cold thin air with the wind in your ears, shot down once more for the fallen angel you never deserved to be.

What shall I do, Mr. Allen?

Shall I tell them I was drunk when I accepted? I *could*, of course, if you think it best, but if I say that too often people will get the idea I'm fried all the time, and for a man who needs steady work that isn't a good image to have projecting itself around the community.

Shall I say I'm going to be too sick to show? The trouble with this is that they've scheduled the gala three months in advance, and to say *now* that I'll be sick *then* may suggest that I got lucky and hit Big Casino, and this isn't too good from my point of view either, because health is very big these days and we live in a town that needs cancerated writers about as bad as a bull blowfly needs a second squirt of Black Flag.

There *could* have been the possibility of asking them to clear it through you at the outset, but I tried that with the Arts Division, ACLU, and what happened? Your Epistle to the Thespians, that's what: cc's flying through the air like pessaries at a campus love-in, pregnant problems aborting in practically everybody's backyard, grim-faced ideological buzzards flapping home to roost in the most improbable places, sacred geese rocketing at full quack through esplanades and public squares, befouling with their startled excrement the fairest freeways in all our New Jerusalem—*well*, Mr. Allen, I sure don't want much more of that and I hope you don't either. But how shall I go about avoiding it?

Would you advise me to turn myself in like a man (which is not in my nature)? Go back where I came from (which seems a reproach on my people who split the joint over two hundred years back)? Pretend I've been brought to bed with Huntington's chorea (which at least has the virtue of rarity)? Get myself hauled up before some Committee so the real truth at last may be known (which, to survive, requires the kind of luck I haven't got)? Square the whole thing off by blowing out my brains (which probably takes sharper shooting than I'm up to)? Or should I just sort of hunker down and let her blow (which depends a good deal on the condition of your hunkers)?

In any event, Mr. Allen, the man doesn't live who can say I've been sneaky about this thing or insensitive to the consequences of my existence to the dedicated community over which you stand your lonely, solitary, but not always silent guard. I've told you frankly, honestly and exactly where the bear sits in the buckwheat. All I ask in return is your advice on how to bag him or get the hell out of his hunting range.

Please send me your thoughts as soon as possible, because the pot is simmering here on the back of the stove, and she's tighter sealed than a bull's you-know-what in chokecherry season, and something's bound to blow a lot sooner than I want it to.

                    Sincerely yours, Dalton Trumbo
cc: Mr. Eason Monroe, Mr. Tom Bradley, Mr. Burt Lancaster, Mr. George Plimpton, The Hon. Mr. Lyndon B. Johnson, The Ninth Earl of Linster, Estate of Mr. Harold Bell Wright, Mr. Haroldson Lafayette Hunt, Mr. Gus Hall, The Rev. Dr. Billy Graham, Al-Ibrahim Institute for Control of Huntington's Chorea

Mr. Steve Allen   May 23, 1969
Dear Mr. Allen:

Well, here I am again. The problem may not seem very important to most of our correspondents, but that makes it no less a problem, and I hope I've dealt with it in a way that will make you proud of me.

The Ninth Earl of Linster, who has been shacked up in Chula Vista these past three months houseguesting on a bewildered pair of old family retainers, informs me that although your letter of February 26 was addressed to *Miss* Beata Inaya, my note of May 21 referred to her as *Mrs*. He feels that the difference between those two forms of address involves a rather substantial difference in the kind of person any lady actually is, and begs me to clear the matter up at my earliest possible convenience, which, luckily, is right now.

I have replied to him as follows:

"My Dear Ninth Earl:

"The marital situation of the lady in question is absolutely none of my business. I know absolutely nothing of her present marital status, nor have I any particular interest in what it may have been, say, a quarter-century ago. I *assume*, however, that at one time she was indeed a single woman.

"It would not in any way affect my own admiration of you-know-who that the lady in question might be one of his supporters, but *if* (a) she is today a single woman (something she has every legal right to be), and *if* (b) that fact is publicized by you-know-who's reactionary rightist political opposition, then (c) her connection with you-know-who will almost certainly be used in such a way as to imply that his feminine support derives exclusively from virgins, maidens and spinsters, thereby costing him a perhaps significant number of votes amongst that large bloc of married, divorced or widowed females which has long infested this not-always-politically-enlightened city.

"It was, perhaps, my unconscious desire to avoid such a split which caused me to refer to the lady as *Mrs*. I leave it to you to determine the relevance, if any, of these observations to the case you have brought to my attention. Most cordially yours, etc., etc."

I hope you will agree with me that this prompt response to Linster of Radford near Cockermouth (who is, in any event, an alien) clarifies more issues than at first glance it would seem to.

                    Sincerely yours, Dalton Trumbo
P.S. I solved that other problem re. being bugged by Cranston, Bell and Rees re. you-know-who by sending a small check signed with my accountant's name rather than my own. I pray, however, that we've got a loyal campaign staff, because you know as well as I do that in these critical times the gander's pragmatic virtue almost always turns into the goose's subversive conspiracy, which means that all hell is bound to break loose if my caper is leaked to our opponents of the extremely reactionary right. Right?

Mr. Steve Allen

Mr. Dalton Trumbo

cc: Mr. Eason Monroe, Mr. Tom Bradley, Mr. Burt Lancaster, Mr. George Plimpton, The Hon. Mr. Lyndon B. Johnson, The Ninth Earl of Linster, Estate of Harold Bell Wright, Mr. Haroldson Lafayette Hunt, Mr. Gus Hall, The Rev. Dr. Billy Graham, Al-Ibrahim Institute for Control of Huntington's Chorea, Princess Conchita Pignatelli, Estate of Miss Brenda Holton.

Mr. Dalton Trumbo   May 29, 1969

Dear Mr. Trumbo:

Mr. Allen is presently in Indianapolis and will be leaving directly for Northern California for a few days. However, he will be back in town next week.

In the meantime, Mr. Allen wanted me to drop you a note acknowledging your recent letters, and he wanted me to let you know that he will be answering them as soon as he returns.

Most cordially, Betty Brew, Secretary to Steve Allen

Miss Betty Brew   June 2, 1969
Secretary to Mr. Steve Allen
Encino, California

Dear Miss Brew:

Thanks for informing me of Mr. Allen's absence from the city and his intention to answer my letters when he returns. I must tell you, however, that from my point of view his Indianapolis and Northern California commitments have not come at a convenient time.

He won't believe this (at first I didn't either) but Sunday evening Mrs. Trumbo and I were invited to dine person to person and face to face with he-knows-who in the house of a mutual friend. Knowing how gross an abuse of free speech and assembly my presence at such an affair would constitute, dreading the impact of a second apostolic interdiction while not yet fully recovered from the first, I heard a voice remarkably like my own begging off with the idiot's excuse that we were departing the city Friday noon for a Mexican holiday which hadn't entered my mind until that moment.

Since a chap in my position has to be even more scrupulous with the truth than Caesar with his wife's, or vice versa, there was nothing for it but to transmute my lie into its opposite by immediate proclamation of a southbound hegira to begin no later than Friday noon, June 6, 1969.

Mrs. Trumbo, I'm sorry to report, didn't take the news at all well. For some years she has been doing whatever she can for a group of young pre-teen-age and hopefully pre-pregnant sub-Aquarians who foregather throughout the mating season (June 1 through August 31) each Saturday afternoon at Happy Jack's Fish Hatcheries, 8041 North San Gabriel Canyon Road in Azusa, where they receive much enlightenment from pisciculture in general, and in particular from unblinking observation of the relatively chaste techniques which characterize the breeding habits of even the most concupiscent among the fishes.

At their last meeting (end of August, 1968), in a somewhat rowdy but nonetheless moving demonstration of gratitude and loyalty, the youngsters unanimously chose Mrs. Trumbo to be Vice-Den Mother for their 1969 season which begins, as anyone with a calendar at hand can see, on Saturday next.

I had written for the occasion a rather stirring First Inaugural Address (based in part on Mr. Allen's Epistle to the Thespians) which can be rattled off in just under forty-seven crackling minutes; and Mrs. Trumbo, having memorized and come to believe it, thought poorly of a command holiday which was bound to spoil what she has lately taken to calling—sentimentally, perhaps, but not unjustifiably—her Vice-Den Mother's Day among the pisciculturians.

Ethics, however, is ethics, and my honor, when it comes to a showdown, invariably takes precedence over hers. Result: we depart Los Angeles International Airport on Western Airlines' Flight Number 601 on Friday, June 6, 1969, for Mexico City, where we shall be met by chartered car, driven forthwith to Cuernavaca, and lodged at Privada de Humboldt 92. Our mailing address, however, will be Apartado 1292, Cuernavaca, Morelos, etc. We can be reached by telephone almost daily between the hours of three and six-thirty a.m., central standard time, at Cuernavaca 2-31-38.

And why, do you ask, have we been put to all this hurly and scurly and involuntary aggravating unexpected burly? Because I, in Sunday's moment of mistruth, had no stern critic at hand to straighten my morals and narrow the range of my political and social pretensions. So much for NCLers who rush off to rival Communists for the political affections of the masses without preschooling their own acolytes in the mysteries of honest unilateral action.

                    Most respectfully, Dalton Trumbo
P.S. The Ninth Earl has somehow leapt to the untidy conclusion that Burt Lancaster is under house arrest as a carrier of Huntington's chorea. Although I have done everything in my poor power to explain that no man on earth can carry a pestilence like H's c (he has to haul it), I might just as well have spent my time hollering down some neighbor's empty grain barrel. He has filed an emergency application with the Chula Vista branch of Travelers Aid for immediate transport to the Control Institute in Oman and Muscat, and compels his entire household, including two of the most dejected old family retainers you've ever seen, to wallow with him thrice daily in tubs of boiling Lysol hugely adulterated with white lie, sheep dip and magnums of granulated loblolly *flambé en brochette*.

Raw-wise, the skins around that house have passed the point of no return, and for some reason I can't fathom old Linster has tried four nights running to deposit the whole begrutten mess (the Sixth Earl married a Scotswoman described by a contemporary as "begrutten of face, large of wen and warp but small woof") at my doorstep. For all his breeding, which I am told has been prodigious, the big L shows every sign of becoming, as we say in my middle-class but hopeful precinct, just one more unwanted and ungrateful *anguis in herba*.

cc: Mr. Eason Monroe, Mr. Tom Bradley, Mr. Burt Lancaster, Mr. George Plimpton, The Hon. Mr. Lyndon B. Johnson, The Ninth Earl of Linster, Estate of Harold Bell Wright, Mr. Haroldson Lafayette Hunt, Mr. Gus Hall, The Rev. Dr. Billy Graham, Al-Ibrahim Institute for Control of Huntington's Chorea, Princess Conchita Pignatelli, Estate of Miss Brenda Holton, Happy Jack Fish Hatcheries

Mr. Dalton Trumbo   June 13, 1969

Dear Mr. Trumbo:

I had a nightmare the other evening. It seemed that at some distant point of future time an enterprising publisher released a portly volume titled "The Trumbo-Allen Letters." The book opens with your clever message of May 7th to the Arts Division of the American Civil Liberties Union, which is followed, of course, by my ponderous rejoinder of May 13th. The third letter is your brief note of May 21st, which clarifies a few points of minor significance. But then, where the reader might expect my response, he instead encounters your letter of May 22nd, your letter of May 23rd, your letter of May 24th, your letter of May 25th, your letter of May 26th, your letter of May 27th and so on—God help us—ad infinitum, ad nauseam, ad wolgast. Right to the end of the book.

At this point the scene quickly shifted, the way it can in dreams—where no stagehands are involved. I not only asked myself, "Where do the polls have Tom Bradley?" but "Where do the Cubans have Eldridge Cleaver?" and "Where do the Nielsen's have Gomer Pyle?"

I awakened with my heart beating mightily, concerning which I have no complaint, for the day will surely come when it will not beat at all. But be that as it may, and I see no reason to be sure it is, the explanation of the dream must be that I was beginning to fear I would never have time to answer your several letters. Or perhaps I was asking myself: is this whole misunderstanding just another example of what can happen when entertainers get involved in politics?

In any event, I have not only had no time to write to you about the Tom Bradley Dinner incident, I have not even had time to write to Mr. Bradley himself; a particular shame since I had planned to suggest specific positions for him on the crucial issues of the day.

Reporter: "Mr. Bradley, what do you think about police brutality?"

Tom B.: "I think people are being entirely too brutal to the police."

Reporter: "Do you think we should recognize the Red Chinese?"

Tom B.: "Well, they all look alike to me."

Reporter: "As a former police lieutenant, what would you say to Mayor Yorty if you encountered him face-to-face at this moment?"

Tom B.: "You're under arrest."

What a pity, as I say, that all this, and more, never reached Tom because of the demands of my schedule.

But, you may retort, what doth it profit me to make such easy jokes when I have a flair for them?

Wrong. I have a typewriter for jokes. I use my flair for other purposes.

But all seriousness aside . . . it ill-behooves us to be joshing like this while our city crumbles about us. Whoever governs this disorganized metropolis, what does he propose to do about such problems as the recent parade held to commemorate Fire Prevention Week, a parade that blocked several fire trucks attempting to report to a nearby conflagration?

Which—fire trucks being red—brings me back to the question of your political affiliation.

You have me, of course, at a considerable disadvantage in that I am unable to know to what extent the straw-man Dalton Trumbo I have criticized corresponds with the *real* Dalton Trumbo. All I know about you is that you are one of our industry's best screenwriters and that at one time you were involved in a public confrontation which led to my including your name in a list of imaginary orchestral aggregations such as *Andy Kirk and his "Clouds of Joy," Horace Heidt and his "Musical Knights," Harry Horlick and "The A&P Gypsies," Earl Warren and the Supremes, Red Nichols and "His Five Pennies,"* and *Dalton Trumbo and "The Unfriendly Ten."* I am reminded at this point (and I'm glad to be reminded, too, because this letter could use a good, funny line right now) of Billy Wilder's observation that of the Unfriendly Ten "only two were really talented; the rest were just unfriendly." I'm sure you were one of the two. If you'll tell me who the other one was, I'll check and see if *he* had anything to do with Tom Bradley's defeat.

It is most generous of you to pretend to honestly solicit my opinion as to whether you should withdraw from or honor your other forthcoming social commitments. On all of your specific questions I must simply beg off. I say again that I don't know if you are presently a Communist. I *do* know that the ACLU was rent by a controversy about this general issue some years ago, and I suspect there are still at least two points of view on the question among members and officers of that admirable organization. I am obviously more or less cemented into my view that Communists—*acting as such*—cannot be trusted. Nor—I readily concede—could *I* be trusted if, holding my present political views, I were a citizen of a Communist society. I am afraid I would be in rather constant, abrasive—perhaps even treasonable—contact with the state because of my conviction that it was embarked on a disastrously erroneous course. But I am not only willing to make the distinction between a man's political function and his function as husband, father, neighbor, dentist, screenwriter, golfing companion, or what-have-you; I absolutely insist on that distinction. Which is to say that, while your letters testify to your wit, charm and good grace, I would nevertheless be forced to oppose you—to hamper you—in your political capacity were you indeed a Marxist.

The fact remains that, while you and I have been composing witty letters to each other, poor Tom Bradley has lost the mayoralty race. All Yorty had to do to defeat him was confuse perhaps five or ten percent of the electorate as regards the issues of racial intemperance and Communist influence. Gus Hall's incredible stupidity in recommending support of Bradley to his followers at a formal Communist Party meeting—however supposedly private—is consistent with the long history of such mistakes on the part of the CP functionaries. It is true that at present perhaps a larger percentage than usual of embittered youth are so disillusioned with the American system that they are willing to entertain a Marxist alternative. I suppose some of them would be willing to rally around the banner of Attila-the-Hun if some fiery spokesman for that ancient cause would insult our present leaders colorfully enough. But with this one exception, Communists are now—as they have been for decades—about as popular with the American electorate as Nazi storm troopers at a Bar Mitzvah. There can be no question that the Gus Hall incident cost Bradley a number of votes in this peculiar community. Certainly the polls show that Bradley lost the race in the last few days, since he was far ahead for several weeks before the contest went to the wire.

While—as I previously made clear—I can understand your feeling hurt at being treated as something of a pariah, I ask you honestly what public capital you think Mr. Yorty would have made out of your hosting a dinner on Mr. Bradley's behalf, had information about the affair come to his attention. As regards my not knowing whether Beata Inaya was a Miss or Mrs., I stand corrected, which is understandable, since I'm wearing surgical hose at the moment. To tell you the truth—inasmuch as the lady signs her letters simply "Beata Inaya"—I didn't even know for sure she was a woman until I met her. I suspected hers was one of those African or Muslim names presently sported by so many of our black brethren along with colorful, flowing robes and "natural" hairdos. In reviewing my own correspondence with the good lady I find that I addressed her on February 26th as Mrs. and on April 3rd as Miss. For all I know, she may be some kind of a Communist, too, who one day acts like a Mrs. and the next day as a Miss, just to throw me off the track. It is clear that the name itself sounds suspiciously un-Waspish. Beata Inaya, indeed! Personally, I've never beaten an Inaya in my life and at a time when the Pope is reneging on beatifications right and left, it ill-behooves a woman arbitrarily to beatify herself.

Well, enough of this chit-chat, which I was about to call Tom-foolery, but will not, out of respect to Mr. Bradley. I repeat, we have our nerve kidding about all this when conditions in the city worsen day by day. Last night the police in the Griffith Park area got a call for help. From three muggers. And just try to bring other actors to line up seriously in support of one worthy cause or another. Polly Bergen cares more about her turtle oil. Debbie Reynolds cares more about her girl scouts. George Jessel is so old he's concerned only with his infirmities. At the moment I believe he is suffering from bleeding Madras.

If you'll forgive me, I must close now as I am overdue in getting out to local authorities a report of an accident I witnessed this morning on an off-ramp of the Ventura Freeway. It seems a Coupe de Ville gave the coupe de grace to a pedestrian.

Yours in haste, Steve Allen
cc: Burt Lancaster, Lance Burtcaster, Burnt Flycaster, Bald Broadcaster, Aristotle Onassis, George Givot, Euripides Pants, Stannous Fluoride.

Mr. Steve Allen   July 17, 1969

Dear Mr. Allen:

I was out of the city when your letter of June 13 arrived. Although it was forwarded to me, the pressure of working away from home prevented me from answering it as promptly as I'd have liked to.

I must now clean up a few matters that accumulated during my absence, after which I shall address myself to a response.

Sincerely, Dalton Trumbo

Mr. Dalton Trumbo   August 12, 1969

Dear Mr. Trumbo:

I thought you would want to add to your Allen-Trumbo files the enclosed copy of a letter Mr. Allen has just received from Mr. Arthur Schlesinger Jr.

Cordially yours, Betty Brew
Secretary to Steve Allen. Enc. (1)

Mr. Steve Allen   August 4, 1969

Dear Mr. Allen:

I have just recently returned from Europe and only now have had an opportunity to read the letters to the ACLU Arts Division.

Your letter seems to me clear and correct, and I would be in strong agreement with it. I have never understood how people who defend communism could consistently associate with an organization dedicated to civil liberties.

Sincerely yours,
Arthur Schlesinger Jr.

Miss Betty Brew   August 28, 1969
c/o Mr. Steve Allen
Van Nuys, California

Dear Miss Brew:

I think I shall never forget Friday, August 15, 1969, as the day I opened an envelope bearing Mr. Allen's new return address and discovered therein, clipped to your thoughtful note, an enclosure which carried the Great Seal of The City University of New York's Albert Schweitzer Chair in the Humanities, the upholstery of which, it said on the back, is stuffed with honeysuckle pollen and twenty-dollar bills.

"Dear Mr. Allen," I read (thinking how much warmer 'Dear *Steve*' would have seemed), "I have just recently returned from Europe and only now have had an opportunity to read the letters to the ACLU Arts Division. Your letter seems to me clear and correct, and I would be in strong agreement with it. I have never understood how people who defend communism could consistently associate with an organization dedicated to civil liberties." And then, with noble simplicity: "Sincerely yours, Arthur Schlesinger Jr."

I confess to you, Miss Brew, that I was more stunned by what that letter was than by what it seemed to say. Although Mr. Schlesinger is perhaps the most prolific correspondent of our time, his and the Pope's thoughts are generally considered too precious to waste on individual citizens or even small groups of them. Because of this, a vast number of Schlesinger judgments, opinions, disavowals, affirmations, admonitions, exhortations, and bad tidings bypass the addressee altogether and go directly to the engraver for mass distribution.

However *my* letter (or rather mine and Mr. Allen's) is what the people at Sotheby's call a "private" Schlesinger. Bells clang all over the place when one of them shows up and the director himself protects it with a ten-guinea bid for openers. It follows that even the Xerox copy of such a find has more cash than sentimental value.

Please be circumspect about having sent it to me. If Mr. Allen discovers that it has fallen into my hands the consequences can be so terrible that—well, for now let's not think of them. We can worry about crossing that particular bridge when we come to it. If worse turns to worst, as it usually does when *my* happiness is at stake, perhaps Mr. Schlesinger, who knows a great deal more about bridges than he pretends, can be persuaded to lend us a hand.

And please, Miss Brew, don't let either of them know that I have written you about bridges or anything else. Mr. Schlesinger has rich and powerful friends on every side of any ocean you choose to cross: Mr. Allen is the most beloved poet, wit, essayist, author, raconteur, comedian, actor, TV personality, stern critic of American society and potential congressman our democratic way of life has yet produced. Such men are easily offended: their wrath, if aroused, consumes continents.

Let us therefore consider this a private letter from me to you. Since it was, after all, your friendly intercession which made Mr. Schlesinger's views known to me, that fervid spirit of reciprocity which saturates our free society calls for some response in kind. But only for you, Miss Brew—only for you, and strictly between ourselves.

Unhappily for both of us, Mr. Schlesinger, when not speaking *ex cathedra*, is one of those soupy writers who requires translation. One must separate what he seems to say from what he says, and then what he says from what he means to say. Not until the broth has been thoroughly clarified is it fair to judge the quality of the ingredients that went into it or the flavor their blending has produced.

The meaning of his first sentence seems relatively clear: I wrote one letter to the ACLU Arts Division and, to the best of my knowledge, Mr. Allen wrote no more than one. Thus when Mr. Schlesinger says he has "had an opportunity to read the letters to the ACLU Arts Division" it is logical to assume that he has read my letter and Mr. Allen's response to it. By changing the end of the first sentence to an *opportunity to read Mr. Trumbo's letter to the ACLU Arts Division and your response to it* we know exactly where we stand.

But we don't know yet exactly where *he* stands, do we? The difficulty, I suspect, resides in that almost imperial *would be in strong agreement*, which, by pairing a volitional auxiliary with a volitional verb, does something that isn't very nice if we accept the convention that any well-behaved volitional verb wants to mate with an auxiliary of simple futurity such as *should*: hence "*should* be in strong agreement."

Yet the letter form, however soothing to pedagogues, fails to enlighten the commonality because it raises in their less cultivated minds two questions of substantial importance: one of simple futurity (*when* would/should he be in agreement?) and another of conditional futurity (*in what circumstances* would/should he be in agreement?).

They are so subtly related that a proper response to one is almost bound to answer the other. For example: "Your letter seems to me clear and correct, and *if asked to take a position on what it says, I should* be in strong agreement with it." Or—do you see what I mean?—something that goes even better than that.

Yet that isn't too good either. What we desperately want to know is not whether Mr. Schlesinger *will* agree with Mr. Allen's letter in some future time, or in some unspecified future circumstance, but whether he agrees with it today, this minute, right now. A conscientious translator trying to solve this typically Arthurian riddle must rely on reasoned analysis of the intent of the full sentence, and, indeed, of the letter as a whole.

Viewed in this light, it is logical to assume that Mr. Schlesinger intended his letter to convey the bracing news that he *did* agree with Mr. Allen's clear and correct statements the instant he read them, and still does. Our translation therefore reads, "Your letter seems to me clear and correct, and I *am* in strong agreement with it." Or, more simply and less passively, "I *strongly agree* with it."

Now we have it, haven't we? Mr. Schlesinger finds Mr. Allen's letter clear and correct and strongly agrees with it. His feelings about mine, as suggested in his next sentence, are antithetical.

But oh Miss Brew, that next sentence! Stand back for a moment. Regard it. "I have never understood how people who defend communism could consistently associate with an organization dedicated to civil liberties."

The first thing that strikes us here is the coupling of present tense *defend* with past tense *could*. Let's dismiss it as misfired elegance, and substitute a *can* for the *could*: "how people who defend communism *can* consistently associate." That helps, doesn't it? Well, yes; but not as much as we hoped. We still have that *consistently* to reckon with.

Mr. Schlesinger doesn't understand how people who defend X can consistently associate with people who are dedicated to Y. Why doesn't he? Why can't they? What holds them back? *You* know, Miss Brew, and so do I, that it's perfectly possible for anybody to join the ACLU and consistently support whichever of its quarrels he has time for, consistently attend its meetings, and consistently pay its dues. This being incontestably true, we must conclude that Mr. Schlesinger doesn't use *consistently* in the sense that one consistently attends church, consistently adheres to a course of action, conducts his life in a consistent manner, or behaves with persistent uniformity. If I know my Schlesinger—and, rather more than less, I do—he is trying to say that there is something inconsistent or incongruous about people who defend communism (and therefore wish to destroy civil liberties) associating with an organization that is dedicated to defending those liberties.

Let us, therefore, change *consistently* to *without incongruity* (or something better of your own choice) and see if it helps: "I have never understood how people who defend communism *can without incongruity* associate with an organization dedicated to civil liberties." That gets us a little closer, don't you think?

But not close enough when we pause to consider the meaning of *communism* with a diminished c. Although the rules of capitalization are as variable as a pimp's virtue, and every writer is a law unto himself, in most dictionaries—the 12-volume O.E.D., Webster's Third Unabridged, Random House Unabridged—the first definition of communism with a lower case c describes a philosophy or system which cannot possibly be considered inimical to the defense of civil liberties. Now if Mr. Schlesinger refers to this good lower case, non-incantatory kind of communism, his letter makes no sense at all.

This becomes particularly apparent if we recall that when he was a much younger man, ardently mindful of Senator Vandenberg's advice to "scare hell out of the country," convinced even before Russia had the bomb that she'd be content with "nothing less than the entire world," playing to the hilt his role of John the Baptist to Joe McCarthy's unexpected messiah, warning his too complacent countrymen against the "awful potentialities of the totalitarian conspiracy" ("It is we or they; the United States or the Soviet Union; capitalism or Communism. . . . We must not be restrained by weakness *when* (italics mine) the moment of crisis arrives . . . we must act swiftly in defense of freedom"), Mr. Schlesinger *always* gave bad Communism a capital *C*.

Not only did he capitalize it, he often characterized it with great specificity as Soviet Communism, Russian Communism, Soviet totalitarianism, etc. Yet now, despite *The New York Times, The New Yorker, The Atlantic* and the dictionaries (Random House Unabridged capitalizes it, Webster's Unabridged regards it as a word generally capitalized), he has lately begun to invite all sorts of confusion and misunderstanding by demoting it to a simple, commonplace, lower case c.

Although no one can be certain when dealing with a mind as subtle and well-connected as Mr. Schlesinger's, I suggest that his reasons are romantic and ideological. He is so fed up with Communism that

he has zapped it into the lower case out of sheer pique, and who can blame him? Certainly not I. Was it not, after all, Lyndon Baines Johnson during his troubles with de Gaulle who commanded the Government Printing Office to place quotation marks around France?

Whatever the truth may be, I think we shall come closer to Mr. Schlesinger's vision of it by changing his lower case communism to upper: *people who defend Communism.* Although it is true that we can't be sure whether the people he is putting the hex on defend Russian, Chinese, Yugoslavian, Czechoslovakian, Hungarian, Albanian, Rumanian, or Cuban Communism. I think it is just clear (and vague) enough to serve Mr. Schlesinger's purposes.

This leaves only *defend* to worry about. Does Mr. Schlesinger use the word in its sense of protect, ward off or repel? In this sense the ACLU for many years has defended the legal rights of Communists to be Communists and of the Communist Party to exist. Surely he can't object to that, since he himself is an absolute wowser on civil liberties and Mr. Allen is wowsier still.

But, one must ask, when the ACLU and Mr. Schlesinger and Mr. Allen defend the civil rights of the Communist Party and its members, don't they actually help the Party to stay in business? If so, is not their defense of its rights a form of assistance, their assistance a form of support, and their support, in any practical sense, a defense not only of Communist rights but of Communism itself?

No. This must not be. It cannot be because it *should* not be. If it were, members of the ACLU wouldn't be able to associate with each other, and Mr. Allen would be cutting Mr. Schlesinger cold on the street if Mr. Schlesinger didn't cut him first.

Perhaps, then, Mr. Schlesinger's *defend* takes the meaning of uphold by speech or argument, to maintain, to vindicate. That seems a lot more likely, don't you think? For his sake, then, as well as clarity's let us change *defend* to *uphold.* Then, carefully underlining the changes we have made, let's assemble the whole thing and see how it looks. To wit:

"Dear Mr. Allen:

"I have just recently returned from Europe and only now had an opportunity to read *Mr. Trumbo's letter to the ACLU Arts Division and your response to it.*

"Your letter seems to me clear and correct, and *I strongly agree with it.* I have never understood how people who *uphold Communism can without incongruity* associate with an organization dedicated to civil liberties.

"Sincerely yours, Arthur Schlesinger Jr."

Since we have followed the form and structure of the original, our translation is not graceful, but the tenses are all straightened out, the purport of the words is clear, and I'll take an oath in any Federal Court of his choice that it exactly reflects the meaning which Mr. Schlesinger wanted to convey when he wrote it.

We emerge from the maze with three small facts: Mr. Schlesinger has read Mr. Allen's letter; he finds it clear and correct; he strongly agrees with it. Our next step is to determine whether the letter with which he agrees makes sense. Let us accept, as our standard for judging it, the idea that reason is the guiding principle of the human mind in the process of thinking; that a logical statement must conform to the laws of correct reasoning; that logic is the process of valid inference; that an inference is valid only when justified by the evidence given to support it; and that any violation of the rule of valid inference (or correct reasoning) produces a fallacious, or illogical, conclusion.

Let's brood for a moment on the following quotations taken in sequence from what I shall henceforth call the Allen-Schlesinger thesis: *(1) I know absolutely nothing of Mr. Trumbo's present political convictions. . . . (2) I assume, however, that at one time he was indeed a Communist. (3) . . . if Mr. Trumbo is today of the Communist persuasion . . . (4) . . . if it could be absolutely certified—or even assumed for purposes of debate—that Mr. Trumbo is today a Communist . . . (5) I haven't the faintest idea as to what Mr. Trumbo's present position on the political spectrum might be. (6) I concede—indeed, I fervently hope—that all of this may be utterly irrelevant in Mr. Trumbo's case. If it is, I would be greatly relieved.*

Question: What is the subject of the Allen-Schlesinger thesis? Answer: "Mr. Trumbo's present political convictions," which thereafter are linked with everything from ruthless marijuana laws and political tyranny to state murder and a strong hint of treason.

Question: What qualifies them to write on this particular subject? Answer: Their confession at the outset that they know absolutely nothing about it. In this respect they are more percipient than a Zhdanov or Goebbels but, in consequence of their percipience, less rational. Everything in their thesis which flows from this anarchic demolition of valid inference and reasoned thought is, by definition, fallacious, illogical, irrational and, for men of such enormous integrity, morally degrading and intellectually disgraceful.

Dare we now admit, against our best hopes and even our prayers, that Mr. Allen and Mr. Schlesinger between them have written almost 1500 deeply patriotic words (not to mention Mr. Allen's later effusions) on a subject about which they know "absolutely nothing"? We not only dare, Miss Brew, I'm afraid we must.

Can the words of men who haven't "the faintest idea" of what they're talking about be classified as anything but gabble? They cannot, Miss Brew: sheer mindless gabble; garbage, as some call it; dreck; pure merde.

What is it that impels a ranking intellectual like Mr. Allen and a Schweitzer humanitarian like Mr. Schlesinger to write all this gabble or dreck or whatever one calls it? That vincible companion of sloth called ignorance, Miss Brew; that infallible solace of closed minds which has sometimes been called "the voluntary misfortune."

The pity of it is that all their ignorance could so easily have been dispelled. Unlike Mr. Allen, who shows every sign of offering himself one day for public service, and Mr. Schlesinger, who has always had one foot in government and the other in somebody's mouth, I am a private citizen to whom the idea of anyone seeking public office has always seemed faintly ridiculous. As past or future politicos, Messrs. Allen and Schlesinger must be prepared at all times to make full disclosure of their professional, political, economic, military and even marital histories: as a private citizen, my political affiliations, whether now or a quarter-century ago, are exempt from such disclosure.

By exempt I mean private. By private I do not mean secret. Hundreds of friends, associates, colleagues, chance acquaintances, employers, and adversaries have discovered from my own lips exactly what my political thoughts and affiliations have been from my twenty-first birthday through every change or lack of it to the present time—not only what they were or are, but when and exactly why they were made or changed.

They are secret only to casual sensation hunters and those who hope to extort information about them under threat of legal or economic reprisal. In that sense they are as secret today as they were twenty-two years ago on that bright October afternoon in Washington, D. C. when I first refused to make public disclosure of political affiliations which I had voluntarily made known, in advance of assignment, to every producer for whom I had worked at Metro-Goldwyn-Mayer during the preceding five years. In every other sense they are as open today as they have always been.

Had Mr. Allen approached me for enlightenment on a subject about which he stood in total ignorance, I should cheerfully have told him all my secrets and blessed his warm, inquiring heart. Had he confided to me his misgivings about the effect on the Bradley campaign of a party at my house, I should have consented at once to its transfer from my address to his. Not because I share his fears or admire him overmuch for harboring them, but because as a rational man I should have been compelled to recognize the objective fact of their existence and to deal with them on that basis.

Do you begin to perceive what I mean, Miss Brew? This part of my letter you may reveal to Mr. Allen and Mr. Schlesinger in any words you choose, for I am offering them the key to their mystery. Whenever they wish to establish a friendly acquaintanceship with me for the purpose of exchanging ideas on subjects of mutual interest (including my past, present and possibly future political opinions and affiliations, but not excluding all else), I shall be happy to accommodate them. At my house. Over my whisky. And, since they are the suppliants, at my convenience. "Ask, dear colleagues," shall I say unto them, "and it shall be given to you; seek, and ye shall find; knock, and it shall be opened."

But do you know something else, Miss Brew? I don't think either of those aging and obsessed evangels will come tapping at my door, because knowledge is the killer of faith and they are of the faithful. They have hallucinated God as the greatest anti-Communist of them all and been completely unhinged by the sight of His glory. It is no longer important to them that they know what they're talking about. It is important only that they talk, since in their theology the act of speech proves the truth of what has been spoken.

Trapped thus between nightmares of qualified good and unqualified evil, they have become what they hate. For such there can be no surcease of gabble, guano, merde, or whatever it is that gushes from their lips and typewriters until the fevers pass and logic resumes its lonely reign. Thus, as the man said, are sweet reason's children strangled in the womb, and noble minds laid low.

Most gratefully yours, Dalton Trumbo
cc: Mr. Eason Monroe, Mr. Thomas Bradley, Mr. Burt Lancaster

September 23, 1969

Mr. Dalton Trumbo

Dear Mr. Trumbo:

Doing six ninety-minute television shows a week has placed such obstacles in the path of my properly fulfilling my obligations as your correspondent that at this point I must beg off, accept your kind invitation to continue our exchange over an amicable glass, and relegate these paper records of our misunderstanding to our respective heirs, assuming our rival philosophies will ultimately permit the continuance of our species on this planet.

Your witty letter of August 28th to my secretary, Miss Brew, obliges me to attempt a response, but I shall not pretend that what follows is any more than a half-hearted attempt to tidy up a few loose ends. At this point, as often is the case in matters of controversy, so many elements have been introduced, above and beyond the original grain of contention, that even if either of us had the luxury of an extended exchange of letters, I suspect we should find it difficult to limit the number and scope of our concerns so as not greatly to confuse any others who might read this correspondence—not to mention each other.

Now, then.

1. You raise what well may be a fair question with your observation that a considerable amount of confusion might have been avoided had I approached you about the matter in the first place. You say, "Had Mr. Allen approached me for enlightenment . . . I should cheerfully have told him all my secrets and blessed his warm, inquiring heart."

This reminds me, though, of the occasion when, as a sixteen-year-old runaway from my Chicago home, I found myself, one chill October afternoon, in front of the Bluebird Café in Del Rio, Texas, with a compulsive hunger that drove me to the lunch counter and forced me to gorge myself though I had not a penny in my pocket. When, after the meal, I confessed as much to the proprietor he called the police and then asked me—as we sat listlessly waiting for the law to arrive—"Why didn't you just *ask* me for something to eat?"

Although I couldn't bring myself to say as much, I think a fair answer would have been, "Because, sir, you would have told me to get the hell out of your restaurant."

In any event, what's past is past.

2. Since you know yourself to a degree that I do not, you naturally have me at a disadvantage when the object of our mutual scrutiny is Dalton Trumbo. When you speculate about *me*, however, then the advantage is mine. It is a simple matter to develop factual evidence about an individual, but when we attribute motivations supposedly explaining his behavior, and indulge in purely theoretical speculation about his beliefs and opinions, our testimony will generally be considerably less reliable. You attribute to me, for example, the view that Communism is an "unqualified evil." Nothing human can be totally evil. The worst atrocity ever committed was an ill-wind that produced some positive result, however slight and however out-of-balance with the enormity of the crime itself. There has never been nor will there ever be the totalitarian dictatorship—whether of the Right or Left—which could not point to certain social achievements; is there anyone beyond the age of ten who would deny it? The near-total law-and-order of totalitarian societies has its attractions, to be sure; the historically crucial question is: are these few material benefits purchased at too high a price when the coin that buys them is the sacrifice of freedoms of belief, speech, assembly, the press and travel?

3. Three single-spaced typewritten pages of your letter of August 28th are devoted to a reinterpretation of Mr. Schlesinger's letter, yielding the unsurprising conclusion that the man's statement is to be taken at its face value, that he means exactly what he *seems* to mean, which is to say that he is puzzled how people can on the one hand defend Communism—which in all times and places, as a matter of public policy, *violates* civil rights and liberties—while on the other hand they profess allegiance to organizations—such as ACLU—which are sworn to defend these same rights and liberties.

A crucial word, of course, in Mr. Schlesinger's observation is "consistently." Obviously it is *logically* inconsistent to proclaim civil liberties in one nation while denying them in another. But there is another sense in which such behavior on the part of American Communists is neither inconsistent nor puzzling, a situation directly analogous to that in which the Catholic Church concedes on the one hand that Protestant rights in Catholic Spain have been infringed upon, in law and in deed, while at the same time insisting that Catholics in the United States are entitled to the same rights as other American citizens.

It is entirely reasonable for Communists-USA to endorse the American Bill of Rights since it proclaims the essential political rights of all Americans. But when Communists assume control of a nation then the rules of the game are radically changed and rationalizations are advanced supposedly justifying limitations upon the civil rights and liberties of *non*-Communists.

You delay an approach to the essence of our argument by raising the irrelevant question as to whether Mr. Schlesinger would distinguish, in his disapproval, among Communism of the Russian, Chinese, Yugoslavian, Czechoslovakian, Hungarian, Albanian, Rumanian or Cuban sort. That no two of these are precisely similar is obvious enough, but the large question is no more necessary than would be the question as to whether, in your disapproval of Fascism, you would be more or less tolerant of it in its German, Italian, Spanish, Japanese or Argentine guise.

It is irrelevant to our purposes—or to mine, at least—to waste time considering the different dictionary meanings of "Communism," the first letter capitalized or not. Obviously there is always a difference between the purely theoretical statement of a philosophy on the one hand and its flesh-and-blood embodiment on the other. In every historical case the ideal is superior to the practice. I see no purpose, therefore, in debating the abstract philosophy of socialism or Communism. What I am here interested in is the undeniably clear record of Communism-in-practice and with—more specifically—the activities of the American Communist party, a political instrument which over the years is on record as endorsing the Hitler-Stalin pact, justifying the Soviet attacks on Poland and Finland, opposing Lend-Lease aid to Europe and assistance to Great Britain before Hitler's surprise attack on Russia, attempting to sweep under the rug of history Stalin's slaughter of millions in his domain, bitter opposition to Franklin Roosevelt during the period of the Soviet-Nazi pact, opposition to the Marshall Plan (Communists wanted Western Europe to collapse, not recover), serving as apologists for the Moscow trials, the crushing of the Hungarian rebellion, the Soviet invasion of Czechoslovakia, and all the rest of the sickening list.

4. Liberals may or may not be opposed in principle to the *economic* theory of Communism (though they will look in vain for evidence of its concrete realization). But by the very definition of the word *liberal* they are logically obliged to oppose the omnipresent despotism of Communist *political* practice and belief. A liberal, as such, may be an atheist, or a devout religionist. But the one thing he cannot possibly be is an apologist for the ruthless imposition of Communist minority party rule that for more than half a century has characterized the exercise of Marxist authority.

That is not to say that Communists, or socialists of other kinds, are wrong in all their criticisms of capitalist practice, or of American foreign or domestic policies. For many years Western capitalism has propped itself up with a certain amount of socialist timber, and Western democracy has come to understand that—mutual annihilation by either nuclear or conventional weapons being an unacceptable alterna-

tive—it will have to come to some sort of terms with the Marxist powers. The more responsible elements in each camp, then, may hope that the other side will mellow and evolve.

Against that hope, there are those who so contemptuously speak the word "*revisionism*." The young nuts of the Progressive Labor Party and Revolutionary Youth Movement—haunted, I suspect, by the dawning awareness of their essential irrelevancy to the American social experience—actually consider China and Albania the only right-thinking Marxist states and view the Soviet Union as revisionist, if not overtly capitalistic and antirevolutionary.

What these fierce but inexperienced dogmatists have yet to discern about the human adventure is that man is *by nature* a revisionist creature, the only conscious one, in fact, that walks our planet. While other species may have their behavior modified by the slow, inexorable force of nature, man is able to take quicker voluntary adaptive steps to bring himself into a more harmonious relationship with his environment. Addiction to rigid dogma and habit, I assert, is an emotional disease that over the course of time greatly incapacitates those individuals and groups that fall victim to it. Not all evolutionary or social adaptations prove beneficial but utter inability to revise behavior to conform with changing circumstances is a sentence of slow death. The Soviets are by nature neither more nor less dogmatic or revisionist than the Chinese; the Russians simply started their revolution 32 years before the Chinese did. It is therefore to be expected that the pace of their political evolution would have wrought greater changes than China has made since 1949.

As a liberal I selfishly hope, of course, that SDS firebrands become even more fanatic and dogmatic. It will make them still more socially irrelevant, even to the most dissatisfied American blacks, poor, and young.

The last thing I will say on this point, for the present, is that even if a liberal were unable to perceive that reason demands his opposition to all forms of tyranny, he ought to be anti-Communist simply because Communists are anti-liberal. When Stalin's armies enlarged the Soviet sphere of influence at the conclusion of the Second World War they almost ignored Conservatives, Reactionaries, Nazis, and Fascists in the areas that came under their control. These pathetic souls had already been defeated, slaughtered in great numbers by the process of war itself, or done in by their own underground movements. The few remaining were in disgrace as having sympathized with Hitler and accordingly posed no threat to Stalin's legions and indigenous Communists. The true threat came from non-Communist socialists and liberal democrats who—though anti-Nazi to the core—enjoyed a popular following and therefore were rivals for the affections of the liberated masses. It was these unfortunates who suffered most tragically at the hands of the Soviet "liberators."

Let us fantasize widespread American dissatisfaction in—say—1975, a growing rebellion of blacks, Latin-Americans, Indians, poor whites, the unemployed, the anti-war young, and then some idiotic repressive act on the part of Wallace-Reagan-Goldwater-J. Edgar Hoover types, leading to popular uprisings, a coup, and a Communist takeover. Would the Party be seriously worried about the Far Right? No, it would need the Extremist Right as a punching bag. The one group it could absolutely not tolerate would be non-Communist leftists who would share popular disaffection but not countenance official terror-campaigns. The non-Communist Left would once again be the first to be sacrificed to the Red firing squads.

5. The cleverest portion of your letter is in the following sentences:

". . . when the ACLU, and Mr. Schlesinger and Mr. Allen, defend the civil rights of the Communist party and its members, don't they actually help the party to stay in business? If so, is not their defense of its rights a form of assistance, their assistance a form of support, and their support, in any practical sense, a defense not only of Communist rights but of Communism itself?"

The question is—as I say—clever, even a bit playful. So let us play with it for a moment. One might as responsibly ask, "When the ACLU and Mr. Trumbo defend the civil rights of the *Nazi* party and its members, don't they actually help the party to stay in business? If so, is not their defense of its rights a form of assistance, their assistance a form of support, and their support . . . a defense not only of Nazi rights but of Nazism itself?"

The paradox, of course, is apparent rather than real. All true libertarians are prepared to defend the *civil rights* of a variety of anti-social or subversive or totalitarian groups which they personally abhor. In the process of defending these rights there is no question but that actual material benefits fall to Communists, Nazis, Ku Kluxers, Minute-Men, John Birchers, and political knuckleheads of all sorts. One may feel the *emotional* temptation to say, "To hell with it; civil rights and liberties ought *not* to be extended to such political idiots; it is really too much to assert that a Communist or Nazi, a Mafia murderer, a Black Panther sniper, a Ku Klux lyncher, ought to be accorded the same constitutional protections as decent, law-abiding American citizens." But of course that is the precise point upon which the rights and liberties of all of us are balanced. The minute we make the mistake of saying that all Americans are entitled to civil liberties and rights *except* Communists or Nazis we have opened a floodgate which it would almost certainly prove impossible to close. Others would care to add to the list Fascists, Pacifists, Liberals, Conservatives, and so on back into the blood-soaked jungles from which we all sprang.

6. You have taken me to task, albeit gently, for having referred to myself as a "stern critic" of American society, perhaps under the misapprehension that the phrase was a fearsome mask held before my face and that what I proposed to criticize sternly was your own political record. No. I meant to suggest that I see much in American *non*-Communist behavior to criticize—from the picture, "*Big Deal*"—for who does

not? Today we are all critics, but I was such when it was a somewhat less popular pastime. After visiting Vietnam in 1963 I did a TV documentary saying we could not win a military victory there with less than one million American troops and that, since we were clearly unwilling to make such an investment, we ought to begin getting out. At the time I was already a veteran of the nuclear test ban debate, the capital punishment controversy, and other scuffles in the marketplace, for all of which activity I was publicly accused by Conservatives—this will make you laugh —of being a Communist!

7. In conclusion, a word about your assumption that I plan one day to run for political office. I do not. In 1961 Norman Cousins advised me to prepare myself to run for the office of U.S. Senator from California. A great many other Democratic party people, chiefly but not solely of liberal persuasion, have since made similar suggestions. For several years my answer was "No, thank you."

Then, in 1965, Congressman James Roosevelt retired, accepted a post at the United Nations, and left ten months of his term to be filled, which called for a special election in his district. I was again urged to run. Since only ten months were involved, I agreed to make the experiment, having received encouragement from Hubert Humphrey and Bobby Kennedy, whose advice I solicited.

A poll showed I would have won handily, but after campaigning for a few weeks I discovered that an obscure clause in the California election code law made it impossible for me to become the Democratic candidate, because I had registered as an Independent. I thereupon withdrew from the race and do not plan to repeat the experience, although I would not have missed it for the world.

8. Lastly, something weighty still seems to block the path toward your understanding of the meaning of my original point. At the risk of boring even myself, let me state it once again, as concisely as possible: (a) at one time you were a mightily active Communist; (b) I do not know whether you are presently a Communist; (why don't you tell us, by the way, and hang the suspense?) (c) if—at the time of the Bradley-Yorty mayoralty campaign in Los Angeles—you *were* still a Communist, then it would have been politically disadvantageous to Mr. Bradley's cause to have it become publicly known that a fundraising party on his behalf had been held in your home.

No doubt upon occasion over the years I have unwittingly vouchsafed public observations that were obscure or ambiguous. This is not one of those occasions.

Most cordially, Steve Allen

Mr. Steve Allen   October 13, 1969

Dear Mr. Allen:

Aside from the owner of the Bluebird Café, who'd have thought that hungry, vagrant, shivering little tyke in Del Rio, Texas, would grow up to be the sort who'd sneak a peek at Miss Brew's mail? Well, I for one. On the off-chance she doesn't snoop yours, please tell her I've just discovered Mr. Bradley didn't know that goddamn party had been scheduled until two weeks after it wasn't held. This means that your spirited croak against free speech and assembly at my address can't properly be called delation because you delated to nobodies, and that doesn't count.

Even were it otherwise, I still feel that the Bishop of Norwich and Exeter held his hackles a bit high when he called informers and delators "an infamous and odious kind of cattle": almost every member of the tribe *I* uncover turns out to be just one more lost, home-loving, duty-driven civil-Samaritan of absolutely paralyzing sincerity, those only fault is a headful of wind littered here and there with small particles of badly organized misinformation. You can't hate a man like that, you can only try to help him.

To that most Christian end, my secretary is preparing a quick-information kit to set you straight on almost everything from marijuana penalties in the USSR (fifteen days for a first-caught user) to the reasons why what you call your black brethren (whose lives will be 176,000,000 years shorter than ours) sport those funny robes, wear those "natural" hairdos (your quotation Marx not mine), and fool-

ishly prefer two names, as in Muhammad Ali, to the five in Stephen Valentine Patrick William Allen. The whole lot, weighing just under three pounds, will be shipped post-paid in a plain brown wrapper.

As for defending the head humanitarian of C.U.N.Y., take one look at that cold, governmental smile, and then head for home. He slings the fastest gun in town and you can't shoot back without blowing Old Glory full of holes. I run a kind of nervous check on him every now and then because when you back him into a serious corner called Bay of Pigs or Congress for Cultural Freedom his talent runs to diddling with the truth instead of telling it.

All that jive about would/should/volition/futurity was, of course, part playfulness, which you suspected, and part gallantry, which you didn't. Any fool can spot the verb of "would be in strong agreement," but "be," for God sake, is copulative, and I certainly wasn't going to say a thing like that in front of Miss Brew.

Sincerely yours, Dalton Trumbo

P.S. I almost forgot the best news of all: the 1958 edition of *March's Thesaurus-Dictionary*, editorially supervised by the same Norman Cousins who tried to roust you off the tube and into the Senate, restricts its "c" listing under **EVILDOER** to *caitiff, cannibal, Communist* and *cut throat*. Your pot.

Sally Kempton:

Cutting Loose

A private view of the Women's Uprising

Once another woman and I were talking about male resistance to Woman's Liberation, and she said that she didn't understand why men never worry about women taking their jobs away but worry only about the possibility that women may stop making love to them and bearing their children. And once I was arguing with a man I know about Woman's Liberation, and he said he wished he had a motorcycle gang with which to invade a Woman's Liberation meeting and rape everybody in it. There are times when I understand the reason for men's feelings. I have noticed that beyond the feminists' talk about the myth of the vaginal orgasm lies a radical resentment of their position in the sexual act. And I have noticed that when I feel most militantly feminist I am hardly at all interested in sex.

Almost one could generalize from that: the feminist impulse is anti-sexual. The very notion of women gathering in groups is somehow anti-sexual, anti-male, just as the purposely all-male group is anti-female. There is often a sense of genuine cultural rebellion in the atmosphere of a Woman's Liberation meeting. Women sit with their legs apart, carelessly dressed, barely made-up, exhibiting their feelings or the holes at the knees of their jeans with an unprovocative candor which is hardly seen at all in the outside world. Of course, they are demonstrating by their postures that they are in effect off duty, absolved from the compulsion to make themselves attractive, and yet, as the world measures these things, such demonstrations could in themselves be seen as evidence of neurosis: we have all been brought up to believe that a woman who was "whole" would appear feminine even on the barricades.

The fact is that one cannot talk in feminist terms without revealing feelings which have traditionally been regarded as neurotic. One becomes concerned about women's rights, as Simone de Beauvoir noted, only when one perceives that there are few personal

advantages to be gained from accepting the traditional women's roles. A woman who is satisfied with her life is not likely to be drawn into the Woman's Liberation movement: there must be advantages for her as a woman in a man's world. To be a feminist one must be to some degree maladjusted to that world, one must be, if you will, neurotic. And sometimes one must be anti-sexual, if only in reaction to masculine expectations. Men do not worry about women taking their jobs because they do not think that women could do their jobs; most men can only be threatened by a woman. in bed. A woman who denies her sexuality, if only for an evening, denies her status as an object of male attention, as a supplicant, successful or not, for male favor. For a woman to deny her sexuality is to attack the enemy in his most valuable stronghold, which is her own need for him.

I became a feminist as an alternative to becoming a masochist. Actually, I always was a masochist; I became a feminist because to be a masochist is intolerable. As I get older I recognize more and more that the psychoanalytical idea that women are natural masochists is at least metaphorically correct: my own masochism derived from an almost worshipful respect for masculine power. In my adolescence I screwed a lot of guys I didn't much like, and always felt abused by them, but I never felt free to refuse sex until after the initial encounter. My tactic, if you can call it a tactic, was to Do It once and then to refuse to see the boy again, and I think I succeeded, with my demonstrations of postcoital detachment, in making several of them feel as rejected by my lovemaking as I had felt by their desire to make love to me without love. Yet I felt in those years that I had irretrievably marked myself a sexual rebel, and I was given to making melodramatic statements like "I'm not the kind of girl men marry." Years later I realized that I had been playing a kind of game, the same game boys play at the age of sexual experimentation, except that, unlike a boy, I could not allow myself to choose my partners and admit that I had done so. In fact, I was never comfortable with a lover unless he had, so to speak, wronged me. Once during my senior year in high school I let a boy rape me (that is not, whatever you may think, a contradiction in terms)

This piece made its appearance in July, 1970, when militant advance forces of women's liberation were marching not only in the streets but also through Newsweek, the Ladies' Home Journal and Evergreen Review; but Kempton had already traveled beyond confrontation politics and its associated malice into a rare and persuasive condition of self-knowledge.

in the bedroom of his college suite while a party was going on next door; afterward I ran away down the stairs while he followed, shouting apologies which became more and more abject as he realized that my revulsion was genuine, and I felt an exhilaration which I clearly recognized as triumph. By letting him abuse me I had won the right to tell him I hated him; I had won the right to hurt him.

I think most American adolescents hate and fear the opposite sex: in adolescence it seems that only one's lovers can hurt one, and I think that even young people who are entirely secure in other relations recognize and would, if they could, disarm the power the other sex has for them. But for adolescent boys, sexual success is not the sole measure of worth. It is assumed that they will grow up and work, that their most important tests will come in areas whose criteria are extra-sexual. They can fail with girls without failing entirely, for there remains to them the public life, the male life.

But girls have no such comfort. Sex occupies even the economic center of our lives; it is, we have been brought up to feel, our lives' work. Whatever else she may do, a woman is a failure if she fails to please men. The adolescent girl's situation is by definition dependent: she *must* attract, and therefore, however she may disguise it, she must compromise the sticky edges of her personality, she must arrange herself to conform with other people's ideas of what is valuable in a woman.

I was early trained to that position, trained, in the traditional manner, by my father. Like many men who are uncomfortable with adult women, my father saw his daughter as a potential antidote to his disappointment in her sex. I was someone who could be molded into a woman compatible with his needs, and also, unlike my mother, I was too impressionable to talk back. So I became the vessel into which he fed his opinions about novels and politics and sex; he fed me also his most hopeful self-image. It reached a point where I later suspected him of nourishing a sort of eighteenth-century fantasy about our relationship, the one in which the count teaches his daughter to read Virgil and ride like a man, and she grows up to be the perfect feminine companion, parroting him with such subtlety that it is impossible to tell that her thoughts and feelings, so perfectly coincident with his, are not original. I had three brothers, as it happened, and another sort of man might have chosen one of them to mold. But my father had himself a vast respect for masculine power. Boys grow up and have to kill their fathers, girls can be made to understand their place.

My father in his thirties was an attractive man, he was witty by adult standards and of course doubly so by mine, and he had a verbal facility with which he invariably demolished my mother in arguments. Masculine power in the intellectual classes is exercised verbally: it is the effort of the male supremacist intellectual to make his woman look clumsy and illogical beside him, to render her, as it were, dumb. His tactic is to goad the woman to attack him and then, resorting to rationality, to withdraw himself from the battle. In my child-

hood experience, subtlety appeared exclusively a masculine weapon. I never saw a woman argue except straightforwardly, and I never saw a woman best a man in a quarrel. My mother tried, but always with the conviction of ultimate failure. She attacked with pinpricks to begin with; in the end, maddened invariably by my father's ostentatious mental absence, she yelled. He was assisted in these struggles by his natural passivity. Withdrawal came easily to him; he hated, as he told us over and over again, scenes. My mother, it seemed to me, was violent, my father cool. And since it also seemed to me that he preferred me, his daughter who never disagreed with him, to his wife who did (that was a fantasy, of course, but one to which my father devoted some effort toward keeping alive), I came to feel that male power, because uncoercible, could only be handled by seduction, and that the most comfortable relation between men and women was the relation between pupil and teacher, between parent and child.

My father taught me some tricks. From him I learned that it is pleasant and useful to get information from men, pleasant because it is easier than getting it for yourself, and useful because it is seductive: men like to give information and sometimes love the inquirer, if she is pretty and asks intelligently. From him I also learned that women are by definition incapable of serious thought. This was a comforting lesson, although it made me feel obscurely doomed, for if I was to be automatically barred from participation in the life of high intellect, there was no reason why I should work to achieve it, and thinking, after all, is difficult work. When I was fifteen my father told me that I would never be a writer because I wasn't hungry enough, by which I think he meant that there would always be some man to feed me. I accepted his pronouncement as I accepted, at that age, all pronouncements which had an air of finality, and began making other career plans.

My task, it seemed to me, was to find a man in whom there resided enough power to justify my acting the child, that is, to justify my acceptance of my own femininity. For I regarded myself as feminine only in my childlike aspect; when I presented myself as a thinking person I felt entirely sexless. The boys in my class regarded me as an intellectual and showed an almost unanimous disinterest in my company. When I was in the eighth grade I lived in trepidation lest I be cited as class bookworm, and defended myself against that threat by going steady with what surely must have been the dumbest boy in our set. He was no fonder of me than I was of him; we needed each other because you had to be part of a couple in order to get invited to parties.

I did not get the opportunity to demonstrate my skill as a child-woman until I became old enough to go out with college boys. My training had equipped me only to attract intelligent men, and a boy who was no brighter than I held no power for me. But for a man who could act as my teacher I could be submissive and seductive—I *felt* submissive and seductive; my awe of the male mind translated easily into an awe of the male person.

I was, I realize now, in tune with the demands of my time. This was in the late Fifties, Marilyn Monroe was the feminine archetype of the period, and Marilyn Monroe was sexy because of her childishness. It is not much of a step from seeing oneself as a child in relation to men to seeing oneself as their victim; obviously a child does not control its environment, obviously a child is powerless before adults. All children are potential victims, dependent upon the world's goodwill. My sense of powerlessness, of feminine powerlessness, was so great that for years I trusted no man who had not indicated toward me a special favor, who had not fallen in love with me. And even toward those who had, I acted the victim, preferring to believe myself the one who loved most, for how could a man retain his power in loving me unless I gave it back to him through my submission? Years later I heard a story about how Bob Dylan so tormented a groupie that she jumped out a window while ten people looked on, and recognized the spirit of my adolescence. I never got myself into a situation even comparably extreme, my fundamental self-protectiveness having permitted me to allow only minor humiliations, but the will was there.

Masochism as clinically defined is more or less exclusively a sexual disorder: masochists are people who derive sexual pleasure from pain. Freudian psychiatrists claim that all women are to one degree or another masochistic in the sexual sense (the male penetrates the female, presumably he hurts her, and presumably she enjoys the pain as part of the pleasure), and many Freudian thinkers extend the use of the term out of the area of sex into the social area and argue that the womanly woman is correctly masochistic, must be masochistic in order to accept the male domination which is necessarily a part even of her extra-sexual life. It seems to me more useful to define masochism, insofar as the word is to be used to describe a non-clinical emotional condition, as the doing of something which one does not enjoy because someone else demands it or even because one's conscience demands it. In this sense clinical masochism can be said to be non-masochistic: if one enjoys being whipped, one is acting directly upon one's own needs, whereas if one allows oneself to be whipped for someone else's pleasure without deriving any pleasure from the act, one is behaving masochistically. A person who acts upon someone else's will, or in accordance with someone else's image of her, or who judges herself by someone else's standards, has allowed herself to be made into an object. A masochist, as I define the term, is a person who consents to be made an object. It is in that sense that I think most women are, or have been at some time in their lives, masochists. For insofar as a woman lives by the standards of the world, she lives according to the standards set by men. Men have laid down the rules and definitions by which the world is run, and one of the objects of their definitions is woman. Men define intelligence, men define usefulness, men tell us what is beautiful, men even tell us what is womanly. Constance Chatterley was a male invention; Lawrence invented her, I used to think, specifically to make me feel guilty because I didn't have the right kind of orgasms.

Lionel Trilling wrote in an essay on Jane Austen that it is the presumption of our society that women's moral life is not as men's, and that therefore we do not expect from women, in fact do not condone in them, the same degree of self-love which we expect and encourage in men. What he meant, I think, was that since women are in a sense given their lives, since women customarily choose a life-style by choosing a man rather than a path, they do not need the self-love which is necessary to carry a man to the places he has to go. Self-love is indeed a handicap to a being whose primary function is supportive, for how is a woman adequately to support another ego when her self-love demands the primacy of her own? Women learn in many ways to suppress their selfishness, and by doing so they suppress also their self-esteem. If most men hold women in contempt it is no greater than the contempt in which women hold themselves. Self-love depressed becomes self-loathing. Men are brought up to command, women to seduce; to admit the necessity of seduction is to admit that one has not the strength to command. It is in fact to accept one's own objecthood, to internalize one's oppression.

Still, I picked up some interesting lore from men, while I was studying to please them. I learned about Eliot from one boy, and about Donne from another, and about Coltrane from a third. A lover turned me on to drugs and also showed me how you were supposed to act when you were high—that is, as if you were not high. I was not surprised that he was better at this than me, cool was beginning to seem more and more a masculine talent, and I had even taken to physical retaliation in arguments, having given up the idea that I would ever win anything by verbal means. I went to Sarah Lawrence instead of Barnard because my boyfriend thought Sarah Lawrence was a more "feminine" school. My parents got divorced and I sided with my father, at least at first, because his appeared to me to be the winning side. Men, I believed, were automatically on the winning side, which was why my oldest brother could afford to withdraw in moral outrage from my father's advances; there was for *him* no danger of branding himself a loser by consorting with my mother. Yet I envied him his integrity. How could I maintain integrity when I was willing to sell out any principle for the sake of masculine attention?

I went to Sarah Lawrence and got to love it without ever taking it very seriously, which I also supposed was the way the boys I loved in those days felt about me. In fact, Sarah Lawrence appeared to me and to most of my friends there as a sort of symbol of ourselves: like the college, we were pretty and slightly prestigious and terribly self-serious in private, but just as we laughed at the school and felt embarrassed to be identified with it publicly (I always felt that if I had been a real student I would have gone to Barnard), so we laughed publicly at our own aspirations. "I like Nancy," a Princeton boy said to me, "except she always starts talking about Kafka promptly at midnight." And I laughed, god how I laughed, at Nancy—how *Sarah Lawrency* to carry on about Kafka—and, by implication, at myself. For I too expressed my intellectualism in effusions. Men expected the effusions, even found them charming, while treating them with friendly contempt. It was important to be charming. A passion for Marxism, stumblingly expressed, an interpretation of *Moby Dick*, these tokens we offered our lovers to prove we were not simply women, but people. Yet though we displayed strong feelings about art and politics, we behaved as if we had not really done the reading. To argue a point logically was to reveal yourself as unfeminine: a man might respect your mind, but he would not love you. Wit, we believed, is frightening in a woman.

In my senior year I met a girl who knew the editor of *The Village Voice*, and after graduation she got me a job there. I went to work as a reporter without having the slightest notion of how to conduct an interview and so, to cover myself, I made up a couple of pieces out of whole cloth. They were about drugs and hippies and homosexuals, the sort of scene pieces *The Voice* later specialized in, but nobody much was writing about that stuff in 1964, and I got several book offers and invitations to cocktail parties, and my father's friends started writing me letters full of sports analogies, saying it was time I entered a main event. In fact, I felt terribly guilty about writing those pieces because they seemed frivolous and sensationalistic, the sort of thing empty-headed girl reporters did when they were too dumb to write about politics, but on the other hand they got me attention, which writing about politics would never have done. I agonized all summer, publicly and privately, over this dilemma, often spending hours telling big strong male reporters how unworthy I felt. They seemed to like it.

I had never thought of myself as ambitious; actually, I think I was too convinced of my basic incompetence to be constructively ambitious, but I quickly saw that a lady journalist has advantages denied to men. For one thing, she never has to pick up a check. For another thing, if she is even remotely serious, people praise her work much more than they would praise the work of a comparably talented man; they are amazed that a woman can write coherently on any subject not confined in interest to the readers of a woman's magazine. And finally, people tell her things they would not tell a man. Many men think the secrets they tell a woman are automatically off the record. They forget that the young woman hanging on their every word is taking it all down—often they confuse her attention with sexual interest. (That is not such an advantage. Some men, rock stars for instance, simply assumed that sex was what I had come for. They would expend a little flattery to assure me that they regarded me as a cut above other groupies, and then they would suggest that we get down to balling. They were often nasty when I refused.)

At any rate, the work was nice, and it gave me a higher status as a sexual object than I had ever had before. But it was also scary. If I was to do well at it I had to take it seriously, and the strongest belief I had retained from my childhood was my idea that nothing I could achieve was worth taking seriously. In the Autumn of 1964 I fell in love with a boy who was not sure he was in love with me, and by the time he decided he was I had quit my job and moved with him to Boston. He styled himself a revolutionary and thought the content of my work hardly worth the effort it took to produce it; I accepted his opinion with relief, telling myself that in any case I had not the emotional energy to handle both a lover and a job. My feeling for him evaporated fairly soon after I discovered that it was reciprocated, though I lived with him for several months after that, partly out of guilt and partly because living with a man made me feel grown-up in a way holding a job never could have done. But finally I left him and took a job as a staff writer on a national magazine, a classy job but underpaid. Instead of complaining about the salary, I took to not showing up for work, justifying my laziness by telling myself that I was selling out anyway by taking an uptown job and that the sooner I rid myself of it, the sooner I would regain my integrity.

In the meantime I had met a grown-up man who was powerful and smart and knocked out by my child act. We spent a few months seducing each other —"You're too young for me," he would say, and I would climb upon his lap, figuratively speaking, and protest that I was not. It was no more disgusting than most courtships. In the end we got married.

Of course, I had to marry a grown-up, a father figure if you will, and my husband, as it turned out, had to marry a child. That is, he had to have an intelligent woman, but one whose intelligence had been, as it were, castrated by some outside circumstances. My youth served that purpose; my other handicaps had not as yet emerged.

Anyway, our romantic personae lasted about a year. For a year he was kind to me and listened to my problems and put up with the psychosomatic diseases which marriage had induced in me, and for a year I brought joy and spontaneity into his drab grown-up existence. Then he began to get tired of being a father and I to resent being a child, and we began to act out what I think is a classic example of contemporary marriage.

It had turned out, I realized with horror, that I had done exactly what middle-class girls are supposed to do. I had worked for a year in the communications industry, and my glamorous job had enabled me to meet a respectable, hardworking man who made a lot of money at *his* glamorous job, and I had settled down (stopped screwing around) and straightened myself out (went into analysis), and all that was missing was babies. I defended myself by assuming that we would be divorced in a year, and sneered a lot at Design Research furniture and the other symbols of middle-class marriage, but still I could not escape the feeling that I had fallen not just into a trap but into a cliché. On the other hand, I loved my husband, and I was still a writer, that is to say, a privileged woman with a life of her own. I could afford, as I began to at that time, to read feminist literature without really applying it to my own situation.

My husband, although he is nice to women, is a male supremacist, very much in the style of Norman Mailer. That is, he invests women with more or less mystical powers of control over the inner workings of the world, but thinks that feminine power is strongest when exercised in child rearing and regards contraception as unnatural. When I had my first stirrings of feminist grievance, he pronounced the subject a bore; I used to follow him from room to room, torturing him with my recitals of the sexist atrocities I was beginning to find in my favorite novels, and when I complained that magazines were paying me less than they paid men, he accused me of trying to blame the world for my own crazy passivity. But we were engaged at that time in the usual internal power struggle, and my feminism seemed to both of us more an intellectual exercise than a genuine commitment. It was not until many months later that he began to accuse me of hating men.

We already knew that he hated women, even that he had good reasons for hating women, but I had up to that time put on such a good display of being cuddly, provocative, sexually uninhibited and altogether unlike those other women that the subject of my true feelings about men had never come up. He knew that I had a compulsion to seduce men, which argues a certain distrust of them, but as the seductions, since our marriage, were always intellectual rather than sexual, they could, if you didn't want to consider their implications, be put down simply to insecurity. I don't think even I realized how I felt. Once I told my husband about a rigmarole a friend and I had made up to dismiss men we didn't like—we would go through lists of names, pointing our fingers and saying, "Zap, you're sterile," and then collapse into giggles; my husband, who has a psychoanalytical turn of mind, thought that was Terribly Revealing and I agreed that it was, but so what? And also, I agreed that it was Terribly Revealing that I liked to pinch and bite him, that I made small hostile jokes and took an almost malicious pleasure in becoming too involved in work to pay attention to him (but only briefly; I never for very long attempted to work when he had other plans), that I would go into week-long depressions during which the bed never got made nor the dishes washed. But the degree of my hostility didn't reveal itself to me until a pattern began to emerge around our quarrels.

We had, since early in the marriage, periodically engaged in bitter fights. Because my husband was the stronger, and because he tends to be judgmental, they usually started when he attempted to punish me (by withdrawing, of course) for some offense. I would dispute the validity of his complaint, and the quarrel would escalate into shouts and blows and then into decisions to terminate the marriage. In the first year my husband always beat me hollow in those battles. I used to dissolve into tears and beg his forgiveness after twenty minutes; I could not bear his rejection and I had no talent at all for conducting a quarrel. I won only when I succeeded in making him

feel guilty; if he behaved badly enough I automatically achieved the moral upper hand for at least a week following the quarrel. But after a while, the honeymoon being over, he began to refuse to feel guilty and I began to resent his superior force. Things rested there until, in the third year of our marriage, we went to live in Los Angeles because of my husband's work. During the year we spent away from home I found that I could not work, and that he was always working, and we suddenly found ourselves frozen into the textbook attitudes of male-female opposition. We fought continually, and always about the same things. He accused me of making it impossible for him to work, I accused him of keeping me dangling, dependent upon him for all emotional sustenance, he accused me of spending too much money and of keeping the house badly, I accused him of expecting me continually to subordinate my needs to his. The difficulty, I realized over and over again without being able to do much about it, was that I had gotten myself into the classic housewife's position: I was living in a place I didn't want to be and seeing people I didn't like because that was where my man was, I was living my husband's life and I hated him for it. And the reason this was so was that I was economically dependent upon him; having ceased to earn my living I could no longer claim the breadwinner's right to attention for my special needs.

My husband told me that I was grown-up now, twenty-six years old, there were certain realities which I had to face. He was the head of the household: I had never questioned that. He had to fulfill himself: I had never questioned that. He housed and fed me and paid for my clothes, he respected my opinions and refused all his opportunities to make love to other women, and my part of the bargain should have become clear to me by now. In exchange for those things, I was supposed to keep his house and save his money and understand that if he worked sixteen hours a day for a year it was no more than necessary for his self-fulfillment. Which was all quite true. Except that it was also necessary for his fulfillment that I should be there for those few hours when he had time for me, and not complain about the hours when he did not, and that I should adapt myself to his situation or else end the marriage. It never occurred to him to consider adapting himself to mine, and it never occurred to me. I only knew that his situation was bad for me, was alien, was in fact totally paralyzing, that it kept me from working, that it made me more unhappy than I had been in my life.

I knew that I was being selfish. But he was being selfish also, the only difference being that his selfishness was somehow all right, while mine was inexcusable. Selfishness was a privilege I had earned for a while by being a writer, that is, a person who had by male standards a worthwhile place to spend her time. As soon as I stopped functioning as a writer I became to my husband and to everyone else a mere woman, somebody whose time was valueless, who had no excuse for a selfish preoccupation with her own wants.

I used to lie in bed beside my husband after those fights and wish I had the courage to bash in his head with a frying pan. I would do it while he slept, since awake he would overpower me, disarm me. If only I dared, I would mutter to myself through clenched teeth, pushing back the realization that I didn't dare not because I was afraid of seriously hurting him—I would have loved to do that—but because even in the extremity of my anger I was afraid that if I cracked his head with a frying pan he would leave me. God, how absurd it was (god, how funny, I would mutter to myself, how amusing, oh wow, what a joke) that my whole life's effort had been directed toward keeping men from leaving me, toward placating them, submitting to them, demanding love from them in return for living in their style, and it all ended with me lying awake in the dark hating my husband, hating my father, hating all the men I had ever known. Probably I had always hated them. What I couldn't figure out was whether I hated them because I was afraid they would leave me or whether I was afraid they would leave me because I hated them.

Because one cannot for very long support such a rage without beginning to go crazy, I tried to think of the problem in political terms. It seemed to me too easy to say that my hatred for men was a true class hatred, that women hate men because women are an oppressed class hungering for freedom. And yet wherever there exists the display of power there is politics, and in women's relations with men there is a continual transfer of power, there is, continually, politics. There are political analogies even to our deepest, our most banal fantasies. Freud maintains that the female terror of the penis is a primary fear, and that the male fear of castration by the vagina is merely a retaliatory fantasy, a guilty fear of punishment. The serf fears the overlord's knout, the overlord, guilty, fears the serf's revenge. Women are natural guerrillas. Scheming, we nestle into the enemy's bed, avoiding open warfare, watching the options, playing the odds. High, and made paranoiac by his observance of my rage, my husband has the fantasy of woman with a knife. He sees her in sexual ecstasy with her eyes open to observe the ecstasy of her partner, with her consciousness awake, her consciousness the knife. It had often been my private boast that even in moments of greatest abandon, I always kept some part of my mind awake: I always searched for clues. Is he mine now, this monster? Have I disarmed him, and for how long? Men are beasts, we say, joking, parodying the Victorian rag, and then realize to our surprise that we believe it. The male has force almost beyond our overpowering, the force of laws, of science, of literature, the force of mathematics and skyscrapers and the Queensboro Bridge; the penis is only its symbol. We cannot share men's pride in the world they have mastered. If you follow that symbolism to its conclusion, we are ourselves that conquered world.

It is because they know that this is true, know it in their bones if not in their heads, that men fear the hatred of women. For women are the true maintenance class. Society is built upon their acquiescence, and upon their small and necessary labors. Restricted to the supportive role, conditioned to excel only at love, women hold for men the key to social order. It is a Marxist truism that the original exploitation, the enslavement which set the pattern for everything which came later, was the enslavement of women by men. Even the lowest worker rests upon the labor of his wife. Where no other claim to distinction exists, a man defines himself by his difference from the supportive sex; he may be a less than admirable man, but at least he is a man, at least he is not a woman.

And if women have fought, they have fought as guerrillas, in small hand-to-hand skirmishes, in pillow wars upon the marriage bed. When they attack frontally, when they come together in groups to protest their oppression, they raise psychic questions so profound as to be almost inadmissable. In E. E. Cummings' play *Him,* there is a scene in which two women sit in a Paris café and order men served up to them like plats du jour; it is an inexpressibly sinister sequence, and it has its counterparts elsewhere in the avant-garde literature of the Twenties. I do not imagine that Cummings approved of men using women like meat, but I am quite sure that he could not have treated the situation with such horror had the sexual roles been reversed. Cummings, like Leonid Andreyev and the other modernists who dealt in surreal images of female dominance, was writing during the early period of feminist protest, and I think they were expressing a fear basic to every man confronted with the idea of women's liberation. When men imagine a female uprising they imagine a world in which women rule men as men have ruled women: their guilt, which is the guilt of every ruling class, will allow them to see no middle ground. And it is a measure of the unconscious strength of our belief in natural male dominance that all of us, men and women, revolt from the image of woman with a whip, that the female sadist is one of our most deep-rooted images of perversion.

And although I believe this male fantasy of feminine equality as a euphemism for feminine dominance to be evidence of the oppressors' neurosis rather than of any supporting fact, it was part of the character of my resentment that I once fancied wresting power from men as though nothing less than total annihilation would satisfy my rage. The true dramatic conclusion of this narrative should be the dissolution of my marriage; there is a part of me which believes that you cannot fight a sexist system while acknowledging your need for the love of a man, and perhaps if I had had the courage finally to tear apart my life I could write you about my hard-working independence, about my solitary self-respect, about the new society I hope to build. But in the end my husband and I did not divorce, although it seemed at one time as if we would. Instead I raged against him for many months and joined the Woman's Liberation Movement, and thought a great deal about myself, and about whether my problems were truly all women's problems, and decided that some of them were and that some of them were not. My sexual rage was the most powerful single emotion of my life, and the feminist analysis has become for me, as I think it will for most women of my generation, as significant an intellectual tool as Marxism was for generations of radicals. But it does not answer every question. To discover that something has been wrong is not necessarily to make it right: I would be lying if I said that my anger had taught me how to live. But my life has changed because of it. I think I am becoming in many small ways a woman who takes no shit. I am no longer submissive, no longer seductive; perhaps it is for that reason that my husband tells me sometimes that I have become hard, and that my hardness is unattractive. I would like it to be otherwise. I think that will take a long time.

My husband and I have to some degree worked out our differences; we are trying to be together as equals, to separate our human needs from the needs imposed upon us by our sex roles. But my hatred lies within me and between us, not wholly a personal hatred, but not entirely political either. And I wonder always whether it is possible to define myself as a feminist revolutionary and still remain in any sense a wife.

There are moments when I still worry that he will leave me, that he will come to need a woman less preoccupied with her own rights, and when I worry about that I also fear that no man will ever love me again, that no man could ever love a woman who is angry. And that fear is a great source of trouble to me, for it means that in certain fundamental ways I have not changed at all.

I would like to be cold and clear and selfish, to demand satisfaction for my needs, to compel respect rather than affection. And yet there are moments, and perhaps there always will be, when I fall back upon the old cop-outs. Why should I trouble to win a chess game or a political argument when it is so much easier to lose charmingly? Why should I work when my husband can support me, why should I be a human being when I can get away with being a child?

Woman's Liberation is finally only personal. It is hard to fight an enemy who has outposts in your head.

HIGH OLD TIMES

Most of the material in this book is now, inevitably, retrospective; though forty years of readers saw it first in Esquire, we can't, nor would we care to, make that claim for an anthology. The four pieces presented here under the general rubric of *High Old Times* were, however, retrospective from their conception: Mencken regarding 1901 from the forty-two-year vantage point of 1943; Runyon dissecting his subject over the span of sixty years, back to his own childhood and indeed far earlier even than that; Ellison looking back from the Fifties over the jazz of the Forties; Joseph Wechsberg lovingly describing a cluttered corner of the Baroque world of Vienna as it will never be again. Now contemporaneity is nice, and this magazine has always abounded with it, while trying to avoid the more degrading excesses of with-it-

ness; but where a gap exists in the historical record, and an author of special qualifications is available to fill it, Esquire has usually been willing to make good the lacuna. Nostalgia is a motive not wholly irrelevant; with magazines as with individuals, everyone feels warm and safe when observing a past which he has survived, and which can't hurt him anymore. But at whatever age, we all find out where we are by looking in every direction, including where we have been; and our proprioceptive sense of the shape we're in is sharpened by improving our knowledge of how we once appeared. Here, then, four contributions to the ongoing evaluation of the background that an organism must perform if it's not to lose its way among its immediate surroundings.

214

H. L. Mencken:

An Evening on the House

All the carnalities denounced in that prissy era flourished in Sunset Park, from crap shooting to hoochie-koochie

In the days of trolley parks, now gone forever, there was almost as much spread between park and park, culturally speaking, as you will now find between nightclubs. Some, catering to what was then called the Moral Element, showed all the hallmarks of Chautauqua, Asbury Park and Lake Mohonk, with nothing stronger on tap than ginger ale, soda pop and sarsaparilla, and no divertisement more provocative to the hormones than quoit-pitching and the flying horses. But in others there was a frank appeal to the baser nature of mankind, and at the bottom of the scale were some that, by the somewhat prissy standards of those days, were veritable sewers of wickedness. One of the latter sort was operated, in the Baltimore I adorned as a young newspaper reporter, by a cashiered police sergeant named Julius Olsen—a man who believed, as he would often say, in living and letting live. His place lay at the terminus of a Class D trolley line that meandered down the harbor side to the shore of one of the affluents of the Patapsco River. Most of his customers, however, did not patronize this trolley line, which was outfitted with senile cars that often jumped the track, and shook the bones out of their passengers when they didn't. Indeed, it was rare to encounter an actual Baltimorean in the place, which had the name of Sunset Park. Nearly all the males who frequented it were sailors from ships berthed along or anchored in the river, and nine tenths of the females were adventuresses from either the Norfolk, Virginia, region, then famous throughout the Eastern seaboard for its levantine barbarities, or the lower tier of Pennsylvania counties, where the Vice Trust, backed by Wall Street, maintained agents in every hamlet.

If there was any among the lady visitors to Sunset who had not lost her honest name long before she ever saw it, the fault was not Julius Olsen's, for he had a ground rule rigidly excluding all others. Every evening at eight o'clock he would take his place at the garish entrance to his pleasure ground, and give his eye to each female who presented herself, whether alone or with an escort. If there was anything in her aspect that raised a suspicion of chastity he would challenge her at once, and hold her up at the gate until she convinced him that her looks were false to her inner nature. Once, as I stood there with him—for I greatly admired his insight into such things and was eager to learn its secrets—a young couple got off the trolley car and made as if to enter. To my unpracticed eye they looked to be the run-of-the-mine yahoos and nothing more: I could detect no stigmata of chemical purity in the lady. But Julius saw deeper than I did, and as the couple came abreast of his sentry post his heavy paw fell upon the shoulder of the young man, and his eyebrows drew together in a fearful frown. "What in hell do you mean," he roared, "to bring a nice young girl to such a goddamn dump as this? Ain't you got no goddamn sense at *all*?" The young fellow, amazed and abashed, stood speechless, and Julius bellowed on. "Don't you know," he demanded, "where you are at? Ain't you ever heerd tell of Sunset Park? Goddamn if I ever seen the like of it in all my born days! Do you want a gang of sailors to bash in your head and make off with your girl? What would you have to say to her mama if that happened? How would you square yourself with her pa? Goddamn if I ain't got a mind to bust you one myself. Now you take her home and don't let me see you around here no more. As for *you*"—turning to the silent and trembling girl—"all I got to say is you better get yourself a better beau. Such damn fools as this one is poison to a religious young lady, and don't you go telling me that ain't what you are. *I know, I* do. Now, scat, the goddamn bothen of you!"

Whereupon he half bowed and half heaved them onto the waiting trolley car, and stood by muttering until it started back to the city.

From all this the maker of snap judgments may conclude that Julius was a Puritan at heart—perhaps even that there was a Y.M.C.A. secretary hidden in him. Nothing could be more untrue. He simply did not want to clutter up his conscience, such as it was, with

H. L. Mencken lived in Baltimore all his life, even while editing magazines published out of New York, and never refused a drink after dark. This memoir of the flaming Baltimore of his youth appeared in December, 1943.

gratuitous and unnecessary burdens. Otherwise he was the complete antinomian, and of all the tough and abandoned trolley parks around the periphery of Baltimore, his Sunset was undoubtedly the worst. Every sort of infamy that the vice crusaders of the time denounced, from crap shooting to hoochie-koochie dancing, and from the smoking of cigarettes by females —then still *contra bonos mores*—to riotous boozing by both sexes, went on within its gates, and there was no dilution of these carnalities by anything of an even remotely respectable nature. If a customer had called for a lemonade the waiters would have fanned him with the billies they carried up their sleeves, and if either of the two comedians in the so-called burlesque show that went on in a big shed had ventured upon a really clean joke, Julius himself would have given him the bum's rush. The striptease had not been invented in that remote era, but everything that the fancy of ribald men had yet concocted was offered. The stock company, like most other such organizations, played a loutish version of *Krausmeyer's Alley* every night, but it was given with variations suggested by the worst conceits of whiskey drummers and medical students. The taste of the time being for large and billowy women, there was no girl in the chorus who weighed less than 170 pounds, and the rear elevation of each and every one of them was covered with bruises from head to foot, all made by the slapsticks of the comedians. In the intervals of the performance on the stage, these ladies were expected to fraternize with the customers. This fraternizing consisted mainly in getting them as drunk as possible, and then turning them over to scamps who dragged them out to a dark spot behind the shed and there went through their pockets. When a customer resisted— which happened sometimes in the case of sailors—the scamps gave him a drubbing, and it was not at all unheard of for the harbor cops to find the clay of a jolly jack-tar in the adjacent river, especially of a Sunday morning, for Saturday night was the big night at Sunset Park, as it was at all such places.

The land cops, who knew Julius when he was a poor flatfoot like themselves and now took a certain amount of fraternal pride in his success in life, made occasional raids upon him, but only under pressure from reformers, and never with any hope or intent of bringing him to heel. Once I was present when a party of reformers undertook a raid in person, with a squad of cops trailing along, theoretically to protect them. Julius, who was on watch as usual at his front gate, let them enter unmolested, but they had hardly

snooped their first snoop before his whole company of goons, male and female, fell upon them, and in two minutes they were in full retreat, with the cops following after to clout them as they ran. The next day he swore out a warrant for their leader, charging him with lifting a diamond sunburst worth $18,000 from one of the chorus girls, and under cover of the ensuing uproar their countercharges were forgotten. Julius had a dozen witnesses willing to swear that they had seen the reformer throttle the girl with one hand and grab the sunburst with the other, and another dozen schooled to testify that they had recovered it only by *force majeure* and in the face of wild slashings with a razor by the accused. The sunburst itself was brought into court, along with five cut-rate jewelers hired to certify to its value, and for a while things looked dark for the poor reformer, for he was a Sunday-school superintendent, and Maryland juries, in those days, always said "Guilty" to Sunday-school superintendents; but his lawyer filed a demurrer on some obscure ground or other.

Rather curiously, there was seldom any serious disorder at Sunset Park—that is, within Julius' definition of the term. Now and then, to be sure, a sailor ran amok and attempted to stage an imitation of some massacre he had seen in Shanghai or Port Said, but he seldom got beyond teeing off, for all of Julius' waiters, as I have said, were armed with billies, and his head bartender, Jack Jamieson, was a retired heavyweight, and worth a thousand men. Even the comedians in his show lent a hand when necessary, and so did the four musicians who constituted the orchestra —the leader, Professor Kleinschmidt, who doubled on piano and violin and fed the comedians; the cornet player, George Mullally; the trombonist, Billy Wilson; and the drummer, Bing-Bing Thompson, himself a reformed sailor. Julius himself never entered these hurly-burlies, but stood on the sidelines to boss his lieges. Even when a customer insulted one of the lady help, say by pasting her in the nose or biting off an ear, the head of the establishment restrained his natural indignation, and let the *lex situs* prevailing at Sunset Park take its course. Only once, indeed, did I ever hear of him forgetting himself, and on that occasion I happened to be present as his guest, for he was always very polite to newspaper reporters, as he was to detectives, precinct leaders, coroners and other such civic functionaries.

It was the opening night of his 1901 season, and I made the uncomfortable trolley trip to the park in the company of Leopold Bortsch, *Totsäufer* of the

Scharnhorst Brewery, who had to attend *ex officio*, for Julius had Scharnhorst beer on tap. Unfortunately, there had been complaints about it of late, as there had been in Baltimore proper, for it was then, and had been for years, the worst malt liquor ever seen in the town. Leopold himself, who had to drink it day in and day out on his tours of customers' saloons, and at the innumerable funerals, weddings, wedding anniversaries, christenings and confirmations that went on in their families, was constrained to admit, in candid moments, that it was certainly doing his kidneys no good. But when a Class A customer had an opening, he had to get it down willy-nilly, and at the same time he had to foment its consumption by all the assembled bibuli. For the first night of Sunset Park, which in a normal week consumed two hundred half barrels, he was expected to stage a really royal show, and to that end the brewery allowed him $100 to spend over the bar. He did not know, as he marched up radiating his best promotional manner, that there was trouble ahead. Specifically, he did not know that Julius, succumbing at last to the endless complaints about Scharnhorst beer (which had by now become so bad that even the Scotch engineers from British ships sometimes gagged at it), had resolved to give a look-in to seven other Baltimore breweries. Nor did he know that all of their seven brews were already on tap at the bar, and that he would find the *Totsäufer* of each and every one lined up before it, to fight him to the death.

It was a shock, indeed, but Leopold was not one to be easily flabbergasted, and his reply was characteristically prompt and bold. The immemorial custom was for a *Totsäufer* to begin proceedings, on such an occasion, by slapping down a five-dollar bill and inviting all comers to have a beer. Leopold slapped down a *ten*-spot. The seven other *Totsäufer*, thus challenged, had to respond in kind, and they did so with panicky dispatch, each, of course, calling for his own beer. Jack Jamieson, for the opening night, had put in two extra bartenders, which, with his regular aides and himself, made five in all, but how could five men, within the space of five minutes, draw 1600 five-cent glasses of beer? It seemed beyond human power, but I saw them do it, and while they were still shoving over the last couple of hundred—by now at least 80 percent foam—Leopold threw down *two* ten-spots, and commanded a double ration of Scharnhorst for all hands. What would the other *Totsäufer* do now? What they would do was instantly apparent. Six of the seven saw him with crisp *twenties*, and simultaneously bellowed orders for wholesale rounds of their own beers. The seventh, Hugo Blauvogel of the Peerless Brewery, raised by peeling off *three* tens.

The situation, as the war correspondents say, now began to develop rapidly. Jack Jamieson relieved it somewhat by palming one of the twenties and one of the tens, and his chief assistant helped a little more by collaring another of the tens, but there remained the sum of $130 for the cash register, and a simple calculation will show that it called for 2600 beers. Half of them had been drawn—God knows how!—before Jack thought of raising the price to ten cents, but

by that time the bar was packed as tightly as a busload of war workers, and great gangs of reinforcements were swarming in from all parts of the park. When the news reached the hoochie-koochie show, where a hundred or more sailors from the Battleship (*censored*), then on a goodwill tour of the Atlantic ports, were spoofing the performers, they arose as one man, and began a lumbering sprint for the bar. Passing the show-shed on their way, they gave the word to its patrons, and in ten seconds the girls and comedians were mauling and jawing one another to empty tables. Not a waiter was left on the floor, and in half a minute more not a girl or comedian was left on the stage, or a musician in the orchestra pit. By the time these artists arrived at the bar the crowd in front of it was twenty men deep, and all semblance of decorum had vanished. The boozers close up were so dreadfully squeezed and shoved that they could hardly get down the beers in front of them, and the later-comers on the outskirts fought in despair for better places. The sailors from the battleship, forgetting chivalry, tried to climb in over the heads of the ladies of the ensemble, and the comedians, musicians and special policemen slugged it out with the waiters. Only the eight *Totsäufer* kept their heads. They went on throwing money into the whirlpool of suds that covered the bar.

Up to this time Julius himself had been at his usual post at the park gate, searching the faces of inpouring fair ones for vestiges of innocence. But he had ears as well as eyes, and though it was a good city block from where he stood to the bar, he eventually picked up the roar that was mounting there, and made off to investigate. The crowd, by now, bulged outside the entrance like a swarm of flies around the bung of a molasses barrel, and hundreds of newcomers were arriving at a gallop and trying to horn and worm their way into it. Julius accordingly ducked to the rear, and entered behind the bar. He was just in time to hear Leopold Bortsch give the signal for the final catastrophe. It consisted of the one word "Wine!" uttered in a kind of scream. "Wine! Wine! Wine!" echoed the massed and macerated boozers. "He's opening wine! He's setting up wine! Hooray! Hooray! Hooray!"

There were, in fact, but five bottles of wine in the whole of Sunset Park, and they had been lying in Jack's cooler for three or four years, awaiting the remote chance that John W. Gates, Stanford White or Charlie Schwab might drop around some evening. The first two were duds, but the remaining three popped with magnificent effect, and as the so-called champagne seethed out of them, the last restraints of civilized society blew off, and the whole company yielded to its *libido boozalis*. In half a minute not a single sailor from the battleship was on the floor: they were all climbing over the merchant mariners and other civilians, and in dozens of cases a sailor thus climbing had another sailor climbing over *him*. Julius, with his long experience as cop and *Wirt*, saw a riot was in the making. "No more!" he roared. "Not another goddamn drink! The bar is closed!"

Alas, it was a bad idea, and even if it had been a

good one it would have come too late to work. As well challenge Behemoth with a spit-blower or Vesuvius with a squirt. Jack and his colleagues, in obedience to the boss's command, downed their tools instantly, but there were plenty of sailors present, both of the Navy and the Merchant Marine, who knew very well which end of a bottle had the cork, and they were over the bar in no time at all. Nor were they bound and hobbled, once they got into action, by the stiff, professional technique of Jack and company. When an outcry for gin came from the far reaches of the crowd they sent a whole bottle of it sailing through the air, and then another. Nor did they hesitate to use bottles on Julius' own head when he plunged into the thick of them, and essayed to lay them out. Of the details of this phase I can give you only hearsay, for I had been working my way out since the beginning of the action, and had by now taken a rather unfavorable post of observation some distance away, behind a large oak tree. But I went to the trouble during the weeks and months following to run down the full story, and these were its principal elements:

1. The rioters emptied not only every container of lawful goods in the park, from beer kegs to sprinklers of Angostura bitters; they also got down a barrel of cologne spirits that Julius used to sophisticate his five-cent whiskey, the contents of forty seltzer siphons, and a bottle of Mickey Finns.

2. Julius' first act, on recovering his faculties, was to get a revolver from his office and go gunning for the eight *Totsäufer*. All had disappeared save Hugo Blauvogel. At him Julius fired six times, missing him every time. The next day he served notice on the Baltimore breweries that any *Totsäufer* sent to the place thereafter would be shot like a dog.

3. The sailors from the Battleship (*censored*), returning aboard at dawn, took with them five of the ladies of the Sunset Park ensemble and both comedians. The officer of the deck refused admission to the ladies, but apparently swore in the comedians as mess attendants, yeomen, chaplain's mates or something of the sort, for a couple of weeks later the men of the whole North Atlantic Fleet staged a show at the Guantanamo base that is still remembered in the Navy as the damnedest ever seen. Its stars were two comics of unprecedented virtuosity. From the first glimpse of their red noses to the last reverberation of their slapsticks, they had the assemblage rolling in the aisles.

Damon Runyon:

They Saw That They Were Naked

In the last piece he ever wrote,
the chronicler of guys and dolls
mentions the unmentionable

Nowadays the average woman does not wear enough undergarments to make a boxing glove for a butterfly, and if you want to know how I acquired this info, why, goodness gracious fellows, I am married, am most observing and have a wonderful mind for detail.

Besides, I worked like a dog on research for this treatise, an explanation I offer because I would not have you think that I sat back somewhere and made notes as a lady put on or took off, which would have been most embarrassing on both sides, I suppose.

The average woman wears a pantie girdle and brassiere, or bra as we say in my set, and it amounts to a reversion to first principles across thousands of years because you read in Genesis that after the old sarpint had conned Eve into munching the forbidden fruit and she in turn sold the idea to her ever-loving husband:

"—the eyes of them both were opened and they knew that they were naked; and they sewed fig leaves together and made themselves aprons."

Well, the girls are practically back to fig leaves in the extent of their underwear. In fact I am not dead sure that a couple of fair-size fig leaves are not more commodious than the pantie girdle and the bra put together.

The pantie girdle is a confection in Lastex and satin or rayon in all colors with detachable supporters to hold up the stockings, if any. The bra is a you-know-what. The pantie girdle was originally a sports proposition but now most women wear it as an all-arounder. It is a combination girdle and pants and supplants the separate girdle and the separate pants.

It is a simple and sensible garment and I think it traces to the Homeric period of Greece. I find that the Greek maidens of that period wore a woolen band called an apodesm as a bra and a zona or woolen band around the waist as a girdle. Of course they wore other garments, but I am specializing here in the substrata,

as you might say, of the female investure.

Maybe I am taking in a little too much territory in assigning just the pantie girdle and the bra to the average woman. A large number, perhaps the majority, though I have not got the time to go around peering and probing, wear with the girdle pantie that oldest of female garments, the slip.

It is a sort of flowing undershirt, the direct descendant of an undergarment of fairly thick material worn by the early Egyptian women. It corresponds to the chemise, pronounced "shimmy" back in my old home town of Pueblo. The early Roman wrens had the equivalent of the Greeks' apodesm in their strophia, worn with a "tunica intima," or under tunic, which was nothing but our old friend the slip or "shimmy."

I used to think that the chief purpose of the slip was to sneak down just below the hem of the overskirt so that other dames could lift their brows at one another when a slip-displayer went past. There is no doubt that some women are born lacking control over their slips and never manage to acquire it, but I think that could be a throwback to a distaff ancestry that once purposely included in the many sinister schemes of the females for the trapping of us blokes this showing of the slip.

In the Middle Ages, when tight-fitting dresses were popular with the French women, they wore a "*cotte*" or fitted chemise over an inner tunic or short chemise and the edge of the "*cotte*" was often embroidered so that when the Janes held up their long skirts as they walked, the bottom of the "*cottes*" showed.

I presume the theory was that the embroidery was more inviting to the masculine orb than anything else the "*cotte*" wearer had to display down there, though of course I am only guessing. The Anglo-Saxon women of the same period wore a garment similar to a chemise that was variously called a kirtle, a smock, a sherte or a camise. Personally, I like the "shimmy" of my old hometown.

It was there as a boy that I became quite familiar with nearly all phases of ladies' underwear of the period of the late '90's because on Monday, which

Seven years after Runyon's death in 1946, Esquire published this quasi-memoir, quasi-historical essay on ladies' underwear. It is hard to imagine what the creator of Miss Sarah Brown would have thought of ladies' underwear if he had lived until the present day.

was washday in my old home town, the backyards of Pueblo were veritable snowbanks of white linen drying in the sun. The vagrant breezes ambling up and down the Arkansas Valley would inflate those voluminous garments known as ladies' drawers until from a distance the town must have looked like one of those barrage-balloon-protected communities of the war.

I used to blush over our department stores' brazen declarations in their ads at certain seasons of the year of bargains in "ladies' picnic drawers." I think I had an impression that they were specially designed for picnics, though of course I am better informed now. I mean I realize that they could have been worn with convenience anywhere.

The first mention of drawers or panties that I am able to discover is in the latter part of the seventeenth century. It seems that the ladies of the stage took to wearing what were known as "caleçons" or opera drawers, a form of tights. In the time of Napoleon, ladies of fashion adopted them and please do not bruit it about, but I hear the Empress Josephine fancied them. I do not know Napoleon's reaction.

We have had two notable periods in which the women have displayed some sense in their underdressing. One is the present. The other is the time of the ancients, of the Greek and Roman maidens I mention above. In the Directoire period, the French women, after a long spell of corsets and bustles and other horrible accouterments of discomfort, went back to the scanty underwear of the oldies for a time.

Prior to this, in both France and England, tightly laced corsets with whalebone stays and big skirts were considered mighty hot stuff by the girls. The corset was laced on over the inevitable chemise, then came an under petticoat and a hoopskirt, called a farthingale in England. The farthingale was followed by a pannier which was similar to the hoop but extended only from the sides, being straight fore and aft. In the eighteenth century the pannier was discarded in favor of the bustle.

In the nineteenth century, about the time of the Restoration, the corset returned. I do not know who invented the corset. In the Minoan or Aegean Age, 2000 B.C., we find evidence of a crude arrangement that indicates that even then the ladies were trying to keep their waistlines down by compression. I do not see why. Personally, I like them a little waisty, and how about you?

Catherine de Medici had a stomach with a slight overhang, as I understand it, and she invented a sort of straitjacket to keep it under control, and the Italian women of the Renaissance had to

adopt a similar device as a fashion, stomachs or no stomachs. They had corsets made of thin steel richly fashioned in ornamental lacework patterns and worn over shifts of cambric linen which had long sleeves.

My narration is not chronological, but in 1825 the skirts began to widen again. Presently the ladies were wearing more undergarments than an artichoke has leaves. Four or five petticoats heavily starched and flounced were considered a fair individual count. A corset went with them, girthed on tighter than a new saddle on a bucking bronco.

After a while the stiff petticoats were replaced by what was called the crinoline, made of several big rings of steel arranged like hoops on a barrel. Under the crinoline, pantalettes reaching to the ankle and ruffled from the knee down were worn. The drawers reaching below the knee, and large enough to hide a couple of watermelons in them when on without attracting undue attention, succeeded the pantalette. They say the Empress Eugenie introduced them. She was the type, men.

In 1874, a National Dress Congress was held in Boston and opened a campaign for hygienic dress for women. It sponsored a union suit made of thick soft wool with high neck and long sleeves which was just jolly in cold weather but which could sometimes itch the behiminy out of the wearer. (Ask Gram'mer, she knows.)

The recollection of this garment also reminds me of another slightly embarrassing feature of those department-store ads back in my home town—"ladies' union suits with drop seats." I mean they were embarrassing to me. I mean I thought they might have left out the more distressing details.

In 1910, the glorious twentieth century, silk underwear for women was brought out—silk bloomers, chemises, short-legged union suits, maybe with those drop seats, too, for all I know to the contrary, petticoats and a new underskirt, the fitted princess slip, et cetera. Now followed the period of the so-called "flaming youth" and the way the girls began shedding their underwear was a caution to cats. Why, fellers, even the "shimmy" went!

They got down to nothing but a bandeau and brief panties or one-piece fitted garments made of glove silk and called "Skin-fits," "Sprites" and such. It was in the late Twenties, I believe, that the girls began borrowing their brothers' shorts and suddenly we had advertisements of "broadcloth briefs" and "athletic shorts for misses," and thus we finally arrive in the present year which as far as ladies' underwear is concerned I think I will entitle "The Age of Reason."

But before leaving you with this vast fund of knowledge about what goes on 'neath yon beautiful broad's exterior draperies, I think I ought to tell you about the spinster lady back in my old home town of Pueblo who had a physical façade like that of Catherine de Medici and who had to call in a Western Union messenger boy to help her lace her corset when she was dressing for the street.

I was one of the corporation Mercurys in those days and I fancied the lady's call because it was good for a ten-cent tip and all you had to do was to grasp the corset laces firmly, put one foot up against the wall to brace yourself and pull until each outlying yard of loose anatomy had been gathered together and tucked within the limits of the corset and she cried sufficient.

In our time, ladies of her contour generally wear what is called a foundation which is a bra and a girdle in one, but they had no fancy truck like that for hefties in that bygone day of which I write. Anyway, I had the misfortune one day to brace myself for the lace-pulling by putting my foot against a door that opened into the street and at the peak of my pull this door flew open and I not only fell into the street but yanked the lady with me.

The sad part of it is that all the laces became undone and the corset fell off and unleashed an extraordinary poundage in all directions at the precise moment that the Rev. Dr. Will Gerard, who was the object of the lady's deepest affection and who had always supposed that she was as slender as she seemed after I had her all pulled in, came calling for her.

Oh, yes, I always felt a little regretful that the good Dr. Will let Romance founder right there on the sidewalk, but I still say after these many years that it was no reason why the lady should repudiate my bill for ten cents.

Ralph Ellison:

THE GOLDEN AGE / TIME PAST

Manners and morals at Minton's, 1941: the setting for a revolution

That which we do is what we are. That which we remember is, more often than not, that which we would have liked to have been; or that which we hope to be. Thus our memory and our identity are ever at odds; our history ever a tall tale told by inattentive idealists.

It has been a long time now, and not many remember how it was in the old days; not really. Not even those who were there to see and hear as it happened, who were pressed in the crowds beneath the dim rosy lights of the bar in the smoke-veiled room, and who shared, night after night, the mysterious spell created by the talk, the laughter, greasepaint, powder, perfume, sweat, alcohol and food—all blended and simmering, like a stew on the restaurant range, and brought to a sustained moment of elusive meaning by the timbres and accents of musical instruments locked in passionate recitative. It has been too long now, some seventeen years.

Above the bandstand there later appeared a mural depicting a group of jazzmen holding a jam session in a narrow Harlem bedroom. While an exhausted girl with shapely legs sleeps on her stomach in a big brass bed, they bend to their music in a quiet concatenation of unheard sound: a trumpeter, a guitarist, a clarinetist, a drummer; their only audience a small, cockeared dog. The clarinetist is white. The guitarist strums with an enigmatic smile. The trumpet is muted. The barefooted drummer, beating a folded newspaper with whisk brooms in lieu of a drum, stirs the eye's ear like a blast of brasses in a midnight street. A bottle of port rests on a dresser, but it, like the girl, is ignored. The artist, Charles Graham, adds mystery to, as well as illumination within, the scene by having

The author of The Invisible Man *participated with amateur trombonist Harold Hayes (then a young editor at Esquire) on a jazz-writing panel at the 1958 Newport festival. Ellison deplored the fact that most jazz history was romanticized and inadequate; the resulting article was part of a section on the Golden Age of Jazz in January, 1959.*

them play by the light of a kerosene lamp. The painting, executed in a harsh documentary style reminiscent of W.P.A. art, conveys a feeling of musical effort caught in timeless and unrhetorical suspension, the sad remoteness of a scene observed through a wall of crystal.

Except for the lamp, the room might well have been one in the Hotel Cecil, the building in 118th Street in which Minton's Playhouse is located, and although painted in 1946, sometime after the revolutionary doings there had begun, the mural should help recall the old days vividly. But the decor of the place has been changed and now it is covered, most of the time, by draperies. These require a tricky skill of those who would draw them aside. And even then there will still only be the girl who must sleep forever unhearing, and the men who must forever gesture the same soundless tune. Besides, the time it celebrates is dead and gone and perhaps not even those who came when it was still fresh and new remember those days as they were.

Neither do those remember who knew Henry Minton, who gave the place his name. Nor those who shared in the noisy lostness of New York the rediscovered community of the feasts, evocative of home, of South, of good times, the best and most unselfconscious of times, created by the generous portions of Negro-American cuisine—the hash, grits, fried chicken, the ham-seasoned vegetables, the hot biscuits and rolls and the free whiskey—with which, each Monday night, Teddy Hill honored the entire cast of current Apollo Theatre shows. They were gathered here from all parts of America and they broke bread together and there was a sense of good feeling and promise, but what shape the fulfilled promise would take they did not know, and few except the more restless of the younger musicians even questioned. Yet it was an exceptional moment and the world was swinging with change.

Most of them, black and white alike, were hardly aware of where they were or what time it was; nor did they wish to be. They thought of Minton's as a sanctuary, where in an atmosphere blended of nostalgia and a music-and-drink-lulled suspension of time they could retreat from the wartime tensions of the town. The meaning of time-present was not their concern; thus when they try to tell it now the meaning escapes them.

For they were caught up in events which made that time exceptionally and uniquely *then*, and which brought, among the other changes which have re-shaped the world, a momentous modulation into a new key of musical sensibility; in brief, a revolution in culture.

So how *can* they remember? Even in swiftly changing America there are few such moments, and at best Americans give but a limited attention to history. Too much happens too rapidly, and before we can evaluate it, or exhaust its meaning or pleasure, there is something new to concern us. Ours is the tempo of the motion picture, not that of the still camera, and we waste experience as we wasted the forest. During the time it was happening the sociologists were concerned with the riots, unemployment and industrial tensions of the time, the historians with the onsweep of the war; and the critics and most serious students of culture found this area of our national life of little interest. So it was left to those who came to Minton's out of the needs of feeling, and when the moment was past no one retained more than a fragment of its happening. Afterward the very effort to put the fragments together transformed them—so that in place of true memory they now summon to mind pieces of legend. They retell the stories as they have been told and written, glamourized, inflated, made neat and smooth, with all incomprehensible details vanished along with most of the wonder—not how it was as they themselves knew it.

It was jumping with good times

When asked how it was back then, back in the Forties, they will smile, then, frowning with the puzzlement of one attempting to recall the details of a pleasant but elusive dream, they'll say: "Oh, man, it was a hell of a time! A wailing time! Things were jumping, you couldn't get in here for the people. The place was packed with celebrities. Park Avenue, man! Big people in show business, college professors along with the pimps and their women. And college boys and girls. Everybody came. You know how the old words to the *Basin Street Blues* used to go before Sinatra got hold of it? *Basin Street is the street where the dark and the light folks meet*—that's what I'm talking about. That was Minton's, man. It was a place where everybody could come to be entertained because it was a place that was jumping with good times."

Or some will tell you that it was here that Dizzy Gillespie found his own trumpet voice; that here Kenny Clarke worked out the patterns of his drumming style; where Charlie Christian played out the last creative and truly satisfying moments of his brief life, his New York home; where Charlie Parker built the monument of his art; where Thelonius Monk formulated his contribution to the chordal progressions and the hide-and-seek melodic methods of modern jazz. And they'll call such famous names as Lester Young and Ben Webster, Coleman Hawkins; or Fats Waller, who came here in the after-hour stillness of the early morning to compose. They'll tell you that Benny Goodman, Art Tatum, Count Basie, and Lena Horne would drop in to join in the fun; that it was here that George Shearing played on his first night in the U.S.; or Tony Scott's great love of the place; and they'll repeat all the stories of how, when and by whom the word "bebop" was coined here—but, withal, few actually remember, and these leave much unresolved.

Usually, music gives resonance to memory (and Minton's was a hotbed of jazz), but not the music then in the making here. It was itself a texture of fragments, repetitive, nervous, not fully formed; its melodic lines underground, secret and taunting; its riffs jeering—"Salt peanuts! Salt peanuts!" Its timbres flat or shrill, with a minimum of thrilling vibrato. Its rhythms were out of stride and seemingly arbitrary, its drummers frozen-faced introverts dedicated to chaos. And in it the steady flow of memory, desire and defined experience summed up by the traditional jazz beat and blues mood seemed swept like a great river from its old, deep bed. We know better now, and recognize the old moods in the new sounds, but what we know is that which was then becoming. For most of those who gathered here, the enduring meaning of the great moment at Minton's took place off to the side, beyond the range of attention, like a death blow glimpsed from the corner of the eye, the revolutionary rumpus sounding like a series of flubbed notes blasting the talk with discord. So that the events which made Minton's *Minton's* arrived in conflict and ran their course, then the heat was gone and all that is left to mark its passage is the controlled fury of the music itself, sealed pure and irrevocable, banalities and excellencies alike, in the early recordings; or swept along by our restless quest for the new, to be diluted in more recent styles, the best of it absorbed like drops of fully distilled technique, mood and emotion into the great stream of jazz.

Left also to confuse our sense of what happened is the word "bop," hardly more than a nonsense syllable, by which the music synthesized at Minton's came to be known. A most inadequate word which does little, really, to help us remember. A word which throws up its hands in clownish self-depreciation before all the complexity of sound and rhythm and self-assertive passion which it pretends to name; a mask-word for the charged ambiguities of the new sound, hiding the serious face of art.

Nor does it help that so much has come to pass in the meantime. There have been two hot wars and that which continues, called "cold." And the unknown young men who brought a new edge to the sound of jazz and who scrambled the rhythms of those who used the small clear space at Minton's for dancing are no longer so young or unknown; indeed, they are referred to now by nickname in even the remotest of places. And in Paris and Munich and Tokyo they'll

tell you the details of how, after years of trying, "Dizzy" (meaning John Birks Gillespie) vanquished "Roy" (meaning Roy Eldridge) during a jam session at Minton's, to become thereby the new king of trumpeters. Or how, later, while jetting over the world on the blasts of his special tilt-belled horn, he jammed with a snake charmer in Pakistan. "Sent the bloody cobra, man," they'll tell you in London's Soho. So their subsequent fame has blurred the sharp, ugly lines of their rebellion even in the memories of those who found them most strange and distasteful.

What's more, our memory of some of the more brilliant young men has been touched by the aura of death, and we feel guilt that the fury of their passing was the price paid for the art they left us to enjoy unscathed: Charlie Christian, burned out by tuberculosis like a guitar consumed in a tenement fire; Fats Navarro, wrecked by the tensions and needling temptations of his orgiastic trade, a big man physically as well as musically, shrunken to nothingness; and, most notably of all, Charlie Parker called "Bird," now deified, worshiped and studied and, like any fertility god, mangled by his admirers and imitators, who coughed up his life and died—as incredibly as the leopard which Hemingway tells us was found "dried and frozen" near the summit of Mount Kilimanjaro—in the hotel suite of a Baroness. (Nor has anyone explained what a "yardbird" was seeking at that social altitude, though we know that ideally anything is possible within a democracy, and we know quite well that upper-class Europeans were seriously interested in jazz long before Newport became hospitable.) All this is too much for memory; the dry facts are too easily lost in legend and glamour. (With jazz we are yet not in the age of history, but linger in that of folklore.) We know for certain only that the strange sounds which they and their fellows threw against the hum and buzz of vague signification that seethed in the drinking crowd at Minton's and which, like disgruntled conspirators meeting fatefully to assemble the random parts of a bomb, they joined here and beat and blew into a new jazz style—these sounds we know now to have become the clichés, the technical exercises and the standard of achievement not only for fledgling musicians all over the United States, but for Dutchmen and Swedes, Italians and Frenchmen, Germans and Belgians, and even Japanese. All these, in places which came to mind during the Minton days only as points where the war was in progress and where one might soon be sent to fight and die, are now spotted with young men who study the discs on which the revolution hatched in Minton's is preserved with all the intensity that young American painters bring to the works, say, of Kandinsky, Picasso and Klee. Surely this is an odd swing of the cultural tide. Yet Stravinski, Webern, and Berg notwithstanding, or more recently, Boulez or Stockhausen—such young men (many of them excellent musicians in the highest European tradition) find in the music made articulate at Minton's some key to a fuller freedom of self-realization. Indeed, for many young Europeans the developments which took place here and the careers of those who brought it about have become the latest episodes in the great American epic. They collect the recordings and thrive on the legends as eagerly, perhaps, as young Americans.

This shrine too has its relic

Today the bartenders at Minton's will tell you how they come fresh off the ships or planes, bringing their brightly expectant and—in this Harlem atmosphere—startlingly innocent European faces, to buy drinks and stand looking about for the source of the mystery. They try to reconcile the quiet reality of the place with the events which fired, at such long range, their imaginations. They come as to a shrine; as we to the Louvre, Notre Dame or St. Peter's; as young Americans hurry to the Café Flore, the Deux Magots, the Rotonde or the Café du Dôme in Paris. For some years now, they have been coming to ask, with all the solemnity of pilgrims inquiring of a sacred relic, to see the nicotine-stained amplifier which Teddy Hill provided for Charlie Christian's guitar. And this is quite proper, for every shrine should have its relic.

Perhaps Minton's has more meaning for European jazz fans than for Americans, even for those who regularly went there. Certainly it has a *different* meaning. For them it is associated with those continental cafés in which great changes, political and artistic, have been plotted; it is to modern jazz what the Café Voltaire in Zurich is to the Dadaist phase of modern literature and painting. Few of those who visited Harlem during the Forties would associate it so, but there *is* a context of meaning in which Minton's and the musical activities which took place there can be meaningfully placed.

Jazz, for all the insistence of the legends, has been far more closely associated with cabarets and dance halls than with brothels, and it was these which provided both the employment for the musicians and an audience initiated and aware of the overtones of the music; which knew the language of riffs, the unstated meanings of the blues idiom, and the dance steps developed from and complementary to its rhythms. And in the beginning it was in the Negro dance hall and nightclub that jazz was most completely a part of a total cultural expression; and in which it was freest and most satisfying, both for the musicians and for those in whose lives it played a major role. As a nightclub in a Negro community then, Minton's was part of a national pattern.

But in the old days Minton's was far more than this; it was also a rendezvous for musicians. As such, and although it was not formally organized, it goes back historically to the first New York center of Negro musicians, the Clef Club. Organized in 1910, during the start of the great migration of Negroes northward, by James Reese Europe, the director whom Irene Castle credits with having invented the fox-trot, the Clef Club was set up on West Fifty-third Street to serve as a meeting place and booking office for Negro musicians and entertainers. Here wage scales were regulated, musical styles and techniques worked out, and entertainment was supplied for such establishments as Rector's and Delmonico's, and for such producers as Florenz Ziegfeld and Oscar Hammerstein. Later, when Harlem evolved into a Negro section, a similar function was served by the Rhythm Club, located then in the old Lafayette Theatre building on 132nd Street and Seventh Avenue. Henry Minton, a former saxophonist and officer of the Rhythm Club, became the first Negro delegate to Local 802 of the American Federation of Musicians and was thus doubly aware of the needs, artistic as well as economic, of jazzmen. He was generous with loans, was fond of food himself and, as an old acquaintance recalled, "loved to put a pot on the range" to share with unemployed friends. Naturally when he opened Minton's Playhouse many musicians made it their own.

Henry Minton also provided, as did the Clef and Rhythm clubs, a necessity more important to jazz musicians than food: a place in which to hold their interminable jam sessions. And it is here that Minton's becomes most important to the development of modern jazz. It is here, too, that it joins up with all the countless rooms, private and public, in which jazzmen have worked out the secrets of their craft. Today jam sessions are offered as entertainment by nightclubs and on radio and television, and some are quite exciting; but what is seen and heard is only one aspect of the true jam session: the "cutting session," or contest of improvisational skill and physical endurance between two or more musicians. But the jam session is far more than this, and when carried out by musicians, in the privacy of small rooms (as in the mural at Minton's) or in such places as Hallie Richardson's shoeshine parlor in Oklahoma City—where I first heard Lester Young jamming in a shine chair, his head thrown back, his horn even then outthrust, his feet working on the footrests, as he played with and against Lem Johnson, Ben Webster (this was 1929) and other members of the old Blue Devils orchestra—or during the after hours in Piney Brown's old Sunset Club in Kansas City; in such places as these with only musicians and jazzmen present, then the jam session is revealed as the jazzman's true academy.

It is here that he learns tradition, group techniques and style. For although since the Twenties many jazzmen have had conservatory training and were well-grounded in formal theory and instrumental technique, when we approach jazz we are entering quite a different sphere of training. Here it is more meaningful to speak, not of courses of study, of grades and degrees, but of apprenticeship, ordeals, initiation ceremonies, of rebirth. For after the jazzman has learned the fundamentals of his instrument and the traditional techniques of jazz—the intonations, the mute work, manipulation of timbre, the body of traditional styles—he must then "find himself," must be reborn, must find, as it were, his soul. All this through achieving that subtle identification between his instrument and his deepest drives which will allow him to express his own unique ideas and his own unique voice. He must achieve, in short, his self-determined identity.

In this his instructors are his fellow musicians, es-

pecially the acknowledged masters, and his recognition of manhood depends upon their acceptance of his ability as having reached a standard which is all the more difficult for not having been rigidly codified. This does not depend upon his ability to simply hold a job but upon his power to express an individuality in tone. Nor is his status ever unquestioned, for the health of jazz and the unceasing attraction which it holds for the musicians themselves lies in the ceaseless warfare for mastery and recognition—not among the general public, though commercial success is not spurned, but among their artistic peers. And even the greatest can never rest on past accomplishments for, as with the fast guns of the old West, there is always someone waiting in a jam session to blow him literally, not only down, but into shame and discouragement.

By making his club hospitable to jam sessions even to the point that customers who were not musicians were crowded out, Henry Minton provided a retreat, a homogeneous community where a collectivity of common experience could find continuity and meaningful expression. Thus the stage was set for the birth of bop.

A musical dueling ground

In 1941 Mr. Minton handed over his management to Teddy Hill, the saxophonist and former band leader, and Hill turned the Playhouse into a musical dueling ground. Not only did he continue Minton's policies, he expanded them. It was Hill who established the Monday Celebrity Nights, the house band which included such members from his own disbanded orchestra as Kenny Clark, Dizzy Gillespie, along with Thelonius Monk, sometimes with Joe Guy, and, later, Charlie Christian and Charlie Parker; and it was Hill who allowed the musicians free rein to play whatever they liked. Perhaps no other club except Clarke Monroe's Uptown House was so permissive, and with the hospitality extended to musicians of all schools the news spread swiftly. Minton's became the focal point for musicians all over the country.

Herman Pritchard, who presided over the bar in the old days, tells us that every time they came, "Lester Young and Ben Webster used to tie up in battle like dogs in the road. They'd fight on those saxophones until they were tired out, then they'd put in long distance calls to their mothers, both of whom lived in Kansas City, and tell them about it."

And most of the masters of jazz came either to observe or to participate and be influenced and listen to their own discoveries transformed; and the aspiring stars sought to win their approval, as the younger tenor men tried to win the esteem of Coleman Hawkins. Or they tried to vanquish them in jamming contests as Gillespie is said to have outblown his idol, Roy Eldridge. It was during this period that Eddie "Lockjaw" Davis underwent an ordeal of jeering rejection until finally he came through as an admired tenor man.

In the perspective of time we now see that what was happening at Minton's was a continuing symposium of jazz, a summation of all the styles, personal and traditional, of jazz. Here it was possible to hear its resources of technique, ideas, harmonic structure, melodic phrasing and rhythmical possibilities explored more thoroughly than was ever possible before. It was also possible to hear the first attempts toward a conscious statement of the sensibility of the younger generation of musicians as they worked out the techniques, structures and rhythmical patterns with which to express themselves. Part of this was arbitrary, a revolt of the younger against the established stylists; part of it was inevitable. For jazz had reached a crisis and new paths were certain to be searched for and found. An increasing number of the younger men were formally trained and the post-Depression developments in the country had made for quite a break between their experience and that of the older men. Many were even of a different physical build. Often they were quiet and of a reserve which contrasted sharply with the exuberant and outgoing lyricism of the older men, and they were intensely concerned that their identity as Negroes placed no restriction upon the music they played or the manner in which they used their talent. They were concerned, they said, with art, not entertainment. Especially were they resentful of Louis Armstrong whom (confusing the spirit of his music with his clowning) they considered an Uncle Tom.

Another misconception:
how to be truly free

But they too, some of them, had their own myths and misconceptions: That theirs was the only generation of Negro musicians who listened to or enjoyed the classics; that to be truly free they must act exactly the opposite of what white people might believe, rightly or wrongly, a Negro to be; that the performing artist can be completely and absolutely free of the obligations of the entertainer, and that they could play jazz with dignity only by frowning and treating the audience with aggressive contempt; and that to be in control, artistically and personally, one must be so cool as to quench one's own human fire.

Nor should we overlook the despair which must have swept Minton's before the technical mastery, the tonal authenticity, the authority and the fecundity of imagination of such men as Hawkins, Young, Goodman, Tatum, Teagarden, Ellington and Waller. Despair, after all, is ever an important force in revolutions.

They were also responding to the nonmusical pressures affecting jazz. It was a time of big bands and the greatest prestige and economic returns were falling outside the Negro community—often to leaders whose popularity grew from the compositions and arrangements of Negroes—to white instrumentalists whose only originality lay in the enterprise with which they rushed to market with some Negro musician's hard-won style. Still there was no policy of racial discrimination at Minton's. Indeed, it was very much like those Negro cabarets of the Twenties and Thirties in which a megaphone was placed on the piano so that anyone with the urge could sing a blues. Nevertheless, the inside-dopesters will tell you that the "changes" or chord progressions and the melodic inversions worked out by the creators of bop sprang partially from their desire to create a jazz which could not be so easily imitated and exploited by white musicians to whom the market was more open simply *because* of their whiteness. They wished to receive credit for what they created, and besides, it was easier to "get rid of the trash" who crowded the bandstand with inept playing and thus make room for the real musicians, whether white or black. Nevertheless, white musicians like Tony Scott, Remo Palmieri and Al Haig who were part of the development at Minton's became so by passing a test of musicianship, sincerity and temperament. Later, it is said, the boppers became engrossed in solving the musical problems which they set themselves. Except for a few sympathetic older musicians it was they who best knew the promise of the Minton moment, and it was they, caught like the rest in all the complex forces of American life which come to focus in jazz, who made the most of it. Now the tall tales told as history must feed on the results of their efforts.

Joseph Wechsberg:

The Concours D'Elégance

The Autoklub was a long jump from the
Staatsoper's fourth gallery but the
claque accepted the charge with valor

Two decades ago I caused a family scandal when my relatives found out that I had become a member of the claque at the Staatsoper in Vienna. Actually the claque was no sinister gang but a rather innocent body of thirty or forty cheerful opera enthusiasts who were given free standing-room admissions in the fourth gallery in return for what Joseph Schostal, the claque chief, termed "artistic applause." Schostal, a tall, forceful man of authoritative stature and a great opera expert, had his definite theories about hand-clapping.

The police were the claque's permanent nightmare. There were four *Kriminal-Inspektoren* in mufti attending every performance, two in the fourth gallery, one in the third gallery, one in the parterre standing room. Inside the opera house small signs read: *"Alle störenden Bei—sowie Missfallsbezeugungen sind verboten"* (All Disturbing Manifestations of Approval and Disapproval Are Prohibited). The interpretation of what was "disturbing" was left to the arbitrary judgment of the *Inspektor* on duty. I remember a performance of *Samson and Delilah*, with the famous contralto Rosette Anday and George Thill, from the Paris Opéra, when Schostal instructed all members of the claque to be careful because *Inspektor* Kramer was on duty. This Kramer, a tough, punctilious man, hated music and the claque and once, after five seidels of Schwechater beer, publicly declared that most operas were "full of noise." In the second act we broke into "spontaneous" applause which didn't quite come off and caused a lot of raised eyebrows among the innocent fourth-gallery patrons. Kramer warned Schostal that should there be one more "disturbing" ovation, we would all meet at police headquarters.

The situation was critical. "Piroshka" Anday was one of our best clients. Schostal had promised her an overwhelming ovation after her great air *"Mon coeur s'ouvre à ta voix."* We had to work fast; Kramer, suspicious and grim, watched us from nearby.

About this time Schostal was joined by Professor Grünauer, a prominent Viennese and the husband of Maria Nemeth, the famous Staatsoper soprano. Schostal was often visited in his headquarters by luminaries of music, literature and politics. When told of Kramer's sinister intentions, Professor Grünauer called upon Schostal to fight it out with Kramer once and for all. The Professor promised his active support.

Madame Anday sang her air in great form and Schostal gave his "cue," nodding his bald head. The claque broke out into a thunderous ovation and the house cheered. Kramer muttered a malediction, took out the feared notebook, wet the pencil with his tongue and asked Schostal all the officially prescribed questions. He then proceeded to write down Professor Grünauer's data. The Professor and Madame Nemeth lived at the Hofburg, parts of the Kaiser's former residence being rented to selected opera stars and other public dignitaries, but Kramer didn't know that. When Professor Grünauer, asked for his residence, truthfully answered, "The Hofburg," Kramer got very angry and told him to shut up. A few enraged opera patrons began to hiss "Quiet! Sh!" but Kramer noisily took down my name and those of four other "lieutenants." We were ordered to appear the next morning at the Polizeipräsidium at Schottenring No. 11.

After the performance we waited for Madame Anday at the stage door and Schostal told her about the incident. The diva was furious and called up Vice-President Pamer of the Polizeipräsidium, an opera lover and a great admirer of Madame Anday, who had also attended the performance. In acid tones she complained about Kramer.

The next morning, Schostal, Professor Grünauer and we five claque members met at the office of Hofrat Ritzberger, chief of the *Strafsektion*. Somebody had notified the press and the room was full of reporters. Schostal didn't disappoint them. He boomed "Guilty!" to the charges raised by Kramer, who stood there, arrogant and tough. Then Schostal made a speech about the immortal merits of the claque. "If

Mr. Wechsberg, a native of Moravia, has contributed more than fifty articles to Esquire since switching, at the suggestion of Arnold Gingrich, from German, Czech and French to English in the 1940's. The Concours d'Elégance *appeared in February, 1945.*

our men had operated in 1875 at the premiere of Bizet's *Carmen* at the Opéra Comique, poor Bizet wouldn't have died so soon," Schostal thundered. "Beethoven, after *Fidelio*, and Wagner, after *Tristan*, would have been saved much grief. Caruso and others have declared that we are an essential part of the opera house. Who is this Kramer to dispute these axioms?"

Hofrat Ritzberger quickly penalized each of us ten schilling (two dollars), the minimum fine, and the clerk gave Schostal an *Erlagschein*, a sort of blank check, to use when sending in the money. Thereupon the press and the bystanders were thrown out of the room, and Schostal, Professor Grünauer and we five "lieutenants" remained alone with the Hofrat. He got up, shook hands with us and apologized to each of us. The whole thing was *sehr peinlich*, a misunderstanding, and the Herr Präsident Pamer was desolate. That night, when Schostal entered the Staatsoper foyer, the four inspectors on duty took off their hats and bowed deeply. Kramer wasn't among them. He had been transferred to the Brigittenau, a tough outlying district, considered the Siberia of Vienna's policemen.

As time went on, Schostal and Hofrat Ritzberger became good friends. After Schostal had appeared for several more "disturbing ovations" the Hofrat said, "I don't want you to get up early and come here all the way from your apartment, Herr Schostal. Take a dozen *Erlagschein*-blanks with you and send in your ten schilling every time they mark you down. Or you can make them out on the first of the month, with the rest of your bills."

The Hofrat's sympathies didn't go to a second group of applauders at the Staatsoper, the claque or Stehparterre Club, under a man named Stieglitz, a slick, tough character who tried to appropriate Schostal's clients. One of our good customers was the tenor, Trajan Grosavescu. Stieglitz attempted to "get" Grosavescu.

One morning preceding a *Carmen* performance with Grosavescu as Don José, Schostal was informed that Stieglitz was planning an anti-Grosavescu putsch that night. All regular members of the claque were warned to be on the alert.

Looking down from the fourth gallery into the parterre standing room, we saw that Stieglitz had divided his forces into two groups, in the right and the left ends of the standing room. This was unusual, the Stehparterre Club being always assembled only at the left side. The first act ended without trouble. The second act began and Grosavescu sang beautifully "*La fleur que tu m'avais jetée.*" When he came to the high B after "*Et j'étais une chose à toi,*" a terrific salvo of applause was started by the right-side Stieglitz group. Experienced operagoers know that the high B isn't the end of the air but is followed by "*Carmen, je t'aime*"—and no one knew this better than the Stieglitz men. The Stieglitz group at the left pretended to be indignant. They started hissing and cried, "Quiet, over there!" ruining Grosavescu's high B. Then Schostal gave his cue and we of the claque came in with legitimate applause which

heightened the confusion. The policemen at the standing room took down the names of the Stieglitz men and some tried to escape. There was a hell of a racket, before the police got them all.

The newspapers and the public got tired of the running war between us and the Stieglitz men. One day in 1924 the soloists of the Staatsoper published a declaration, each singer of the house pledging his "word of honor." Henceforth no artist could get in touch "with any member of the applauding bodies," directly or indirectly. Those breaking their word of honor would be instantly thrown out of the Staatsoper.

The afternoon before the performance of *Cavalleria Rusticana* and *Pagliacci*, with Vera Schwarz as Nedda and Alfred Piccaver as Canio, Schostal was notified to call up U-88-5-94. This was the secret telephone number of Alfred Piccaver. Schostal took a cab and went to the tenor's apartment on Brahmsplatz. Madame Piccaver looked grave as she said, "Go into the bathroom." This was serious. When faced with problems of real magnitude Piccaver always retired to the bathroom.

Piccaver was sitting on the edge of the bathtub. He shook hands with Schostal and sighed deeply. He said he was so sorry for Schostal but there was of course nothing he could do, word of honor and so on. As Schostal was about to leave, still wondering why Piccaver had summoned him, the tenor pointed down to the floor, saying, "You've lost something." Schostal bent down and picked up two twenty-schilling bills from under the washbasin. Only after he left did the claque chief remember that forty schilling was exactly what Piccaver paid him for one evening.

There was tension in the fourth gallery that night when the claque entered, led by Schostal. We didn't lift a finger after the "prologue" in *Pagliacci*, or after Vera Schwarz's air. But after Piccaver's "*Vesti la giubba*" we gave the tenor an ovation that shook the house. The next night they gave *Faust*. None of the singers dared to contact Schostal, "directly or indirectly." "We won't work for any of them," Schostal said. "But after the ballet give all you have. That will stump them."

The performance was uninspired and there was scant applause for the singers, but the ovation for the ballet was deafening. The next morning two divas sent their husbands to renew their pacts with Schostal. The other singers followed, one by one, and the hell with their word of honor.

On a Friday night in 1926, after a dull performance of Richard Strauss's *Die Ägyptische Helena*, two grey-haired, well-groomed gentlemen of the Captain-of-Industry type met Schostal at the opera foyer and invited him for a coffee to the Café Heinrichshof, across the Ringstrasse. They introduced themselves as the sole Austrian representatives of the automobile firms Lancia, Fiat and Auburn-Cord.

The following afternoon, the Concours d'Elégance, the yearly automobile beauty contest under the auspices of the aristocratic Autoklub and the outstanding social event of the season, would take place in the Schönbrunn Schlosshof. The three winning cars would get gold ribbons and a great deal of publicity, all of which would be dandy for the automobile firms. Having heard of Schostal's uncanny promotion successes, the gentlemen wondered if he would care to do something for their cars by subtly influencing the judges and the audience at the Schlosshof in favor of Lancia, Fiat and Auburn-Cord.

"Suppose you would bring with you a hundred of your men, well-dressed and sort of aristocratic-looking," the younger Captain of Industry suggested. "A little applause in favor of our cars, as they pass the judges, might work wonders." They would pay Schostal one thousand schilling and the cost of the men, adding that subtlety had to be the keynote of the operation. It was agreed that each of the hundred men would get two schilling and one sandwich as *Wegzehrung* and that the gentlemen would provide for tickets and transportation.

The two men placed their own limousine and their chauffeur at Schostal's disposal. All night Schostal rode through Vienna, hiring men for the Concours. Members of the claque were ordered under the opera arcades the next afternoon at two. A few grumbled, having made dates for the weekend, but Schostal threatened to take their names off the list for *Meistersinger*, with Friedrich Schorr, Slezak, Lehmann and Mayr, on Sunday night, unless they would call off their girls and come to Schönbrunn. The men promised to be there, no girl on earth being worth missing a great *Meistersinger* performance. Schostal rode to Piowatti, where some of the claque's regular members were having a late snack, *Würstel mit Kren*; at the Café Lustbader he hired eighteen men, at the moment not looking too aristocratic, wearing pulled-up shirt sleeves and playing billiards; at the Café Central nine men were aroused from their chess game and ordered up for duty. The next morning Schostal was taken to the auto dealers' showrooms where the gentlemen showed him the three automobiles selected for the Concours: a sleek, light-blue Fiat, a stunning, longish, black Lancia coupe, and a cream-colored Auburn-Cord. Not an automobile expert, Schostal had the dealers turn on the engines of the cars since he would only recognize them acoustically by the sound of their motors.

At two p.m. two autobuses, hired from the *Gemeinde Wien*, drove on under the arcades. There was a roll call and Schostal made a formal inspection of his men. Some of us, not up to the high aristocratic standard of the occasion, had to be sent back to have our shoes shined and to get more discreet ties. The buses stopped at a hidden corner of the Schönbrunn Park and Schostal gave us last-minute instructions. "No rough stuff today," he said. "Give out with inconspicuous but moderately strong applause.

Don't forget you are supposed to be part of the upper classes."

We went into the Schlosshof in small groups, looking blasé, with slightly raised eyebrows, as we thought young men of nobility would look. The claque chief was nervous. It is one thing to applaud a magnificent performance by Jeritza or Lehmann and another to work for automobiles that sing no high C and would race past us before one could say "*Götterdämmerung*." A few of our men tried to date handsome countesses, and Immerglück, an old member of the opera claque and an outspoken *Sozialdemokrat*, got into an argument with an expropriated baron.

The first cars drove by and from the bored audience came a trickle of applause. They had an amateurish way of clapping their hands, the gentlemen being afraid of dropping their monocles. The ladies wore long gloves and lorgnettes and applauded, clapping the back of their hands, a sight which drove Schostal almost crazy.

There was the high-pitched sound of an engine and Schostal sat up straight. "That rhythm," he said. "Like the beginning of the *Walküre* prelude. That must be the Lancia." A black coupe drove on in front of the jury. Schostal arose and nodded his head, and a sudden, terrific salvo of applause went down on the doddering aristocrats. Two members of the jury woke up from their stupor. A cream-colored car was next. Schostal nodded again, and there was another thunderous ovation. People in the audience began to applaud themselves, nothing being so contagious as well-staged applause. By this time all our men were really warmed up and when the light-blue Fiat appeared, there was the sort of ovation we usually gave when we wanted to force the repetition of an air sung by Slezak or Lehmann. Some men cried "Bravo!" producing a mad, relentless machine-gun fire with their hands, and old Immerglück jumped on his seat and cried, "*Hoch Slezak!*" which, he said later, was meant to be, "*Hoch Fiat!*"

In the face of such unheard-of public acclamation the judges could but award the three gold ribbons to the Lancia, Fiat and Auburn-Cord automobiles, with additional prizes going to the Steyr and Tatra. After the Concours there was a final *Vergatterung* in a hidden corner of the Park. The Captains of Industry, beaming with joy, carried large rolls of silver schillings, and Schostal gave each man two schilling and a large sandwich from a laundry basket. Fourteen were missing at the pay formation, evidently having established promising contacts with the young ladies of the *Hocharistokratie*. Schostal, in a benevolent mood, said they would get their money at night, after the opera performance.

PASSING FANCIES

Esquire has seen four decades of fads, crazes, whims, rages, grand obsessions. Let us call them, collectively, passing fancies. In lucky times, the magazine has had the first word; in other times it has had the last. This section is about nine passing fancies, from the myth of Churchill to the cult of Tarzan, from the greatest hotels to the greatest center fielder.

A few words about *Latins Are Lousy Lovers*: In 1936, when the piece appeared, it carried a by-line, *Anonymous*. There were two reasons for this, one bad, one understandable. The bad one—and it didn't seem as bad then as it does now—was that a woman writer's place certainly wasn't in a man's magazine. The understandable one—and it seemed more understandable then than it does now—was the feeling that the author's name had to be suppressed to protect her innocence. As you might imagine, *Latins Are Lousy Lovers* was considered a bit risqué for its time, so Helen Lawrenson appeared as Anonymous. On the next page, the proper name has been restored, fearlessly.

A Few Words About Breasts by Nora Ephron shows how far we've come, how much times have changed. While one's own opinion of one's own body is hardly a passing fancy, everyone else's opinion of that body certainly is. Nora Ephron's

formative years were the Fifties; had they been the Seventies it might have all been different.

In *The Totemization of Sir Winston Churchill*, the writer comes upon the subject in extreme old age: "The inevitable cigar, jutting out of his mouth, gives an impression of having been put there by someone else, as children stick an old pipe into a snowman." That was how Malcolm Muggeridge saw Old Winston in retirement on the French Riviera.

Richard Joseph's *The Three Greatest Hotels in the World* reveals the cream of the hotel crop of 1967. *Tarzan Revisited* by Gore Vidal reflects the whims of one writer's youth; *The Homecoming of Willie Mays* by Murray Kempton reflects the whims of one writer's experience. William Faulkner's *Impressions of Japan* is a look at Japan in the late Fifties; George Frazier's *Cold Thoughts on the Hot Medium* is a look at television of the late Sixties. And, finally, there is Tennessee Williams' one-act play, *A Perfect Analysis Given By a Parrot*. At one time—in America, in New York, in Esquire—*the play was the thing*. Williams, master of the form, contributed numerous dramatic works to the magazine. It was with pride that we published them then—and it's with pride that we offer this one a second time.

Helen Lawrenson:

Latins Are Lousy Lovers

Patriotic American beauty dares all
to prove that the composite Cuban is not
so hot as he's cracked up to be

First of all, I want to make it clear that this is not the wail of a downhearted frail who was scorned and is therefore taking a cad's revenge. The following observations are not based on personal experience alone, but on the testimony of other disillusioned damsels, as well. I have listened to their plaints in ladies' rooms, nightclubs, tearooms, boudoirs, on boats and on beaches; and I wish to acknowledge my indebtedness to those unwept, unhonored and unsung American women who have trusted and Given All in Cuba and Mexico, Central and South America, Spain and Puerto Rico—not to mention various encounters with visiting Latins on their own hearthstones in Ohio, Maine, Mississippi and both Dakotas. I, myself, have just returned from five months in Cuba, where I did a little fieldwork on my own; and I believe that it is high time someone exploded the mythical superiority of Latins as lovers and relegated it to its proper place, along with other half-baked, but quaint, traditions, such as the saying that ashes in your coffee make you drunk, that if you don't save all your baby teeth, your second set will be puppies' teeth, or that if you don't move, the bee won't sting you. (Ah, so you've been caught on that one, too!)

It is a common belief all over the world that Latin men are the best lovers and Americans the worst. With an American flag of washable bunting draped prominently—but with careless grace—around my chest, and balancing an American eagle on my head, I hereby rise to state that this is a hoax. I will not only state it; hell, I will prove it. In order to facilitate matters, let us divide the subject into three parts: The Latin at Large, The Latin at Home, and The Latin in Bed. All right, Miss America, take it away!

From now on, I will say Cubans, because I have taken a special course in Cubans, but you can substitute Venezuelans or Andalusians or Argentines, because,

from what the rest of the girls say, they are practically interchangeable as far as this subject is concerned.

THE LATIN AT LARGE

In the first place, they are generally short in stature. When anyone asks you if you want to meet another Cuban, it's customary to say, "All right. Is he over five foot four?" (She Stoops to Conquer Cubans can be taken physically, therefore, as well as morally and spiritually.) They are not only short; they are thin, too, with narrow shoulders and wide hips: in other words, like the Flapper Age trousers—bell-bottomed. Their teeth—if any—are either frayed stumps or dazzling with gold. They wear straw Kellys too large or too small, badly fitting suits, and shoes that pinch their feet—and they have little feet. Of course, they do have nice eyes—that is, when they aren't cross-eyed. Their hair is oily and usually needs cutting. They spit a great deal. They are always scratching themselves.

That is the typical Cuban for you. That is, that is what they're like if they look like Cubans. Most Cubans don't look like Cubans. They look like Germans, Italians, Swedes, Polacks, and clerks from Yonkers. It makes my heart bleed to think of the boatloads of hopeful females who go down there every year on cruises, trusting to find a nation of Cesar Romeros. If they do find one, the odds are ten to one that he's another American tourist. As one more disappointed maiden put it, on her return to Manhattan, "The worst Americans are better than the best Cubans. I mean, the Americans you see here digging ditches or driving ice wagons or riding in the subways are all handsomer and better built than the most highly publicized Don Juans in Havana."

In the second place, although part of their claim to superiority in amorous dalliance is based on an assumption of gallantry, they are not gallant in a practical way. They meet you at a bar for cocktails at five-thirty, make violent love to you—and then go home for dinner. They will meet you afterward and renew their spirited attack, but for the space of a couple of

Published anonymously in 1936, Latins Are Lousy Lovers may be the most notorious piece in this magazine's history and bears one of the most famous titles in any magazine's history. It was the author's Esquire debut.

hours, their mad love is abated. They appreciate their home cooking, and, of course, foreign young women cannot be invited—or, at any rate, they aren't—into the sanctity of the typical Cuban home. They pay you fantastic compliments that no half-wit would believe, but they never send you flowers or give you presents. I take that back. A South American gave a girl I know an old coin, and a New York blonde once got a clock and an Eversharp pencil from a Cuban who said he was enslaved by her eyes, that he was blinded by the golden sunshine of her hair, that he would cut off his right arm for her, in short, that he would die for her. (They are fond of fancying themselves as impetuous, violent folk, ready to draw their machetes at the drop of a sombrero.) They are, however, great on photographs and practically the moment they meet you will pull out their pictures, inscribe them passionately, and present them to you, blissfully confident that forever afterward you sleep with their images under your pillow by night and plastered onto your mirror by day, where you can spend long hours in adoration.

They are convinced that all American women worship them; and they love American women because they're so free and easy. With their money, they forget to add. There are very few who object to acting as amiable escorts to American girls who foot the bills. In fact, some of them can be said really to live only during the tourist season, when they emerge like butterflies to meet all incoming ships. The rest of the year, they just languish around, recounting their exploits and saving their strength.

They are good dancers, as a rule, although the belief that every Cuban is a born hoofer is a fallacy. When they *are* good, they are superlatively so, but there are plenty of them who can step on your feet just as often and just as heavy as the boys back home. They are definitely not good drinkers. A couple of highballs and they are sitting on top of the world. One more, and they slip down in their chairs, practically parallel with the floor. All Latins have trouble with their livers and if they drink too much they get very sick. One Cuban says, "When I drink more than two drinks, my kidneys resent it, and my liver abets them." Their sense of humor expresses itself for the most part in jokes which were thrown out of the Minsky circuit ten years ago. They adore American slang but are always five to ten years behind. (Last winter I met a Cuban who had just caught up with "It's the cat's pajamas!") Anything approaching subtlety will leave them blankfaced and untouched, but the simplest reference to the bathroom and the elimination

processes of the digestive tract will plunge them into uncontrollable hysterics. They also appreciate any suggestion of sex, provided it is elementary enough. Judged by their standards, the greatest wits in the world have been the little boys who scribble on fences and the comfort-station-wall decorators. The national type of joke most prevalent is a charming little game known as the *pega*. It is couched in the form of question and answer and is the ultimate in obscene simplicity. Naturally, examples cannot be given at this time, but the question is frequently something like, "Have you got a few minutes to spare?" And when the victim answers "Yes, why?"—(and they always answer; even though they've been hearing this form of joke daily all their lives, they never seem to catch on) —the answer is, "Well then, do thus and so"—(fill in with any of the dirtier phrases you remember from your childhood). This will render them incapacitated by laughter for ten minutes.

While the above may seem irrelevant, I believe it to have a bearing on the general subject, since it depicts sidelights on the qualities of the Latin at Large as a companion. And after all, a certain amount of companionship—sometimes known as the preliminaries—is customary before getting down to the brass tacks of *amor*.

THE LATIN AT HOME

In his own home, the Cuban man is absolute king, lord and master. He demands service and he gets it—hand and foot. Although he practically never takes his wife out—and seldom stays home with her—he is insanely jealous and keeps constant tab on her by bribing the servants, tapping the telephone wires, and a general spy system as elaborate as that of the Jesuits. He telephones his home every hour or so as part of the checkup. If his wife says she is going to the hairdresser's, the modiste's or the milliner's, he makes sure to telephone there, too. If she goes to a movie, he runs over and sees the same picture so that he can question her on it during dinner that night. When he stays out all night, he almost never notifies his wife, but if he telephones and says he won't be home, he makes a point of going home within an hour.

The Cuban husband is practically never at home, except for meals. He goes out night after night, to political meetings, the club, poker games, jai-alai games, cockfights, cabarets, dances, parties, dinners, sidewalk cafés— or to visit his mistress—and his wife stays home. Once a month, he may spend an evening at the movies with her; a couple of times a year he takes her to large charity fiestas; and on special occasions, like the Fourth of July or the President's Saint's Day, he may invite her out and buy her a glass of sherry. One man I know married his wife when she was sixteen and has never let her out at night since. She is now thirty-two. She has never even been permitted to go alone in the daytime to do her shopping or to a beauty parlor or to the movies. Although she is the mother of three children, the only person she can go to these places with is her older sister, and then she must travel in a closed automobile, never in a streetcar or bus, where other men might look at her. Her husband initiated her into this regime immediately after they returned from their honeymoon. Right then, he began leaving her in the house while he went out; and night after night, she used to sit at an upstairs window alone and watch him sitting in a gay party at the sidewalk café across the street. Nor is he an ignorant country yokel. He is a member of Congress; he has traveled in the United States and in Europe; he likes music, dancing and night life; and he is considered worldly and charming by the women he meets outside of his home.

This is by no means an isolated case, although not all Cubans carry the system to such extremes. However, they do not take their wives to nightclubs, cabarets or public restaurants. When they go out for a good time—which is about six nights out of the week—their helpmates stay at home. As one man said, "Certainly my wife stays home where she belongs. Furthermore, I never allow her to have girl friends. When she starts to become friendly with another woman—go to the movies with her or to the hairdresser's, right away I forbid her to see her anymore. Women together talk and breed trouble. My wife must live for me alone and for what time I can find to give her." Which might be said to be the definitive word on the subject.

THE LATIN IN BED

And now we come to the point of the piece. God knows, the Cuban man spends enough time on the subject of sex. He devotes his life to it. He talks it, dreams it, reads it, sings, dances it, eats it, sleeps it—does everything but do it. That last is of course not literally true, but it is a fact that they spend far more time in words than in action. Sitting in their offices, rocking on the sidewalk in front of their clubs, drinking at cafés, they talk hour after hour about sex. When the University of Habana had a football team, they used to drive their American coach crazy by sitting in the dressing room before a game and describing their exploits—play by play—with the girls they took out the night before. A smart American who makes an appointment to discuss business with a Cuban at a café always makes the Cuban sit with his back to the street; because if he does not, the Cuban will eye every woman who passes and, like as not, at a crucial point of the business transaction, will interrupt to make anatomical comments on some pretty who is just going by. They telephone each other at their offices during business hours to describe in minute detail a new conquest. According to them, they always had their first affair at the age of two. This may account for their being all worn out at twenty-three. Makers of aphrodisiacs do a thriving business: Spanish fly, yohimbim, marijuana cigarettes, cocaine, Baum Bengue. (Even the horses at Oriental Park have ginger put under their tails.) You can pick up any Cuban newspaper and see, on the second or third page, right smack in the middle of the news, a big ad—"Men! Let Science help you! Merely a matter of the hormones." Etc., etc.

This lack of masculine energy does not prevent them from talking a great game. They boast of their prowess, their anatomical proportions, and their methods. (To hear them talk of what is known to Drs. Van der Velde, Stopes, *et al.* as the love-play, you'd think they invented it. Certain they are, at least, that it has been revealed to them alone out of all mankind in a sort of divine and mystic annunciation kept secret from the rest of the world.) But if you believe the testimony of their womenfolk, when it actually comes to the test, they apparently suffer from tropical amnesia. In other words, they're talkers, not doers.

According to Cuban technique, love is a game of chess. Now it's your move; now it's mine—whoops, I caught you! If I do this, she will do that. If she says that, it means I should do this. They will spend hours figuring out unnecessary progressive steps in an amorous campaign, and when their objective is finally obtained, they are apparently too exhausted by strategy to do much about it. Through the years, they have managed to work out an extraordinarily and elaborately complicated system of sexual attack, which only they know the meaning of; and they are perfectly happy to putter around with this for months at a time, making telephone calls, writing notes, conferring with their friends (they are inveterate gossips and cannot make an amorous move without running off beforehand and afterward to consult with all their male friends), and making a great to-do about symbols and signals and point counter point.

They believe in quantity, not quality, also. Every man has his wife and his mistress of the moment. In addition, he has to find time to attend to the demimondaines (dancers, singers, nightclub hostesses or just women about town), the concubines (maids, dance-hall girls, little *achinadas* and *mulaticas*), and to the regular professional prostitutes. (They are great frequenters of houses of ill fame, making their rounds as a matter of course, and Mr. Dewey would have a difficult time in Habana. He certainly would lack the taxpayers' wholehearted support.) Besides this, in each one of these classes of women, he has someone he's working up to the proper pitch of surrender—dropping in to see occasionally, buying a glass of beer for, calling on the telephone—and, also in each class, he has someone he's got marked out to start paying attention to when he gets around to it, or when a vacancy occurs in the regular lists or on the scrub team. You can easily see how all of this keeps him extremely busy—he even has to devote afternoons, and frequently mornings, to it—so that he doesn't find quite so much time for actual practice.

Nevertheless, living in this constant aura of sex, the Cuban grows serenely sure that he is more adept amorously than other men—particularly Americans. In this impenetrable vanity of theirs, they are unlike any other nation. The elderly American, at least, occasionally lets a bit of cynicism slip into his attitude. He admits that the gift of a diamond bracelet, a mink coat or a car may possibly have influenced the young lady of his choice, but the Cuban, be he ever so ancient, fat, bald and wrinkled, is perpetually convinced that his personal charms alone are what render him irresistible. To see him is to love him, he reasons.

They are a curious mixture of Spanish tradition, American imitation and insular limitation. This explains why they never catch on to themselves. I think the reason for their initial vanity is that, early in life, they start frequenting what, for want of a better word, are known as fancy women. (I know a better word but I won't use it here.) These women, for obvious business reasons, flatter them extravagantly, make them think they're superlative lovers—and the men never find out otherwise. I suppose no one ever has the heart to tell them. And everything with which they come in contact the rest of their lives serves to perpetuate the myth: the books they read, the songs they sing, the testimony of their fellow countrymen—who are, as I have said, anything but reticent—and the continued plaudits of their womenfolk. One case I heard of—submitted by a fellow fieldworker—had to do with a noted Casanova, famed not only in Habana but as far as Pinar del Rio for his amatory skill. When subjected to an impartial test, it turned out that his routine could be classified as Amateur College Boy,

Class G-6, but that immediately on completion of said simple routine, he sat up in bed and exclaimed, "Am I not wonderful? Am I not wonderful?"

In short, as the result of an extensive female survey, my conclusions are that offhand I would swap you five Cubans, three South Americans and two slightly used Spaniards for one good Irish-American any night in the week. I feel sorry for the women of Cuba. Theirs not to reason why, theirs but to try and try.

I am hereby offering a plea for Latin womanhood. Too long have they suffered under adversity's rod. Any upstanding American man who wants to do a humane deed knows where to go now. My advice to the American male is, Go South, young man, Go South. It's open season for putting the horns on Cuban manhood. They'll look like a race of moose when you get through with them, and you will have served to remove national stigma and explode a worldwide myth.

If this all sounds like an embittered and chauvinistic diatribe against Cubans, I can only say that I did not mean it as such. It is merely that I happen to like American men, and I have been aroused to a high pitch of indignation by hearing them constantly maligned. You cannot spend an hour in the society of any Latin male without hearing what bad lovers Americans are. "Of course American men know nothing of sex!" is the theme song of the tropics. I thought that our own home boys might like to know they've been severely underrated and they no longer need tremble before foreign competition in the most popular of indoor sports.

William Faulkner:
IMPRESSIONS OF JAPAN

"The scenery is beautiful but the faces are better still"

The engines are long since throttled back; the overcast sinks slowly upward with no semblance whatever of speed until suddenly you see the aircraft's shadow scudding the cottony hillocks; and now speed has returned again, aircraft and shadow now rushing toward one another as toward one mutual headlong destruction.

To break through the overcast and fling that shadow once more down, upon an island. It looks like land, like any other air-found landfall, yet you know it is an island, almost as if you saw both seabound flanks of it at the same instant, like a transparent slide; an island more miraculously found in the waste of water than Wake or Guam even, since here is a civilization, an ordered and ancient homogeny of the human race.

It is visible and audible, spoken and written too: a communication between man and man because human speaks it; you hear and see them. But to this one western ear and eye it means nothing because it resembles nothing which that western eye remembers; there is nothing to measure it against, nothing for memory and habit to say, "Why, this looks like the word for house or home or happiness"; not even just cryptic but acrostic too, as though the splashed symbols of the characters held not mere communication but something urgent and important beyond just information, promising toward some ultimate wisdom or knowledge containing the secret of man's salvation. But then no more, because there is nothing for western memory to measure it against; so not the mind to listen but only the ear to hear that chirrup and skitter of syllables like the cries of birds in the mouths of children, like music in the mouths of women and young girls.

The faces: Van Gogh and Manet would have loved them: that of the pilgrim with staff and pack and dusty with walking, mounting the stairs toward the Temple in the early sunlight; the Temple lay brother or perhaps servant, his gown tucked about his thighs, squatting in the gate of the compound before begin-

ning, or perhaps having already set it into motion, the day; that of the old woman vending peanuts beneath the gate for tourists to feed the pigeons with: a face worn with living and remembering, as though not one life had been long enough but rather every separate breath had been needed to etch into it all those fine and myriad lines; a face durable and now even a comfort to her, as if it had by now blotted up whatever had ever ached or sorrowed behind it, leaving it free now of anguishes and the griefs and the enduring: here is one anyway who never read Faulkner and neither knows nor cares why he came to Japan nor gives one single damn what he thinks of Ernest Hemingway.

He is much too busy to have time to bother about whether he is happy or not, quite dirty, perhaps five years old, past-less and apparently immune even from parents, playing in the gutter with the stub of a cigarette.

The bowl of mountains containing the lake is as full of hard rapid air as the mouth of a wind tunnel; for some time now we have been thinking that maybe it is already too late to take a reef in the mainsail: yet there it is. It is only a skiff yet to the western eye it is as invincibly and irrevocably alien as a Chinese junk, driven by a battered U.S.-made outboard engine and containing a woman in a kimono beneath an open paper parasol such as would have excited no comment in a sunny reach of the English Thames, as fragile and invulnerable in the center of that hard blue bowl of wind as a butterfly in the eye of a typhoon.

The geisha's mass of blue-black lacquered hair encloses the painted face like a helmet, surmounts, crowns the slender body's ordered and ritual posturing like a grenadier's bearskin busby, too heavy in appearance for that slender throat to bear, the painted fixed expressionless face immobile and immune also above the studied posturing: yet behind that painted and lifeless mask is something quick and alive and elfin: or more than elfin: puckish: or more than puckish even: sardonic and quizzical, a gift for comedy, and more: for burlesque and caricature: for a sly and

The eleventh Nobel Prize winner of the sixteen to appear in Esquire, William Faulkner served as a cultural representative of the U.S. State Department in 1955. This piece grew out of that experience.

vicious revenge on the race of men.

Kimono. It covers her from throat to ankles; with a gesture as feminine as the placing of a flower or as female as the cradling of a child, the hands can be concealed into the sleeves until there remains one unbroken chalice-shape of modesty proclaiming femininity where nudity would merely parade mammalian femaleness. A modesty which flaunts its own immodestness like the crimson rose tossed by no more than one white flick of hand, from the balcony window—modesty, than which there is nothing more immodest and which therefore is a woman's dearest possession; she should defend it with her life.

Loyalty. In her western clothes, blouse and skirt, she is merely one dumpy and nondescript young woman, though in kimono at the deft balanced rapid tripping glide she too comes into her own share of that national heritage of feminine magic. Though she has more than that; she partakes of her share of that other quality which women have in this land which was not given them by what they have on: loyalty, constancy, fidelity, not for, but at least one hopes not without, reward. She does not speak my language nor I hers, yet in two days she knows my countryman's habit of waking soon after first light so that each morning when I open my eyes a coffee tray is already on the balcony table; she knows I like a fresh room to breakfast in when I return from walking, and it is so: the room done for the day and the table set and the morning paper ready; she asks without words why I have no clothes to be laundered today, and without word asks permission to sew the buttons and darn the socks; she calls me wise man and teacher, who am neither, when speaking of me to others; she is proud to have me for her client and, I hope, pleased that I try to deserve that pride and match with courtesy that loyalty. There is a lot of loose loyalty in this land. Even a little of it is too valuable to be ignored. I would wish that all of it were deserved or at least appreciated as I have tried to do.

This is the same rice paddy which I know back home in Arkansas and Mississippi and Louisiana, where it replaces now and then the cotton. This one is merely a little smaller and a little more fiercely cultivated, right up to the single row of beans which line the very edge of the irrigation canals, the work here done by hand where in my country machines do it since we have more machines than we have people; nature is the same: only the economy is different.

And the names are the same names too: Jonathan and Winesap and Delicious; the heavy August foliage is blue-grey with the same spray which we use. But there the resemblance ceases: every single apple enclosed in this twist of paper until that whole tree to this western eye becomes significant and festive and ceremonial like the symbolical tree of the western rite of Christmas. Only it is more significant here: where in the West there is one small often artificial tree to a family, wrested from the living dirt to be decked in ritual tinsel and then to die as though the tree were not the protagonist of a rite but the victim of a sacrifice, here not one tree to a family but every tree of all is dressed and decked to proclaim and salute older gods than Christ: Demeter and Ceres.

Briefer and faster now, toward the journey's nearing end: goldenrod, as evocative of dust and autumn and hay fever as ever in Mississippi, against a tall bamboo fence.

The scenery is beautiful but the faces are better still. The swift supple narrow grace with which the young girl bows and in that same one glowing motion recovers, tougher through very tenderness than the rigid culture which bent her is as the willow bough itself to the hard gust which can never do more than sway it.

The tools they use evoke the ones Noah must have built his ark with, yet the framework of the house seems to rise and stand without nails in the fitted joints or even the need for nails, as if here were a magic, an art in the simple building of man's habitations which our western ancestors seemed to have lost somewhere when they moved.

And always the water, the sound, the plash and drip of it, as if here were a people making constant oblation to water as some peoples do to what they call their luck.

So kind the people that with three words the guest can go anywhere and live: Gohan; Sake; Arrigato.

And one more word:

Tomorrow now the aircraft lightens, a moment more and the wheels will wrench free of the ground, already dragging its shadow back toward the overcast before the wheels are even tucked up, into the overcast and then through it, the land, the island gone now which memory will always know though eye no longer remembers.

Sayonara.

Richard Joseph:

THE THREE GREATEST HOTELS IN THE WORLD

Start with ambience and aroma, then continue down the checklist.
These three rate highest and Conrad Hilton owns none of them

What makes *un grand hôtel* grand? What distinguishes the few really great hotels of the world, which are travel destinations within themselves, from the hundreds that are merely good? Size it certainly is not; the Conrad Hilton is the world's largest, yet nobody ever decided to stay over in Chicago just to spend the night in one of its twenty-five hundred rooms. Generally, the smaller a hotel is, the greater are its chances of entering the *grand luxe* category. So it is that the knowing traveler seeks out such small gems as the ninety-nine-room Gritti Palace in Venice and the fifty-room La Réserve at Beaulieu in the south of France. Nevertheless size is no bar to greatness; even in skyscraping Manhattan the thousand-room Plaza is a landmark.

Some criteria are measurable. Hotelmen sometimes work with the phrase "number of people behind each bed"—the ratio of staff to guests. The more people there are waiting on you, usually, the better the service you'll get. "Unit cost" is another figurable factor—the rooms are likely to be more spacious and luxurious in a two-hundred-room hotel costing $10,000,000 than in a four-hundred-room hotel at the same price, although other elements, such as land costs, do enter the equation. Spaciousness contributes to a hotel's feeling of opulence and elegance; on a balance sheet it's a liability.

Which is why few, if any, Hilton hotels in the United States qualify for greatness, while a number of Hilton International hotels are candidates. Most of the domestic hotels were planned or renovated in accordance with Conrad Hilton's philosophy of making every square foot of space produce revenue, but the international hotels, built by investors in the countries in which they are located, are often designed with an eye to national prestige.

Researchers for the Cornell University School of Hotel Administration grade hotels with the help of a ten-page checklist of two hundred ninety-four items, including "Closets: convenience, doors, shelves, hangers, hooks, floor and housekeeping," and "Busboys: attitude, conduct, uniforms, cleanliness." In deciding on final ratings, however, the school points out: "There is not, nor can there be any mathematical formula which will establish the number [of stars] to be given to any hotel."

The fact is that all hotel ratings are subjective judgments based on a great number of imponderable factors. Even the redoubtable *Guide Michelin*, confidently bestowing one, two, three or no stars on restaurants, backs away from the task of rating hotels; merely listing them in order of preference according to size and price categories, with "pleasant hotels" printed in red.

Most important to a hotel's excellence, or lack of it, are the manager and staff—the hoteliers and veteran travelers can smell a good hotel, literally. Dust, age and mustiness smell and, conversely, cleanliness and fresh air have their own distinctive scents. Four or five good sniffs around a lobby, and the sophisticated visitor already has a good idea of the whole housekeeping setup.

Another imponderable is the ambience—the general mood, atmosphere, spirit, feeling of a hotel—and it comprises everything from the selections played by the string ensemble in the lounge, or piped in over the P.A. system, to the temper of the concierge's wife when he took off for work that morning. Tradition is important, and here the newer hotels, which haven't had time to develop a patina, are handicapped. Clientele can contribute much to a hotel; the checking-in of a Winston Churchill will set an entire staff on its collective toes (conversely the arrival of an Arab chieftain with a wifely retinue can tear a hotel apart), and a Hemingway, Maugham, Bemelmans or Joseph Wechsberg writing about a place will establish an *esprit de corps* for years to come.

A hotel's bars and public rooms help set a hotel's status in the community—which the guest quickly senses. Smart *Madrileños* have been packing the bar

Esquire's travel editor for twenty-seven years, Richard Joseph has, by his own count, checked into over 1000 hotel rooms, visited 120 countries, traveled a distance equivalent to six round trips to the moon. His report here identifies the best hotels of 1967.

of the Palace Hotel at eight p.m. for years; and French journalists stopped writing cracks about the Paris Hilton when *le tout Paris* took up its Le Western bar. Another factor is a hotel's location; in an in-town hotel it is convenience and fashionableness, while in a resort hotel it's mainly the view.

Putting all these criteria together in a hat, shaking them up well and then throwing the hat out of the window, we've come up with our own list of the three greatest hotels in the world: New York's Plaza, the Gritti Palace overlooking the Grand Canal in Venice, and the Mauna Kea, on the beach on Hawaii island.

Opened in 1907, The Plaza has won such titles as the Dowager Queen of American Hotels, and The Last of the Big Splendors. Together with the St. Regis, Pierre, Gotham, and the Sherry-Netherland, it has survived, been refurbished and prospered while such grand old-timers as the Ritz-Carlton, Park Lane, Savoy-Plaza, Madison, Chatham, New Weston, Astor, Sheraton East (the old Ambassador) and the Gladstone all fell victims to rising land values and changing travel patterns. Its eighteen stories were designed along the lines of a French Renaissance château, and more than any other American hotel The Plaza has exemplified the elegance of a continental *hôtel de grand luxe*.

Hundreds of New Yorkers lined the curbs of the Grand Army Plaza and Fifty-ninth Street on October 1, 1907, to witness the opening of what was described as "the greatest hotel in the world." They'd been drawn by the hotel's advance publicity, featuring the fact that it had cost $12,000,000 (the equivalent of about $60,000,000 today), and by a full-dress fire drill by a horse-drawn fire company. At nine a.m. they saw the first guest draw up in his limousine; he was Alfred Gwynne Vanderbilt, the millionaire sportsman, whose father, Cornelius Vanderbilt, believed to be the richest man in America, lived in a baronial mansion just across the street.

The first entry on the new register was "Mr. & Mrs. Vanderbilt and servant." The next one was Mr. and Mrs. William G. Roelker of Newport, who had the grace to add "and maid" instead of "servant." They were followed quickly by Oliver Harriman, of the railroad millions, George Jay Gould, John Wanamaker, John "Bet-a-Million" Gates, Benjamin W. Duke of the tobacco family, and—carrying a diamond-and-ruby-headed cane and escorting the beautiful Lillian Russell—"Diamond Jim" Brady.

Guest lists at various opening-day functions included the names of Mark Twain, Billie Burke, Charles Dillingham, David Belasco, Oscar Hammerstein and Maxine Elliott.

Opening the doors of their automobiles and carriages in a gold-and-fawn-broadcloth uniform trimmed with gold lace collar and cuffs was the tall young doorman, Tom Clifford, who was to occupy this post for the following forty-five years.

The whole pattern of The Plaza's career, in fact, was set right at the beginning. New York's great social parties were held in the original grand ballroom, and today The Plaza is still the setting for the Junior Assemblies, the Junior League's Debutante Ball, the Grosvenor Debutante Ball and the Gotham Debutante Ball. Many of the big fund-raising functions are held here—"Name a disease, and The Plaza has a ball for it," one cynic said—as well as such other society affairs as the $175-per-ticket April-in-Paris Ball.

The Plaza has often been the scene of fine, small scandals. There was the time that Mrs. Patrick Campbell shocked the world but set a precedent by smoking a cigarette in the Palm Court; and the memorable day when Enrico Caruso, enraged by the ticking of the electric clock in his room, swung at it with his cane—and knocked out every clock in the hotel, since The Plaza was the first to have an automatic clock system in all rooms. Cary Grant raised hell when he was served three English muffin halves and discovered that the fourth had been withheld by the kitchen to be used as a base for Eggs Benedict; and Elizabeth Taylor once found her luggage full of Plaza linen, bath fixtures and a Martini carafe—packed by Montgomery Clift before she had checked out.

The Plaza has been host to Everybody. "Eloise," created by Kay Thompson, romped around its rooms and halls; and the hotel was in a state of siege in 1964 when The Beatles stayed there on their first American tour. Although John F. Kennedy used the Carlyle as his New York home while he was President, he once wore a string tie, and a gun belt under his dinner jacket, while Jacqueline Kennedy was his dance-hall girl with a rose in her hair at a Wild West Ball at The Plaza. His sister Pat had her wedding reception at The Plaza when she married Peter Lawford, and so did Jean Kennedy for her marriage to Stephen Smith, and Eunice Kennedy almost missed being a bridesmaid at a friend's wedding there when she was delayed by a storm at sea.

On the day in 1960 that Dick Nixon had to concede the election to John F. Kennedy, he took the bad taste out of his mouth by lunching with his wife at The Plaza. President and Mrs. William Howard Taft came to The Plaza often, Harry Truman used to have lunch there with his daughter, and a dinner at which President Eisenhower appeared ended up in a bomb scare when a waiter mistook a photographer's range finder for an infernal machine.

But The Plaza today is much more than distinguished names and a great tradition. A $9,000,000 restoration completed last year was the latest stage in a continuing program of alteration, reconstruction and refurbishment that keeps the hotel's plant as fresh and contemporary as it was when it opened. Decorative motifs remain enduringly traditional, so the basic look of the place doesn't change, but everything else about it does.

The Oak Bar, for instance, was originally all-male when it was opened back in 1912, but its Edwardian atmosphere hasn't been too badly disturbed by the introduction of heterosexual drinking when it reopened after repeal of Prohibition. With its great bar, fine paneling and murals, oak tables and big, comfortable leather chairs, it's still one of the most civilized saloons in town. The adjoining Oak Room was also an all-male sanctuary until Prohibition, and it's still for-men-only at lunchtime. Women are permitted

The Plaza, New York

The Gritti Palace, Venice

The Mauna Kea Beach Hotel, Hawaii

from dinner on, and the stately room has long been an after-theatre meeting place. George Jessel, Helen Hayes, Judith Anderson, Lucius Beebe, Richard Rodgers, Beatrice Lillie, Edna Ferber and Mary Martin were among the nightly habitués, and George M. Cohan took his place at a corner banquette almost every afternoon. Today a bronze plaque put up by the Lambs marks the Cohan corner.

Early guests dining in The Plaza's corner restaurant gazed through the tall windows at the coaching meets on Fifth Avenue, and the hansom cabs coming out of Central Park. Today the scenery has changed but the atmosphere hasn't. There are the same marble walls, handsome furnishings and superb service. Now called the Edwardian Room, it is one of New York's most gracious restaurants.

In the two years since the Mauna Kea Beach Hotel has been open, it has established itself—in the mind of this observer, at least—as the greatest resort hotel on earth. It is, in fact, a compendium of superlatives. It sits on a tract leased from the Parker Ranch, the largest ranch under single ownership in the United States, at the foot of 13,796-foot-high Mauna Kea, the highest island mountain in the world. Its cost of $15,000,000 for a hundred-fifty-four-room hotel puts its unit cost at about $100,000 per room, certainly the highest of any resort hotel.

Nobody but a Rockefeller can spend that sort of money, and nobody but Laurance Rockefeller could have spent it with such superb taste. Drawing on his experience in developing Colonial Williamsburg as well as Caneel Bay, Dorado Beach and other outstanding resorts, the brother of New York's Nelson Rockefeller and Chase Manhattan's David Rockefeller set out quite purposefully to create the most magnificent resort hotel the world had ever seen, operating under a mandate from then-Governor William Quinn to develop a whole new Hawaiian tourist area to get people the hell away from Waikiki.

The result was an architectural and decorative triumph (Honor Award of the American Institute of Architects, one of *Fortune* Magazine's Ten Best Buildings of 1966). The visitor's basic impression is one of light and spaciousness. Every guest room with its own lanai open to the sky; long, cool, tiled-floor corridors punctuated by flowered courtyards and islands of trees and shrubbery. Walking through it is like strolling through an open-air museum and art gallery—past Hawaiian quilts hung as tapestries, bronze ceremonial drums and red-and-gold scroll boxes from Thailand, Japanese and Chinese scrolls and paintings, New Guinea carvings and masks, brass candelabra from Hindu temples, an antique wood and brass chest from Zanzibar, an Ainu kimono, Buddhist figures from all over the Orient. Every art object was checked with the New York Museum of Primitive Art for authenticity and value.

The art show continues into every guest room. Hawaiian floral prints on the walls, punctuated by framed collections of Pacific seashells. Tunisian copper dishes used as side tables. Bedspreads and upholstery material woven in Thailand under the direction of a Shan princess, red lacquer bar boxes made in Kyoto, woven mats from Samoa, furniture from Italy and Hong Kong.

Surrounding all this are thirty acres of gardens, and around the whole business is Robert Trent Jones's $2,000,000 golf course—and the figure is *not* included in the $15,000,000 cost of the hotel. The third hole, across a deep inlet where the ocean throws spray thirty feet high against a black lava shoreline, has already won fame as one of the most spectacular par threes in the world.

A resort is known for the sports it offers, and the Mauna Kea has them all. On a few favored days of the year, you can even swim in the morning and ski—*snow* ski, that is—in the afternoon, but on any day you can swim, sail, surf, motorboat, outrigger canoe, water-ski, skin dive, snorkel or play tennis on the hotel's two championship hard-surface courts. The Mauna Kea is on the Kona Coast, one of the greatest fishing grounds in the Pacific. There's bonefish in the shallows, and charter boats sail from a marina a mile and a half from the hotel for Pacific blue, black, silver and striped marlin (some of the blacks going over a thousand pounds); bonito, yellowfin and albacore tuna, blue dolphin and wahoo. For horseback riding you go out into the adjacent 260,000-acre Parker Ranch, where the hotel operates a ranch-house annex, twelve miles away and 2500 feet high on the mountain slope. You can overnight here, and go on jeep-hunting forays for bighorn sheep and mountain goats, wild boar and pheasant.

Although it can't yet compete with such older hotels as The Plaza in the luster of its guest list, the Mauna Kea has gathered its quorum of celebrities. They include Vice-President and Mrs. Humphrey; Jacqueline Kennedy and children; and two Presidential candidates, declared and undeclared, George Romney and Nelson Rockefeller. The bag has also included Arnold Palmer, Jack Nicklaus, Gary Player and Billy Casper, and such variegated achievers as Bing Crosby, Julie Andrews, Stavros Niarchos and Wernher Von Braun.

Our third great hotel brings us back to the world of cachet, tradition, age and elegance, and here the Gritti Palace is the greatest of them all—which is surprising, because it's less than twenty years old. Although it was built in the sixteenth century as the palace of Andrea Gritti, a Venetian merchant, warrior and statesman who became Doge in 1523, it wasn't converted into a hotel until 1948—yet you'd be willing to swear that you read about Keats staying at the Gritti, or about something happening there to Henry James; it has that sort of atmosphere.

As the Venetian flagship of the C.I.G.A. (*Compagnia Italiana dei Grandi Alberghi*) group which includes such luxury hotels as the Excelsior and

Grand in Rome, Florence, Turin, Genoa and Naples —and the Lido Excelsior Palace and the Royal Danieli in Venice—it has been furnished with magnificent seventeenth- and eighteenth-century antiques, carpeted with rich Oriental rugs and lighted with Murano chandeliers. Oil paintings and gilded mirrors line the walls. C.I.G.A. officials are more concerned with having the Gritti serve as a showplace than with its turning a big profit, so Manager Fred Laubi (who also directs the Lido Excelsior) cuts no corners.

Actually it would be a tough scene to spoil. The dining room and the dining and drink terrace look out on the Grand Canal and the domed and sculptured Basilica of Santa Maria della Salute on the opposite bank. Blue-and-white-striped awnings shade the terrace when the sun is strong, and black-and-gold gondolas tie up at the hotel's blue-and-white mooring poles.

You get the whole ambience of the place as you climb onto the hotel dock from the motorboat that has carried you from the railroad station or airline terminal. The welcoming delegation makes you feel like de Gaulle. A white-jacketed bellboy takes your arm—if you're female, aged or hungover; the doorman takes your bags from the deckhand; somebody from the reception staff salutes and greets you (by name, if you've ever been there before), and even Laubi might be standing by.

Laubi's lobby is small, restrained, underplayed. Soft lights; the prevailing color is Gritti blue, a soft shade; quiet voices are made even softer by the thick rugs and the heavy drapery. At the reception desk, a clerk says something like, "We've kept 221 for you, Signor X, you liked it so well last time."

A quiet elevator takes you to your room, where, if you like blue-eyed anemones, there's a bouquet of them on the dressing table; otherwise flowers to complement the room. Out of a hundred ten staff members, only four were replaced last year; the others remember that Gloria Swanson wants only roses or carnations in her room. And fresh carnations every day, please, for Prince Bernhard of The Netherlands, who never goes out without his boutonniere.

If your drink is beer-and-Burgundy, Fontana, the barman, will remember it from last time and his shudder won't be visible. But sometime during your visit he might, as a friend, try to switch you over to his pretty petit Gritti cocktail: one part Bitter Campari, and two parts white vermouth, with a few drops of China Martini.

Gritti people are aghast at the notion of a check-out time. You leave whenever it's time to make your plane or train, or pick up your car, and the motorboat is waiting at the dock without your ordering it. And, if you're anything like a regular guest, Laubi has already penciled in your name for 221 at the time of your usual visit.

"Our whole idea is to run the Gritti for the individual guest," he says, "not for the group member —and certainly not for the convenience of the staff or management. We want each guest to feel that his room is really his—that nobody has been there before him, and that it will be waiting for him when he gets back."

But the best commentary on the Gritti Palace is contained in the writings of its guests. "The most satisfying hotel in the world," John Gunther called it, while Elizabeth Taylor and Eddie Fisher wrote in the hotel's Golden Book that everything was the greatest. (Obviously it wasn't.)

Georges Simenon, the Belgian novelist, wrote "C'est un sort de 'décoration' internationale d'être reçu ici comme dans un palais de Venise, le dernier du monde, hélas! Et le dernier où l'on a conservé la beauté de la vie."

Wrote Somerset Maugham, "There are few things in life more pleasant than to sit on the terrace of the Gritti when the sun about to set bathes in lovely color the Salute which almost faces you. You see that noble building at its best and the sight adds to your satisfaction. For at the Gritti you are not merely a number as you are in those vast caravansaries that are now being built all over the world; you are a friend who has been welcomed as he stepped out of his motorboat, and when you sit down to dinner at the very same table that you sat at the year before, and the year before that, when you see that your bottle of Soave is in the ice pail, waiting for you, as it has been year after year, you cannot but feel very much at home."

Hemingway put it more succinctly in *Across the River and Into the Trees.*

"'The hell with it,' the Colonel said. 'Take us to the Gritti.' '*Con piacere,*' the boatman said."

Malcolm Muggeridge:

THE TOTEMIZATION OF SIR WINSTON CHURCHILL

Through twilight days he lingers, last illusion of a departed grandeur

The arrival of Sir Winston Churchill on the Riviera has become as regular and invariable an occurrence as Mardi Gras and Battle of Flowers. At Nice Airport the photographers turn out yet once more, and M. le Préfet or M. le Sous-Préfet or just M. le Maire waits on the tarmac. It has all happened many times before, and everyone knows what is expected of him. Local reporters from the *Agence France-Presse* and the *Nice-Matin* stand around in the vague expectation that there may be a story. Air-travelers waiting for their planes and spectators on the airport roof are glad enough to have something to look at. They cluster as near as possible to where the great man descends and, when they see him, raise a faint cheer, to which he responds by shakily lifting up his fingers in a V-sign.

The inevitable cigar, jutting out of his mouth, gives an impression of having been put there by someone else, as children stick an old pipe into a snowman. His face is glazed and vacant: it might be immensely old or just born—the eyes faded and watery, the features muzzy, somehow out of focus, like a photograph when the camera has moved. One has a sense, under the surface varnish, of an inward melancholy. It is an illusion to suppose that those who cling tenaciously to life necessarily want to go on living. They often long to die and, like Lear, hate those who would upon the rack of this tough world stretch them out longer. Their survival may be due to some reflex action. By lingering on, they may be expiating an undue rage to live. Bernard Shaw told his biographer, Hesketh Pearson, that each night, when he lay down to sleep, he hoped not to awaken the following morning. Is Sir Winston, perhaps, a like case, except that the chains which keep him earthbound eat mostly into the flesh, whereas Shaw's lacerated a mind which would not subside?

Sir Winston's prodigious constitution has miraculously carried him through all strains and hazards, and

Presently Esquire's regular book reviewer, Malcolm Muggeridge has also contributed numerous articles to the magazine, among them this profile of Sir Winston. It was published in June, 1961.

left intact his capacity to eat and drink with enjoyment. The cautions and abstinences which normally accompany old age, and which his doctors prescribe, are not for him. He can still go through the motions of responding to applause. Cheers penetrate his deafness (which he resolutely refuses to alleviate with a hearing aid) when words cannot. The instinct, inculcated through years of practice, to brace himself for public appearances still operates. As he goes to his car, nowadays with two nurses in his entourage, his footsteps are surprisingly steady, his bearing, ostensibly, alert. Old politicians, like old actors, revive in the limelight. The vacancy which afflicts them in private momentarily lifts when, once more, they feel the eyes of an audience upon them. Their old passion for holding the center of the stage guides their uncertain footsteps to where the footlights shine, and summons up a wintry smile when the curtain rises.

Thus, from time to time, Churchill manages to find his way, alone and unaided, into the House of Commons. This is the scene he knows best; this the place where he has spent so many breathless hours of his long life. He returns to it by instinct—to the stale air, the untidy benches, the drone of unmeant and unheeded speeches, the pallid Front Bench faces, the occasional exclamations of approval or dissent, the laughter so easily and so fatuously aroused, all the drab panoply of a mid-twentieth-century Parliament. When his bulky form appears, whoever may be speaking, whatever may be under discussion, the proceedings are, in effect, temporarily suspended. All eyes rest on him, in the galleries as on the floor of the House. With exaggerated obeisance, he makes his bow to Mr. Speaker, and advances upon his old seat below the gangway. Then, after some long-drawn-out byplay with his handkerchief or a throat lozenge, he leans across to ask a neighboring M.P., in a sepulchral whisper, what the business is before the House, and who the Member is (pointing at him) on his feet. It may well be Macmillan or Gaitskell whom he cannot identify. His eyes seldom intimate recognition, and, when they do, it is from an old recollection. With the years, distant memories grow clearer. The present and the recent past are hidden from view under thick clouds of forgetfulness.

Attention remains fixed on him. As he well knows, no speech will be heard, no question received other than desultory consideration while he is there. Honorable and Right Honorable Members, on both sides of the House, continue to be preoccupied with his strange, eerie presence among them. When he gets up to go, their eyes follow him, as they did when he came in. After he has gone, and they have resumed their business, it takes a little while for them to get back onto their own pedestrian wavelength. The atmospherics created by his incursion only gradually subside. What is it about him which makes him, even in his decrepitude, still tower above the others, and hold them in thrall? Not warmth of character—he is rather horrible. Not past services—in the House of Commons, of all places, it is true that (to use a phrase Shakespeare puts into the mouth of Timon of Athens) men bar their doors before the setting sun. Not famous orations—like all rhetoric, his wear badly. Few today can listen without squirming even to the wartime speeches, which were so stirring at the time, about blood, sweat and tears, and fighting on the beaches.

He has become a kind of totem. His continued existence provides a link with departed glory. Though his sun may have set, still, as long as he is there, some glow lingers about the western sky in which others may participate. He is produced, as totems are, to keep up tribal morale, which otherwise would sag under the weight of unfamiliar and disconcerting circumstances. Britannia no longer rules the waves, but did when Churchill was First Lord of the Admiralty; narrower still and narrower shall our bounds be set, not wider still and wider, as Conservative ladies fervently proclaim when they sing *Land of Hope and Glory*; but he it was who said that he had not become His Majesty King George VI's Principal Secretary of State in order to preside over the dissolution of his Empire. Brave words, which had to be eaten during his postwar premiership, when the dissolution of the British Empire went on apace! Even so, the Conservative ladies continue to derive comfort and reassurance from them.

On the Riviera nowadays Sir Winston usually stays at the Hotel de Paris in Monte Carlo, as guest of Mr. Aristotle Onassis, who owns the place. Or Mr. Onassis will take him for a cruise, along with Maria Callas, on his sleek yacht *Christina*, named, in the circumstances somewhat embarrassingly, after his former wife, Tina Onassis. When the party goes ashore at some little holiday port, again there are cheers— "Vive Churchill!"—from groups of boatmen and fishermen and tourists who gather in the Mediterranean sun to look at him, and at Miss Callas, and even at Mr. Onassis. Those who saw Churchill, as I did, walk down the Champs Elysées with General de Gaulle, on his first visit to liberated Paris, when he seemed the embodiment of a resurrected Europe (at least, so we thought it then), might ruminate philosophically on the *bizarreries* of fame. How strange that applause, so tumultuous and heartfelt on the

great stage of history, should, only a few years later, find this faint, frivolous echo in so diminished a setting! Does he detect and note the difference? Who can tell? It is still applause. Mr. Onassis is no General de Gaulle, certainly, but an attentive, considerate and generous host; *Christina* no man-of-war, but a commodious and elegant yacht. V is for victory; and, though that victory was won, it seems an eternity ago, and brought scant benefit and many woes, a V-sign made by its originator is still appreciated in Monte Carlo and along the Côte d'Azur.

The Hotel de Paris, where Mr. Onassis accommodates Sir Winston, is one of the few remaining old-style expensive hotels on the Riviera. The others are steadily being eliminated by *le camping*, which, in accordance with the spirit of the age, thrives by taking a little money from a lot of people rather than a lot of money from a few. There is nothing of *le camping* about the Hotel de Paris. The bars and dining rooms and lounges are kept in restful and perpetual twilight. As far as is humanly possible, the outside world is excluded. Residents, if so inclined, may make their way to the neighboring Casino by an underground passage without submitting themselves to the elements even to the extent of crossing the road. The service is alert and efficient, and the cuisine justly famed throughout, and, indeed, beyond the Alpes-Maritimes; the suites are ample and luxurious, and the charges astronomical—though not, of course, for Mr. Onassis' guests, who pay nothing. Outside, Rolls-Royces and Cadillacs are neatly berthed side by side, awaiting their owners' pleasure. Sir Winston keeps mostly to his suite, and appears only rarely in the public parts of the hotel. On the occasions when he is respectfully wheeled, in his invalid chair, into the dining room, the other diners all look up, eager to catch a glimpse of him. For them, too, he is a totem, whose effect is to reinforce their conviction that, whether or not there will always be an England, there will assuredly always be a Hotel de Paris.

Before Sir Winston's friendship with Mr. Onassis ripened into their present intimacy, he used to stay in the Villa Pausa at Roquebrune, some two miles further along the coast, with his literary agent, Mr. Emery Reves. This, too, is an ample residence, with a spacious stairway, and a large expanse of walls, which show off to advantage Mr. Reves's valuable collection of Impressionist paintings. It was formerly owned by Coco Chanel, famous for *haute couture* and perfume, who tamed its Italianate luxuriance into the quiet shades of grey she preferred, preserving, in the large garden, a similar color scheme by planting lavender under the old olive trees. Mlle. Chanel, long ago when she was the great friend of the Duke of Westminster, knew Sir Winston well. She used, she told me once, to play cribbage with him, and found it expedient to let him win always. In those far-off days, Mr. Reves was still in his native Hungary, and Adolf Hitler, the unconscious instrument which brought him and Sir Winston together in Mlle. Chanel's former villa, still in his native Austria. Such are the small, but still intriguing, byways of history's harsh course. Under the Reves regime, the Villa Pausa's decor has

been preserved, though its chatelaine, Wendy Russell, has superimposed a certain degree of Americanization upon the household arrangements, daintily attiring the maids in coffee-shop pink nylon—a shade to which she is addicted, and which predominates in her own elegant boudoir.

As they say in Roquebrune, when conversation turns on the Reves ménage, made famous by Sir Winston's visits: "*C'est une vie en rose là-haut.*"

Mr. Reves, like Mr. Onassis, is a rich man. Sir Winston's hosts usually are. The difference is that, whereas Mr. Onassis' wealth is derived from shipping, Mr. Reves's has been derived from Sir Winston. He has the, I should suppose, almost unique distinction in our rough island history of having benefited financially by associating with a Churchill. By astute and pertinacious syndication of Sir Winston's writings, he has enriched himself, and, of course, to a far greater degree, Sir Winston. Thus, when Mr. Reves entertained Sir Winston, he was, in a sense, looking after a valuable property. The property continues to be valuable. Though Sir Winston no longer produces, his works go marching lucratively on through the media of film, radio and television. His paintings continue to have a brisk sale as Christmas cards in the United States, and *Winston Churchill: The Valiant Years* has recently provided American and British televiewers with yet another version of his famous war memoirs. The totem is effective at long range, like a guided missile, as well as by direct contact.

A ready means of being cherished by the English is to adopt the simple expedient of living a long time. I have little doubt that if, say, Oscar Wilde had lived into his nineties, instead of dying in his forties, he would have been considered a benign, distinguished figure, suitable to preside at a school prize-giving, or to instruct and exhort scoutmasters at their jamborees. He might even have been knighted. A notable example of the operation of the same principle was Queen Victoria, who, in the earlier years of her reign, was so detested by her subjects that it was considered highly dubious whether the Monarchy would survive her death. Her gross and pudgy figure repelled them, as did her morbid protraction of the normal period of mourning after the death of Albert, the Prince Consort. This unfavorable impression was intensified by her lack of consideration for her heir, later Edward VII, and by her curious associates like John Brown, the Scottish baillie at Balmoral, who was permitted gross familiarities, at any rate in speech, and who, anyway, was nearly always drunk. By the time of the Queen's Diamond Jubilee, however, all was changed. She had sat so long on the throne that her stupidities had become endearing eccentricities, and her arrogance an old lady's whimsicality. Her turgid and heavily underlined journals were lovingly edited, and to this day are liable to raise a snicker rather than a yawn. Dreadful statues

of her, turned out by the score, were erected in prominent places throughout the country, and even shipped to far-off lands like India, where they still stand unsuitably in Calcutta, New Delhi and Pakistan's Lahore.

If this unpleasing old Germanic lady thus achieved fame and popular esteem just by becoming very old, how much more so is this the case with Sir Winston, who has notable achievements to his credit, and who has displayed, in the course of his turbulent political career, exceptional verve and resourcefulness. Yet even Sir Winston, as few now care to remember, has had periods of exclusion from office, and of intense unpopularity, particularly among his associates in the political party he happened to belong to at the time. I recall very well, in the middle Thirties, when I was working on the London *Evening Standard*, how Churchill used to come occasionally to the office. Lord Beaverbrook, the owner of the *Evening Standard*, had engaged him to write regular articles on current affairs at what was then considered an exceptionally high fee. What a dispirited and disgruntled figure he was in those days! Any political journalist would have been happy to give long odds against his ever holding office again, let alone becoming Prime Minister. The Tories, whom he had rejoined when their political fortunes revived, could not abide him. He found a point of attack in their India policy, which, when it was put into effect in a more extreme form some ten years later by a Labour Government, he approved without a murmur. At the time of King Edward VIII's abdication, he was howled down in the House of Commons when he attempted to make a plea on the King's behalf. Here, too, as the exiled Duke of Windsor found to his chagrin, Churchill in opposition was one thing, Churchill in office another. The nomadic Duke and Duchess of Windsor received no more consideration from their former champion when he was in a position to do them favors than they did from Mr. Attlee, who owed them none.

Now all this is forgotten. Churchill is very old, and so any breath of criticism of his character or achievement is considered to be not only in execrable taste, but almost blasphemous. This is a pity, if only because it detracts from his undoubted greatness. For a man as human and humorous and audacious as Churchill has been to be turned into a totem, serving to protract illusions of grandeur, is a sad end to a splendid career. How fortunate were those Hindu rulers whose philosophy required them to retire to the forest for their last years, and thus disengage their minds from earthly preoccupations in order to prepare themselves for the death which could not be long delayed.

It is, of course, true that Churchill's totem role is particularly required just now, when his country's fortunes are visibly declining. He was the last Prime Minister able to produce authentic Great Power credentials at international gatherings. Though, in fact, in his dealings with Stalin and Roosevelt, he was increasingly a junior partner, he appeared to be an equal. At the ill-omened Yalta meeting, he was mostly overborne, and sometimes treated with scant consideration by his two associates, but in the final winding-up scenes they allowed him an equal status with themselves. He had the dubious distinction of being photographed, his Russian fur hat rakishly on one side, as one of the three pillars of the modern world, who, it was confidently believed, would draw the frontiers and establish the conditions for an era of enduring peace and prosperity. Things, as we now know, took quite a different turn. Even so, the English are still inclined to look nostalgically into their old photograph album, which recalls grander circumstances than they now enjoy. Among the studio portraits it contains, Sir Winston's is particularly prized.

Few men of action have been able to make a graceful exit at the appropriate time. Napoleon's retirement to St. Helena was enforced, restless and cantankerous; Lloyd George, for the last twenty-three years of his life excluded from office, continued till the end to hover round public affairs, managing to persuade himself that he was contributing to their course and direction. Even Sir Oswald Mosley, whose meteoric career in party politics ended ingloriously in the British Union of Fascists and incarceration during the war years, continues still to believe that the call will come for him to take over the Government. Power-addiction, like any other, becomes in the end incurable. Its victims continue to crave for the drug even when it cannot be procured, or, if it could, when their systems are too enfeebled to react, other than fitfully and wanly, to its stimulus.

How much better for Churchill's reputation if he had brought himself, or been persuaded, to retire from active politics after his electoral defeat in 1945! Then his enormous services were a fresh memory instead of a too-often-told tale. The rhetoric which gloriously saved us from surrender to the Nazis had not staled with constant repetition; the great esteem in which he was rightly held had not degenerated into sycophancy, nor been used to sustain a legendary destiny which precludes effectively grappling with a real one.

It was not to be. He discarded the role of national leadership, which he had so richly earned, in favor of party leadership, for which he was ill-fitted and which ill became him. The red dispatch boxes, toys of office, held their old allure, and for them he threw away, or at any rate clouded, the memory of the time when he had been the spokesman, not of a class or a party, but of a nation and a cause. His postwar premiership was confused, meandering and self-willed—much more so than is even now recognized or admitted. He hung on as long as he dared, and as long as the poltroonery of his associates permitted. When, at last, he went, he bequeathed us Anthony Eden, who, in one ill-judged, ill-planned and fatuous venture at Suez, lost to, of all people, the Egyptians what Winston Churchill's heroic wartime leadership had saved from the Nazis. History, which is always ironic, has rarely produced a greater irony than this.

Surely, it will be contended, Sir Winston's place in history is sufficiently assured irrespective of how the twilight of his days may be spent. Is it not the case that, as has so often been remarked, his deeds will live, and his writing be read, as long as England's fate interests mankind, and the English language continues to be spoken? As for his writing—I am not so sure. Participants in public events are seldom reliable chroniclers of them. Their egos are too involved, their views are too prejudiced, for them to achieve an historian's detachment. They find it difficult to recollect in tranquility, and therefore to endow with enduring interest, what so excited them at the time. Effective men of action, by their very nature, have little sense of perspective. They are too obsessed with their own lines to be interested in the play; too avidly concerned with the present to trace its relation to the past and the future. Tactics obsess them to the exclusion of strategy. Like Napoleon, their only true principle is *"On s'engage, et après on voit."* History cannot be written in such a spirit. Gibbon, who as an officer in the Militia was a ludicrous figure and at the Board of Trade a fiasco, could with exquisite clarity, skill and elegance unravel the story of Rome's decline and fall. Napoleon, on the other hand, when, on St. Helena, he looked back on the dramatic events in which he had played so dramatic and decisive a part, had nothing of any particular interest or significance to say about them.

In Sir Winston's case the question is complicated by his rhetorical style, which, though it has been greatly admired by his contemporaries, posterity may well find distasteful. Already his memoirs of the First World War have begun to pall. Who today can stomach passages like:

"Once more now in the march of centuries Old England was to stand forth in battle against the mightiest thrones and dominations. Once more in defense of the liberties of Europe and the common right must she enter upon a voyage of great toil and hazard across waters uncharted, towards coasts unknown, guided only by the stars. Once more 'the far-off line of storm-beaten ships' was to stand between the Continental Tyrant and the dominion of the world. . ."?

It would not be surprising if his memoirs of the Second World War came, before very long, to create a like impression of being gaseous, overwritten, and, in the light of subsequent events, too inappropriate to deserve attention.

History, in any case, is the story of the victor. When I first went to India, in 1924, little Indian boys were taught at school that their country was torn with conflicts and prostrate until the English landed on its shores. Thenceforth, all was well. Now they are taught the exact opposite—that their country languished until the English were chased away. Which version is true? The answer probably is: neither. However unjustly or inaccurately, Sir Winston's place in history will depend on who, from the turmoil and discontents of our time, is seen to emerge as the victor.

Nora Ephron:

A FEW WORDS ABOUT BREASTS

Shaping up absurd

have to begin with a few words about androgyny. In grammar school, in the fifth and sixth grades, we were all tyrannized by a rigid set of rules that supposedly determined whether we were boys or girls. The episode in *Huckleberry Finn* where Huck is disguised as a girl and gives himself away by the way he threads a needle and catches a ball—that kind of thing. We learned that the way you sat, crossed your legs, held a cigarette and looked at your nails, your wristwatch, the way you did these things instinctively was absolute proof of your sex. Now obviously most children did not take this literally, but I did. I thought that just one slip, just one incorrect cross of my legs or flick of an imaginary cigarette ash would turn me from whatever I was into the other thing; that would be all it took, really. Even though I was outwardly a girl and had many of the trappings generally associated with the field of girldom—a girl's name, for example, and dresses, my own telephone, an autograph book—I spent the early years of my adolescence absolutely certain that I might at any point gum it up. I did not feel at all like a girl. I was boyish. I was athletic, ambitious, outspoken, competitive, noisy, rambunctious. I had scabs on my knees and my socks slid into my loafers and I could throw a football. I wanted desperately not to be that way, not to be a mixture of both things but instead just one, a girl, a definite indisputable girl. As soft and as pink as a nursery. And nothing would do that for me, I felt, but breasts.

I was about six months younger than everyone in my class, and so for about six months after it began, for six months after my friends had begun to develop—that was the word we used, develop—I was not particularly worried. I would sit in the bathtub and look down at my breasts and know that any day now, any second now, they would start growing like everyone else's. They didn't. "I want to buy a bra," I said to my mother one night. "What for?" she said. My mother was really hateful about bras, and by the time my third sister had gotten to the point where she was ready to want one, my mother had worked the whole business into a comedy routine. "Why not use a Band-Aid instead?" she would say. It was a source of great pride to my mother that she had never even had to wear a brassiere until she had her fourth child, and then only because her gynecologist made her. It was incomprehensible to me that anyone could ever be proud of something like that. It was the 1950's, for God's sake. Jane Russell. Cashmere sweaters. Couldn't my mother see that? *"I am too old to wear an undershirt."* Screaming. Weeping. Shouting. "Then don't wear an undershirt," said my mother. "But I want to buy a bra." "What for?"

I suppose that for most girls, breasts, brassieres, that entire thing, has more trauma, more to do with the coming of adolescence, with becoming a woman, than anything else. Certainly more than getting your period, although that too was traumatic, symbolic. But you could *see* breasts; they were there; they were visible. Whereas a girl could claim to have her period for months before she actually got it and nobody would ever know the difference. Which is exactly what I did. All you had to do was make a great fuss over having enough nickels for the Kotex machine and walk around clutching your stomach and moaning for three to five days a month about The Curse and you could convince anybody. There is a school of thought somewhere in the women's lib/women's mag/gynecology establishment that claims that menstrual cramps are purely psychological, and I lean toward it. Not that I didn't have them finally. Agonizing cramps, heating-pad cramps, go-down-to-the-school-nurse-and-lie-on-the-cot cramps. But unlike any pain I had ever suffered, I adored the pain of cramps, welcomed it, wallowed in it, bragged about it. "I can't go. I have cramps." "I can't do that. I have cramps." And most of all, gigglingly, blushingly: "I can't swim. I have cramps." Nobody ever used the hard-core word. Menstruation.

For a time, Nora Ephron wrote a monthly column on women. In addition to this article, which appeared in 1972, she also wrote about such subjects as Helen Gurley Brown, Erich Segal, and Rod McKuen.

God, what an awful word. Never that. "I have cramps."

The morning I first got my period, I went into my mother's bedroom to tell her. And my mother, my utterly-hateful-about-bras mother, burst into tears. It was really a lovely moment, and I remember it so clearly not just because it was one of the two times I ever saw my mother cry on my account (the other was when I was caught being a six-year-old kleptomaniac), but also because the incident did not mean to me what it meant to her. Her little girl, her first-born, had finally become a woman. That was what she was crying about. My reaction to the event, however, was that I might well be a woman in some scientific, textbook sense (and could at least stop faking every month and stop wasting all those nickels). But in another sense—in a visible sense—I was as androgynous and as liable to tip over into boyhood as ever.

I started with a 28AA bra. I don't think they made them any smaller in those days, although I gather that now you can buy bras for five year olds that don't have any cups whatsoever in them; trainer bras they are called. My first brassiere came from Robinson's Department Store in Beverly Hills. I went there alone, shaking, positive they would look me over and smile and tell me to come back next year. An actual fitter took me into the dressing room and stood over me while I took off my blouse and tried the first one on. The little puffs stood out on my chest. "Lean over," said the fitter (to this day I am not sure what fitters in bra departments do except to tell you to lean over). I leaned over, with the fleeting hope that my breasts would miraculously fall out of my body and into the puffs. Nothing.

"Don't worry about it," said my friend Libby some months later, when things had not improved. "You'll get them after you're married."

"What are you talking about?" I said.

"When you get married," Libby explained, "your husband will touch your breasts and rub them and kiss them and they'll grow."

That was the killer. Necking I could deal with. Intercourse I could deal with. But it had never crossed my mind that a man was going to touch my breasts, that breasts had something to do with all that, petting, my God they never mentioned petting in my little sex manual about the fertilization of the ovum. I became dizzy. For I knew instantly—as naïve as I had been only a moment before—that only part of what she was saying was true: the touching, rubbing, kissing part, not the growing part. And I knew that no one would ever want to marry me. I had no breasts. I would never have breasts.

My best friend in school was Diana Raskob. She lived a block from me in a house full of wonders. English muffins, for instance. The Raskobs were the first people in Beverly Hills to have English muffins for breakfast. They also had an apricot tree in the back, and a badminton court, and a sub-scription to *Seventeen* magazine, and hundreds of games like Sorry and Parcheesi and Treasure Hunt and Anagrams. Diana and I spent three or four afternoons a week in their den reading and playing and eating. Diana's mother's kitchen was full of the most colossal assortment of junk food I have ever been exposed to. My house was full of apples and peaches and milk and homemade chocolate-chip cookies—which were nice, and good for you, but-not-right-before-dinner-or-you'll-spoil-your-appetite. Diana's house had nothing in it that was good for you, and what's more, you could stuff it in right up until dinner and nobody cared. Bar-B-Q potato chips (they were the first in them, too), giant bottles of ginger ale, fresh popcorn with melted butter, hot fudge sauce on Baskin-Robbins jamoca ice cream, powdered-sugar doughnuts from Van de Kamp's. Diana and I had been best friends since we were seven; we were about equally popular in school (which is to say, not particularly), we had about the same success with boys (extremely intermittent) and we looked much the same. Dark. Tall. Gangly.

It is September, just before school begins. I am eleven years old, about to enter the seventh grade, and Diana and I have not seen each other all summer. I have been to camp and she has been somewhere like Banff with her parents. We are meeting, as we often do, on the street midway between our two houses and we will walk back to Diana's and eat junk and talk about what has happened to each of us that summer. I am walking down Walden Drive in my jeans and my father's shirt hanging out and my old red loafers with the socks falling into them and coming toward me is . . . I take a deep breath . . . a young woman. Diana. Her hair is curled and she has a waist and hips and a bust and she is wearing a straight skirt, an article of clothing I have been repeatedly told I will be unable to wear until I have the hips to hold it up. My jaw drops, and suddenly I am crying, crying hysterically, can't catch my breath sobbing. My best friend has betrayed me. She has gone ahead without me and done it. She has shaped up.

Here are some things I did to help:

Bought a Mark Eden Bust Developer.

Slept on my back for four years.

Splashed cold water on them every night because some French actress said in *Life* magazine that that was what *she* did for her perfect bustline.

Ultimately, I resigned myself to a bad toss and began to wear padded bras. I think about them now, think about all those years in high school I went around in them, my three padded bras, every single one of them with different sized breasts. Each time I changed bras I changed sizes: one week nice perky but not too obtrusive breasts, the next medium-sized slightly pointy ones, the next week knockers, true knockers; all the time, whatever size I was, carrying around this rubberized appendage on my chest that occasionally crashed into a wall and was poked inward and had to be poked outward—I think about all that and wonder how anyone kept a straight face through it. My parents, who normally had no restraints about needling me—why did they say nothing as they watched my chest go up and down? My friends, who would periodically inspect my breasts for signs for growth and reassure me—why didn't they at least counsel consistency?

And the bathing suits. I die when I think about the bathing suits. That was the era when you could lay an uninhabited bathing suit on the beach and someone would make a pass at it. I would put one on, an absurd swimsuit with its enormous bust built into it, the bones from the suit stabbing me in the rib cage and leaving little red welts on my body, and there I would be, my chest plunging straight downward absolutely vertically from my collarbone to the top of my suit and then suddenly, wham, out came all that padding and material and wiring absolutely horizontally.

Buster Klepper was the first boy who ever touched them. He was my boyfriend my senior year of high school. There is a picture of him in my high-school yearbook that makes him look quite attractive in a Jewish, horn-rimmed glasses sort of way, but the picture does not show the pimples, which were air-brushed out, or the dumbness. Well, that isn't really fair. He wasn't dumb. He just wasn't terribly bright. His mother refused to accept it, refused to accept the relentlessly average report cards, refused to deal with her son's inevitable destiny in some junior college or other. "He was tested," she would say to me, apropos of nothing, "and it came out 145. That's near-genius." Had the word underachiever been coined, she probably would have lobbed that one at me, too. Anyway, Buster was really very sweet—which is, I know, damning with faint praise, but there it is. I was the editor of the front page of the high-school newspaper and he was editor of the back page; we had to work together, side by side, in the print shop, and that was how it started. On our first date, we went to see *April Love* starring Pat Boone. Then we started going together. Buster had a green coupe, a 1950 Ford with an engine he had hand-chromed until it shone, dazzled, reflected the image of anyone who looked into it, anyone usually being Buster polishing it or the gas-station attendants he constantly asked to check the oil in order for them to be overwhelmed by the sparkle on the valves. The car also had a boot stretched over the back seat for reasons I never understood; hanging from the rearview mirror, as was the custom, was a pair of angora dice. A previous girl friend named Solange who was famous throughout Beverly Hills High School for having no pigment in her right eyebrow had knitted them for him. Buster and I would ride around town, the two of us seated to the left of the steering wheel. I would shift gears. It was nice.

There was necking. Terrific necking. First in the car, overlooking Los Angeles from what is now the Trousdale Estates. Then on the bed of his parents' cabana at Ocean House. Incredibly wonderful, frustrating necking, I loved it, really, but no further than necking, please don't, please, because there I was absolutely terrified of the general implications of going-a-step-further with a near-dummy and also terrified of his finding out there was next to nothing there (which he knew, of course; he wasn't that dumb).

I broke up with him at one point. I think we were apart for about two weeks. At the end of that time I drove down to see a friend at a boarding school in Palos Verdes Estates and a disc jockey played *April Love* on the radio four times during the trip. I took it as a sign. I drove straight back to Griffith Park to a golf tournament Buster was playing in (he was the sixth-seeded teen-age golf player in Southern California) and presented myself back to him on the green of the 18th hole. It was all very dramatic. That night we went to a drive-in and I let him get his hand under my protuberances and onto my breasts. He really didn't seem to mind at all.

"Do you want to marry my son?" the woman asked me.

"Yes," I said.

I was nineteen years old, a virgin, going with this woman's son, this big strange woman who was married to a Lutheran minister in New Hampshire and pretended she was Gentile and had this son, by her first husband, this total fool of a son who ran the hero-sandwich concession at Harvard Business School and whom for one moment one December in New Hampshire I said —as much out of politeness as anything else— that I wanted to marry.

"Fine," she said. "Now, here's what you do. Always make sure you're on top of him so you won't seem so small. My bust is very large, you see, so I always lie on my back to make it look smaller, but you'll have to be on top most of the time."

I nodded. "Thank you," I said.

"I have a book for you to read," she went on. "Take it with you when you leave. Keep it." She went to the bookshelf, found it, and gave it to me. It was a book on frigidity.

"Thank you," I said.

That is a true story. Everything in this article is a true story, but I feel I have to point out that that story in particular is true. It happened on December 30, 1960. I think about it often. When it first happened, I naturally assumed that the woman's son, my boyfriend, was responsible. I invented a scenario where he had had a little heart-to-heart with his mother and had confessed that his only objection to me was that my breasts were small; his mother then took it upon herself to help out. Now I think I was wrong about the incident. The mother was acting on her own, I think: that was her way of being cruel and competitive under the guise of being helpful and maternal. You have small breasts, she was saying; therefore you will never make him as happy as I have. Or you have small breasts; therefore you will doubtless have sexual problems. Or you have small breasts; therefore you are less woman than I am. She was, as it happens, only the first of what seems to me to be a never-ending string of women who have made competitive remarks to me about breast size. "I would love to wear a dress like

250

that," my friend Emily says to me, "but my bust is too big." Like that. Why do women say these things to me? Do I attract these remarks the way other women attract married men or alcoholics or homosexuals? This summer, for example. I am at a party in East Hampton and I am introduced to a woman from Washington. She is a minor celebrity, very pretty and Southern and blonde and outspoken and I am flattered because she has read something I have written. We are talking animatedly, we have been talking no more than five minutes, when a man comes up to join us. "Look at the two of us," the woman says to the man, indicating me and her. "The two of us together couldn't fill an A cup." Why does she say that? It isn't even true, dammit, so why? Is she even more addled than I am on this subject? Does she honestly believe there is something wrong with her size breasts, which, it seems to me, now that I look hard at them, are just right. Do I unconsciously bring out competitiveness in women? In that form? What did I do to deserve it?

As for men.

There were men who minded and let me know that they minded. There were men who did not mind. In any case, I always minded.

And even now, now that I have been countlessly reassured that my figure is a good one, now that I am grown-up enough to understand that most of my feelings have very little to do with the reality of my shape, I am nonetheless obsessed by breasts. I cannot help it. I grew up in the terrible Fifties—with rigid stereotypical sex roles, the insistence that men be men and dress like men and women be women and dress like women, the intolerance of androgyny—and I cannot shake it, cannot shake my feelings of inadequacy. Well, that time is gone, right? All those exaggerated examples of breast worship are gone, right? Those women were freaks, right? I know all that. And yet, here I am, stuck with the psychological remains of it all, stuck with my own peculiar version of breast worship. You probably think I am crazy to go on like this: here I have set out to write a confession that is meant to hit you with the shock of recognition and instead you are sitting there thinking I am thoroughly warped. Well, what can I tell you? If I had had them, I would have been a completely different person. I honestly believe that.

After I went into therapy, a process that made it possible for me to tell total strangers at cocktail parties that breasts were the hang-up of my life, I was often told that I was insane to have been bothered by my condition. I was also frequently told, by close friends, that I was extremely boring on the subject. And my girl friends, the ones with nice big breasts, would go on endlessly about how their lives had been far more miserable than mine. Their bra straps were snapped in class. They couldn't sleep on their stomachs. They were stared at whenever the word "mountain" cropped up in geography. And *Evangeline*, good God what they went through every time someone had to stand up and recite the Prologue to Longfellow's *Evangeline*: "... *stand like druids of eld* .../ *With beards that rest on their bosoms.*" It was much worse for them, they tell me. They had a terrible time of it, they assure me. I don't know how lucky I was, they say.

I have thought about their remarks, tried to put myself in their place, considered their point of view. I think they are full of shit.

Gore Vidal:

Tarzan Revisited

An urbane man of letters looks back nostalgically
at the Complete Works of Edgar Rice Burroughs
and concludes that for sheer daydreaming
the Best Man is still the Ape Man

There are so many things the people who take polls never get around to asking. Fascinated as we all are to know what our countrymen think of great issues (approving, disapproving, "don't-knowing," with that same shrewd intelligence which made a primeval wilderness bloom with Howard Johnson signs), the pollsters never get around to asking the sort of interesting personal questions our new-Athenians might be able to answer knowledgeably. For instance, how many adults have an adventure serial running in their heads? How many consciously daydream, turning on a story in which the dreamer ceases to be an employee of I.B.M. and becomes a handsome demigod moving through splendid palaces, saving maidens from monsters (or monsters from maidens: this is a jaded time). Most children tell themselves stories in which they figure as powerful figures, enjoying the pleasures not only of the adult world as they conceive it but of a world of wonders unlike dull reality. Although this sort of Mittyesque daydreaming is supposed to cease in maturity, I suggest that more adults than we suspect are bemusedly wandering about with a full Technicolor extravaganza going on in their heads. Clad in tights, rapier in hand, the daydreamers drive their Jaguars at fantastic speeds through a glittering world of adoring love objects, mingling anachronistic historic worlds with science fiction. "Captain, the time-warp's been closed! We are now trapped in a parallel world, inhabited entirely by women with three breasts." Though from what we can gather about these imaginary worlds they tend to be more Adlerian than Freudian: The motor drive is the desire not for sex (other briefer fantasies take care of that) but for power, for the ability to dominate one's environment through physical strength. I state all this with perfect authority because I have just finished rereading several books by the master of American daydreamers, Edgar Rice Burroughs, whose works today, as anyone who goes into a drugstore

or looks at a newsstand can see, have suddenly returned to great popularity.

When I was growing up, I read all twenty-three Tarzan books, as well as the ten Mars books. My own inner storytelling mechanism was vivid. At any one time, I had at least three serials going as well as a number of old faithful reruns. I used Burroughs as a source of raw material. When he went to the center of the earth à la Jules Verne (much too fancy a writer for one's taste), I immediately worked up a thirteen-part series, with myself as lead, and various friends as guest stars. Sometimes I used the master's material, but more often I adapted it freely to suit myself. One's daydreams tended to be Tarzanish pre-puberty (physical strength and freedom) and Martian post-puberty (exotic worlds and subtle *combinazione* to be worked out). After adolescence, if one's life is sufficiently interesting, the desire to tell oneself stories diminishes. My last serial ran into sponsor trouble when I was in the Second World War and was never renewed.

Until recently I assumed that most people were like myself: daydreaming ceases when the real world becomes interesting and reasonably manageable. Now I am not so certain. Pondering the life and success of Burroughs leads one to believe that a good many people find their lives so unsatisfactory that they go right on year after year telling themselves stories in which they are able to dominate their environment in a way that is not possible in this overorganized society.

"Most of the stories I wrote were the stories I told myself just before I went to sleep," said Edgar Rice Burroughs, describing his own work. He is a fascinating figure to contemplate, an archetype American dreamer. Born 1875, in Chicago, he was a drifter until he was thirty-six. Briefly, he served in the U.S. Cavalry; then he was a gold miner in Oregon, a cowboy in Idaho, a railroad policeman in Salt Lake City; he attempted several businesses that failed. He was perfectly in the old-American grain: the man who could take on almost any job,

Gore Vidal's by-line has appeared fifteen times in Esquire, under articles, essays, stories, and plays. This essay appeared in 1963.

who liked to keep moving, who tried to get rich quick, but could never pull it off. And while he was drifting through the unsatisfactory real world, he consoled himself with an inner world where he was strong and handsome, adored by beautiful women and worshiped by exotic races. Burroughs might have gone to his death an unknown daydreamer, if he had not started reading pulp fiction. He needed raw material for his own inner serials and once he had used up his favorite source, Rider Haggard, he turned to the magazines. He was appalled at how poor the stories were. They did not compare with his own imaginings. He was like a lover of pornography who, unable to find works which excite him, turns to writing them. Burroughs promptly wrote a serial about Mars and sold it to *Munsey's*. His fellow daydreamers recognized a master. In 1914 he published his first book, *Tarzan of the Apes* (Rousseau's noble savage reborn in Africa), and history was made. To date the Tarzan books have sold over twenty-five million copies in fifty-six languages. There is hardly an American male of my generation who has not at one time or another tried to master the victory cry of the great ape as it once bellowed forth from the androgynous chest of Johnny Weismuller, while a thousand arms and legs were broken by attempts to swing from tree to tree in the backyards of the republic. Between 1914 and his death in 1950, Burroughs, the squire of Tarzana, California (a prophet honored by his own land), produced over sixty books, while enjoying the unique status of being the first American writer to be a corporation. Burroughs is said to have been a pleasant, unpretentious man who liked to ride and play golf. Not one to disturb his own unconscious with reality, he never set foot in Africa.

With a sense of recapturing childhood, I have just reread several Tarzan books. It is fascinating to see how much one recalls after a quarter century. At times the sense of *déjà vu* is overpowering. It is equally interesting to discover that one's memories of *Tarzan of the Apes* are mostly action scenes. The plot had slipped one's mind. It is a lot of plot, too. The beginning is worthy of Conrad. "I had this story from one who had no business to tell it to me, or to any other. I may credit the seductive influence of an old vintage upon the narrator for the beginning of it, and my own skeptical incredulity during the days that followed for the balance of the strange tale." It is 1888. The young Lord and Lady Greystoke are involved in a ship mutiny ("there was in the whole atmosphere of the craft that undefinable something which presages disaster"). They are put ashore on the west coast of Africa. They build a tree house. Here Burroughs is at his best. He tells you the size of the logs, the way to hang a door when you have no hinges, the problems of roofing. All his books are filled with interesting details on how things are made. The Greystokes have a child. They die. The "man-child" is taken up by Kala, a Great Ape, who brings him up as a member of her tribe of apes. Burroughs is a rather vague anthropologist. His apes have a language. They are carnivorous. They can, he suspects,

mate with human beings. Tarzan grows up as an ape; he kills his first lion (with a full nelson); he teaches himself to read and write English by studying some books found in the cabin. The method he used, sad to say, is the currently fashionable "look-see." Though he can read and write, he cannot speak any language except that of the apes. He gets on well with the animal kingdom, with Tantor the elephant, Ska the vulture, Numa the lion (Kipling has added his grist to the Burroughs dream mill). Then white people arrive: Professor Archimedes Q. Porter and his daughter Jane. Also, a Frenchman named D'Arnot who teaches Tarzan to speak French, which is confusing. By coincidence, Jane's suitor is the current Lord Greystoke, who thinks the Greystoke baby is dead. Tarzan saves Jane from an ape. Then he puts on clothes and goes to Paris where he drinks absinthe. Next stop, America. In Wisconsin, he saves Jane Porter from a forest fire; then he nobly gives her up to Lord Greystoke, not revealing the fact that *he* is the real Lord Greystoke. Fortunately in the next volume, *The Return of Tarzan*, he marries Jane and they live happily ever after in Africa, raising a son John, who in turn grows up and has a son. Yet even as a grandfather, Tarzan continues to have adventures with people a foot high, with descendants of Atlantis, with the heirs of a Roman legion who think that Rome is still a success. All through these stories one gets the sense that one is daydreaming, too. Episode follows episode with no particular urgency. Tarzan is always knocked on the head and taken captive; he always escapes; there is always a beautiful princess or high priestess who loves him and assists him; there is always a loyal friend who fights beside him, very much in the Queequeg tradition which Leslie Fiedler assures us is the burning of the fuel supply of the American psyche. But no matter how difficult the adventure, Tarzan, clad only in a loincloth with no weapon save a knife (the style is contagious), wins against all odds and returns to his shadowy wife.

These books are clearly for men. I have yet to meet a woman who found Tarzan interesting: no identification, as they say in series land.

Stylistically, Burroughs is—how shall I put it?—uneven. He has moments of ornate pomp, when the darkness is "Cimmerian"; of redundancy, "she was hideous and ugly"; of extraordinary dialogue: "Name of a name," shrieked Rokoff. "Pig, but you shall die for this!" Or Lady Greystoke to Lord G.: "Duty is duty, my husband, and no amount of sophistries may change it. I would be a poor wife for an English lord were I to be responsible for his shirking a plain duty." Or the grandchild: "Muvver," he cried, "Dackie doe? Dackie doe?" "Let him come along," urged Tarzan. "Dare!" exclaimed the boy turning triumphantly upon the governess, "Dackie do doe yalk!" Burroughs' use of coincidence is shameless even for a pulp writer. In one book he has three sets of characters shipwrecked at exactly the same point on the shore of Africa. Even Burroughs finds this a bit much. "Could it be possible [muses Tarzan] that fate had thrown him up at the very threshold of his own beloved jungle?" It was possible, of course; anything can happen in a daydream.

Though Burroughs is innocent of literature and cannot reproduce human speech, he does have a gift very few writers of any kind possess: he can describe action vividly. I give away no trade secrets when I say that this is as difficult for a Tolstoi as it is for a Burroughs (even William). Because it is so hard, the craftier contemporary novelists usually prefer to tell their stories in the first person, which is simply writing dialogue. In character, as it were, the writer settles for an impression of what happened rather than creating the sense of a happening. Tarzan *in action* is excellent.

There is something basic in the appeal of the 1914 Tarzan which makes me think that he can still hold his own as a daydream figure, despite the sophisticated challenge of his two contemporary competitors, Ian Fleming and Mickey Spillane. For most adults, Tarzan (and John Carter of Mars) can hardly compete with the conspicuous consumer consumption of James Bond or the sickly violence of Mike Hammer, but for children and adolescents, the old appeal continues. All of us need the idea of a world alternative to this one. From Plato's Republic to Opar to Bondland, at every level, the human imagination has tried to imagine something better for itself than the existing society. Man left Eden when we got up off all fours, endowing most of his descendants with nostalgia as well as chronic backache. In its naïve way, the Tarzan legend returns us to that Eden where, free of clothes and the inhibitions of an oppressive society, a man can achieve in reverie his continuing need, which is, as William Faulkner put it in his high Confederate style, to prevail as well as endure. The current fascination with LSD and non-addictive drugs —not to mention alcoholism—is all part of a general sense of frustration and boredom. The individual's desire to dominate his environment is not a desirable trait in a society which every day grows more and more confining. Since there are few legitimate releases for the average man, he must take to daydreaming. James Bond, Mike Hammer and Tarzan are all dream-selves, and the aim of each is to establish personal primacy in a world which in reality diminishes the individual. Among adults, the increasing popularity of these lively inferior fictions strikes me as a most significant (and unbearably sad) phenomenon.

Murray Kempton:

The Homecoming of Willie Mays

On the beginning of the end of a magnificent career

He was twenty when he began these voyagings, and he is supposed to have said then that this first trip around the league was like riding through a beautiful park and getting paid for it. Out of all those playgrounds, only Wrigley Field in Chicago is still used for baseball; everywhere else he is older than any piece of turf upon which he stands.

All has changed save him. No one else is still playing in the major leagues who was there when he arrived. Five managers are younger than he. In his first spring he saw the Braves in Boston; in his golden summer, he met them in Milwaukee; now, with the turning of his leaves, he finds them in Atlanta.

Before the New York Mets had ever played one game as a team, Willie Mays had already hit more home runs than all but six players then in the Hall of Fame. By now, he has stolen more bases than Rabbit Maranville, hit for more bases than either Ty Cobb or Babe Ruth, caught more fly balls than Tris Speaker, scored more runs than Honus Wagner and driven in more than Ted Williams.*

You have to come early to the Mets' warm-ups to be certain of seeing Mays; more days than not, his most extensive exposure to the public gaze comes at batting practice with the other pinch hitters, those "extra men" left over after the starting lineup has been named. He takes his cuts two hours before game time with the Jim Beauchamps, the Dave Marshalls, the Ed Kranepools; he has hit more than four times as many home runs as all three of these playmates put together. It is very soon noticed that Willie Mays is the only one among them who runs to the box when his turn comes. "I'm gonna *kill* you cockseekers

*These notations come from the Sporting News' Baseball Record Book. They are not offered as argument for Mays' superiority to anyone else but simply as a rough measure of his altitude in what is a range of mountaintops. Willie Mays may well be able to look at eye level at any other peak, except, of course, Babe Ruth. The best way to appreciate Ruth's place beyond all comparison is to notice achievements of his that few of us would associate with him. The whole history of the game encompasses only thirty players who stole home plate more than eight times in their careers; and one of them was Babe Ruth. There are six pitchers in the Hall of Fame who were parsimonious enough to have yielded an average of less than two-and-a-half earned runs a game over their lifetimes; they are, in order of excellence: Ed Walsh, Mordecai Brown, Christy Mathewson, Rube Waddell, Walter Johnson, and Babe Ruth.

In 1972 Murray Kempton served as Esquire's sports columnist. This reflection on a baseball legend ran in the September issue.

today," he laughs. He fouls off two pitches then drives one to the grass just past the infield. "That's a hit," he cries. "You *got* to give me that." They rule him out; "Cockseekers," he grumbles and wanders away to pick up balls for Coach Eddie Yost to hit to the fielders.

Here there bounds intact his image as eternal child. For here he takes his ease; he need fear no tests this night. But then there arrives an afternoon when he has been inscribed to start; and there falls upon him in the batting cage a desperation like the prisoner's in his cell. The face cherished by his countrymen along with Ernie Banks's as the last unaffectedly accommodating black one suddenly evokes some photograph from Attica, the nostrils flared, the eyes hot, the temper sour and nothing between him and despair except self-esteem.

Negroes who went young into the world put on and never quite took off a mask that carried them through the ordeal of inspection by great numbers of white people; Louis Armstrong was over sixty before he gave way to those occasional dark flashes that suggested how ancient was his bitterness and how often renewed by the condescensions of the middle class. Willie Mays had generally kept the mask of careless joy whenever the audience was larger than two dozen persons; still a private reputation, of having grown sullen with the years, had followed him back to New York and his new teammates had been surprised to find him exerting himself to please them.

He had been especially cheerful after the first evening he had suited up with the team and the occasion had arisen for a pinch hitter and Manager Yogi Berra had sent in John Milner instead of the Willie Mays for whose sight the crowd was crying. Happiness, then, must be an arrival at some place when everything is no longer expected of you; and contentment some assurance that this could be a workday when nothing at all is asked of you except to sit and watch.

But this day he was down to play and the young Mets who had joked with a man-child a few hours before looked now upon a brooding god. His life has been one long responsibility, more often met than not, but always feared. For nearly eighteen years he had carried the Giants. His memory is scarred by the recollection of fainting spells in locker rooms; of the team collapsing around him in 1959 while he alone held the gate with a broken finger and hit five home runs in the last two dreadful weeks of the season; of the arrival at the third game of last year's championship series so exhausted that, with no one out, a run already in and Tito Fuentes on second, he could only bunt and leave the decision up to Willie McCovey.

He does not want the load. He shouts for the bat boy to hurry and help him with his warm-up throws—"fuggin kids"—the playmate any other time, but now the imperial despot at bay.

Berra had him leading off. Mike Torrez, the Montreal pitcher, was not yet five years old the afternoon in 1951 when Willie Mays threw out Billy Cox from center field in the Polo Grounds, a ball traveling three hundred sixty feet to catch a fast man who had to run only ninety. Torrez paid his respects to this shrine by throwing two balls, the first wickedly close to the cap, the second evilly close to the chest. Willie Mays then watched a strike and another ball—he seemed as squat, as archaic, as immobile as some pre-Columbian figure of an athlete—then melted to protect himself with a foul tip and walked at last.

Ted Martinez came up to drive a long ball to right center and two outfielders turned and fled toward the wall with a gait that at once informed the ancient, glittering eyes of Willie Mays that men run like this when they have given up on the catch and hope only for a retrieval from the wall. Mays gunned around second and then, coming into third, quite suddenly slowed, became a runner on a frieze, and turned his head to watch the fielders. He was inducing the mental error; he had offered the illusion that he might be caught at home, which would give Ted Martinez time to get to third.

And only then did Willie Mays come down the line like thunder, ending in a heap at home, with the catcher sprawled in helpless intermingling with him and the relay throw bouncing through an unprotected plate and into the Montreal dugout. He was on his feet at once; his diversion had already allowed Martinez to run to third and he jumped up now to remind the umpire, in case he needed to, that when the ball goes into the dugout each runner is entitled to one more base. Ted Martinez was waved home and those two runs were the unique possession of Willie Mays, who had hit nothing except one tipped foul.

You remembered how often it had been said that Willie Mays knows more ways to beat you than anyone who ever played the game. But that was no more than comment; and here was presence; and all historical memory was wiped out for this moment when Willie Mays had paused at third as if to array himself as proclamation of an army with banners. It was beyond any mere note of excitement; it was the tone of absolute authority. When we hear it in the blues, it comes less often from the Delta than from Kansas City. It grows in the bones of scuffling, isolated country childhoods. It is much more broadly country Southern than it is uniquely black. The only baseball player before Jackie Robinson and Willie Mays who

played with that almost brutal abandon we call the black style was Enos Slaughter of the Cardinals, a native of Roxboro, North Carolina. You read the tone in Faulkner when Boon Clatterbuck stands beside the wagon "turbaned like a Paythan and taller than anyone there. . . . 'Them that's going,' he said, 'get in the goddam wagon. Them that ain't get out of the goddam way.'" You can hear it in the old Venuti-Lang record of *Farewell Blues*, where there is a deal of slush and then a kind of stuttered note on the trombone and Jack Teagarden pushing everyone else aside. Boon Clatterbuck throwing his whiskey bottle away, Jack Teagarden almost clearing his throat, Willie Mays arraying himself for the charge—three pauses to assemble the irascible, occasionally even vicious dignity of the Southern country boy's announcement that he is taking command of the city ones.

Those were all the runs the Mets would have that afternoon; and they would be just enough to win. Willie Mays did nothing else except catch two fly balls and thus twice routinely set a new record for total putouts by an outfielder in the whole twentieth century. In the locker room Yogi Berra did one of the minor managerial duties he was taught by Casey Stengel, in this case catering to the susceptibilities of the journalists for mythmaking. "I think Willie timed that throw," he attested. "I've seen him do that before. He slows down and tries to hit the plate at the same time as the throw to make it hard on the catcher." "Yogi lies a lot," said Willie Mays affectionately. "You can't time no throw like that."

And he departed for Philadelphia and on Saturday drove in the first run with a double and scored the winning run after a walk, and the next day he beat the Phillies with a home run; the next Wednesday he scored the only run in a Met defeat; and Thursday he singled to break a tie with the Cubs after having played fourteen innings. He had returned to New York from San Francisco as half a pensioner; yet he had played six games and had produced or scored the winning run in five of them. In Chicago he hurt his finger, scrambling for some fragment of first base; he was healing and infrequently seen for the next two weeks. By June 8, he was healthy and marked down to start against the Reds. By then he had come to bat thirty-seven times as a Met and gotten on base nineteen of them; even so, as the shadow of responsibility came once more toward him, he again withdrew into that brooding silence from which no diplomatic jape of his teammates could coax him forth; isolated in the rubbing room, he left them to wait on the field until just before the game began.

It began and would end most alarmingly. The Commissioner of Baseball had come to Shea Stadium in May to wonder aloud what sort of dynasty was being built here; but Bowie Kuhn is the stockholder type, which is to say that he fell off a horse when he was four years old, or suffered some such blow to his reason, and has since been conditioned to see in any transient rise of an issue the promise of unbreaking ascent. The Mets had since settled back to the scrabbling of the accustomed existence of teams able to trust their arms and their gloves more than their bats;

and now they would win a close game and then they would lose another. And this day, in the first inning, the Reds fell for four runs on Tom Seaver, the league's most effective pitcher last year. The Mets built a run in the first; Seaver righted himself thereafter but the game remained at four to one until the fifth when Mays singled off the pitcher's shoulder and there followed two runs. Tony Perez hit a home run, and the Mets came to the bottom of the ninth behind, five to three. Ed Kranepool pinch-hit a gentle single; and then Willie Mays was up. He swung so hard at the first pitch that his hat flew off; the respect of two successive balls was offered him and then, more viciously than before, he swung and shot a single like a 40mm. shell to left field. As often happens with him, you felt that the pitch had fooled him and that, in his passion, he had simply overpowered it. The note of authority had been struck; he was on first and Kranepool on second and there were no outs. The note vibrated in the air and there it died. Bud Harrelson bunted and Perez came down from first and seized the ball and threw out Kranepool at third. That killed it; the next two hitters expired on grounders and Mays was left at third.

He had had two hits for three official at-bats; yet afterward his solitary gloom was impenetrable. It had been an afternoon to stir uneasy prospects. There were so many small things: a lead runner thrown out at third base, the foundation stone of the pitching staff inexplicably shaky, such big hitters as the roster holds failing—all signs that the Mets would never know the comfort of being enough ahead or the resignation of being enough behind. No, it would go on all summer, one more of those desperate adventures with an incomplete team that Willie Mays had known so often before with the Giants until the familiar horror of those final weeks whose reiterated torment had brought him, as long ago as 1965, to confess how permanently drained he was: "No. There is nothing in baseball that can get me excited anymore." And yet there is not another Met who has known the ordeal of a close pennant race more than once in his career; and Willie Mays has been there eight times before. So, more and more, they would have to turn to him with too much of the load, and this would be another one of those cruel summers that, for just a little while, in the sun with the extra men, he had been able to entertain the illusion of escaping. Scowling, he strode through the children who had waited for him at the gate and alone he drove away, his face fixed in its contempt for destiny; everything that he had proved through all those years was worthless to appease him; nothing was ahead of him but the implacable duty of needing to prove everything all over again. Fuggin kids.

George Frazier:

Cold Thoughts on the Hot Medium

Reflections on the stylelessness of TV

The one has that tight-lipped smile, as if he'd just smelled something unpleasant, and the other is so insufferably pixieish, so excruciatingly unfunny, that he makes me want to throw up. Still, godawful as they are, Huntley and Brinkley may not be entirely to blame for their pedestrian performances. After all, television itself can hardly disavow a certain responsibility, since, in giving them exposure, it endorses their ineptitude, condones their singular lack of anything even remotely resembling charisma. But by now it seems clear that one of the authentic tragedies of our time is that television, which is almost incontestably the most influential taste-maker in the history of communications, has betrayed its trust, offering us, except on rare occasions, not stylishness, but the dreadful likes of Andy Williams.

Those outfits he wears, like something out of a mail-order catalog, like something not-to-be-believed in the window of a Midwest department store; that colossal cheek with which, come Christmastime, he inflicts his wife and children on his viewers! Where, one wonders, does he get those clothes? Were they left over from some ancient Perry Como program—and, in any case, isn't there somebody with enough authority and taste to tell him what a revolting, what a foolish, figure he cuts? And, oddly, he isn't all that bad a vocalist, either—no Sinatra, of course, no Arthur Prysock, no Tony Bennett, no Brook Benton, no Bill Henderson, no Buddy Greco, but far from the bottom of the barrel just the same. But those clothes and that foisting of his family on us—things like that make you wonder.

They make you wonder exactly what television has in mind. Is it deliberately endeavoring to endear itself to the lowest common denominator; is it cagily trying to make the stupid and the slovenly feel self-assured by exposing them to personalities who, with few ex-

ceptions, could hardly be less housebroken, and not merely in the matter of what they wear, but in their unctuous obsequiousness, their uninspired efforts at wit and humor, their indifference to the beauty and resonance of the English language?

But, to be perfectly fair, there are, and have been, a number of offenders more flagrant than either Andy Williams or the heavenly twins of the NBC news department.

Art Linkletter, for one, can be pretty disgusting—that coyness, those clothes, those clichés, and, of course, that sly, sanctimonious device of getting away with the risqué and downright dirty by quoting the innocent indecencies of little children. And, besides him, there are people like the once-impressive John Daly, who now acts so coyly on *What's My Line?*; and a sports announcer named Gowdy, who once observed that the ballplayer Wes Parker "was originally born in Chicago"; and Allen Ludden, whose only evidence of talent would seem to be an inane grin; and— But there is no need to go on, for what is rather more significant is that television gives such incompetents gainful employment.

I have certain theories about the tastelessness of television and one of them is that David Sarnoff has just about as much to answer for as to be proud of. After all, if the most imposing figure in an industry (and television is much more an industry than an art) is undiscriminating, lesser men engaged in the same line of endeavor are likely to follow suit. And for all his technological enterprise and imagination, the General (as he has yet to resent being called) has never had any real sense of style. Over the not inconsiderable years, Mr. Sarnoff has either committed or taken no action against a great many reprehensible bits of business that have impeded the artistic progress of a medium which he practically created and for which his enthusiasm is unquestioned. What I am thinking of are, among other outrages, the appointment of his son, Lieutenant Robert (Somebody Up There Likes Me) Sarnoff to a position of prodigious power, a power, by the way, that he has demonstrated

George Frazier, a columnist for The Boston Globe, has been for many years one of Esquire's strongest voices on matters of class, taste, and good manners. This essay ran in 1967 and is an example of the numerous columns Frazier wrote for the magazine.

an almost unique inability to administer, at least with an eye to the art of the matter; the cashiering of Sylvester (Pat) Weaver, a man of impeccable taste and one of television's very few authentic geniuses; the "live" telecast of only the opening ceremonies of the Tokyo Olympic Games; and, naturally, the care and feeding of Jack Paar.

In our time, at least on television, there has been no better interviewer than Paar. That much we must acknowledge, for he was probing, irreverent, and provocative. He stripped interviews of the inane amenities and got right to the heart of things, and, as a result, our midnights were touched by the magic of truth, by a candor that television had rarely, if ever, exhibited before. But having acknowledged this much, one is left with what was atrocious. And some of the things he did were inexcusable, not the least of them being his granting exposure, week after week, to such tiresome Hungarians as Zsa Zsa Gabor. And largely because he had such nervy pretensions to taste and style, Paar was perhaps the least stylish, the most tasteless, figure in the short and simpleminded annals of television. His arrogance in enfranchising somebody as noisy and vulgar and uninformed as Peggy Cass to voice her views on the Berlin Wall! His unpardonable nepotism in burdening his audience with the inarticulate presence of his daughter Randy! His leering; his outhouse humor; his shameless weeping! He was simply unforgivable. And as for his lack of even the slightest chic, one night, looking at Robert Montgomery's red-and-blue-striped necktie, he gushed, "I gotta get me a tie like that." And perhaps he should, although it would probably be more discreet if he arranges for membership in the Racquet Club first.

But the point is less that Jack Paar was lacking in grace than that the Sarnoffs and NBC took him to task, not for his major offenses, but for a relatively harmless joke about a water closet. Night after night he promoted the non-books either written by him or ghosted for him and his second bananas; program after program he promoted personal appearances by his announcer and his orchestra leader. Certainly, if NBC had had any genuine concern for the common weal, it would have censored him for all this self-service and for what was one of the most disgraceful attacks ever made on another person. This was his vicious comment on the late Dorothy Kilgallen's physical appearance. It was television's most contemptible moment and the next time some well-meaning but muddled organization contemplates giving a plaque for public service to either of the Sarnoffs, it would do well to bear in mind what, of a meretricious midnight, was said about Miss Kilgallen by Jack Paar, whom the General and the Lieutenant had incubated, encouraged, and endorsed.

Still, it would be a gross injustice as well as slanted journalism to exempt all but the Sarnoffs from culpability. After all, mediocrity or worse is the measure of television and if NBC has those two, why, CBS had its Aubrey, while ABC, except for a few people like Howard K. Smith and Edward P. Morgan, is almost unrelievedly awful. Red Skelton, *The Beverly Hillbillies*, Jack E. Leonard, Buddy

Hackett, Bess Meyerson, *Petticoat Junction*, Joan Rivers, the Oscar awards, and the simpering of Bert Parks on the Miss America pageant, those things sum up the tastelessness of television; they, and also, of course, Huntley and what's-his-name. Those shows, those personalities—they are why so many discriminating people confine their viewing largely to the old movies on *The Late Show*. Lewis Stone and Herbert Marshall and C. Aubrey Smith—now there was style!

Yet the objection to most newscasters is not (as it is to so much else that's ghastly about television) that they are incompetent, but that they have no wit, no subtlety, no insight, no feeling for the nuances of the language. Naturally, there are those who argue that there is no place for such graces in a mass medium like television, and most of the time it seems that they have a point. Yet more than a decade ago—on the evening of March 9, 1954—Edward R. Murrow proved how much in error they are. That was when, on his and Fred Friendly's *See It Now*, he dissected, and with a scalpel, not a hacksaw, the demagoguery of Joseph R. McCarthy. Here is his peroration:

"This is no time for men who oppose Senator McCarthy's methods to keep silent or for those who approve. We can deny our heritage and our history but we cannot escape responsibility for the result. There is no way for a citizen of a republic to abdicate his responsibilities. As a nation we have come into our full inheritance at a tender age. We proclaim ourselves, as indeed we are, the defenders of freedom, what's left of it, but we cannot defend freedom abroad by deserting it at home. The actions of the junior Senator from Wisconsin have caused alarm and dismay amongst our allies abroad and given considerable comfort to our enemies, and whose fault is that? Not really his, he didn't create this situation of fear, he merely exploited it and rather successfully. Cassius was right, 'The fault, dear Brutus, is not in our stars, but in ourselves.' . . . Good night, and good luck.''

Now Murrow is in the ground and never again will we know the reassurance of that "Good night, and good luck" coming to us "live" from amid the rubble of the Blitz. Yet there is the legacy he left us. It was one aspect of Murrow's greatness that he trained men, if only by precept, to report and interpret the news with distinction and dedication. The trouble with Huntley and Brinkley is that, unlike Eric Sevareid and Howard K. Smith, and indirectly, Walter Cronkite and Harry Reasoner, they never had the benefit of being "Murrow's boys," and for that they are to be pitied, for the ones who were are now the very special, the only really eloquent, voices in the wasteland of television. They have a touch of the poet in their prose, the sagacity of a seer in their assessments. To them, the world we live in is something more than merely a matter of headlines. It is a place of fun and sadness and shiny dreams, and Ed Murrow's boys are our observers, our interpreters, the elegant little essays of Eric Sevareid like pages out of Walter Pater, the wry *obiter dicta* of Harry Reasoner as warm and amusing and graceful as a column by Red Smith. But let me cite some Scripture. For instance, there was this by Reasoner on the day the creator of 007 was gathered to his fathers:

"None of us ever expected to have to write Ian Fleming's obituary so soon; it is a real shock, as if Tarzan had died. It is really as if the grown-ups had won. Because we all assumed, all the time, that Fleming thought he was James Bond, just as each of us did. We all sat back and worried about our cigarettes and our extra drink and felt a little fatigued at the thought of love, but Bond went ahead with all the things that the grown-ups said were impractical: he smoked like Peter Lorre and drank like Humphrey Bogart and ate like Sidney Greenstreet and used up girls like Errol Flynn and then went out to a steam bath and came out looking like Clark Gable. It was all so reassuring that we never stopped to think that all these people are dead until Fleming died. . . .

"In a world where almost all the writers are so grown-up and dull that they take both the Russians and sex seriously, we will miss Mr. Fleming."

And this is what he had to observe of the marriage vows heard round the world:

"Elizabeth Taylor, the American actress, and Richard Burton, the Welsh actor, were married today in Montreal. The couple met two years ago while they were working on a picture in Rome, and have been good friends ever since."

And Eric Sevareid? Well, there has never been anyone on television, except perhaps Murrow himself, quite so civilized, quite so stylish. Here, for instance, is what he had to say—and extemporaneously at that! —on Election Night last November when it was announced that Edward Brooke, a Negro, had defeated Endicott Peabody, the grandson of the legendary Rector of Groton, for a seat in the Senate of the United States:

"There's another kind of drama, it seemed to me, in what's happened up in Massachusetts. There's a kind of a beautiful irony in this election of Mr. Brooke to the Senate, defeating Chub Peabody. Here's the Peabody family, an old and distinguished family of New England, comes from the old abolitionist tradition, the father an Episcopal bishop, I believe; the grandfather I think was head of Groton School. You remember Peabody's mother in her seventies not long ago went down into Florida and was arrested for picketing and demonstrating on behalf of Negro rights. The kind of family in enlightened New England that made an Edward Brooke and his career possible over the years. And one was raised up and has defeated a Peabody now. I find something kind of beautiful about this. I don't know why."

And here, in part, is Sevareid's *ave atque vale* to Walt Disney:

"It would take more time than anybody has around the daily news shops to think of the right thing to say about Walt Disney.

"He was an original; not just an American original, but an original, period. He was a happy accident; one of the happiest this century has experienced; and judging by the way it's been behaving in spite of all Disney tried to tell it about laughter, love, children, puppies, and sunrises, the century hardly deserved him.

"He probably did more to heal or at least to soothe troubled human spirits than all the psychiatrists in the world. There can't be many adults in the allegedly civilized parts of the globe who did not inhabit Disney's mind and imagination at least for a few hours and feel better for the visitation.

"It may be true, as somebody said, that while there is no highbrow in a lowbrow, there is some lowbrow in every highbrow.

"But what Walt Disney seemed to know was that while there is very little grown-up in a child, there is a lot of child in every grown-up. To a child this weary world is brand new, gift wrapped; Disney tried to keep it that way for adults. . . .

"By the conventional wisdom, mighty mice, flying elephants, Snow White and Happy, Grumpy, Sneezy and Dopey—all these were fantasy, escapism from reality. It's a question of whether they are any less real, any more fantastic than intercontinental missiles, poisoned air, defoliated forests, and scrap iron on the moon. This is the age of fantasy, however you look at it; but Disney's fantasy wasn't lethal. People are saying we'll never see his like again."

And then, separating the men from the boys and with such style as is alien to Huntley and Brinkley, his last two words:

"We'd better."

Thomas B. Morgan:

What Makes Sammy Jr. Run?

First, anger made Sammy run, and now it's irony:
no matter how big you make it,
you never make it all the way

In a typical ten-day period recently, Sammy Davis Jr. had this schedule: the final week of an eighteen-day engagement at the Copacabana (sixteen performances interspersed with general frolicking, a record date, television and radio interviews, and two visits with Cye Martin, his tailor); a one-night stand in Kansas City to receive an Americanism award from the American Legion; one night at home in Hollywood; and the opening night of a two-week date in Las Vegas at the Sands Hotel, the management of which has a contract with him for the next four years, eight weeks a year, at $25,000 per week. The schedule could have been extended. The day after closing in Vegas, Davis was due for three weeks in Hollywood at the Moulin Rouge, another night-club with which he has a five-year million-dollar deal, followed by two weeks in Australia, followed by an Eastern tour. Photographer Burt Glinn and I, however, arbitrarily pursued Davis through that ten-day period. Since this short, skinny, one-eyed, broken-nosed, umber-colored singer-dancer-musician-actor-mimic may be, as Milton Berle has said, "the greatest entertainer in the world," and may even be, as Groucho Marx has decided, "better than Al Jolson, who could only sing," we wanted to find out what we could, naturally, about what makes Sammy Jr. run.

Like most men, Davis lives a life of quiet desperation. The only differences are that he has little privacy to live it in and that on the average of twice a night, thirty weeks a year, he must stand in a spotlight and be Sammy Davis Jr.—cosmic, sentimental, bursting with energy, and immensely talented—no matter how he feels inside. If he were an average performer, the challenge might not be so great.

"But you see," says Davis, "what I do is different. Most Negro performers work in a cubicle. They walk on, entertain, and sing twelve songs before they say good evening. They never make any personal contact with the audience. Long time ago, I knew I could only make it if I broke through this wall. I was convinced that a Negro boy could do comedy—you know the kind I mean. Not the yassuh, nossuh thing. I decided I could make it as a person, like Jolson or Danny Kaye made it. Well, to do that, you have to be honest with an audience. You got to have antennae and feel what they want. And you have to try to keep your personal feelings from interfering with your communication."

The Davis act has a basic structure—songs, impersonations, dancing, laced together with comic patter or sentimental chitchat. The structure never changes, yet every performance is different.

"The patter between songs," says Davis, "is something that can't be planned. You can't write it if you're going to be honest. I can vary the act at any minute with a signal to Morty Stevens, my conductor. I snap my fingers a certain way and he knows we are going to go into *Let's Face the Music*. I tap my foot just so, and it's going to be *Old Black Magic*. If you're honest, you can feel the right way to get to them every time. Otherwise, Dullsville, Ohio. I don't mean all good shows are alike, either. You've got three kinds of shows—a routine show, a fun show, and a performance show. The fun show is lots of tumult and laughs. The performance show is the one, like opening night, where you belt it all the way. What I do works because I am trying to be honest.

"You take most of the material in my act: aside from the songs, I don't do any bits that I didn't contribute to. I have a choreographer—Hal Loman—but we work out the dances together. Nothing fancy about my dancing. I like to make clear sounds with the taps. Bojangles—that's Bill Robinson, who taught me a lot—he used to say, 'Make it so the people can understand it.' That's what I try to do.

"Sometimes the impersonations get in the way. They blur your image with the people and you die as a performer without a distinction of your own. I used to do a song called *Why Can't I Be Me?* That's the story of most of my life. Every guy wants to sound like himself. But I keep the impersonations in the act

Until recently, Mr. Morgan was Press Secretary to New York's Mayor John V. Lindsay, but before that he was a copious magazine writer, contributing to Esquire profiles of Blaze Starr, John Wayne, Bennett Cerf and Teddy Kennedy, among others. This article on Sammy Davis Jr. appeared in October, 1959.

because the audience wants them. They're like a frame. The audience says, gee, that's his best stuff, what's he going to give us next?

"The big thing is understanding the songs and projecting them honestly. When I sing *I Got Plenty o' Nuttin'*, I think about a guy who is happy with his life. Doesn't make any difference how *I* feel. I think how *he* feels. When you have that, daddy, you don't need any tricks. All I want is they should like me—say this is a nice guy. Just let them give me one thing—applause—and I'm happy."

Nightclub audiences do curious things when Davis is onstage. For one, they are prone to give him standing ovations. For another, they tend to gasp out telling comments—telling about themselves as well as the performer. Early in his act, Davis comes on wearing a grey porkpie hat, black suit, black shirt, white tie, with a trench coat flung over his shoulder, a cigarette in one hand and a glass of whiskey-colored water in the other. He blows smoke into the microphone, sips the drink, and says, "My name is Frank Sinatra, I sing songs, and we got a few we'd like to lay on ya." Davis puts the drink on the piano, throws the trench coat on the floor, and begins *The Lady Is a Tramp*. The audience always applauds wildly and somebody is certain to cry out: "My God, he even looks like Sinatra," or words to that effect. A broken-nosed Negro does not look much like Sinatra, even though the latter is no work of art himself, but the illusion of Davis' voice and visage and movements, plus the complete rapport which has been established between entertainer and entertainees, produces a kind of Sinatrian hallucination.

For the full sixty minutes of his act, Davis sustains this kind of communication. It could be defined as an atmosphere of colorlessness in which he not only makes the audience forget that he is a Negro, but also makes it forget that it is white. This is why one of his closing bits has a special irony that is all Davis. He is sitting on a stool in a circle of light. He has, it seems, almost sung himself out in an effort to entertain. His coat and tie are off. He takes a few deep breaths and suddenly he brightens. "What do you say?" he asks. "Let's all get in a cab and go up to my place!" For one goofy moment, nobody laughs. Here is the source of his power and also the reason for his private desperation. In the spotlight, he and they are colorless. In the real world, he is a colored man who has made it and yet can never make it all the way. When the applause finally comes, it is deafening. The performance drives to a rocking, exploding, belting finish, and Davis is gone. As someone once said, "The only thing that could follow that act is World War Three."

Thus driving and thus driven, Sammy Davis made $1,200,000 last year—over half from nightclubs and the rest from records, TV, and movies. When you say it slowly, it sounds like a lot of money, but his net is considerably less. Besides taxes (he's in the ninety percent bracket), he has eleven people on his payroll: valet, secretary, conductor-arranger, drummer, guitarist, office manager, typists (for answering fan mail), and various assistants; his overhead is $3,500 a week.

His agent takes ten percent. And even though his father retired from the act in 1959, because of a heart attack, and his uncle, Will Mastin, moved over from dance manager to manager in 1958, he still splits what is left equally with them, and presents the act to the public as the Will Mastin Trio featuring Sammy Davis Jr.

The three-way split of the profits is unique in show business. Davis believes he must spend on the "millionaire" level, yet the contract with father and uncle provides him with a mere thirty-three percent, of which still another ten percent goes to a group of Chicago investors.

Davis has not saved much money nor has he put his earnings to work for him with any conspicuous success. He owns a piece of an unspectacular restaurant in Hollywood and has an interest in a line of sports shirts ("Creations by Sammy Davis Jr.") and a hand grip for cameras. He put money into some TV and movie properties. But mostly the money goes for living well, if not too wisely. It would be surprising if it went any other way.

Davis was born in Harlem, December 8, 1925. His mother, father, and uncle were all in show business. He went onstage before he was three in a theatre in Columbus, Ohio. He did a talking act with Uncle Will when he was three and a half. He appeared in a movie, *Rufus Jones for President*, made at Warner Brothers' Long Island studios, at age four. The next year, in the midst of singing *I'll Be Glad When You're Dead, You Rascal You* at the Republic Theatre in Manhattan, he was pulled off the stage by a member of the Gerry Society, which enforced child-labor laws in those days. Until he was eleven, he trouped with his uncle's fifteen-person vaudeville act. When the authorities became suspicious, his father put cork on his face, stuck a cigar in his mouth, and passed him off as a dancing midget. In 1936, the vaudeville act was disbanded and the Will Mastin Trio, a straight dancing act, was born. They danced in beer gardens and theatres all over the East, making as little as $30 a week (for the trio) and spending part of the time on relief. Davis' education consisted of less than two years in school and a few lessons from a now-and-then tutor.

In 1943, Davis was drafted into the Army. He passed the Air Corps cadet tests, but Negroes with less than two years of college training were not being accepted. He was transferred to the Infantry, in which he took basic training in one of the earliest integrated units. Three times he was rejected for overseas duty because of an athletic heart. Toward the end of the war, he was transferred again, to Special Services. In camp shows, he developed as a singer and mimic. "What was more important," says Davis, "I met a sergeant by the name of Bill Williams who gave me about fifty books to read. He's really the guy who educated me."

After the war, with Davis' songs and impersonations added to the act, the trio's luck improved. They traveled six months with Mickey Rooney, who encouraged Davis to develop all of his talents instead of concentrating on just one. Frank Sinatra, whom first met in 1940, got them three weeks on t the Capitol on Broadway in 1947. In spite rable reviews, nothing happened. They toured West Coast with Jack Benny, through whose help they were booked into Ciro's, Hollywood, in 1951. Herman Hover, the owner of Ciro's, offered them $300 a week to open a show starring Janis Paige. The trio held out for $350. Finally, Arthur Silber, their agent, put up $50 of his own for the first week, and the contract was signed. The act caught fire. By the second week, the Will Mastin Trio was costarred with the headliner. They moved on to a date at the Chez Paree in Chicago at $1,250 a week and were not headed again.

After twenty-three years, Davis had become an overnight sensation. In the eight years that followed, the trio went round and round on the nightclub circuit—New York, Miami, Chicago, Las Vegas, and Hollywood. Davis made eleven record albums for Decca Records. He took intermittent turns as a guest performer on TV—notably *The Comedy Hour* and *The Steve Allen Show*. He appeared in *Mr. Wonderful* on Broadway—a mediocre show that ran for a year because it was cheaper for Davis' growing audience to see him in a theatre than in a nightclub. In Hollywood, he made *Anna Lucasta* and the spectacular *Porgy and Bess*. The money poured in.

"After that night in Ciro's," Davis recalls, "every day for three years I had a new chick—wine, women, and song. After the war, I'd been hungry and mad, baby. You couldn't work certain hotels because of the Negro bit. Certain headliners refused to go on with us because we stole the show. I was so hungry. I was trying to do everything. We used to do an hour-and-forty-minute show. I could do fifty impersonations. Play the drums. Play the trumpet. Play the bass fiddle. Play the piano. Dance. Sing. Tell jokes.

"Well, then we made it. It's the old story of the guy who doesn't have it and then gets it. He fluffs friends. He does a hundred things wrong. He *knows* he's doing wrong, see, but he can't stop.

"I bought twelve suits at a time—$175 a whack. I bought tailor-made shirts, cars—fast ones. Once I bought twenty-one pairs of shoes from Lefcourt in New York. All my life, I wanted to buy something in a store and not ask how much. I lost all sense of value. I had credit everywhere and just signed my name. Between 1951 and 1954, I must have blown $150,000. My head got *so big*. I wanted to pick up every check and pay every tip. The first time I was booked into the Copa in New York, I bought a pack of cigarettes and left the girl change from a twenty-dollar bill. I wanted to do that because once I went in there as a nobody and they put me on the side. I bought a Cadillac El Dorado. I bought gold cigarette cases for everybody. I remembered when, for Christmas presents, my dad and uncle and I used to exchange a carton of cigarettes. Every day was like Christmas. I got snotty. Everybody I saw, it was, 'Hello, chickee. Love ya, baby. See you later.'

"It takes a terribly long time to learn how to be a success in show business. People flatter you all the time. You are *on* all the time. And if you're a Negro, you find yourself using your fame to make it socially. Let's face it. The biggest deals with the big moguls are made in a social way, around the pool, that sort of thing. If you're not there, well, you're not *there*. So I used to think the greatest thing in the world was to be invited to a movie star's house.

"Things got bad. One night in Vegas, I lost $39,000 playing blackjack. That's how bad it was. There's nobody who's got that much money to lose.

"I feel I've been changing. If a man doesn't change, he isn't one to swing with. But his friends stick by him while he's changing.

"November 19, 1954, I'm driving along with a buddy at eight in the morning near San Bernardino on the way to Hollywood. It was a beautiful, typical, happy California morning. A car pulled out of a blind drive and I hit it going fifty-five or sixty. The steering wheel hit me in the face. I got the car stopped and ran over to see if the lady in the other car was all right. She was, until she looked at me. She turned green. Then I felt my left eye. They took me to the hospital and Dr. Owen O'Connor and Dr. Frederick Hull removed the eye. If they hadn't done that, I might have gone blind in a month. I spent three, four days in total darkness. I began thinking about my faults. I was sure God had saved my life. That's when I began to change.

"I met a rabbi at a Jewish benefit in Las Vegas and got interested in Judaism. I found the faith gave me something I'd been missing—peace of mind—so I converted. When I am home, in Hollywood, I try to attend services whenever I can. For a long time, I was reluctant to go into a synagogue. I was afraid people would think I was trying to pull something. While we were working on *Porgy and Bess*, Sam Goldwyn thought I was kidding when I said I wanted to be excused for the High Holy Days. Then he had to believe me when I said I would take off anyway.

"I admit the Jewish thing had been a bit of a problem. It couldn't have been more of a problem if I'd have had my eyes fixed and become Japanese. But I think everyone has to find God his own way. Sometimes it takes something like the loss of an eye to get you thinking about it. Life is very confused and you need something. I accept the Jewish idea of God. As I see it, the difference is that the Christian religion preaches love thy neighbor and the Jewish religion preaches justice. I think justice is the big thing we need."

Davis has not been without a sense of humor about his religious conversion. During his nightclub act he is likely to say, "I could have starred in *The Defiant Ones*, but I lost the part when they found out I was Jewish," or "The Irish kept me out of the St. Patrick's Day Parade for *two* reasons." On the *Porgy and Bess* set he looked accusingly at German-speaking director Otto Preminger and said: "You made lampshades out of my people." But the justice he seeks, of course, is the most elusive of human ideals. Instead, there is irony, which Sammy Davis runs from and into almost every day of his life.

During his stay in New York last spring, Davis' dressing room was a small, seedy, two-room suite on the third floor of the Hotel Fourteen, which adjoins the Copacabana. One night after his late show, the average crowd of thirty people was milling in the twelve-by-fifteen-foot living room. Among them were Sidney Poitier, the actor, and Archie Moore, the fighter; Fran Warren, the singer, and Althea Gibson, the tennis star; three plainclothes cops ("just friends"), and a Mrs. Goldman and her daughter ("We're fans!") from Queens, Long Island, and twenty-or-so other people who were helping themselves to the liquor, watching TV, and fooling around with the expensive portable stereo rig on the mantel—yakking and puffing as though none of the satires on show biz had ever been written.

Davis was in the bedroom, wearing a white terry-cloth robe with a torn pocket and drinking bourbon-and-Coke from a sterling-silver goblet, which a friend had given him. With him were his valet, Murphy Bennett; his secretary, Dave Landfield, who looks a little like Rip Torn and is an aspiring actor; and a man from Hollywood, one Abby Greshler, who seemed proudest of the fact that he originally brought Dean Martin and Jerry Lewis together as a team. Greshler was there to organize a movie vehicle for Davis based on Joey Adam's novel, *The Curtain Never Falls*, about a Broadway-Hollywood star and heel. As usual, Davis was conducting his business in a fishbowl. He has no secrets from his valet, his secretary, or from almost anyone else. In exchange, his employees are deeply attached to him. A guest once said to his valet: "Tell you what, Murphy, I'll kill Sammy, and you come work for me." Bennett replied: "If Sammy dies, I'll just have to go with him."

Davis was passionately convinced that *The Curtain Never Falls* with himself in the lead would be an important step forward for all Negro actors and entertainers.

"So the hero in the book is Jewish," he said. "We make him a Negro. It works, motivation and everything. Look, I want to make it as a movie actor. I always wanted to act, but what chance was there? I remember when the reviews came out for *Mr. Wonderful*—everyone was crying about the beating we took and I was walking on air because Brooks Atkinson said I was a believable actor. Atkinson said that. Or you take *Porgy and Bess*. Now I simply *had* to play Sportin' Life. I mean, he was me. I worked to get that part. My friends—Frank and all the rest—worked to get it for me. So one night after Sam Goldwyn saw me perform, he called me into his office and pointed his finger. 'You,' he said, 'you are Sportin' Life.' Let me tell you, I mean, playing that part was the gasser of my life."

"Well, this'll be great, too," said Greshler.

"The way I see it, Abby, the movie positively can't preach. It's got to show it. Here's this hero. He knows there are only three ways a colored cat can make it: as a fighter, ballplayer, or entertainer. He's got to make it, see? I remember one time a guy asked me, 'How far you going to make it, Sammy?' and I said, 'I've got an agent, some material, and talent.' So the guy says, 'Yes,' but you're colored.' And I said, 'I can beat all this.' Now this is what the hero in the movie

wants. Only he's ready to renounce everything he is to make it. He's a character who's ashamed of his father, see? That's the way we'll do it. People have to believe it's honest."

"They will, Sammy, they will," said Greshler.

Davis and Greshler shook hands, resealing their contract, which would never be more formal than that until the money talk began in Hollywood. Davis turned and walked into the living room to join his guests. In the crowd, he looked smaller than he seems onstage. He is about five foot six and weighs only a hundred and twenty-five pounds. His hair, combed flat, is neither brown nor black, but somewhere in between. It is next to impossible to determine which eye is the blind one. He has a U-shaped scar across the bridge of his nose, which was broken in the 1954 accident. His face is thin, the jaw slightly underslung. As Bob Sylvester once said, he looks as though he had been hit in the face with a shovel.

Davis spied Sidney Poitier, who is husky and tall and reminds you of an unspoiled Belafonte who can also act.

"Sidney!" cried Davis. "I'm glad to see you, baby!"

Sidney Poitier embraced him, lifting him off his feet. The room, which had been shaking with noise, became quiet, except for some shooting on the TV, and Tony Bennett lisping on the stereo.

"Everybody's got to see it, baby," said Davis, turning to a clot of people on his blind side. "I mean, you have to see Sidney in *Raisin*. Only the end—a definite gas!"

Now Davis embraced Poitier, then backed away, bending over, shoulders hunched, hands dangling in a precise imitation of Poitier in *A Raisin in the Sun*, crying: "I'm thirty-five and what am I—I'm *nothing*!"

A girl laughed, "Oh, you're something, Sam, and you're only thirty-three," and everyone laughed with her.

"She's got to die," said Davis, pinching her cheek. "If she makes one more remark, death!"

The crowd began to thin out after a while. Poitier and Moore and many of the people that no one knew departed. Davis paused to say good-bye as each one left. At the door, he did a short bit with a girl who asked him how he was getting along with the head doctor. Davis has had some psychoanalysis, but he is rarely in Hollywood long enough to accomplish much.

"Well, I've had a little, baby," said Davis. "I'm still sick, but I understand it now, see what I mean? I told the doc I didn't want to understand myself, I just wanted to be better. So he says, what you got, a cold or something—what better?"

Then Davis kissed her cheek and sent her on her way. A hard core of a dozen cordial-to-very-close friends remained. Dave Landfield, the secretary, strapped on one of the two gun belts hanging in the closet and practiced his fast draw.

"Not that way, Dave! Dave—God, I could draw faster with a pencil and paper," Davis said. "Get the thumb on the hammer, man, and do it all in one motion."

Over his bathrobe, Davis buckled on a gun belt

a single-action Colt .45 six-shooter. He tied
ther things above his knee. He drew the gun,
it three times over his trigger finger, and
ought it down smartly into the holster. He drew
again, very fast, cocking and dry-firing in a split second. Then he twirled the gun vertically, horizontally,
over and back into the holster. (In Hollywood, Davis
has a collection of thirty Western guns and, next to
Mel Tormé, he is the fastest nonprofessional draw in
town. Once I saw him hold a bottle at waist level,
throw the bottle to the floor, and draw, cock, and
shoot before it hit the carpet. "I love things Western,"
he says. "Morty, Dave, Arthur Silber, and I go to
Phoenix and dress up in the tailor-made jeans and
the tailor-made shirts, the cowboy hats, .45's on our
hips and Winchesters in the saddle holsters. We ride
out like cowboys and talk about the south forty, tip
the hat back with the thumb, and chew on filter
cigarettes.") Davis demonstrated the fast draw a few
more times.

"You dig, baby?" asked Davis.

Landfield nodded and Davis retired to the bedroom
to dress. As he hung up his gun belt, he said to me:
"I'm crazy to make a Western. Can you imagine a
colored Western—they'll never do it! But if they do,
it'll be the first time they let the Indians win!"

From the Hotel Fourteen, Davis and the hard core
of friends rode three cabs to the Hotel New Yorker.
Davis was living there in the penthouse. (Going up
in the elevator, I remembered a story I had once
heard about Bert Williams, a great Negro song-and-
dance man of twenty-five years ago. When Williams
played New York, he also rented a penthouse at a
midtown hotel. The only difference was that his lease
required him to enter and leave the hotel by the service elevator. One night, Eddie Cantor was riding up
with Williams and asked him if it bothered him using
the service elevator. "Mr. Cantor," Williams said,
"the only thing that bothers me is applause." A great
deal of progress has been made since then, I thought,
but there was still a strong trace of Williams in
Sammy Davis Jr.) Parties of varying intensity were
held every night at the penthouse during Davis'
eighteen-day engagement at the Copacabana and this
night was no exception. When Davis arrived, three
Copa girls, a former owner of the Chez Paree in
Chicago, Davis' lawyer, another one of Davis' assistants named John Hopkins, and comedian Jack Carter and his date were waiting. Hopkins and Murphy
Bennett tended bar. Landfield sent out for hamburgers and Davis turned up the stereo. The hamburgers
arrived and talking stopped as the guests leaped to the
feast. In a twinkling, the hamburgers were gone.
Everyone got one, even the pretty girl reclining on
the floor underneath an oak bench—everyone, that is,
except Davis.

"It's a definite steal," he said, cheerfully, but for an
instant he looked as though he would have liked a
hamburger.

The party broke well after dawn. Only a few bitter-
enders remained when Davis' father and stepmother
came in from their room down the hall. They had
flown to New York from Hollywood, where they live

with Sammy Jr., for a vacation and to see him at the
Copacabana.

"How's my baby?" asked Sam Sr., and kissed Sam
Jr.

"I'm fine, Dad."

Davis stepped back to examine his father. The
older man is taller and heavier and the family resemblance is faint. He wore a new suit.

"You're getting fat, Dad," said Davis.

"I'm going to get fat as I want to."

"Well, then, get into your old clothes. Nothing
looks worse than a fat man in a Continental suit."

"See what kind of a boy I have," said Sam Sr., and
the two men embraced, laughing.

To me, Sam Sr. said: "We have a fine house out
there. We all live in it together—the wife and me,
Sam's two sisters, grandmother, and Sammy. A fine
house, yes! Believe me, it's a kick for a man who was
born on West Thirty-ninth Street."

(Sam Jr. was proud of the house, too. It had been
built by Judy Garland on the side of one of the Hollywood hills, just up the road from where Davis'
friend, James Dean, used to live. Davis had bought
the house a few years ago for a reported $75,000.
Built on three levels, it provided an apartment for
Davis' grandmother and more-or-less private quarters
for the family of Sam Sr. The upper floor—living
room, bedroom, terrace and guest room—was Davis'
domain, furnished with white rugs, mostly black
furniture, and gigantic lamps. The terrace overlooked
the inevitable swimming pool. The most unusual
piece of furniture was Davis' bed, which was twice
the size of the average double bed; otherwise, the
house was ordinary-California-expensive without
being lavish.)

"It is a fine house," Davis said. "It means a lot to
me. Someday, I'd like to arrange to spend some time
there."

Davis finally went to bed that morning at eight.
He was up at noon in high spirits. After lunch at
P. J. Clarke's with Dorothy Kilgallen, the columnist,
he walked crosstown. Everywhere he went, people on
the street spoke to him, a bus driver pulled over to
the curb to shake his hand, and teen-agers chased him
for his autograph. A few days earlier he had been
taking such a stroll on Seventh Avenue and had
obliged a middle-aged lady with his signature. A
crowd had formed and had followed him to the door
of a haberdashery. From inside, he had seen a hundred noses pressed to the window. The crowd had
grown, tying up traffic on the street. At last, an irate
police sergeant had forced his way into the shop.

"Mr. Davis," the policeman had said, "you got a
crowd outside."

"I didn't bring them," Davis had said.

"I'll call some more cops for you."

"No, I'll get out all right."

"How can you stand it?"

"I worked twenty years for this, sergeant. I can
wait."

Now as he walked, Davis enjoyed the waves and
glances of passersby again. "This sort of thing started
a couple of years ago," he said to me. "All of a sudden,

it was there. People knew *me*. Then I was sure I was sure I'd made it." His high spirits lasted through a sloppy recording session at Decca studios late in the afternoon. He was not in good voice and, besides, the songs were not right for him. When Dave Landfield, the secretary, asked him, "What next?" Davis said: "Well, Dave, baby, it's a definite leave from here in two-oh minutes, maybe even one-five, followed by a definite cab, which will speed me to Danny's Hide-a-Way for a little din-din. Then it will be another cab-ola to the Hotel Fourteen, that is, one-four. After that, chickee, it is a definite lay-down with closed eyes and Morpheus dropping little things in them for about forty winks, until I awake again, as myself—like refreshed—ready to go on."

Davis laughed. When he is very happy, indeed, his talk often becomes a combination of hip, show biz, jazz, and, of course, English. It is in-group lingo of the kind he shares with his Hollywood friends—Frank Sinatra, Dean Martin, Peter Lawford, Eddie Fisher, and Tony Curtis—who are members of a determinedly informal organization known as "the clan."

In about one-five, Davis said to me, "Let's split," which meant *leave*, and we rode a definite cab to Danny's Hide-a-Way, a midtown restaurant in which Davis frequently dined. He ate his one big meal of the day with gusto. At seven, I followed him to the hat-check counter where he retrieved his derby, cape, and umbrella. A teen-age girl asked for his autograph. Davis signed a postcard for her.

"Thank you, Sammy," she said.

"You're welcome," he said, walking toward the door.

A heavy-set blond man, waiting to get to the hat-check room, said: "That's very nice, but why don't you do that in the *street*—"

A car was waiting for Davis. He stood inconclusively on the sidewalk. He looked through the window into Danny's trying to spot the man. Then he got into the car. By the time he arrived at the Hotel Fourteen, he was deeply hurt and enraged.

"What a Jackson!" he said.

"What's a Jackson?" I asked.

"A Jackson is some guy who calls a Negro 'Jackson' or 'Bo,'" he explained. "I'd like ten seconds with that rat!"

What can happen to Davis at any time, no matter how high he is flying, had happened.

Davis' early show was, in many subtle ways, below par. His timing was off. He did not kid with the audience. The beat of his songs was slower. It was not a happy show. Afterward, he returned to the dressing room, changed into the terry-cloth robe, and lay on the couch. Mike Silver, the drummer who travels with him, sat in a chair with his sticks in his hands, watching TV. Murphy Bennett straightened the bedroom. Davis was almost as alone as he ever is.

"I've never, never tried to be anything but what I am," he said. "I am a Negro. I'm not ashamed. The Negro people can mark a cat lousy for that and they won't go to see him perform. Well, we have Negroes here every night. If you go hear a Negro and see some Negroes in the audience, then you know how they stand. They'll ignore a guy who's marked lousy, see? So, I've never been the kind of guy who was ashamed. See, it's a matter of dignity. That's what makes something like that Jackson so tough on you. One time I went on in San Francisco and a guy down in the front row says to another guy, 'I didn't know he was a nigger,' and walked out. It's tough to play against that. In the Army, the first time anybody called me a bad name, I cried—the tears! I had spent all my life with my dad and uncle. I was loved. I was Charlie-protected. But now, this is the thing that is always just around the corner. It's like you can't get into El Morocco because you're colored. See?"

Davis' second show that night was better than the first, but he still seemed chilled. About four a.m., accompanied by fifteen men and women, he went to a West Side nightclub. Legally, it was closing time, but the bartender gathered up bottles, mix, ice, and glasses and carried the makings into a large back room. Cecil Young and three fourths of a Canadian jazz quartet were having a last drink before calling it a night. Like the patrons, the fourth member of the quartet—the bass fiddler—had already gone home. Seeing Davis, Cecil Young began telephoning around to find another fiddle player. When the man arrived, sleepy-eyed, the jam session began. Davis, Young, the Canadians, and the new man played wildly and wonderfully for ninety minutes. Davis sat in on drums, blew the trumpet, and sang scat with Cecil Young. When it was over, the hurt was gone.

During a break, Cecil Young had said to me: "Jazz isn't polite, son. Jazz is, pardon the expression, screw you. If you don't like it, well, that's all. But if you do like it, then I like you, dig? With jazz, you thumb your nose when they don't like you. You get the message out, daddy."

Davis picked up the check for his friends and the group moved over to his penthouse.

A few days later, Davis landed in Las Vegas after overnight stops in Kansas City and Hollywood. Murphy Bennett had arrived a day ahead of him and had set up the suite at the Sands Hotel which would be Davis' home for the next two weeks. The stereo was rigged and 250 records (from Davis' collection of 20,000) were stacked neatly in the bedroom. There was fresh ice in the ice bucket and the silver goblet had been polished. After the rehearsal and a steam bath, Davis settled on a couch in the living room to relax until it was time to dress for the opening.

Jack Entratter, manager of the Sands, telephoned to report that five hundred reservations had been turned down for the dinner show. A friend called to tell Davis that his wife, Loray White Davis, was in Las Vegas divorcing him. Davis had been married in 1958 and had separated from his wife in less than three months. During the separation, a settlement had been made, but this was the first Davis had heard of the Nevada divorce proceedings. He shrugged. It was all over long ago. Another friend called to give him the latest on the romance of his friend Eddie Fisher who, with Elizabeth Taylor, was exciting Las Vegas and the world at that time.

Davis sighed. "Vegas I like," he said. "I feel like I've come home. You know I've performed in this town like twenty-nine times. We used to come in here before we were anything and when there were only a couple of hotels. The Sands I like. I was offered $37,500 a week to go into another hotel, but I turned it down. Very low pressure here. Easy. It builds, but the pace is slower. You're running all the time, and then it's nice to come down to the Vegas pace."

Davis called to Landfield, the secretary.

"Hey, baby, call up Keely [Smith] and Louis [Prima] and tell them we'll be over after our show tonight. And find out what the Count [Basie] is doing. We'll swing with him tonight. And chicks. Chicks, we need. Ah, it's like a vacation. You can tumult all night, sleep all day, get a little sun—sun, I need—play a little blackjack. Oh, fine!" And he lay back on the couch, running.

Tennessee Williams:

A Perfect Analysis Given By a Parrot

A Play in one act

The set: *The interior of a St. Louis tavern, which may be represented by a backdrop painted in the style of the colored comics. There should be two door-frames, one exterior and the other to the Ladies' Room. The other essential properties are a small round table and a jukebox. The light is focused on the table.*

Into this lighted area enter two girls in the late afternoon of their youth, which is close to forty. They are FLORA *and* BESSIE. FLORA *is thin to the point of emaciation and* BESSIE *is correspondingly stout. They are dressed much alike. Both have on big cartwheel hats and black dresses and long black gloves, but the cartwheel hats are in vividly contrasting colors,* BESSIE'S *being magenta and* FLORA'S *chartreuse. When and if they want to look at each other, it is necessary to tilt their heads far back. They are both loaded with ornaments, brass hoops and bangles, so that every movement is accompanied by a small percussion. A grotesque and garish effect should prevail in everything.*

BESSIE (*as they enter*): Wild horses couldn't hold you in that cab!

FLORA: Two more blocks and we couldn't of paid the fare!

BESSIE: "Driver, driver, stop here, this place looks lively!"

FLORA: It did, outside!

BESSIE: Yes, it looked like a tacky funeral parlor! A snare and a delusion if I've ever seen one!

FLORA: Am I responsible?

BESSIE: Yes!

FLORA: We passed five places I would of been willing to stop at, including Dante's Inferno! But you kept telling the driver, "Go on, go on," like it was a chariot race in a Roman forum!

This play first appeared. in Esquire's Silver Anniversary issue, October, 1958. At the time of publication, Tennessee Williams was polishing up Sweet Bird of Youth *for its Broadway opening.*

BESSIE: He sure in hell took us out of the lively district!

FLORA: At your insistence, honey—a child shall lead them! But now that we're here we might as well make the best of it.

BESSIE: And how are we going to go about doing that?

FLORA: By setting down here and getting organized, honey. The waiter is cute.

BESSIE: I ask one favor of you, and only one!

FLORA: What is that, Bessie?

BESSIE: Don't get us involved with th' waiter.

FLORA (*sweetly and clearly*): *Waiter?*

BESSIE: I think we'd better take account of finances before he comes. How much've you got left?

FLORA: Six bits and a bunch of these little round paper things.

BESSIE: Mills!

FLORA: How much're they worth?

BESSIE: One tenth of one cent!

FLORA: Heigh-ho! (*Tosses them into the air.*)

BESSIE (*bitterly*): Somebody seems to be in awfully good spirits! (FLORA *has rushed to the jukebox and started it playing Funiculi Funicula.* THE WAITER *comes to the table, a plump little Italian in a green apron.*) Waiter, this place is just a tissue of lies!

WAITER: Why do you call it that, lady?

BESSIE: Outside is a sign that says "Dancing and Floor Show Every Saturday Night!" But where is the dancing and where is any floor show?

WAITER: The band is quit, ladies.

BESSIE: Oh, I see! How ducky! That solves all our problems!

FLORA: When does the joint liven up?

WAITER: Ladies, at one o'clock the joint is jumping!

BESSIE: Five of nine, and the joint is paralyzed.

FLORA: We're members of the Women's Auxiliary of the Jackson Haggerty Post of the Sons of Mars in Memphis!

BESSIE: Come up here for the National Convention!

FLORA: However, we've got separated from Charlie and Ralph, the boys who came up in our party!

BESSIE: So now we're just out "on the town"!

FLORA: But haven't located a single boy that we know!

BESSIE: Never have seen a convention in such confusion!

FLORA: *Nobody* knows where *anybody's* located!

BESSIE: We've wo'n ou'selves out jus' tryin' t' get *hold* of people!

FLORA: The earth has swallowed up ev'ry boy that we came with!

BESSIE: We always go to the annual convention, but this one has been a terrible—

FLORA: *Disappointment!* But two girls by themselves can have a good deal of fun as long as they know how to be good sports about it.

BESSIE: As long as they can agree on major issues. We'll have two beers.

WAITER: Nickel glasses or twenty-six ounces for a dime?

(FLORA *throws up her hands and* BESSIE *clasps her bosom.*)

BESSIE: Bring us two fish bowls!

FLORA: Of liquid amber, please!

(THE WAITER *withdraws.*)

FLORA (*looking after him*): Kind of cute, huh?

BESSIE: Honey, no man that broad in the beam is cute.

FLORA: *Chacun à son goût.* (*Calling*): Waiter, don't any Son of Mars come here?

WAITER (*returning with fish bowls*): Two of 'em come in just before you ladies.

BESSIE: Honest t' God?

WAITER: One of the two was drippin' wet with water!

FLORA: What!

BESSIE: How come?

WAITER: He said they had dropped paper sacks full of water out of the hotel windows and one of these paper sacks had landed on his head and busted open and spilt all the water on him.

(BESSIE *and* FLORA *scream with amusement but* THE WAITER *continues to look horrified at the incident.*)

FLORA: Aren't they cards?

BESSIE: Don't they think of the craziest things to do?

FLORA: That's what I like about them!

BESSIE: That's what I *love!*

FLORA (*chuckling appreciatively*): You know what they are? Just *great—big—overgrown—Boys!*

BESSIE: My girl friend and I have took in ev'ry convention since—

FLORA: Time immemorial—yes! I wonder which hotel they dropped the paper sacks out of?

BESSIE: I bet you it was the Statler.

FLORA: Why the Statler?

BESSIE: The Statler's always so lively!

FLORA: It might just as well have been the Coronado, or the Jefferson.

BESSIE: Not the Jefferson.

FLORA: Why not the Jefferson?

BESSIE: The Jefferson's such a dignified hotel.

FLORA: There is no such thing!

BESSIE: Well, there is only one hotel in America that I am right down sentimental about.

FLORA: Which one is that?

BESSIE: The Sherman Hotel in Chicago! (*Rolling her eyes and shaking her bangles.*) Shades of the 1926 Convention! Best of 'em all without a single exception!

FLORA: It all depends on the crowd you get thrown with!

BESSIE: Sociability's all that really counts! Although the Sons are a serious organization. In many respects.

FLORA: The country would be in a terrible fix without them.

BESSIE: You're not whistling *Dixie!* But I tell you, the boys are terrible cutups!

WAITER: You heard what they done on Washington Avenue?

FLORA: No!

BESSIE: What?

WAITER: They stripped the clothes off a girl an' sent her home in a Yellow Taxicab!

(*Comedy cross-out of light.* THE GIRLS *throw their heads way back and split their sides.*)

FLORA (*finally catching her breath*): I double-dog-dare ennybody to try that on *me!* (*She sweeps the deserted café with a challenging glance.*)

BESSIE: A Son of Mars wouldn't blow his nose on this place.

FLORA: Well, you was all for stoppin' at th' Statler.

BESSIE: And what's wrong with the Statler?

FLORA: When did we ever have any luck at the Statler?

BESSIE: Twice.

FLORA: In whose recollection?

BESSIE: Mine! You wasn't along.

FLORA: Nope, I guess I wassent.

BESSIE: But you've heard me speak of that restaurant man from Chicago?

FLORA: Heard you speak of him? Continually—yes. . . .

BESSIE: The Statler was where I made that man's acquaintance.

FLORA: And well do I remember how that turned out.

BESSIE: I don't regret it; I have no regret whatsoever.

FLORA: Bessie, you've got no pride where men are concerned.

BESSIE (*slowly and sententiously*): No, I've got no pride where men are concerned, and you haven't got any pride where men are concerned and nobody's got any pride where men are concerned. That's how it is, so let's face it! I'm not coldhearted and when I get out with a boy I am just as anxious as he is to have a good time.

FLORA: More.

BESSIE: Yes, that's right, often more. That is to say, I always go halfway with him.

FLORA: More than halfway, honey.

BESSIE: Yes, I sometimes even go more than

halfway and I see no reason why I should be criticized for it.

FLORA: Nobody's spoken a word of criticism.

BESSIE: I do my part to create some happiness in the world, even if it's just for one night only. It isn't a crime to give a good time and a pleasant memory, even to a stranger.

FLORA: Whoever said that it was?

BESSIE: Some people seem to take that attitude.

FLORA: I certainly never.

BESSIE: You talked about pride as if I didn't have any. (*She leans way back with considerable effort in order to stare at Flora from under the brim of the cartwheel.*)

FLORA (*quickly*): I said *false* pride, not pride. There's a difference, Bessie.

BESSIE: That's exactly what I was pointing out.

FLORA: All I mean is a girl mustn't compromise with her self-respect.

BESSIE: She don't need to—and I don't see why she should.

FLORA: That's exactly the point I was making.

BESSIE: Except you sometimes go to the other extreme.

FLORA: *I* do?

BESSIE: Uh-huh.

FLORA: Extreme of what, may I ask?

BESSIE: *Self—respect!*

FLORA: You mean I'm not a good sport?

BESSIE: That is just the opposite of my meaning.

FLORA: Your meaning is private as far as I am concerned.

BESSIE: The trouble with you is your mind wanders off a subject but you go right on chopping your gums together as if you weighed every single word that was spoken. (*Powdering furiously.*) That's what makes it so difficult to talk with you!

FLORA: Oh—foot! (*She looks slowly and wearily away from her girl friend, but* BESSIE'S *look remains on* FLORA. FLORA'S *head begins to droop like a heavy flower on a thin stem.*)

BESSIE (*suspiciously*): A penny for your thoughts, Miss Merriweather.

FLORA: I had my character read this afternoon.

BESSIE: Who by? A gypsy?

FLORA: No, it was read by a parrot.

BESSIE: Are you kidding?

FLORA: No. I gave a man a dime and he opened the parrot's cage and the parrot hopped out and stuck his head in a box and picked up a piece of paper in his beak. I took the piece of paper, and guess what it said?

BESSIE: How would I guess what it said on that piece of paper?

FLORA: I'll tell you, Bessie. "You have a sensitive nature, and are frequently misunderstood by your close companions!"

BESSIE: Huh!

FLORA: Imagine it, Bessie. A perfect analysis given by a parrot!

BESSIE: I don't have very much faith in that sort of thing.

(FLORA *tilts her head way back to give her girl friend a long and critical look.*)

BESSIE (*nervously*): Well?

FLORA: Wipe your chin off, Bessie. You've got foam on it.

BESSIE: Thank you, Miss Merriweather. (*A pause.*) May I ask you a question?

FLORA (*suspiciously*): What, Miss Higginbotham?

BESSIE: Are you still keeping up those Youthful Beauty treatments?

FLORA: I had a Youthful Beauty treatment this afternoon.

BESSIE: How are you satisfied with what they're doing?

FLORA: I have noticed one hundred percent improvement in my skin since I started taking those Youthful Beauty treatments, Bessie.

BESSIE: I'm glad you've noticed it, honey.

FLORA: Why, haven't you?

BESSIE (*lighting a cigarette*): Flora, your main beauty problem is not blackheads. It's large pores, honey.

FLORA (*with fierce conviction*): I haven't a single blackhead left in my face, just a few little whiteheads, and this little do-hickey here which is just a spot where I squeezed out one with a hairpin!

BESSIE: Well, Flora, your problem is skin and you might as well face it.

FLORA: Everyone's problem is skin, including yours, Bessie. But of course your primary problem is keeping down *weight*.

BESSIE: I am a type that can carry a good deal of weight because I have large bone structure. However, it's always been well-distributed on me.

FLORA: As long as you won't face facts, it's no use talking. Complacency's one thing and—optimism's another!

BESSIE: What does a man look at with greater int'rest, a straight-back chair or a rocker?

FLORA: Depends on the man an' the relative size of the rocker.

(BESSIE *tilts her head way back to study* FLORA'S *face, but gravity brings it back down with a jolting motion.*)

FLORA (*continuing sweetly*): You know what would do you an awful lot of good, Bessie?

BESSIE: No. What?

FLORA: Bending exercise!

BESSIE: I thought you was going to say "Yogi"—but who wants to bend?

FLORA: Everyone does who wants to keep youthful contours! You've got to resign yourself to making some effort, unless you prefer to let things take their course. (*A reflective pause, then slowly and gravely*): Nature is not on the side of a girl over thirty.

BESSIE: For once in your life you are not just whistling *Dixie*! (*Another brief meditation.*)

FLORA (*brightly*): Honey, why don't you and I play golf on Sundays?

BESSIE: Have you struck oil on your property?

FLORA: What's that got t' do with it?

BESSIE: Expense! It's a millionaire's sport!

FLORA: It's not so expensive except you pay caddies and all. (*Continued on page 287*)

BESSIE: And all is correct. Buying the balls, losing them and buying more. You can't take up golf without an initial outlay of something like thirty-five dollars. And that's the beginning—only!

FLORA (*plaintively*): You don't have to lose balls, do you?

BESSIE (*vaguely*): Maybe you don't have to, but you do.

FLORA: Well, outdoor sports are a wonderful basis for friendship.

BESSIE (*gravely*): You mean with men?

FLORA: Uh-huh.

BESSIE: Eunice McPheeters, to mention a case in point, has been playing golf for going on fifteen years. Has she ever made such brilliant contacts with men?

FLORA: Probably has; don't see enny reason t' doubt it! Consider the number and types of men that play golf!

BESSIE: Consider—Eunice! Her face is frozen in a perpetual sneer. A girl like her could be marooned on an island and, though outnumbered fifty to one by males, escape without even so much as a mild flirtation!

FLORA: You don't appreciate Eunice. Eunice has got common sense and it shows in her face.

BESSIE: Is that what shows in her face?

FLORA: Any girl's been through what Eunice Mc-Pheeter's been through with her home situation and all can't be expected to look upon life as one continual joy ride.

BESSIE: But why talk of golf as the be-all and end-all of living?

FLORA: Who did, and who ever does?

BESSIE (*vaguely*): Eunice and you—although she does and you don't.

FLORA: I'm just attempting to think of something to help you.

BESSIE: Accept my thanks, my heartfelt appreciation—but please don't strain your thinking apparatus!

FLORA: Sarcasm, Bessie?

BESSIE: No, honey, but I came out for the purpose of seeking diversion. That's my whole purpose in leaving my hotel bedroom. If you're in accord with that purpose—good! If otherwise—good-bye! Separation is simple. You go to the Statler and I to the Coronado, or whichever way you prefer it, but don't try to pull me into a state of depression! I've had rotten luck with men. Not once but always! You've had your share of disappointments also. So far, so good. But when you start harping on Yogi—on Eunice's home situation—girlie, good-bye! We have come to the sad, sweet parting! I mean of the ways. . . .

(*She takes a long drink of beer, gags and spews it up.* BOTH GIRLS *scramble back from the table in time to avoid a deluge. The incident is immediately forgotten.*)

FLORA (*dreamily*): Bessie—

BESSIE: Huh?

FLORA: After Howard, you know you let yourself go.

BESSIE: Just like you after Vernon. I went through an awful period for a while. . . .

FLORA: You took a negative attitude toward things. Acted as if all hope had gone out of life. But instead of wasting away, you put on flesh. Honestly, Bessie, you blew up like a balloon!

BESSIE: I used to wear a sixteen.

FLORA: Bessie, that must've been long before I knew you.

BESSIE: In 1930.

FLORA: That recently, honey?

BESSIE: I had no figure problem until the Winter of 1932. But you were always bedeviled by your complexion. Isn't that so?

FLORA: Only because I have such a fine-grained skin.

BESSIE (*doubtfully*): Possibly, but also—

FLORA: What?

BESSIE: You never have hit on a really becoming hairdo!

FLORA: What's wrong with the one I got last week at Antoinette's?

BESSIE: Honey, the upswept style is not for your face. Every type of face requires a different style of hairdo, just in the way diff'rent figures can't put on the same type of clothes. Now what you call for is horizontal lines because of the distance between your chin and your forehead.

FLORA (*slowly*): I haven't forgotten the time you called me "Horse-Face."

BESSIE: All I meant is you have the *long* type of face the same as I have the *broad* one. Now what you need is bushing out at the temples, the *aureole* type.

FLORA: Oriole? like a bird?

BESSIE: No, honey. The spelling is diff'rent. But never mind that. What I mean is Antoinette's is not a good friend of yours—not from the grotesque things which they do to your face!

(*A pause.* FLORA *stares at her friend and her lips begin to tremble. Slowly her face droops downward on the delicate stem of her throat and the cartwheel hides her tears.*)

BESSIE (*gently and sorrowfully*): You harp on Yogi and Eunice McPheeter's golf, and claim that your sensitive nature is misunderstood by everyone but a parrot! But let me give you some well-intended advice—and tears, tears, tears! A regular fountain of them! (*She opens her purse and produces assorted cosmetics.*) Repair the ravages and we'll go to the Statler.

(BESSIE *has picked up a lipstick and* FLORA *a sheet of Kleenex, when all at once the front door of the tavern erupts on a pair of* MALE FIGURES *in the blue-and-white summer parade uniforms of the Sons of Mars. One crouches by the door and the other leaps over his back, which action is repeated until they arrive at the girls' table where they abruptly halt, blow shrill blasts on toy bugles and extend their elbow. Electrified with joy,* THE GIRLS *have sprung to their feet.* BESSIE *seizes one's arm,* FLORA *the other's, and they strut gaily around the table, singing* Mademoiselle From Armentières, *as*

THE CURTAIN FALLS

GREAT STORIES

We have been presenting fiction for forty years. We have been presenting lists for a long time too. So when the occasion for composing this introduction arose and we went looking for an index to the range and height of what we've done in fiction, we were naturally appalled to find that nowhere does there exist a handy reference recording the greatness of our achievement. Now let those who come after search here, for among the writers who have all these years kept us attentive to the story, there are—briefly—the following: Stanley Elkin, William Faulkner, Alec Waugh, Thomas Williams, Ernest Hemingway, Norman Mailer, Arthur Miller, John Steinbeck, Erskine Caldwell, Charles Jackson, Bruce Jay Friedman, Vladimir Nabokov, Geoffrey Household, James Purdy, Philip Roth, Budd Schulberg, James B. Hall, John Dos Passos, Ray Bradbury, A. E. Coppard, Joyce Cary, Meyer Levin, Richard Yates, William Styron, James Jones, Ben Hecht, Jesse Stuart, André Maurois, Oliver La Farge, Gabriel García Márquez, Jerry Bumpus, Kurt Vonnegut Jr., John Graves, Richard Brautigan, Pietro Di Donato, John Updike, Langston Hughes, Alberto Moravia, Robert Lowry, Mavis Gallant, Robie Macauley, Joyce Carol Oates, Mark Schorer, John Cheever, Reed Whittemore, Brendan Behan, Mark Harris, Herbert Gold, Frank O'Connor, Thomas Wolfe, Terry Southern, Richard Wright, R. V. Cassill, Evan S. Connell Jr., Saul Bellow, Irwin Shaw, Albert Camus, S. N. Behr-man, Wallace Stegner, Allan Seager, John Wain, Jack Kerouac, Georges Simenon, Wright Morris, Thomas Berger, George P. Elliott, Harvey Swados, John Barth, Nelson Algren, Herbert Wilner, Tennessee Williams, Truman Capote, Dorothy Parker, Flannery O'Connor, William Inge, Jorge Luis Borges, Don DeLillo, John O'Hara, Franz Werfel, Paul Bowles, James T. Farrell, W. Somerset Maugham, Gore Vidal, F. Scott Fitzgerald, Vance Bourjaily, Kingsley Amis, Robert Penn Warren, Howard Nemerov, Chester Himes, Heinrich Böll, Leo Litwak, Lawrence Durrell, Willard Marsh, Ivan Gold, Grace Paley, Alfred Chester, Edward Hoagland, Max Steele, Italo Calvino, Alan Paton, Isaac Bashevis Singer, Bernard Malamud, Evelyn Waugh, J. F. Powers, Jonathan Strong, Leonard Michaels, Reynolds Price, John Gardner, Dashiell Hammett, Cynthia Ozick, Alain Robbe-Grillet, Graham Greene, Edward Albee, J. P. Donleavy, William Humphrey, Jakov Lind, Gina Berriault, Harold Brodkey, Leslie Fiedler, Niccolo Tucci, James Leo Herlihy, Thomas Pynchon, Irvin Faust, Yukio Mishima, William Burroughs, Joseph Heller, Maxim Gorki, Conrad Aiken, William Golding, Barton Midwood, Siegfried Lenz, Louis Auchincloss, Robert Coover, Richard Fariña, Ring Lardner Sr., D. H. Lawrence, Morley Callaghan, Luigi Pirandello, Thomas Mann, Theodore Dreiser, Sean O'Faolain, James Baldwin, William Saroyan, and J. D. Salinger. This said, we say amen.

Irwin Shaw:

The Eighty-Yard Run

Fifteen years ago a run on the football field,
and a girl's kiss,
assured him he would go places

The pass was high and wide and he jumped for it, feeling it slap flatly against his hands, as he shook his hips to throw off the halfback who was diving at him. The center floated by, his hands desperately brushing Darling's knee as Darling picked his feet up high and delicately ran over a blocker and an opposing linesman in a jumble on the ground near the scrimmage line. He had ten yards in the clear and picked up speed, breathing easily, feeling his thigh pads rising and falling against his legs, listening to the sound of cleats behind him, pulling away from them, watching the other backs heading him off toward the sideline, the whole picture, the men closing in on him, the blockers fighting for position, the ground he had to cross, all suddenly clear in his head, for the first time in his life not a meaningless confusion of men, sounds, speed. He smiled a little to himself as he ran, holding the ball lightly in front of him with his two hands, his knees pumping high, his hips twisting in the almost-girlish run of a back in a broken field. The first halfback came at him and he fed him his leg, then swung at the last moment, took the shock of the man's shoulder without breaking stride, ran right through him, his cleats biting securely into the turf. There was only the safety man now, coming warily at him, his arms crooked, hands spread. Darling tucked the ball in, spurted at him, driving hard, hurling himself along, his legs pounding, knees high, all two hundred pounds bunched into controlled attack. He was sure he was going to get past the safety man. Without thought, his arms and legs working beautifully together, he headed right for the safety man, stiff-armed him, feeling blood spurt instantaneously from the man's nose onto his hand, seeing his face go awry, head turned, mouth pulled to one side. He pivoted away, keeping the arm locked, dropping the safety man as

Of all of Irwin Shaw's many short stories, we have two favorites, "The Girls in Their Summer Dresses" and "The Eighty-Yard Run," which latter we have the pleasure of printing again here because, thank goodness, we had the honor of printing it the first time, in 1941. A search through our files indicates we had no such luck in the case of that other beauty.

he ran easily toward the goal line, with the drumming of cleats diminishing behind him.

How long ago? It was autumn then and the ground was getting hard because the nights were cold and leaves from the maples around the stadium blew across the practice fields in gusts of wind and the girls were beginning to put polo coats over their sweaters when they came to watch practice in the afternoons. . . . Fifteen years. Darling walked slowly over the same ground in the spring twilight, in his neat shoes, a man of thirty-five dressed in a double-breasted suit, ten pounds heavier in the fifteen years, but not fat, with the years between 1925 and 1940 showing in his face.

The coach was smiling quietly to himself and the assistant coaches were looking at each other with pleasure the way they always did when one of the second stringers suddenly did something fine, bringing credit to them, making their $2,000 a year a tiny bit more secure.

Darling trotted back, smiling, breathing deeply but easily, feeling wonderful, not tired, though this was the tail end of practice and he'd run eighty yards. The sweat poured off his face and soaked his jersey and he liked the feeling, the warm moistness lubricating his skin like oil. Off in a corner of the field some players were punting and the smack of leather against the ball came pleasantly through the afternoon air. The freshmen were running signals on the next field and the quarterback's sharp voice, the pound of the eleven pairs of cleats, the "Dig, now, *dig!*" of the coaches, the laughter of the players all somehow made him feel happy as he trotted back to midfield, listening to the applause and shouts of the students along the sidelines, knowing that after that run the coach would have to start him Saturday against Illinois.

Fifteen years, Darling thought, remembering the shower after the workout, the hot water steaming off his skin and the deep soapsuds and all the young voices singing with the water streaming down and towels going and managers running in and out and the sharp sweet smell of oil of wintergreen and everybody clapping him on the back as he dressed and Packard, the captain, who took being captain very seriously, coming over to him and shaking his hand and saying, "Darling, you're going to go places in the next two years."

The assistant manager fussed over him, wiping a cut on his leg with alcohol and iodine, the little sting making him realize suddenly how fresh and whole and solid his body felt. The manager slapped a piece of adhesive tape over the cut and Darling noticed the sharp clean white of the tape against the ruddiness of the skin, fresh from the shower.

He dressed slowly, the softness of his shirt and the soft warmth of his wool socks and his flannel trousers a reward against his skin after the harsh pressure of the shoulder harness and thigh and hip pads. He drank three glasses of cold water, the liquid reaching down coldly inside of him, soothing the harsh dry places in his throat and belly left by the sweat and running and shouting of practice.

Fifteen years.

The sun had gone down and the sky was green behind the stadium and he laughed quietly to himself as he looked at the stadium, rearing above the trees, and knew that on Saturday when the 70,000 voices roared as the team came running out onto the field, part of that enormous salute would be for him. He walked slowly, listening to the gravel crunch satisfactorily under his shoes in the still twilight, feeling his clothes swing lightly against his skin, breathing the thin evening air, feeling the wind move softly in his damp hair, wonderfully cool behind his ears and at the nape of his neck.

Louise was waiting for him at the road, in her car. The top was down and he noticed all over again, as he always did when he saw her, how pretty she was, the rough blonde hair and the large, inquiring eyes and the bright mouth, smiling now.

She threw the door open. "Were you good today?" she asked.

"Pretty good," he said. He climbed in, sank luxuriously into the soft leather, stretched his legs far out. He smiled, thinking of the eighty yards. "Pretty damn good."

She looked at him seriously for a moment, then scrambled around, like a little girl, kneeling on the seat next to him, grabbed him, her hands along his ears, and kissed him as he sprawled, head back, on the seat cushion. She let go of him, but kept her head close to his, over his. Darling reached up slowly and rubbed the back of his hand against her cheek, lit softly by a streetlamp a hundred feet away. They looked at each other, smiling.

Louise drove down to the lake and they sat there silently, watching the moon rise behind the hills on the other side. Finally he reached over, pulled her gently to him, kissed her. Her lips grew soft, her body sank into his, tears formed slowly in her eyes. He knew, for the first time, that he could do whatever he wanted with her.

"Tonight," he said. "I'll call for you at seven-thirty. Can you get out?"

She looked at him. She was smiling, but the tears were still full in her eyes. "All right," she said. "I'll get out. How about you? Won't the coach raise hell?"

Darling grinned. "I got the coach in the palm of my hand," he said. "Can you wait till seven-thirty?"

She grinned back at him. "No," she said.

They kissed and she started the car and they went back to town for dinner. He sang on the way home.

Christian Darling, thirty-five years old, sat on the frail spring grass, greener now than it ever would be again on the practice field, looked thoughtfully up at the stadium, a deserted ruin in the twilight. He had started on the first team that Saturday and every Saturday after that for the next two years, but it had never been as satisfactory as it should have been. He never had broken away, the longest run he'd ever made was thirty-five yards, and that in a game that was already won, and then that kid had come up from the third team, Diederich, a blank-faced German kid from Wisconsin, who ran like a bull, ripping lines to pieces Saturday after Saturday, plowing through, never getting hurt, never changing his expression, scoring more points, gaining more ground than all the rest of the team put together, making everybody's All-American, carrying the ball three times out of four, keeping everybody else out of the headlines. Darling was a good blocker and he spent his Saturday afternoons working on the big Swedes and Polacks who played tackle and end for Michigan, Illinois, Purdue, hurling into huge pileups, bobbing his head wildly to elude the great raw hands swinging like meat cleavers at him as he went charging in to open up holes for Diederich coming through like a locomotive behind him. Still, it wasn't so bad. Everybody liked him and he did his job and he was pointed out on the campus and boys always felt important when they introduced their girls to him at their proms, and Louise loved him and watched him faithfully in the games, even in the mud, when your own mother wouldn't know you, and drove him around in her car keeping the top down because she was proud of him and wanted to show everybody that she was Christian Darling's girl. She bought him crazy presents because her father was rich, watches, pipes, humidors, an icebox for beer for his room, curtains, wallets, a fifty-dollar dictionary.

"You'll spend every cent your old man owns," Darling protested once when she showed up at his rooms with seven different packages in her arms and tossed them onto the couch.

"Kiss me," Louise said, "and shut up."

"Do you want to break your poor old man?"

"I don't mind. I want to buy you presents."

"Why?"

"It makes me feel good. Kiss me. I don't know why. Did you know that you're an important figure?"

"Yes," Darling said gravely.

"When I was waiting for you at the library yesterday two girls saw you coming and one of them said to the other, 'That's Christian Darling. He's an important figure.'"

"You're a liar."

"I'm in love with an important figure."

"Still, why the hell did you have to give me a forty-pound dictionary?"

"I wanted to make sure," Louise said, "that you had a token of my esteem. I want to smother you in tokens of my esteem."

Fifteen years ago.

They'd married when they got out of college. There'd been other women for him, but all casual and secret, more for curiosity's sake, and vanity, women who'd thrown themselves at him and flattered him, a pretty mother at a summer camp for boys, an old girl from his hometown who'd suddenly blossomed into a coquette, a friend of Louise's who had dogged him grimly for six months and had taken advantage of the two weeks when Louise went home when her mother died. Perhaps Louise had known, but she'd kept quiet, loving him completely, filling his rooms with presents, religiously watching him battling with the big Swedes and Polacks on the line of scrimmage on Saturday afternoons, making plans for marrying him and living with him in New York and going with him there to the nightclubs, the theatres, the good restaurants, being proud of him in advance, tall, white-teethed, smiling, large, yet moving lightly, with an athlete's grace, dressed in evening clothes, approvingly eyed by magnificently dressed and famous women in theatre lobbies, with Louise adoringly at his side.

Her father, who manufactured inks, set up a New York office for Darling to manage and presented him with three hundred accounts and they lived on Beekman Place with a view of the river with fifteen thousand dollars a year between them, because everybody was buying everything in those days, including ink. They saw all the shows and went to all the speakeasies and spent their fifteen thousand dollars a year and in the afternoons Louise went to the art galleries and the matinees of the more serious plays that Darling didn't like to sit through and Darling slept with a girl who danced in the chorus of *Rosalie* and with the wife of a man who owned three copper mines. Darling played squash three times a week and remained as solid as a stone barn and Louise never took her eyes off him when they were in the same room together, watching him with a secret, miser's smile, with a trick of coming over to him in the middle of a crowded room and saying gravely, in a low voice, "You are the handsomest man I've ever seen in my whole life. Want a drink?"

Nineteen twenty-nine came to Darling and to his wife and father-in-law, the maker of inks, just as it came to everyone else. The father-in-law

waited until 1933 and then blew his brains out and when Darling went to Chicago to see what the books of the firm looked like he found out all that was left were debts and three or four gallons of unbought ink.

"Please, Christian," Louise said, sitting in their neat Beekman Place apartment, with a view of the river and prints of paintings by Dufy and Braque and Picasso on the wall, "please, why do you want to start drinking at two o'clock in the afternoon?".

"I have nothing else to do," Darling said, putting down his glass, emptied of its fourth drink. "Please pass the whiskey."

Louise filled his glass. "Come take a walk with me," she said. "We'll walk along the river."

"I don't want to walk along the river," Darling said, squinting intensely at the prints of paintings by Dufy, Braque and Picasso.

"We'll walk along Fifth Avenue."

"I don't want to walk along Fifth Avenue."

"Maybe," Louise said gently, "you'd like to come with me to some art galleries. There's an exhibition by a man named Klee—"

"I don't want to go to any art galleries. I want to sit here and drink Scotch whisky," Darling said. "Who the hell hung those goddamn pictures up in the wall?"

"I did," Louise said.

"I hate them."

"I'll take them down," Louise said.

"Leave them there. It gives me something to do in the afternoon. I can hate them." Darling took a long swallow. "Is that the way people paint these days?"

"Yes, Christian. Please don't drink any more."

"Do you like painting like that?"

"Yes, dear."

"Really?"

"Really."

Darling looked carefully at the prints once more. "Little Louise Tucker. The Middle-Western beauty. I like pictures with horses in them. Why should you like pictures like that?"

"I just happen to have gone to a lot of galleries in the last few years. . . ."

"Is that what you do in the afternoon?"

"That's what I do in the afternoon," Louise said.

"I drink in the afternoon."

Louise kissed him lightly on the top of his head as he sat there squinting at the pictures on the wall, the glass of whiskey held firmly in his hand. She put on her coat and went out without saying another word. When she came back in the early evening, she had a job on a woman's fashion magazine.

They moved downtown and Louise went out to work every morning and Darling sat home and drank and Louise paid the bills as they came up. She made believe she was going to quit work as soon as Darling found a job, even though she was taking over more responsibility day by day at the magazine, interviewing authors, picking painters for the illustrations and covers, getting actresses to pose for pictures, going out for drinks with the right people, making a thousand new friends whom she loyally introduced to Darling.

"I don't like your hat," Darling said, once, when she came in in the evening and kissed him, her breath rich with Martinis.

"What's the matter with my hat, Baby?" she asked, running her fingers through his hair. "Everybody says it's very smart."

"It's too damned smart," he said. "It's not for you. It's for a rich, sophisticated woman of thirty-five with admirers."

Louise laughed. "I'm practicing to be a rich, sophisticated woman of thirty-five with admirers," she said. He stared soberly at her. "Now, don't look so grim, Baby. It's still the same simple little wife under the hat." She took the hat off, threw it into a corner, sat on his lap. "See? Homebody Number One."

"Your breath could run a train," Darling said, not wanting to be mean, but talking out of boredom, and sudden shock at seeing his wife curiously a stranger in a new hat, with a new expression in her eyes under the little brim, secret, confident, knowing.

Louise tucked her head under his chin so he couldn't smell her breath. "I had to take an author out for cocktails," she said. "He's a boy from the Ozark mountains and he drinks like a fish. He's a Communist."

"What the hell is a Communist from the Ozarks doing writing for a woman's fashion magazine?"

Louise chuckled. "The magazine business is getting all mixed up these days. The publishers want to have a foot in every camp. And anyway, you can't find an author under seventy these days who isn't a Communist."

"I don't think I like you to associate with all those people, Louise," Darling said. "Drinking with them."

"He's a very nice, gentle boy," Louise said. "He reads Ernest Dobson."

"Who's Ernest Dobson?"

Louise patted his arm, stood up, fixed her hair. "He's an English poet."

Darling felt that somehow he had disappointed her. "Am I supposed to know who Ernest Dobson is?"

"No, dear. I'd better go in and take a bath."

After she had gone, Darling went over to the corner where the hat was lying and picked it up. It was nothing, a scrap of straw, a red flower, a veil, meaningless on his big hand, but on his wife's head a signal of something . . . big city, smart and knowing women drinking and dining with men other than their husbands, conversation about things a normal man wouldn't know much about, Frenchmen who painted as though they used their elbows instead of brushes, composers who wrote whole symphonies without a single melody in them, writers who knew all about politics and women who knew all about writers, the movement of the proletariat, Marx, somehow mixed up with five-dollar dinners and the best looking women in America and fairies who made them laugh and half-sentences immediately understood and secretly hilarious and wives who called their husbands, "Baby." He put the hat down, a scrap of straw and a red flower, and a little veil. He drank some whiskey straight and went into the bathroom where his wife was lying deep in her bath, singing to herself and smiling from time to time like a little girl, paddling the water gently with her hands, sending up a slight spicy fragrance from the bath salts she used.

He stood over her, looking down at her. She smiled up at him, her eyes half closed, her body pink and shimmering in the warm, scented water. All over again, with all the old suddenness, he was hit deep inside him with the knowledge of how beautiful she was, how much he needed her.

"I came in here," he said, "to tell you I wish you wouldn't call me 'Baby.'"

She looked up at him from the bath, her eyes quickly full of sorrow, half-understanding what he meant. He knelt and put his arms around her, his sleeves plunged heedlessly in the water, his shirt and jacket soaking wet as he clutched her wordlessly, holding her crazily tight, crushing her breath from her, kissing her desperately, searchingly, regretfully.

He got jobs after that, selling real estate and automobiles, but somehow, although he had a desk with his name on a wooden wedge on it, and he went to the office religiously at nine each morning, he never managed to sell anything and he never made any money.

Louise was made assistant editor and the house was always full of strange men and women who talked fast and got angry on abstract subjects like mural painting, novelists, labor unions. Negro short-story writers drank Louise's liquor, and a lot of Jews, and big solemn men with scarred faces and knotted hands who talked slowly but clearly about picket lines and battles with guns and lead pipe at mine-shaft heads and in front of factory gates. And Louise moved among them all, confidently, knowing what they were talking about, with opinions that they listened to and argued about just as though she were a man. She knew everybody, condescended to no one, devoured books that Darling had never heard of, walked along the streets of the city, excited, at home, soaking in all the million tides of New York without fear, with constant wonder.

Her friends liked Darling and sometimes he found a man who wanted to get off in the corner and talk about the new boy who played fullback for Princeton, and the decline of the double wingback, or even the state of the stock market, but for the most part he sat on the edge of things, solid and quiet in the high storm of words. "The dialectics of the situation . . . the theatre has been given over to expert jugglers . . . Picasso?

What man has a right to paint old bones and collect ten thousand dollars for them? . . . I stand firmly behind Trotsky . . . Poe was the last American critic. When he died they put lilies on the grave of American criticism. I don't say this because they panned my last book, but. . . ."

Once in a while he caught Louise looking soberly and consideringly at him through the cigarette smoke and the noise and he avoided her eyes and found an excuse to get up and go into the kitchen for more ice or to open another bottle.

C ome on," Cathal Flaherty was saying, standing at the door with a girl, "you've got to come down and see this. It's down on Fourteenth Street, in the old Civic Repertory, and you can only see it on Sunday nights and I guarantee you'll come out of the theatre singing." Flaherty was a big young Irishman with a broken nose who was the lawyer for a longshoreman's union, and he had been hanging around the house for six months on and off, roaring and shutting everybody else up when he got in an argument. "It's a new play, *Waiting for Lefty*, it's about taxi drivers."

"Odets," the girl with Flaherty said. "It's by a guy named Odets."

"I never heard of him," Darling said.

"He's a new one," the girl said.

"It's like watching a bombardment," Flaherty said. "I saw it last Sunday night. You've got to see it."

"Come on, Baby," Louise said to Darling, excitement in her eyes already. "We've been sitting in the Sunday *Times* all day, this'll be a great change."

"I see enough taxi drivers every day," Darling said, not because he meant that, but because he didn't like to be around Flaherty, who said things that made Louise laugh a lot and whose judgment she accepted on almost every subject. "Let's go to the movies."

"You've never seen anything like this before," Flaherty said. "He wrote this play with a baseball bat."

"Come on," Louise coaxed, "I bet it's wonderful."

"He has long hair," the girl with Flaherty said. "Odets. I met him at a party. He's an actor. He didn't say a goddamn thing all night."

"I don't feel like going down to Fourteenth Street," Darling said, wishing Flaherty and his girl would get out. "It's gloomy."

"Oh, hell!" Louise said loudly. She looked coolly at Darling, as though she'd just been introduced to him and was making up her mind about him, and not very favorably. He saw her looking at him, knowing there was something new and dangerous in her face and he wanted to say something, but Flaherty was there and his damned girl, and anyway, he didn't know what to say.

"I'm going," Louise said, getting her coat. "I don't think Fourteenth Street is gloomy."

"I'm telling you," Flaherty was saying, helping her on with her coat, "it's the Battle of Gettysburg, in Brooklynese."

"Nobody could get a word out of him," Flaherty's girl was saying as they went through the door. "He just sat there all night."

The door closed. Louise hadn't said good-night to him. Darling walked around the room four times, then sprawled out on the sofa, on top of the Sunday *Times*. He lay there for five minutes looking at the ceiling, thinking of Flaherty walking down the street talking in that booming voice, between the girls, holding their arms.

Louise had looked wonderful. She'd washed her hair in the afternoon and it had been very soft and light and clung close to her head as she stood there angrily putting her coat on. Louise was getting prettier every year, partly because she knew by now how pretty she was, and made the most of it.

"Nuts," Darling said, standing up. "Oh, nuts."

He put on his coat and went down to the nearest bar and had five drinks off by himself in a corner before his money ran out.

T he years since then had been foggy and downhill. Louise had been nice to him, and in a way, loving and kind, and they'd fought only once, when he said he was going to vote for Landon. ("Oh, Christ," she'd said, "doesn't *anything* happen inside your head? Don't you read the papers? The penniless Republican!") She'd been sorry later and apologized for hurting him, but apologized as she might to a child. He'd tried hard, had gone grimly to the art galleries, the concert halls, the bookshops, trying to gain on the trail of his wife, but it was no use. He was bored, and none of what he saw or heard or dutifully read made much sense to him and finally he gave it up. He had thought, many nights as he ate dinner alone, knowing that Louise would come home late and drop silently into bed without explanation, of getting a divorce, but he knew the loneliness, the hopelessness, of not seeing her again would be too much to take. So he was good, completely devoted, ready at all times to go anyplace with her, do anything she wanted. He even got a small job, in a broker's office and paid his own way, bought his own liquor.

Then he'd been offered the job of going from college to college as a tailor's representative. "We want a man," Mr. Rosenberg had said, "who as soon as you look at him, you say 'There's a university man.'" Rosenberg had looked approvingly at Darling's broad shoulders and well-kept waist, at his carefully brushed hair and his honest, wrinkleless face. "Frankly, Mr. Darling, I am willing to make you a proposition. I have inquired about you, you are favorably known on your old campus, I understand you were in the backfield with Alfred Diederich."

Darling nodded. "Whatever happened to him?"

"He is walking around in a cast for seven years now. An iron brace. He played professional football and they broke his neck for him."

Darling smiled. That, at least, had turned out well.

"Our suits are an easy product to sell, Mr. Darling," Rosenberg said. "We have a handsome, custom-made garment. What has Brooks Brothers got that we haven't got? A name. No more."

"I can make fifty, sixty dollars a week," Darling said to Louise that night. "And expenses. I can save some money and then come back to New York and really get started here."

"Yes, Baby," Louise said.

"As it is," Darling said carefully, "I can make it back here once a month, and holidays and the summer. We can see each other often."

"Yes, Baby." He looked at her face, lovelier now at thirty-five than it had ever been before, but fogged over now as it had been for five years with a kind of patient, kindly, remote boredom.

"What do you say?" he asked. "Should I take it?" Deep within him he hoped fiercely, longingly, for her to say, "No, Baby, you stay right here," but she said, as he knew she'd say, "I think you'd better take it."

He nodded. He had to get up and stand with his back to her, looking out the window, because there were things plain on his face that she had never seen in the fifteen years she'd known him. "Fifty dollars is a lot of money," he said. "I never thought I'd ever see fifty dollars again." He laughed. Louise laughed, too.

Christian Darling sat on the frail green grass of the practice field. The shadow of the stadium had reached out and covered him. In the distance the lights of the university shone a little mistily in the light haze of evening. Fifteen years. Flaherty even now was calling for his wife, buying her a drink, filling whatever bar they were in with that voice of his and that easy laugh. Darling half-closed his eyes, almost saw the boy fifteen years ago reach for the pass, slip the halfback, go skittering lightly down the field, his knees high and fast and graceful, smiling to himself because he knew he was going to get past the safety man. That was the high point, Darling thought, fifteen years

ago, on an autumn afternoon, twenty years old and far from death, with the air coming easily into his lungs, and a deep feeling inside him that he could do anything, knock over anybody, outrun whatever had to be outrun. And the shower after and the three glasses of water and the cool night air on his damp head and Louise sitting hatless in the open car with a smile and the first kiss she ever really meant. The high point, an eighty-yard run in the practice, and a girl's kiss and everything after that a decline. Darling laughed. He had practiced the wrong thing, perhaps. He hadn't practiced for 1929 and New York City and a girl who would turn into a woman.

Somewhere, he thought, there must have been a point where she moved up to me, was even with me for a moment, when I could have held her hand, if I'd known, held tight, gone with her. Well, he'd never known. Here he was on a playing field that was fifteen years away and his wife was in another city having dinner with another and better man, speaking with him a different, new language, a language nobody had ever taught him.

Darling stood up, smiled a little, because if he didn't smile he knew the tears would come. He looked around him. This was the spot. O'Connor's pass had come sliding out just to here ... the high point. Darling put up his hands, felt all over again the flat slap of the ball. He shook his hips to throw off the halfback, cut back inside the center, picked his knees high as he ran gracefully over two men jumbled on the ground at the line of scrimmage, ran easily, gaining speed, for ten yards, holding the ball lightly in his two hands, swung away from the halfback diving at him, ran, swinging his hips in the almost girlish manner of a back in a broken field, tore into the safety man, his shoes drumming heavily on the turf, stiff-armed, elbow locked, pivoted, raced lightly and exultantly for the goal line.

It was only after he had sped over the goal line and slowed to a trot that he saw the boy and girl sitting together on the turf, looking at him wonderingly.

He stopped short, dropping his arms. "I . . ." he said, gasping a little though his condition was fine and the run hadn't winded him, "I . . . . Once I played here."

The boy and the girl said nothing. Darling laughed embarrassedly, looked hard at them sitting there, close to each other, shrugged, turned and went toward his hotel, the sweat breaking out on his face and running down into his collar.

Ray Bradbury:

The Illustrated Man

Here is a story of strange power that you'll never forget.
It's about a hideously fat man, the ghastly pictures tattooed on his body,
and the woman that he loved—to death.
You'll retell it over and over. . .

H ey, the Illustrated Man!"

A calliope screamed, and Mr. William Philippus Phelps stood, arms folded, high on the summer-night platform, a crowd unto himself.

He was an entire civilization. In the Main Country, his chest, the Vasties lived—nipple-eyed dragons swirling over his fleshpot, his almost feminine breasts. His navel was the mouth of a slit-eyed monster—an obscene, in-sucked mouth, toothless as a witch. And there were secret caves where Darklings lurked, his armpits, adrip with slow subterranean liquors, where the Darklings, eyes jealously ablaze, peered out through rank creeper and hanging vine.

Mr. William Philippus Phelps leered down from his freak platform with a thousand peacock eyes. Across the sawdust meadow he saw his wife, Lisabeth, far away, ripping tickets in half, staring at the silver belt buckles of passing men.

Mr. William Philippus Phelps' hands were tattooed roses. At the sight of his wife's interest, the roses shriveled, as with the passing of sunlight.

A year before, when he had led Lisabeth to the marriage bureau to watch her work her name in ink, slowly, on the form, his skin had been pure and white and clean. He glanced down at himself in sudden horror. Now he was like a great painted canvas, shaken in the night wind! How had it happened? Where had it all begun?

It had started with the arguments, and then the flesh, and then the pictures. They had fought deep into the summer nights, she like a brass trumpet forever blaring at him. And he had gone out to eat five thousand steaming hot dogs, ten million hamburgers, and a forest of green onions, and to drink vast red seas of orange juice. Peppermint candy formed his brontosaur bones, the hamburgers shaped his balloon flesh, and strawberry pop pumped in and out of his heart valves sickeningly, until he weighed three hundred pounds.

"William Philippus Phelps," Lisabeth said to him in the eleventh month of their marriage, "you're dumb and fat."

That was the day the carnival boss handed him the blue envelope. "Sorry, Phelps. You're no good to me with all that gut on you."

"Wasn't I always your best tent man, boss?"

"Once. Not anymore. Now you sit, you don't get the work out."

"Let me be your Fat Man."

"I *got* a Fat Man. Dime a dozen." The boss eyed him up and down. "Tell you what, though. We ain't had a Tattooed Man since Gallery Smith died last year. . . ."

That had been a month ago. Four short weeks. From someone, he had learned of a tattoo artist far out in the rolling Wisconsin country, an old woman, they said, who knew her trade. If he took the dirt road and turned right at the river and then left. . . .

He had walked out across a yellow meadow, which was crisp from the sun. Red flowers blew and bent in the wind as he walked, and he came to the old shack, which looked as if it had stood in a million rains.

Inside the door was a silent, bare room, and in the center of the bare room sat an ancient woman.

Her eyes were stitched with red resin-thread. Her nose was sealed with black wax-twine. Her ears were sewn, too, as if a darning-needle dragonfly had stitched all her senses shut. She sat, not moving, in the vacant room. Dust lay in a yellow flour all about, unfootprinted in many weeks; if she had moved it would have shown, but she had not moved. Her hands touched each other like thin, rusted instruments. Her feet were naked and obscene as rain rubbers, and near them sat vials of tattoo milk—red, lightning-blue, brown, cat-yellow. She was a thing sewn tight into whispers and silence.

Perhaps Ray Bradbury's most striking story, "The Illustrated Man" was three years in the writing and entailed fifty thousand words of rewriting before the author found his "Pet Milk" conclusion. Pet Milk? "You'll understand what I mean," Bradbury explained in our July, 1950, issue, "if you examine a Pet Milk can with its picture of a cow coming out of a can on which there is a picture of a cow coming out of a can on which there is a picture of a cow coming out of a can. . . ."

Only her mouth moved, unsewn: "Come in. Sit down. I'm lonely.here."

He did not obey.

"You came for the pictures," she said in a high voice. "I have a picture to show you, first."

She tapped a blind finger to her thrust-out palm. "See!" she cried.

It was a tattoo-portrait of William Philippus Phelps.

"Me!" he said.

Her cry stopped him at the door. "Don't run."

He held to the edges of the door, his back to her. "That's me, that's me on your hand!"

"It's been there fifty years." She stroked it like a cat, over and over.

He turned. "It's an *old* tattoo." He drew slowly nearer. He edged forward and bent to blink at it. He put out a trembling finger to brush the picture. "Old. That's impossible! You don't know *me*. I don't know *you*. Your eyes, all sewed shut."

"I've been waiting for you," she said. "And many people." She displayed her arms and legs, like the spindles of an antique chair. "I have pictures on me of people who have already come here to see me. And there are other pictures of other people who are coming to see me in the next one hundred years. And you, you have come."

"How do you know it's me? You can't see!"

"You *feel* like the lions, the elephants, and the tigers, to me. Unbutton your shirt. You need me. Don't be afraid. My needles are as clean as a doctor's fingers. When I'm finished with illustrating you, I'll wait for someone else to walk along out here and find me. And someday, a hundred summers from now, perhaps, I'll just go lie down in the forest under some white mushrooms, and in the spring you won't find anything but a small blue cornflower. . . ."

He began to unbutton his sleeves.

"I know the Deep Past and the Clear Present and the even Deeper Future," she whispered, eyes knotted into blindness, face lifted to this unseen man. "It is on my flesh. I will paint it on yours, too. You will be the only *real* Illustrated Man in the universe. I'll give you special pictures you will never forget. Pictures of the Future on your skin."

She pricked him with a needle.

He ran back to the carnival that night in a drunken terror and elation. Oh, how quickly the old dust-witch had stitched him with color and design. At the end of a long afternoon of being bitten by a silver snake, his body was alive with portraiture. He looked as if he had dropped and been crushed between the steel rollers of a print press, and come out like an incredible rotogravure. He was clothed in a garment of trolls and scarlet dinosaurs.

"Look!" he cried to Lisabeth. She glanced up from her cosmetic table as he tore his shirt away. He stood in the naked bulb-light of their car-trailer, expanding his impossible chest. Here, the Tremblies, half-maiden, half-goat, leaping when his biceps flexed. Here, the Country of Lost Souls, his chins. In so many accordion pleats of fat, numerous small scorpions, beetles, and mice were crushed, held, hid, darting into view, van-

ishing, as he raised or lowered his chins.

"My God," said Lisabeth. "My husband's a freak."

She ran from the trailer and he was left alone to pose before the mirror. Why had he done it? To have a job, yes, but, most of all, to cover the fat that had larded itself impossibly over his bones. To hide the fat under a layer of color and fantasy, to hide it from his wife, but most of all from himself.

He thought of the old woman's last words. She had needled him two *special* tattoos, one on his chest, another for his back, which she would not let him see. She covered each with cloth and adhesive.

"You are not to look at these two," she had said.

"Why?"

"Later, you may look. The Future is in these pictures. You can't look now or it may spoil them. They are not quite finished. I put ink on your flesh and the sweat of you forms the rest of the picture, the Future —your sweat and your thought." Her empty mouth grinned. "Next Saturday night, you may advertise! The Big Unveiling! Come see the Illustrated Man unveil his picture! You can make money in that way. You can charge admission to the Unveiling, like to an Art Gallery. Tell them you have a picture that even *you* never have seen, that *nobody* has seen yet. The most unusual picture ever painted. Almost alive. And it tells the Future. Roll the drums and blow the trumpets. And you can stand there and unveil at the Big Unveiling."

"That's a good idea," he said.

"But only unveil the picture on your chest," she said. "That is first. You must save the picture on your back, under the adhesive, for the following week. Understand?"

"How much do I owe you?"

"Nothing," she said. "If you walk with these pictures on you, I will be repaid with my own satisfaction. I will sit here for the next two weeks and think how clever my pictures are, for I make them to fit each man himself and what is inside him. Now, walk out of this house and never come back. Good-bye."

"Hey! The Big Unveiling!"

The red signs blew in the night wind: NO ORDINARY TATTOOED MAN! THIS ONE IS "ILLUSTRATED"! GREATER THAN MICHELANGELO! TONIGHT! ADMISSION 10 CENTS!

Now the hour had come. Saturday night, the crowd stirring their animal feet in the hot sawdust.

"In one minute—" the carny boss pointed his cardboard megaphone—"in the tent immediately to my rear, we will unveil the Mysterious Portrait upon the Illustrated Man's chest! Next Saturday night, the same hour, same location, we'll unveil the Picture upon the Illustrated Man's *back*! Bring your friends!"

There was a stuttering roll of drums.

Mr. William Philippus Phelps jumped back and vanished; the crowd poured into the tent, and, once inside, found him reestablished upon another platform, the band brassing out a jig-time melody.

He looked for his wife and saw her, lost in the crowd, like a stranger, come to watch a freakish thing, a look of contemptuous curiosity upon her face. For, after all, he was her husband, and this was a thing she didn't know about him herself. It gave him a feeling of great height and warmness and light to find himself the center of the jangling universe, the carnival world, for one night. Even the other freaks—the Skeleton, the Seal Boy, the Yoga, the Magician, and the Balloon—were scattered through the crowd.

"Ladies and gentlemen, the great moment!"

A trumpet flourish, a hum of drumsticks on tight cowhide.

Mr. William Philippus Phelps let his cape fall. Dinosaurs, trolls, and half-women-half-snakes writhed on his skin in the stark light.

Ah, murmured the crowd, for surely there had never been a tattooed man like this! The beast eyes seemed to take red fire and blue fire, blinking and twisting. The roses on his fingers seemed to expel a sweet pink bouquet. The tyrannosaurus rex reared up along his leg, and the sound of the brass trumpet in the hot tent heavens was a prehistoric cry from the red monster throat. Mr. William Philippus Phelps was a museum jolted to life. Fish swam in seas of electric-blue ink. Fountains sparkled under yellow suns. Ancient buildings stood in meadows of harvest wheat. Rockets burned across spaces of muscle and flesh. The slightest inhalation of his breath threatened to make chaos of the entire printed universe. He seemed afire, the creatures flinching from the flame, drawing back from the great heat of his pride, as he expanded under the audience's rapt contemplation.

The carny boss laid his fingers to the adhesive. The audience rushed forward, silent in the oven vastness of the night tent.

"You ain't seen nothing yet!" cried the carny boss.

The adhesive ripped free.

There was an instant in which nothing happened. An instant in which the Illustrated Man thought that the Unveiling was a terrible and irrevocable failure.

But then the audience gave a low moan.

The carny boss drew back, his eyes fixed.

Far out at the edge of the crowd, a woman, after a moment, began to cry, began to sob, and did not stop.

Slowly, the Illustrated Man looked down at his naked chest and stomach.

The thing that he saw made the roses on his hands discolor and die. All of his creatures seemed to wither, turn inward, shrivel with the arctic coldness that pumped from his heart outward to freeze and destroy them. He stood trembling. His hands floated up to touch that incredible picture, which lived, moved and shivered with life. It was like gazing into a small room, seeing a thing of someone else's life, so intimate, so impossible that one could not believe and one could not long stand to watch without turning away.

It was a picture of his wife, Lisabeth, and himself.

And he was killing her.

Before the eyes of a thousand people in a dark tent in the center of a black-forested Wisconsin land, he was killing his wife.

His great flowered hands were upon her throat, and her face was turning dark and he killed her and he killed her and did not ever in the next minute stop killing her. It was real. While the crowd watched, she died, and he turned very sick. He was about to fall straight down into the crowd. The tent whirled like a monster bat wing, flapping grotesquely. The last thing he heard was a woman, sobbing, far out on the shore of the silent crowd.

And the crying woman was Lisabeth, his wife.

In the night, his bed was moist with perspiration. The carnival sounds had melted away, and his wife, in her own bed, was quiet now, too. He fumbled with his chest. The adhesive was smooth. They had made him put it back.

He had fainted. When he revived, the carny boss had yelled at him, "Why didn't you *say* what that picture was like?"

"I didn't know, I didn't," said the Illustrated Man.

"Good God!" said the boss. "Scare hell outa everyone. Scared hell outa Lizzie, scared hell outa me. Christ, where'd you *get* that damn tattoo?" He shuddered. "Apologize to Lizzie, now."

His wife stood over him.

"I'm sorry, Lisabeth," he said, weakly, his eyes closed. "I didn't know."

"You did it on purpose," she said. "To scare me."

"I'm sorry."

"Either it goes or I go," she said.

"Lisabeth."

"You heard me. That picture comes off or I quit this show."

"Yeah, Phil," said the boss. "That's how it is."

"Did you lose money? Did the crowd demand refunds?"

"It ain't the money, Phil. For that matter, once the word got around, hundreds of people wanted in. But I'm runnin' a clean show. That tattoo comes off! Was this your idea of a practical joke, Phil?"

He turned in the warm bed. No, not a joke. Not a joke at all. He had been as terrified as anyone. Not a joke. That little old dust-witch, what had she *done* to him and how had she done it? Had she put the picture there? No; she had said that the picture was unfinished, and that he himself, with his thoughts and his perspiration, would finish it. Well, he had done the job all right.

But what, if anything, was the significance? He didn't want to kill anyone. He didn't want to kill Lisabeth. Why should such a silly picture burn here on his flesh in the dark?

He crawled his fingers softly, cautiously down to touch the quivering place where the hidden portrait lay. He pressed tight, and the temperature of that spot was enormous. He could almost feel that little evil picture killing and killing and killing all through the night.

I don't wish to kill her, he thought, insistently, looking over at her bed. And then, five minutes later, he whispered aloud: "Or *do* I?"

"What?" she cried, awake.

"Nothing," he said, after a pause. "Go to sleep."

The man bent forward, a buzzing instrument in his hand. "This costs five bucks an inch. Costs more to peel tattoos off than put 'em on. Okay, jerk the adhesive."

The Illustrated Man obeyed.

The skin man sat back. "Christ! No wonder you want that off! That's ghastly. *I* don't even want to look at it." He flicked his machine. "Ready? This won't hurt."

The carny boss stood in the tent flap, watching. After five minutes, the skin man changed the instrument head, cursing. Ten minutes later he scraped his chair back and scratched his head. Half an hour passed and he got up, told Mr. William Philippus Phelps to dress, and packed his kit.

"Wait a minute," said the carny boss. "You ain't done the job."

"And I ain't going to," said the skin man.

"I'm paying good money. What's wrong?"

"Nothing, except that damn picture just won't come off. Damn thing must go right down to the bone."

"You're crazy."

"Mister, I'm in business thirty years and never seen a tattoo like this. An inch deep, if it's anything."

"But I've got to get it off!" cried the Illustrated Man.

The skin man shook his head. "Only one way to get rid of that."

"How?"

"Take a knife and cut off your chest. You won't live long, but the picture'll be gone."

"Come back here!"

But the skin man walked away.

They could hear the big Sunday-night crowd, waiting.

"That's a big crowd," said the Illustrated Man.

"But they ain't going to see what they came to see," said the carny boss. "You ain't going out there, except with the adhesive. Hold still now, I'm curious about this *other* picture, on your back. We might be able to give 'em an Unveiling on this one instead."

"She said it wouldn't be ready for a week or so. The old woman said it would take time to set, make a pattern."

There was a soft ripping as the carny boss pulled aside a flap of white tape on the Illustrated Man's spine.

"What do you see?" gasped Mr. Phelps, bent over.

The carny boss replaced the tape. "Buster, as a Tattooed Man, you're a washout, ain't you? Why'd you let that old dame fix you up this way?"

"I didn't know who she was."

"She sure cheated you on this one. No design to it. Nothing. No picture at all."

"It'll come clear. You wait and see."

The boss laughed. "Okay. Come on. We'll show the crowd part of you, anyway."

They walked out into an explosion of brassy music.

He stood monstrous in the middle of the night, putting out his hands like a blind man to balance himself in a world now tilted, now rushing, now threatening to spin him over and down into the mirror before which he raised his hands. Upon the flat, dimly lighted table top were peroxides, acids, silver razors, and squares of sandpaper. He took each of them in turn. He soaked the vicious tattoo upon his chest, he scraped

at it. He worked steadily for an hour.

He was aware, suddenly, that someone stood in the trailer door behind him. It was three in the morning. There was a faint odor of beer. She had come home from town. He heard her slow breathing. He did not turn. "Lisabeth?" he said.

"You'd better get rid of it," she said, watching his hands move the sandpaper. She stepped into the trailer.

"I didn't want the picture this way," he said.

"You did," she said. "You planned it."

"I didn't."

"I know you," she said. "Oh, I know you hate me. Well, that's nothing. I hate you, I've hated you a long time now. Good God, when you started putting on the fat, you think anyone could love you then? I could teach you some things about hate. Why don't you ask me?"

"Leave me alone," he said.

"In front of that crowd, making a spectacle out of me!"

"I didn't know what was under the tape."

She walked around the table, hands fitted to her hips, talking to the beds, the walls, the table, talking it all out of her. And he thought: *Or did I know? Who made this picture, me or the witch? Who formed it? How? Do I really want her dead? No! And yet....* He watched his wife draw nearer, nearer, he saw the ropy strings of her throat vibrate to her shouting. This and this and *this* was wrong with him! That and that and *that* was unspeakable about him! He was a liar, a schemer, a fat, lazy, ugly man, a child. Did he think he could compete with the carny boss or the tent-peggers? Did he think he was sylphine and graceful, did he think he was a framed El Greco? Da Vinci, huh! Michelangelo, my eye! She brayed. She showed her teeth. "Well, you can't scare me into staying with someone I don't want touching me with their slobby paws!" she finished, triumphantly.

"Lisabeth," he said.

"Don't Lisabeth me!" she shrieked. "I know your plan. You had that picture put on to scare me. You thought I wouldn't *dare* leave you. Well!"

"Next Saturday night, the Second Unveiling," he said. "You'll be proud of me."

"Proud! You're silly and pitiful. God, you're like a whale. You ever see a beached whale? I saw one when I was a kid. There it was, and they came and shot it. Some lifeguards shot it. Jesus, a whale!"

"Lisabeth."

"I'm leaving, that's all, and getting a divorce."

"Don't."

"And I'm marrying a man, not a fat woman—that's what you are, so much fat on you there ain't no sex!"

"You can't leave me," he said.

"Just watch!"

"I love you," he said.

"Oh," she said. "Go look at your pictures."

He reached out.

"Keep your hands off," she said.

"Lisabeth."

"Don't come near. You turn my stomach."

"Lisabeth."

All the eyes of his body seemed to fire, all the snakes to move, all the monsters to seethe, all the mouths to widen and rage. He moved toward her— not like a man, but a crowd.

He felt the great blooded reservoir of orangeade pump through him now, the sluice of cola and rich lemon pop pulse in sickening sweet anger through his wrists, his legs, his heart. All of it, the oceans of mustard and relish and all the million drinks he had drowned himself in in the last year were aboil; his face was the color of a steamed beef. And the pink roses of his hands became those hungry, carnivorous flowers kept long years in tepid jungle and now let free to find their way on the night air before him.

He gathered her to him, like a great beast gathering in a struggling animal. It was a frantic gesture of love, quickening and demanding, which, as she struggled, hardened to another thing. She beat and clawed at the picture on his chest.

"You've got to love me, Lisabeth."

"Let go!" she screamed. She beat at the picture that burned under her fists. She slashed at it with her fingernails.

"Oh, Lisabeth," he said, his hands moving up her arms.

"I'll scream," she said, seeing his eyes.

"Lisabeth." The hand moved up to her shoulders, to her neck. "Don't go away."

"Help!" she screamed. The blood ran from the picture on his chest.

He put his fingers about her neck and squeezed. She was a calliope cut in mid-shriek.

Outside, the grass rustled. There was the sound of running feet.

Mr. William Philippus Phelps opened the trailer door and stepped out.

They were waiting for him. Skeleton, Midget, Balloon, Yoga, Electra, Popeye, Seal Boy. The freaks, waiting in the middle of the night, in the dry grass.

He walked toward them. He moved with a feeling that he must get away; these people would understand nothing, they were not thinking people. And because he did not flee, because he only walked, balanced, stunned, between the tents, slowly, the freaks moved to let him pass. They watched him, because their watching guaranteed that he would not escape. He walked out across the black meadow, moths fluttering in his face. He walked steadily as long as he was visible, not knowing where he was going. They watched him go, and then they turned and all of them shuffled to the silent car-trailer together and pushed the door slowly wide. . . .

The Illustrated Man walked steadily in the dry meadows beyond the town.

"He went that way!" a faint voice cried. Flashlights bobbled over the hills. There were dim shapes, running.

Mr. William Philippus Phelps waved to them. He was tired. He wanted only to be found now. He was tired of running away. He waved again.

"There he is!" The flashlights changed direction. "Come on! We'll get the bastard!"

When it was time, the Illustrated Man ran again. He was careful to run slowly. He deliberately fell down twice. Looking back, he saw the tent stakes they held in their hands.

He ran toward a far crossroads lantern, where all the summer night seemed to gather; merry-go-rounds of fireflies whirling, crickets moving their song toward that light, everything rushing, as if by some midnight attraction, toward that one high-hung lantern— the Illustrated Man first, the others close at his heels.

As he reached the light and passed a few yards under and beyond it, he did not need to look back. On the road ahead, in silhouette, he saw the upraised tent stakes sweep violently up, up, and then *down*!

A minute passed.

In the country ravines, the crickets sang. The freaks stood over the sprawled Illustrated Man, holding their tent stakes loosely.

Finally they rolled him over on his stomach. Blood ran from his mouth.

They ripped the adhesive from his back. They stared down for a long moment at the freshly revealed picture. Someone whispered. Someone else swore, softly. The Thin Man pushed back and walked away and was sick. Another and another of the freaks stared, their mouths trembling, and moved away, leaving the Illustrated Man on the deserted road, the blood running from his mouth.

In the dim light, the unveiled Illustration was easily seen.

It showed a crowd of freaks bending over a dying fat man on a dark and lonely road, looking at a tattoo on his back which illustrated a crowd of freaks bending over a dying fat man on a. . . .

John Updike:

Deus Dixit

Four years at Harvard leave their mark on a man;
it is less clear what they do to a god

The world is mocked—belittled, perforated—by the success of one's contemporaries in it. The world of deeds and wealth, which to a child appears a gaudy heaven staffed with invincibly brilliant powers, is revealed as a tattered heirloom limply descending from one generation of caretakers to the next. In the ten years since our graduation, one of my Harvard classmates has become a Congressman; another a bit movie actor, whose specialty is playing the "goofy" guy in those beach-party movies that costar Fred MacMurray and Elvis Presley; a third a professor of Celtic languages at Brandeis. Three others have annual incomes of over a hundred thousand a year. Which these three are, the class report (a fat red paperback) does not say. Nor does it say anything, beyond a curt forwarding address in Kabul, of my old tennis opponent Gish Imra, whose fate has been the noblest and strangest of all; for, if I read the newspapers right, he has become not merely a god but God.

The rumor of divinity haloing his slight and sallow person seemed, when I knew him, a kind of undergraduate joke. I understood only that his father was the "profoundly venerated" chieftain of the Shīgar tribe of Nuristan. Two years ago when his father died, in an assassination so ambiguous in its effect that both the Russians and the C.I.A. were rumored to be responsible, the newspapers printed some helpful, if not entirely enlightening, background material. I synopsize briefly.

The region of Central Asia now called (though not by its own inhabitants) Afghanistan has been overswept by many political and religious tides—Greek and Arab from the west, Mongol from the north, Buddhist and Hindu from the east. The old Afghan chroniclers, surprisingly, call themselves the Children of Israel and claim descent from King Saul. Under the

Kushan dynasty, derived from the Yue-chi tribe that expelled the Parthians in the first century A.D., the Buddhist religion was established. Huns ousted the Buddhists; Turkish adventurers brought Islam; Genghis Kahn devastated the dynasty of Ghor. Aloof from these conversions and counter-conversions stood the mysteriously fair-skinned people of the Hindu Kush, a mountain range in the region north of Kabul traditionally known as Kafiristan, "The Country of Unbelievers." The region is impenetrably wild. The mountains are so steep some valleys are in shadow for six months of the year. Landslides of loose scree are frequent. Mulberries grow, and the ibex flourishes. A legend traces the human inhabitants back to stragglers from the army of Alexander the Great, who crossed the Hindu Kush on his way to the Indus in 327 B.C. But Alexander did battle in the Kunar Valley with a blond and warlike race called, then, the Aspasians. The Kafirs worshiped a pantheon of gods that included Imra the Creator and Gish the God of War, drank gross amounts of wine, kept slaves, robbed strangers, lived in tall wooden houses, and spoke, valley to valley, mutually unintelligible dialects of Dardic. Their women were, and are, renowned for handsomeness.

In 1895, the amir Abdur Rahman, with British complicity, on the provocation that the Russians might annex the area, sent his gigantic commander Ghulam Haider Khan on a campaign to convert the Kafirs by the sword—the last such conversion in history. The Kafirs succumbed, and the region was christened Nuristan, "The Country of Light." However, one pocket of resistance remained, in the remote valley inhabited by the Shīgar tribe. Winter snows sealed the valley off, and the legions of Ghulam Haider Khan turned back. In celebration, the Shīgars, who numbered not more than twenty thousand, gave their chief, my tennis friend's great-grandfather, the name Gish Imra—as if we were to call a President Thor Jehovah. Probably the Shīgar chieftains were already semidivine. The ancient ceremony, for instance, whereby on the day of the vernal equinox the chief

In a recent issue of The Hudson Review, critic William Pritchard cited John Updike as the leading novelist of his generation. Prolific as Updike is, and as inventive, we were interested to discover—when we sifted through for the story we most wanted to reprint—that in titling his latest novel Rabbit Redux, Updike may have found his own precedent in our September, 1965, issue.

would take for himself as much treasure (consisting of lapis lazuli from Badakhshan, rubies from the famous mine in the Jagdalak Pass, and, in recent times, wristwatches from Switzerland) as he could hoist with a straight right arm onto an altar five feet high, has many analogues in Frazer.

While the religious antecedents of this throne are obscure, its modern political career is a matter of record. The first Gish Imra was a prodigious brute who maintained his tribe, of necessity, in a state of impregnable ferocity. No European traveler or Moslem emissary is known to have returned from an audience with him, and in Nuristani art he is always represented simply as the sun—with blank features, circular face, and stylized radii. His son, who succeeded him in 1915, traveled with a bodyguard of two thousand men to Kabul to exchange rugs, pledges, and mulberry butter with the amir Habibullah, who had recently extended leniency to the Ghilzais and Mangals of Khost. Thus begins the recognized autonomy of the Shīgars under the amir. Shīgar tribesmen fought beside Amanullah in his war with the British in the Summer of 1919, but remained aloof when, ten years later, his excessively progressive regime collapsed under pressure from the fanatical south. The second Gish Imra died, at the age of ninety-three, in 1946, whereupon his son, who in the Nineteen Thirties had enjoyed some small celebrity in café society and in the League of Nations, succeeded him. An unhappy and thoroughly Europeanized man, the third Gish Imra, when he was not wintering in Cannes or Menton, fortified himself against the tireless machinations of the amirate with perhaps excessive helpings of American advice and French cuisine. Our mission in his court, headed by the shadowy "Major Damon," was never officially acknowledged, and Congressional investigations came to nothing. The French foodstuffs, including truffles and goose livers, were imported into the fastnesses of the Hindu Kush by means of goat caravans.

My friend had been tutored at home, schooled in Bern, and sent to Harvard as a political gesture, much as his father had gone to Oxford. His tennis, learned in Switzerland, was stronger from the backcourt than at the net. His backhand was slightly wristy, his serve loopy and fat; but his forehand, administered with a powerful straight right arm, came off the bounce with a pace that constantly surprised me, for Gish Imra could not have weighed more than one hundred and fifteen pounds. He drove a little red M.G. with countless gears, and it was in this car that we went, on one occasion, into Boston, still in our tennis whites, to have dinner together. It was late in the spring, and perhaps the approaching end of our senior year had prompted his unexpected invitation. Gish kept habitually aloof, and after his sophomore year did not have roommates. I had met him when we were both freshmen, working off our physical-education requirements with tennis, which I had learned on some pitted public courts in Pennsylvania. My game, then as now, in I suppose the American style, disdained strategy and solid ground strokes for a hopeful mishmash of reckless, glamorous "gets" and satisfying overhead smashes. Despite his smaller size and soft serve, he beat me as often as I beat him. We were well matched, and each spring, until we graduated, on one of those sudden soft days when the classroom windows are thrown open and the Radcliffe girls venture down to the Charles with their books and bicycles, he would call me up and in his formal and, though humorless, faintly mischievous voice offer to renew our competition. I was pleased to accept. After a winter of sitting I needed the exercise, and I suppose, having this half-comic sense of his "divinity," I was flattered.

I recall our dinner imperfectly. I remember that it was still daylight outside, that the restaurant was the Nile (since moved), and that the manager had frowned at our bare legs as we walked in. I remember the glow of the jukebox selector on my left, and the thoughtful pallor of my companion's face, and the startling ease with which he downed two very dry gimlets. But I do not remember the conversation that led up to the brief exchange I will never forget. It must have been by way of "Cross-currents." Though he was a Government major and I in Mathematics, we were, that year, taking one course in common—an eccentric Comp. Lit. concoction called "Cross-currents in Nineteenth-Century Thought." The course, taught by a beetle-browed ironist from the University of Chicago, dealt with four thinkers—Nietzsche, Marx, Kierkegaard, and Dostoevski—who in their various styles paddled against the liberal, progressivist mainstream of their century. I dimly recall expressing to Gish my enthusiasm for Kierkegaard, and perhaps I confessed, in passing, the fact that I, like Kierkegaard, was a Lutheran.

He looked at me sharply; there was not much amiability in his face. Though his skin was as fair as mine, there was something taut and flattened in the spread of his small-boned features. "Do you believe in it?"

"I don't know. Part of it, I suppose."

"Which of it?"

I began to blush. I realized that in a primitive byway of my being I had "revered" my slight friend and had regarded him, for all the times I had victimized his backhand, with what used to be called "superstitious awe"; so that I felt unworthy and embarrassed in the face of his questioning.

He insisted, "Do you believe in personal immortality?"

I assumed that, being a god, he was certainly pious and said, to placate him, "Why not? It can't be disproved."

"I can't see it," Gish said.

Though the remark seemed addressed, calmly, more to himself than to me, my heart sank, and kept sinking, through the abysmal depths of this somehow authoritative denial.

"But it's not supposed to be *seen*," I pleaded. "It must be believed. Belief is the option we've been given."

He shook his head, regretfully, inexorably. His voice was small and high-pitched, yet took a certain resonance from the firmness of his enunciation. "It's a hoax," he said. "I agree with Marx. It's a method whereby the powerful keep the ignorant from rebelling."

I must have been so shocked that my mind erased itself, for the next thing I recall is Gish laughing, mischievously, and saying, presumably in connection with the theme of ignorant credulity, "Do you want to hear an Afghanistani legend? This is how the belly of the ibex became white. When God made the Great Flood, when you say Noah built his ark, the ibex ran into the mountains. The waters kept rising, and the ibex went from mountain to mountain, until at last he came to the highest of all, to Tirich Mir, and there he stood, waiting. The water rose to his feet, to his knees, to his belly; and then it subsided." Gish showed me, with slender hands and wrists flat like female wrists, the soft motion of the subsiding. "And that," he said, "is why the belly of the ibex is white." His voice was gentle and bitter and the light in his grey eyes was, yes, gay.

Though the class report, for all its fat red bulk, as nothing in it but a Kabul forwarding address, the newspapers have printed a little about his postgraduate career. Becoming king (if that is what it is) upon his father's violent death, the fourth Gish Imra has reversed all liberal trends in the Shigar state. Contact with the south and the Kabul administration has dwindled; radios were destroyed by tribal decree; strangers venture into the region at their own risk and may expect to be robbed. Certain brutal aspects of the cult of worship, which had fallen into disuse, have been revived, in the name of cultural autonomy. My friend, seeking a policy, "can't see" the reign of his unhappy father and looks toward his grandfather, who left the mountains amid two thousand bodyguards, and even beyond, toward his great-grandfather, the sun.

John O'Hara:

The Little Mysteries of Pomp and Circumstance

Two stories written in the Forties and drawn
from the work still unpublished
at the time of O'Hara's death in 1970

1: At the Cothurnos Club

Although the Cothurnos Club was founded by actors, a limited number of writers and painters are taken in from time to time, and that is how I chance to be a member. It is the pleasantest of places; in the reading and writing rooms pin-drop quiet prevails, while in the bar and billiard room and dining room there is very little likelihood of a man's feeling lonesome. Especially is this true of the dining room where most of the members eat at a large round table. After I had been honored by admission to the club I took to lunching there nearly every day and that was how I happened to notice Mr. Childress. He always ate alone at a small table against the wall. He never seemed to speak to anyone, for surely the nod that he gave the men at the round table could not be taken as a greeting. A few days ago I asked Clem Kirby, who put me up for the club, to tell me about the reclusive Mr. Childress. "Has he been a member long?" I said.

"Oh, yes," said Kirby. "About thirty years, I should say."

"But was he always like that? I don't see why a man like that joins a club, he's so antisocial."

Kirby smiled. "Maybe it's hard to believe, but up till about ten or twelve years ago George Childress was just the opposite of what you see today. Full of beans. Witty. Here every day, down in the bar, drinking with the boys and so on."

"What does he do?" I asked.

"He paints, or did. He was what's commonly called a fashionable portrait painter, and he made a lot of money, and while I don't think anyone could call George stingy, he took care of his money. He hasn't done anything in recent years. That's probably why you've never heard of him."

"Vaguely I have," I said.

John O'Hara's work did not appear in Esquire again, after the appearance of Little 'Chita in our August, 1936, issue; this because the author honored a prior commitment to The New Yorker. But after his death his estate released to us the two short stories that are reprinted here from our July, 1972, issue.

"He married Hope Westmore," said Kirby.

"Oh, of course," I said. "That's where I've heard of him. Hope Westmore's husband. She was one of my all-time favorite actresses. So that's George Childress. Are they still married?"

"Married, yes," said Kirby. "But of course—" Clem did not finish his sentence. His eyes turned sad. "I'll tell you about George.

"He wasn't exactly a practical joker, but he was something of the sort, especially with, well, someone like you, a new member. He'd find out all he could about you, and then before being introduced to you he'd discuss your work, whatever it was, in your hearing, and I may say the opinions he'd come out with would be devastating. He did it, of course, to get a rise out of new members. A cruel trick. What you younger fellows nowadays call a rib. He had several tricks like that. He also invented another one, with a new twist.

"He would join a group of fellows in the bar, all old members except one. Everybody was on to the trick but the new member. George would be introduced and he'd be his most charming, affable self. Then slowly he would get the conversation around to the theatre and he would say, 'What was the name of that actress a few years back. Terribly good actress. Beautiful. But drank herself out of every job she had?' And he'd pretend to rack his brains, trying to recall the name. The fellows who were in on the trick would also pretend to search their memories, and of course what would happen would be that the new member, trying to be helpful, would volunteer a name. Now George's point was that he never got the same answer twice, or did very seldom.

"Well, I see you know what happened. You're right. One day we were down in the bar and there was a new member, a young fellow, and when George couldn't remember the actress' name the young fellow popped up with a name, and of course the name was Hope Westmore."

"Good Lord," I said. "What happened?"

"Well," said Clem Kirby, "there was a stillness that I thought would never end. You've seen for yourself,

289

George is a powerfully built man and I've never seen anyone exercise such self-control. But he took a deep breath and said, 'You see, gentlemen, I never get the same answer twice,' and then he excused himself. As far as I know that's the last time George has been in the bar."

"What about Hope Westmore? Was it true?" I said.

Kirby looked at me long and steadily. "I don't see that that makes the slightest difference," he said. ⚎

2: All I've Tried To Be

The building was not old as office buildings go. It had two elevators and a mail chute and a directory of tenants that was ornamental as well as practical. Throughout the building there were Savage burglary-alarm stations, the kind that set off a signal at police headquarters if the night watchman failed to make his stop at each station every hour. After twenty years the building was still no worse than the second-tallest in the town, and had been the best investment the Masons had ever made. The lodge owned the building, but even without the members' efforts it would have averaged eighty-percent occupancy through the years. In a larger town, or in a great city, the building would not have attracted any attention; it was only twelve stories high and there was nothing about the architecture that would have frightened Fouilhoux or Hood. Nevertheless Miss Lapham, visiting the building for the first time, was favorably impressed. The brightwork on the elevator doors and mail chute and directory had a nice patina and as she waited for one of the elevators she looked up at the marble ceiling, as one will while waiting for an elevator, and she was sure that there was not a speck of dust in the ceiling corners. The man she was going to interview, Mr. Lewis C. Craymer, ran the building, she knew, and she admired the way he ran it.

The elevator operator was a girl who bore a very, very slight resemblance to Dorothy Lamour. "Three, please," said Miss Lapham.

"Right," said the girl. She seemed to be counting the time she waited, or possibly was silently going through a song. In any case she suddenly closed the elevator door, as though she had reached the end of a count or a song, and took Miss Lapham to the third floor. "Three out," she said. "If you're looking for Craymer, it's to your right and another right."

"How'd you know I was looking for Craymer?" said Miss Lapham, with a smile.

The girl smiled back. "The other offices on this floor are the dynamite company, and I didn't think you'd be in the market for dynamite."

"You're right, but I might be looking for a job or something."

"They only employ the one woman and she'll be here forever," said the girl. "All the rest are men."

"That ought to be interesting, being the only woman," said Miss Lapham.

"It's plenty interesting where you're *going*," said the girl, closing the elevator door.

Miss Lapham could not be sure whether the girl's manner indicated esprit de corps or disrespect toward Craymer. She went around to his door and knocked.

"Come in," a man's voice sang out.

She entered a small reception room-outer office, which was unevenly divided by an old-fashioned oak fence, the kind once dear to country lawyers and justices of the peace. Beyond was a larger office, separated from the smaller by a wood-and-glass partition. The two rooms got the theme of their furniture and decoration from the oak fence. At a quick glance Miss Lapham was almost sure that there was nothing in either room, including the typewriter in the anteroom, that was newer than the fence. As she had observed earlier, the building was not remarkably old but *was* remarkably well cared for. But Mr. Craymer's offices were of another day, and so was Mr. Craymer. It was like walking through the Presbyterian Hospital in New York and opening a door at random and discovering an abdominal operation being performed by a bearded man in a Prince Albert.

Mr. Craymer was clean-shaven, except for a small moustache, and he wore an ordinary three-button sack suit, but he wore a heavy gold watch chain, with a collegiate gold charm and an old-time large-size fraternity badge. His grey hair was parted in the middle. A nail-scissors job had been done on his cuffs, but not on his nails, and his stiff collar was cleaner than his shirt by at least one day's wear. He came around from behind his desk to greet her. "This must be Miss Lapham," he said.

"That's right," she said.

"I'm delighted to see you. Have a chair. I've just been getting things, uh. . . ." He removed a pile of cardboard folders from a chair and dusted it off with a rumpled handkerchief. The chair was on one side of the desk, which was roll-topped and so crowded with papers that there was scarcely room for the outstandingly modern article, the telephone. "I was just signing some letters," he said. "My secretary only comes in in the morning." He cleared his throat.

"Go right ahead," she said.

He took an extraordinarily long time reading each letter, frowning and clearing his throat and apparently having trouble concentrating on the correspondence. Miss Lapham looked about her. Besides the desk and chairs there was a large plain table on which were stacks of papers of assorted sizes; several piles of cardboard letter files on the composition floor (there was only one small green rug on the floor, under her feet); wire wastebaskets; a black tufted-leather sofa with a Navajo blanket folded in a corner; an oak filing cabinet with some of the tabs written on and some not; and a small safe with a letterpress on top. She noticed also a pencil sharpener screwed into the wall, and quite naked without the covering that is intended to hold the vermicular pencil peelings; a check protector under the pigeonhole compartments of the desk; a russet leather shotgun case under the sofa; a man's pair of rubbers, also under the sofa; several rubber-tire ashtrays; two unused memo pads for 1947 and 1948, which advertised the neighboring dynamite company; four blackened silver loving cups with crossed tennis rackets on two of them; a battery lamp, suitable for camping, boating, the farm, and countless other uses; and a large silver-plated carafe and tray and three Coca-Cola glasses on the plain-topped table. There were Venetian blinds on the three windows and the window glass was spotlessly clean.

"Mm-hmm," said Mr. Craymer, nodding to his letters. He had been standing; now he sat down in the swivel chair. "This office, we've been so . . . I don't see how we ever get anything . . . I'm sorry, Miss Lapham. Do you smoke?"

"I have some."

"Here. Try a—have you ever tried one of these? They're Fatimas. No gold tips, but finest quality. That's the slogan. . . . Now then, the *Standard* wants some help from me. Is that correct? Did you just start there?"

"I started Monday."

"And you're from?"

"Originally Cleveland, Ohio, but more recently New York."

"Is that so? Well, I imagine a writer can get a lot of experience working on a paper like the *Standard*. I happen to believe in the country doctor, too, you know." He scratched his head behind his ear. "Whenever one of the younger chaps comes to me for advice, I tell them they ought to practice in a small town first, before specializing. Now what was it you wanted to know exactly?"

"Well, part of my job, at least till I learn my way around, I'm supposed to go back in the files and write the thirty-years-ago and twenty-years-ago-today stuff. I guess you've read them."

"I certainly never miss them. I'm in them so often. One or the *other*."

"Well, somebody sent us this photograph and asked why we didn't run it, but the only trouble was they didn't send the names of the people in the picture. Mr. Pierson said he recognized you, but you were the only one."

"Who's Mr. Pierson?"

"Why, he's the composing-room foreman."

"Oh, Jake Pierson. Jake, of course. The printer. Is that what he is? Composing foreman." Mr. Craymer nodded. "I've seen him going to work, to and fro all these years, and I never knew exactly what he did. Well, let me have a look at the picture."

She handed him the photograph and he immediately smiled. "Oh, my yes. Now I wonder who on earth sent you this. That's me, all right. I can give you the names right off the reel. There's m'self, with the cap in my hand."

"Can you give them to me left to right?"

"Very well. This short fellow, that's Henry Crowell."

"Henry H. Crowell, of the Keystone National?"

"Henry Crowell. Correct. Next to him is Sam Biggers. That's Samuel T. Biggers, the lawyer. Then myself. Lewis C. Craymer. Then Van Vandergrift. He's living in Philadelphia. Theodore P. Vandergrift, retired now, but formerly with Union Carbide. Very well-to-do. *Very* well-to-do. Arthur Schneider. He was killed at I *think* it was Belleau Wood. With the Marines, I know."

"Belleau Wood?" said Miss Lapham.

"Oh, this picture's over thirty years old. This was

taken before the First War. You can't put this with your thirty-years-ago. A lot of people would know right away. Then here's dear old Charlie Watkins, my doubles partner for years. You'll see his name on two of those trophies over there. Charlie lives in New York City, and I'm sure if you were in the newspaper game there you've heard of Charlie. Charles W. Watkins. He has a house on East Seventy-ninth Street, New York City, and a large country place at Amagansett, Long Island, where I've visited him many, many times."

"Charles W. Watkins. What does he do?"

"Oh, Wall Street. He's in all kinds of activities in the banking world, and still owns property here in town that I handle for him. Was there a letter with this picture? I wonder who sent it?"

"An anonymous letter, that's all."

"Man's or lady's handwriting, would you suppose?"

"I couldn't tell. It was printed. It just said 'I think many of your readers would be interested in this old photograph of prominent local citizens,' or something to that effect. It was a nice note."

"I don't remember the picture at all. I don't remember who took it or why, but of course I know where. It was taken at the old Tennis Club. This was our old team. Charlie played first man and he and I were the first doubles team. We beat all the good teams in this part of the state. In those days they didn't have as many country clubs, golf courses that is, but every town big and little had a tennis team. Let's see, now, Charlie played at Yale. Henry at Princeton. Sam at Haverford. Van wasn't on the team at Lehigh, but he played a lot. Arthur Schneider at Princeton, not on the team, and I played on the team at Lafayette. I guess there weren't many better club teams in the whole East, when you think of it. How many other towns could boast of so many varsity players? And we had a ladder, you know. You weren't always sure of your place on the team, just because you made it once. We were always challenging each other, taking each other down a peg, so to speak."

"Did you have a name for your team?"

"Why, just the Gibbsville Lawn Tennis Club team. We always traveled by motor, too. The Watkins had a big Locomobile, and the Schneiders had a Lozier. There was room for all of us in one car, and a chauffeur, but not for our duds. After a match there'd always be *some* kind of party. A dance, sometimes, or a dinner party. We'd start out for a place like Scranton, or Fort Penn, in the morning. Have a very light lunch. Chicken sandwich or something on that order, and play our match in the afternoon. Take a cold shower —couldn't always get hot water when you turned on the hot-water tap. Then dress and go to some party or other, and usually drive home the same night. Those distances don't seem very great now, but the roads in those days were a different proposition. Latham did you say your name was? No, it was Lathrop was the name of some people I knew then. They were Wilkes-Barre people. Before you were born. How old would you say I was?"

"I could never guess."

"Well, of course you know to some extent."

"Well, if you were twenty-two and out of college in 1916, before the First War. That's thirty-three years ago. You'd have to be fifty-five."

"You hit it right on the head. Fifty-five and play volleyball three times a week. Do you board in town or what?"

"I'm living at the Y.W."

"Well, if you'd like me to keep an eye out for an apartment, I sometimes hear of them, you know. It isn't my special line, but naturally I hear from time to time. It must get very boring for an attractive young girl, at the Y.W."

"Well, of course I've only been here less than a week. I only started Monday."

"That's true. You haven't met many people, I suppose."

"Not many."

"I'd like to see you get acquainted with some of the young people. I don't necessarily mean the country-club crowd. I resigned there, a few years ago. I like a more active game than golf, and the people there—well, I used to go there and I'd know every single man, woman, and child, but there's a different crowd there now. It isn't what it used to be. Some of us'd rather go to one of the roadhouses, and of course I being a bachelor, I have a small but comfortable bachelor apartment where I do my own entertaining. More like New York than you usually find in a town this size. Nobody bothers me, you know. My little place is over a store that's closed at six o'clock and the people downstairs go home and I might as well be living a thousand miles away, unless I happen to want friends to drop in. What I mean to say is, a man does his work, and then he's entitled to his own private life."

"I agree with you."

"Good. You've been married, I suppose?"

"No."

"I suppose you're like me in that respect."

"What respect is that?"

"Well, I could never tie myself down to one girl. It wouldn't have been fair to the girl I married. For instance if I were a married man now, I'd go home for dinner and all evening I'd be thinking of an attractive young lady that came and interviewed me."

"Well, I hope you're not going to forget me just because you're not married."

"Far from it. Anything but. In fact, I'd like to take you out to dinner this very evening, if you don't mind my terrible old car. I've made a trade on a new one and they're letting me keep this till the new one arrives. I'll sort of hate to part with it, but. . . ."

"Mr. Craymer, did you send this picture to the paper?"

"Did I send the picture? I never saw the damned thing before in all my life. What made you think that?"

"I had to ask you. I just had to ask you, that's all."

"God in heaven. Do you think a gentleman would do a thing like that? I never heard of such a thing in all my life. Why did you ask that question?"

"I had to. It's been on my mind."

"But do you mean to say that after spending an hour in my company you still had to ask that question?"

"I had to ask you."

"Did someone put you up to it? Is that why? Someone at your office?"

"No, nobody put me up to it."

"I don't understand you, young woman."

The door opened and the elevator girl, dressed in her street clothes, appeared in the outer room. They looked at her and she at them. She said, "Oh," and went out again. Miss Lapham stood up: "I didn't realize it was so late."

"I don't understand you," said Craymer. "Look at the picture. Look at it again. Study the kind of people that are my friends, that I grew up with. Then ask yourself, 'How could I ask that question?'"

"I'm sorry, Mr. Craymer. I realize it was a mistake."

"The greatest mistake of your life. My dear young woman—if you don't know people better than that, then you can't expect to get anywhere in writing. You have to know people to write about them. The great masters all knew human nature, and you've just been showing how *little* you know."

"I'll go now, Mr. Craymer," she said gently. "The elevator girl'll still be in your building."

"Oh, the hell with her," he said. "I want you before you go to give me your word of honor—you don't believe I sent that picture to the paper."

"I give you my word of honor. I don't believe you sent it."

"Thank you," he said. "If I thought anybody believed that of me—I wouldn't know *what* to do. All I've ever stood for, all I've ever tried to be. I'm fifty-five years old, and all my life I've believed there were some things you did and some things you didn't."

"Mr. Craymer, why don't you take me to dinner?"

"You sure you want me to?"

"Quite sure," she said.

He took a deep breath. "Well, of course I will. But you've been very naughty. Very naughty. But I'll take you to dinner."

Graham Greene:
When Greek Meets Greek

Mr. Fennick welcomed the peer's son to St. Ambrose's
as a spider would a fly,
while Lord Driver had plans of his own

When the chemist had shut his shop for the night he went through a door at the back into a hall that served both him and the flats above, and then up two flights and a half of stairs, carrying an offering of a little box of pills. The box was stamped with his name and address; Priskett, 14, New End Street, Oxford. He was a middle-aged man with a thin moustache and scared, evasive eyes; he wore his long white coat even when he was off duty as if it had the power of protecting him like a King's uniform from his enemies. A door was marked with a visiting card Mr. Nicholas Fennick, B.A.: the chemist rang three short times.

The man who opened the door was sixty years old at least, with snow-white hair and a pink babyish skin. He wore a mulberry velvet dinner jacket, and his glasses swung on the end of a wide black ribbon. He said with a kind of boisterousness, "Ah, Priskett, step in, Priskett."

"I brought you some more of my pills."

"Invaluable, Priskett. If only you had taken a degree—the Society Apothecaries would have been enough—I would have appointed you resident medical officer of St. Ambrose."

"How's the college doing?"

"Give me your company for a moment in the common room, and you shall know all."

Mr. Fennick led the way down a little dark passage cluttered with mackintoshes; Mr. Priskett, feeling his way uneasily from mackintosh to mackintosh, kicked in front of him a pair of girl's shoes. "One day," Mr. Fennick said, "we must build . . ." and he made a broad confident gesture with his glasses that seemed to press back the walls of the common room: a small round table covered with a landlady's cloth, three or four shiny chairs and a glass-fronted bookcase containing a copy of *Every Man His Own Lawyer*. "My

It was the early Forties when Graham Greene wrote this story and brought it out in Esquire, and of course it was also the time of Germany's air attack on England. Greene's home had been destroyed in the bombing, and yet, as this story shows, he could still laugh and care that others did so too.

niece Elizabeth," Mr. Fennick said, "my medical adviser." A very young girl with a lean, pretty face nodded perfunctorily from behind a typewriter. "I am going to train Elizabeth," Mr. Fennick said, "to act as bursar."

Mr. Priskett said humbly, "And what do you think of the college, Miss Fennick?"

"My name's Cross," the girl said. "I think it's a good idea. I'm surprised my uncle thought of it."

"In a way it was—partly—my idea."

"I'm more surprised still," the girl said firmly.

Mr. Priskett, folding his hands in front of his white coat as though he were pleading before a tribunal, went on: "You see I said to your uncle that with all these colleges being taken over by the military and the tutors having nothing to do they ought to start teaching by correspondence."

"A glass of audit ale, Priskett," Mr. Fennick suggested. He took a bottle of brown ale out of a cupboard and poured out two gaseous glasses.

"Of course," Mr. Priskett pleaded. "I hadn't thought of all this—the common room, I mean, and St. Ambrose's."

The girl said briskly, "As I see it, Uncle is running a swindle called St. Ambrose's College, Oxford."

"Not a swindle, my dear. The advertisement was very carefully worded." He knew it by heart; every phrase had been carefully checked with his copy of *Every Man His Own Lawyer* open on the table. He repeated it now in a voice full and husky with bottled brown ale. "War conditions prevent your going up to Oxford. St. Ambrose's—Tom Brown's old college—has made an important break with tradition. For the period of the war only it will be possible to receive tuition by post wherever you may be, whether defending the Empire on the cold rocks of Iceland or on the burning sands of Libya, in the main street of an American town or a cottage in Devonshire. . . ."

"You've overdone it," the girl said. "It won't catch anybody but saps."

"There are plenty of saps," Mr. Fennick said. "But I'll skip that bit. 'Degree-diplomas will be granted at the end of three terms instead of the usual three years.'" He explained: "That gives a quick turnover. One can't wait for money these days. 'Gain a real Oxford education at Tom Brown's old college. For full particulars of tuition fees, battels, etc. write to the Bursar.' "

"And do you mean to say the University can't stop that?"

"Anybody," Mr. Fennick said with a kind of pride, "can start a college anywhere. I've never said it was part of the University."

"But battels—battels mean board and lodging."

"In this case," Mr. Fennick said, "it's quite a nominal fee—to keep your name in perpetuity on the books of the old firm—I mean the college."

"And the tuition. . . ."

"Priskett here is the science tutor. I take history and classics. I thought that you, my dear, might tackle—economics?"

"I don't know anything about them."

"The examinations, of course, have to be rather simple—within the capacity of the tutors. (There is an excellent public library here.) And another thing—the fees are returnable if the diploma-degree is not granted."

"You mean. . . ."

"Nobody will ever fail," Mr. Priskett brought breathlessly out.

"And you are really getting results?"

"I waited, my dear, until I could see the distinct possibility of at least six hundred a year for the three of us before I wired you. And today—beyond all my expectations—I have received a letter from Lord Driver. He is entering his son at St. Ambrose's."

"But how can he come here?"

"In his absence, my dear, on his country's service. The Drivers have always been a military family. I looked them up in *Debrett*."

"What do you think of it?" Mr. Priskett asked with anxiety.

"I think it's rich. Have you arranged a boat race?"

"There, Priskett," Mr. Fennick said proudly, raising his glass of audit ale. "I told you she was a girl of ideas."

II

Directly he heard his landlady's feet upon the stairs the elderly man with the grey shaven head began to lay his wet tea leaves around the base of the aspidistra. When she opened the door he was dabbing the tea leaves in tenderly with his fingers. "A lovely plant, my dear."

But she wasn't going to be softened at once: he could tell that: she waved a letter at him. "Listen," she said, "what's this Lord Driver business?"

"My name, my dear: a good Christian name like Lord George Sanger had."

"Then why don't they put Mr. Lord Driver on the letter?"

"Ignorance, just ignorance."

"I don't want any hanky-panky from my house. It's always been honest."

"Perhaps they didn't know if I was an esquire or

just a plain mister, so they left it blank."

"It's sent from St. Ambrose's College, Oxford: people like that ought to know."

"It comes, my dear, of your having such a good address, W. 1. And all the gentry live in Mewses." He made a halfhearted snatch at the letter but the landlady held it out of reach.

"What are the likes of you writing to Oxford College about?"

"My dear," he said with strained dignity, "I may have been a little unfortunate: it may even be that I have spent a few years in chokey, but I have the rights of a free man."

"And a son in quod."

"Not in quod, my dear. Borstal is quite another institution. It is—a kind of college."

He was usually in the end too much for her. Before his first stay at the Scrubs he had held a number of positions as manservant and even butler: the way he raised his eyebrows he had learned from Lord Charles Mansville: he wore his clothes like an eccentric peer, and you might say that he had even learnt the best way to pilfer from old Lord Bellew who had a penchant for silver spoons.

"And now, my dear, if you'd just let me have my letter?" He put his hand tentatively forward: he was as daunted by her as she was by him: they sparred endlessly. This time it was his victory. She slammed the door. Suddenly, when the door had closed, he made a little vulgar noise at the aspidistra. Then he put on his glasses to read.

His son had been accepted for St. Ambrose's, Oxford. The great fact stared up at him above the sprawling decorative signature of the President. Never had he been more thankful for the coincidence of his name. "It will be my great pleasure," the President wrote, "to pay personal attention to your son's career at St. Ambrose's. In these days it is an honor to welcome a member of a great military family like yours." Driver felt an odd mixture of amusement and of genuine pride. He'd put one over on them, but his breast swelled within his waistcoat at the idea of having a son at Oxford.

But there were two snags. It was apparently an old Oxford custom that fees should be paid in advance, and then there were the examinations. His son couldn't do them himself: Borstal would not allow it, and he wouldn't be out for another six months. Besides the whole beauty of the idea was that he should receive the gift of an Oxford degree as a kind of welcome home.

A peer could always get credit, and if there was any trouble after the degree had been awarded, he could just tell them to sue and be damned. No Oxford college would like to admit that they'd been imposed on by an old lag. But the examinations. A funny little knowing smile twitched the corners of his mouth: a memory of the Scrubs five years ago and the man they called Daddy, the Reverend Simon Milan. He remembered the tall, lean aristocratic parson with his iron-grey hair and his narrow face like a lawyer's which had gone somehow soft inside with too much love. He knew where he could find Mr. Milan: he was employed in a boardinghouse near Euston Square, and for a few drinks he would do most things—he would certainly make out some fine examination papers. "I can just hear him now," Driver told himself ecstatically, "talking Latin to the warders."

<h1 style="text-align:center">III</h1>

It was autumn in Oxford: people coughed in the long queues for sweets and cakes: and the mists from the river seeped into the cinemas past the commissionaires on the lookout for people without gas masks. A few undergraduates picked their way through the evacuated swarm: they always looked in a hurry: so much had to be got through in so little time before the army claimed them. There were lots of pickings for racketeers, Elizabeth Cross thought, but not much chance for a girl to find a husband: the oldest Oxford racket has been elbowed out by the black markets in Woodbines, toffees, tomatoes.

There had been a few days last spring when she had treated St. Ambrose's as a joke, but when she saw the money actually coming in, the whole thing seemed less amusing. Then for some weeks she was acutely unhappy—until she realized that of all the wartime rackets this was the most harmless: her uncle paid income tax, and they even to some extent actually educated people. The saps, when they took their diploma-degree, would know several things they hadn't known before.

But that didn't help a girl to find a husband.

She came moodily out of the matinee, carrying a bunch of papers she should have been correcting. There was only one "student" who showed any intelligence at all, and that was Lord Driver's son. The papers were forwarded from "somewhere in England" via London by his father: she had nearly found herself caught out several times on points of history, and her uncle she knew was straining his rusty Latin to his limited limit.

When she got home she knew that there was something in the air: Mr. Priskett was sitting in his white coat on the edge of a chair and her uncle was finishing a stale bottle of beer. When something went wrong he never opened a new bottle: he believed in happy drinking. They watched her come in in silence:

"Good evening," Elizabeth said: Mr. Priskett looked at Mr. Fennick and Mr. Fennick frowned. "Is Mr. Priskett out of pills?"

Mr. Priskett winced.

"I've been thinking," Elizabeth said, "that as we are now in the third term of the academic year, I should like a raise in salary."

Mr. Priskett drew in his breath sharply, keeping his eyes on Mr. Fennick.

"I should like another three pounds a week."

Mr. Fennick rose from the table; he whistled ferociously in the top of his dark ale; his frown beetled. The chemist scraped his chair a little backward. And then Mr. Fennick spoke.

"We are such stuff as dreams are made on," he said and hiccupped slightly.

"You've been correcting the English papers."

"Unless you allow me to think, to think rapidly and deeply, there won't be any more examination papers," Mr. Fennick said.

"Trouble?"

"I've always been a Republican at heart. I don't see why we want a hereditary peerage."

"*A la lanterne*," Elizabeth said.

"This Lord Driver: why should an accident of birth . . . ?"

"He refuses to pay?"

"It isn't that. It's right that he should have credit. But he's written to say that he's coming down tomorrow to see his boy's college. The old fat-headed sentimental fool," Mr. Fennick said.

"It just needs brain. I'll meet him at the station with a taxi, and take him to—say Balliol. Lead him straight through into the inner quad, and there you'll be just looking as if you'd come out of the Master's Lodging."

"He'll know it's Balliol."

"He won't. Anybody who knew Oxford couldn't be sap enough to send his son to St. Ambrose's."

"Of course it's true. These military families are a bit crass."

"You'll be in an enormous hurry. Consecration or something. Whip him around the Hall, the Chapel, the Library, and hand him back to me outside the Master's. I'll take him out to lunch and see him into his train. It's simple."

Mr. Fennick said broodingly, "Sometimes I think you're a terrible girl, terrible. Is there nothing you wouldn't think up?"

"I believe," Elizabeth said, "that if you're going to play your own game in a world like this, you've got to play it properly."

It really all went off very smoothly. He found Elizabeth at the barrier. Something about him worried her: it wasn't his clothes or the monocle he never seemed to use—it was something subtler than that. It was almost as though he were afraid of her, he was so ready to fall in with her plans. "I don't want to be any trouble, my dear, any trouble at all. I know how terribly busy the President must be."

When she explained that they would be lunching together in town, he even seemed relieved. "It's just the bricks of the dear old place," he said. "You mustn't mind my being a sentimentalist, my dear."

"Were you at Oxford?"

"No, no. The Drivers, I'm afraid, have neglected the things of the mind."

"Well, I suppose a soldier needs brains?"

He took a sharp look at her, and then answered in quite a different sort of voice. "We believed so in the Lancers." All the way up from the station he was silent, taking little quiet sideways peeks at her, appraising, approving.

"So this is St. Ambrose's," he said in a hearty voice just beside the porter's lodge and she pushed him quickly by, through the first quads toward the Master's house on whose doorstep with a B.A. gown over his arm stood Mr. Fennick posed like a piece of garden statuary. "My uncle, the President," Elizabeth said.

"A charming girl, your niece," Driver said as soon as they were alone together: he had really only meant to

make conversation, but as soon as he had spoken the old two crooked minds began to move in harmony.

"She's very home-loving," Mr. Fennick said. "Our famous elms," he went on, waving his hand skywards. "St. Ambrose's rooks."

"Crooks?" Driver said with astonishment.

"Rooks. In the elms. One of our great modern poets wrote about them. 'St. Ambrose elms, oh St. Ambrose elms,' and about 'St. Ambrose rooks calling in wind and rain.' "

"Pretty. Very pretty."

"Nicely turned, I think."

"I meant your niece."

"Ah, yes. This way to the Hall. Up these steps. So often trodden, you know, by Tom Brown." He added thoughtfully, "She'll make a fine wife—and mother."

"Young men are beginning to realize that the flighty ones are not what they want for a lifetime."

They stopped by mutual consent on the top step: they nosed toward each other like two old blind sharks who each believes that what stirs the water close to him is tasty meat.

"Whoever wins her," Mr. Fennick said, "can feel proud. She'll make a fine hostess . . ." as the future Lady Driver, he thought.

"I and my son," Driver said, "have talked seriously about marriage. He takes rather an old-fashioned view. He'll make a good husband. . . ."

They walked into the hall, and Mr. Fennick led the way round the portraits. "Our founder," he said, pointing at a full-bottomed wig. He chose it deliberately: he felt it smacked a little of himself. Before Swinburne's portrait he hesitated: then pride in St. Ambrose's conquered caution. "The great poet Swinburne," he said. "We sent him down."

"Expelled him?"

"Yes. Bad morals."

"I'm glad you are strict about those."

"Ah, your son is in safe hands at St. Ambrose's."

"It makes me very happy," Driver said. He began to scrutinize the portrait of a nineteenth-century divine. "Fine brushwork," he said. "Now religion— I believe in religion. Basis of the family." He said with a burst of confidence, "You know our young people ought to meet."

Mr. Fennick gleamed. "I agree."

"He'll be on leave in a week or two. Why shouldn't he take his degree in person?"

"Well, there'd be difficulties."

"Isn't it the custom?"

"Not for postal graduates. The Vice-Chancellor likes to make a small distinction. . . . But, Lord Driver, in the case of so distinguished an alumnus I suggest that I should be deputed to present the degree to your son in London."

"I'd like him to see his college."

"And so he shall in happier days. So much of the college is shut now, I would like him to visit it for the first time when its glory is restored. Allow me and my niece to call on you."

"We are living very quietly."

"Not serious financial trouble, I hope?"

"Oh, no, no," Driver assured him.

"I'm so glad. And now let us rejoin the dear girl."

IV

It always seemed to be more convenient to meet at railway stations. The coincidence didn't strike Mr. Fennick who had fortified himself for the journey with a good deal of audit ale but it struck Elizabeth. The college lately had not been fulfilling expectations, and that was partly due to the laziness of Mr. Fennick: from his conversation lately it almost seemed as though he had begun to regard the college as only a step to something else—what she couldn't quite make out. He was always talking about Lord Driver and his son Frederick and the responsibilities of the peerage. His Republican tendencies had quite lapsed. "That dear boy" was the way he referred to Frederick, and he marked him 100 percent for classics. "It's not often Latin and Greek go with military genius," he said. "A remarkable boy."

"He's not so hot on economics," Elizabeth said.

"We mustn't demand too much book learning from a soldier."

At Paddington Lord Driver waved anxiously to them through the crowd: he wore a new suit—one shudders to think how many coupons had been gambled away for the occasion. A little behind him was a very young man with a sullen mouth and a scar on his cheek.

Mr. Fennick bustled forward: he wore a black raincoat over his shoulders like a cape and carrying his hat in his hand he disclosed his white hair venerably among the porters.

"My son—Frederick," Lord Driver said. The boy sullenly took off his hat and put it on again quickly: they wore their hair in the army very short.

"St. Ambrose's welcomes her new graduate," Mr. Fennick said.

Frederick grunted.

The presentation of the degree was made in a private room at Mount Royal. Lord Driver explained that his house had been bombed—a time bomb, he added, a rather necessary explanation since there had been no raids recently. Mr. Fennick was satisfied if Lord Driver was: he had brought up a B.A. gown, a mortarboard and a Bible in his suitcase, and he made quite an imposing little ceremony between the book table, the sofa and the radiator, reading out a Latin oration and tapping Frederick lightly on the head with the Bible. The degree-diploma had been expensively printed in two colors by an Anglo-Catholic firm. Elizabeth was the only uneasy person there. Could the world, she wondered, really contain two such saps? What was this painful feeling growing up in her that perhaps it contained four?

After a little light lunch with bottled brown beer—"Almost as good, if I may say so, as our audit ale," Mr. Fennick beamed—the President and Lord Driver made elaborate moves to drive the two young people out together. "We've got to talk a little business," Mr. Fennick said, and Lord Driver hinted, "You've not been to the flickers for a year, Frederick." They were driven out into bombed, shabby Oxford Street while the old men rang cheerfully down for whisky.

"What's the idea?" Elizabeth said.

He was good looking: she liked his scar and his sullenness: there was almost too much intelligence and purpose in his face. Once he took off his hat and scratched his head: Elizabeth again noticed his short hair. He certainly didn't look a military type. And his suit, like his father's, looked new and ready-made. Hadn't he had any clothes to wear when he came on leave?

"I suppose," she said, "they are planning a wedding."

His eyes lit gleefully up. "I wouldn't mind," he said.

"You'd have to get leave from your C.O., wouldn't you?"

"C.O.?" he asked with astonishment, flinching a little like a boy who has been caught out, who hasn't been prepared beforehand with that question. She watched him carefully, remembering all the things that had seemed odd to her since the beginning.

"So you haven't been to the movies for a year," she said.

"I've been in service."

"Not even an Ensa show?"

"Oh, I don't count those."

"It must be awfully like being in prison."

He grinned weakly, walking faster all the time, so that she might really have been pursuing him through the Hyde Park gates.

"Come clean," she said. "Your father's not Lord Driver."

"Oh yes he is."

"Any more than my uncle's President of a College."

"What?" He began to laugh—it was an agreeable laugh, a laugh you couldn't trust but a laugh which made you laugh back and agree that in a crazy world like this all sorts of things didn't matter. "I'm just out of Borstal," he said. "What's yours?"

"Oh, I haven't been in prison yet."

He said, "You'll never believe me, but all that ceremony—it looked phony to me. Of course the Dad swallowed it."

"And my uncle swallowed you. . . . I couldn't quite."

"Well, the wedding's off. In a way I'm sorry."

"I'm still free."

"Well," he said, "we might discuss it," and there in the pale autumn sunlight of the park they did discuss it—from all sorts of angles. There were bigger frauds all round them; officials of the Ministries passed carrying little portfolios: controllers of this and that purred by in motorcars, and men with the big blank faces of advertisement hoardings strode purposefully in khaki with scarlet tabs down Park Lane from the Dorchester. Their fraud was a small one by the world's standard, and a harmless one! the boy from Borstal and the girl from nowhere at all—from the draper's counter and the semidetached villa. "He's got a few hundred stowed away," said Fred. "He'd make a settlement if he thought he could get the President's niece."

"I wouldn't be surprised if Uncle had five hundred. He would put it all down for Lord Driver's son."

"We'd take over this college business. With a bit of capital we could really make it go. It's just chicken feed now."

They fell in love for no reason at all, in the park, on a bench to save twopences, planning their fraud on the old frauds they knew they could outdo. Then they went back, and Elizabeth declared herself before she'd got properly inside the door. "Frederick and I want to get married." She almost felt sorry for the old fools as their faces suddenly lit up simultaneously because everything had been so easy, and then darkened with caution as they squinted at each other.

"This is very surprising," Lord Driver said, and the President said, "My goodness, young people work fast."

All night the two old men planned their settlements, and the two young ones sat happily back in a corner, watching the elaborate fence, with the secret knowledge that the world is always open to the young.

Dashiell Hammett:
Albert Pastor at Home

It's hard on the racketeers when a big guy called Lefty
yearns to see his hometown

Lefty comes in and drops his suitcase and kicks the door shut and says, "How's it, kid?"

I get up to shake hands with him and say, "How's it, Lefty?" and see he has got a goog or black eye that is maybe a week old and some new skin growing in alongside his jaw. I am too polite to stare at these things. I ask, "Well, how'd you find the old hometown?"

"I just looked behind the railroad depot and there it was," he replies jokingly. "Is there anything in the bottom drawer?"

There is a bottle of Scotch in the bottom drawer. Lefty says it is not good Scotch because he does not want anybody to think he can be fooled by stuff that is made in this country, but he drinks it in a way that would not hurt the feelings of the man that made it in any country.

He unbuttons his vest and says, "Kid, I'm here to tell you it was one swell visit. This big city stuff is all oke, but when you go back to the place you was born and the kids you run around with and your family and—Say, kid, I got a kid brother that ain't eighteen yet and you ought to see him. Big as me except for weight and a couple inches of height and can he throw hands. When we put the gloves on down the cellar mornings—what a kid, kid! Even when I was in shape I would've had trouble holding him. You ought to see him, kid."

I think that it will be all right to refer to those things on Lefty's face now, so I say, "I'd like to. Why don't you bring him on? Any boy that can get to your ponem like that ought—"

Lefty puts a hand to the eye that is not in as good shape as the other one and says, "That ain't his. That's—" He laughs and takes his hand away from his eyes and takes a jewelry box out of his coat pocket and passes it to me. "Take a look at that."

In the box there is a watch that looks like platinum

attached to a chain that looks like platinum. I think they are.

Lefty says, "Read what's on it."

On the back of the watch it says *To Albert Pastor* (which is the way Lefty writes his name when he has to) *with the gratitude of the members of the Grocers' Protective Association*.

"Grocers' Protective Association," I say slowly, "that sounds like—"

"A racket!" he finishes for me and laughs and bangs my desk with his hand. "Call me a liar if you want, but back there in my hometown, this little burg that ain't got a quarter million people in it—but get me right, a swell little burg just the same—they got racketeers!"

I would not want to call Lefty a liar even if I thought he was a liar because he would have been heavyweight champion of the world before he left the ring to go in business with me if they did not have rules you are supposed to fight by in the ring and if he did not have a temper which kept him forgetting they had rules you were supposed to fight by. So I say, "Is that so?"

Lefty says that is so. He says, "You could've knocked me over with the District Attorney's office. Big city stuff back there! Ain't that a howl? And my old man being shook down along with the rest of them." He reaches for the bottle of Scotch that he says is not good.

"Your old man is a grocer?" I ask.

"Uh-huh, and he always wanted me to follow in his own footsteps," Lefty says, "and that's the real reason he didn't have no use for my fistic career. But that's all right now—now that I retired from the arena. He's a swell old guy when you're old enough to understand him and we got along fine. I give him a sedan and you'd ought to see the way he carries on about it. You'd think it was a Dusenberg."

"Was it?" I ask.

Lefty says, "No, but you'd think it was a Rolls the way he carries on about it. Well, I'm there a couple days and he lets off about these bums that'd been

Dashiell Hammett contributed this story to Esquire's inaugural issue, joining therein the company of John Dos Passos, Ernest Hemingway, Morley Callaghan, Gilbert Seldes, Ring Lardner Jr., and James T. Farrell.

lining up the grocers round town—join the protective association or else, with not many takers for the else. It seems the grocer business ain't none too good by its own self and paying alimony to these mugs don't help it none. The old man's kind of worried.

"I don't say nothing to him, but I go off by myself and do some thinking and I think, what's the matter with me going to see these babies and ask them do they want to listen to reason or have I got to go to work on them? I can't see nothing wrong with that idea. Can you?"

"No, Lefty," I say, "I can't."

"Well, neither could I," Lefty says, "and so I did and they don't think they want to listen to reason. There's a pair of them in the protective association office when I come in—just about what I expected—they know the words, but they ain't got the motions right yet. There was a third one come in after a while, but I'm sweating good by that time and handy pieces has been broke off some of the furniture, so I make out all right, and the old man and some of the others get together and buy me this souper with some of the dues they'd've had to pay next month if there'd been any protective association left." He puts the watch and chain back in the box and puts the box back in his pocket. "And how's *your* father's horse?" he asks.

I take the envelope with the money in it out of my pocket and give it to him. "There's your end," I say, "only Caresse's not in. You know—the little fat guy around on Third Avenue."

"I know him," Lefty says. "What's the matter with him?"

"He says he's paid so much for protection now that he's got nothing left to protect," I say, "and he won't stand for the boost."

Lefty says, "So?" He says, "That's the way, soon's I get out of town these babies think they can cut up." He stands up and buttons his vest. "Well," he says, "I guess I'll go round to see that baby and ask him does he want to listen to reason or have I got to go to work on him?"

Luigi Pirandello:

With Other Eyes

A story in which the action is entirely restricted
to the arena of a woman's mind

As she turned away from the window, with a sigh, Anna noticed that her husband had forgotten that morning to disturb his bed, as was his custom when he did not want the servants to know that he had not slept in his own bedroom. She leaned her elbows on the bed and then stretched out, pressing her blonde head on the pillows and closing her eyes as if to enjoy in the freshness of the linen her husband's dreams.

Her husband was going away that evening, and she had come into his room to prepare his bags. When she opened the wardrobe she heard a squeak in one of the inside compartments, and started back in alarm. Gathering her skirts around her legs, she took a walking stick with a curved handle from the corner and tried to open the door with it. When she pulled, instead of the door, a bright steel blade came out of the stick. This was so unexpected that she shuddered and let the handle of the stick fall.

Kicking aside the sword blade, she pulled out the compartment, full of old discarded clothes of her husband. In a sudden burst of curiosity she began to arrange them and, as she replaced a faded old jacket, she felt something in the pocket which crackled like a letter. She wondered what the letter could be which had lain there forgotten for so many years. In this way Anna discovered the photograph of her husband's first wife.

Pale with excitement she ran to the window, and stood for quite a while staring at this unknown image.

The huge cape and old-fashioned clothes prevented her at first from seeing how beautiful that face was.

But as soon as she realized the features, disconnecting them from the clothes of the period, she was struck by the eyes, and was filled with a feeling of jealousy and hatred; her jealousy was posthumous, but her hate was mixed with the contempt which she had felt for the other woman, when she had married her present husband. That was eleven years after the domestic tragedy which had suddenly destroyed his first household.

Anna had hated that woman, because she could not understand how she could have been unfaithful to the man whom she now adored. She also hated her because her own parents had opposed her marriage to Brivio, as if he were responsible for the disgrace and violent death of the unfaithful wife.

She knew this must be Victor's first wife; the woman who had killed herself! This was proved by the inscription on the back of the photograph: "To my darling Victor, from his Almira. November 11, 1913."

Anna's knowledge of her death was very vague. All she knew was that, when her husband discovered he was being deceived, with the impassiveness of a judge, he compelled her to take her own life.

At the moment she recalled with satisfaction her husband's condemnation, because she was exasperated by that "darling Victor" and that "his Almira," as if that woman had wanted to show how close were the bonds which existed between her and Victor, just simply to annoy her.

This first emotion of hate prompted by her sense of rivalry was followed by a feminine curiosity to examine the features of that face, a curiosity almost restrained by that strange consternation which one experiences on seeing something that has belonged to someone who died a tragic death, a consternation all the more profound in her case because it was bound

In 1921, with the presentation of Six Characters in Search of an Author, *Luigi Pirandello broke enough rules to cause a riot in Rome. In 1934, when this story appeared in* Esquire, *people were busy rioting over jobs. But Pirandello was still breaking the rules.*

302

up with her love for the husband, who had once belonged to this other woman.

Looking at the face, Anna immediately noticed how unlike her own it was. And at once she wondered in her heart how on earth her husband could ever have loved this woman—though he certainly must have thought her beautiful—if he could then fall in love with a person as different as herself.

Even to her this face seemed beautiful, much more beautiful than her own, and in the picture she seemed to be a brunette, and to think that those lips had kissed her husband's! But why those sad lines around the mouth? Why the melancholy in those intense eyes? The whole face inspired deep sympathy, and Anna was almost annoyed by the gentle and real kindness which these features expressed. With a sudden movement of repulsion and disgust she seemed to see in those eyes the same expression as she noticed in her own, when she looked at herself in the mirror in the morning, and thought of her husband, after they had spent the night together.

She had scarcely time to hide the photograph in her pocket when her husband appeared in the doorway and jokingly said:

"What have you been doing? As usual, you've been putting things in order, I suppose! God help me, now I'll never be able to find anything!"

Noticing the sword stick on the ground, he added:

"Aha! So you've been fencing with the clothes in the wardrobe?"

He gave one of those laughs of his which seemed to issue only from his throat, and as he laughed he looked at his wife as if he were asking her the reason for his laughter. As he looked at her, his sharp, black, restless eyes blinked rapidly.

Victor Brivio treated his wife like a child who was incapable of anything more than that ingenuous and almost infantile love with which she had surrounded him, which often bored him, and to which he had proposed to pay attention only from time to time, even then showing a certain condescension mixed with irony. It was as if he wanted to say: "Oh, very well! For the time being I'll be a child like you. A man has to do that sort of thing, but don't let us waste too much time over it!"

Anna had let the old jacket fall, in which she had found the photograph. He picked it up with the point of the stick, went to the window and called to his servant in the garden. When the boy appeared in front of the window, Brivio threw the faded coat in his face saying: "This is for you."

"Now you will have less to dust," he added, turning to

his wife, "and to set in order, I hope!"

Again he uttered that forced laugh of his, his eyelids blinking rapidly.

Her husband had often before left the city, and not only for a day, but also for a night, as on this occasion. Affected by the discovery of the photograph, Anna had a curious fear of being alone, as she weepingly confessed to her husband.

Victor Brivio was completely absorbed in his own affairs and was fussing about being late, so he did not receive his wife's unusual complaint very sympathetically.

"What! Why? Come, come, don't be a baby!"

He left the house in a rage without even saying good-bye.

Anna started, as the door banged behind him. There were tears in her eyes as she hastened to her room to go to bed.

"You can go," said Anna to her maid who was waiting. "I'll undress myself. Good night."

She began to undress rapidly, staring at the floor in front of her. As her clothes slipped to the floor, she remembered that the photograph was there, and she had the feeling that those sad eyes were looking at her compassionately. She stooped resolutely to pick up her clothes, and threw them, without folding them, on a chair at the foot of the bed, as if she would thus be able to avoid the image of the dead woman, by leaving the photograph hidden.

As soon as she was in bed, she closed her eyes, and forced herself to think of the route her husband would take to the railway station. She was anxiously fighting the thoughts which had compelled her all day to observe and study her husband. She knew what obsession had caused her to do this, and she wanted to get rid of it.

She had the vague sensation that for the last three years, from the moment that she left her father's house, she had been living in a vacuum of which she was only just beginning to be conscious. She had not noticed this emptiness before, because she had filled it with her love, all unaided. Now she noticed it, because during the entire day she had held her love in abeyance, in order to see, to watch, to judge.

"He did not even say good-bye," she thought, and again she began to cry, as if this thought were the real reason for her tears.

She sat up in bed, and suddenly reached out her hand to get her handkerchief. Now it was useless to pretend that she should not and could not look again at the photograph. She found it and turned on the light again.

How differently she had imagined this woman! Now that she looked at the real face, she had a sense of remorse for the feelings which the imaginary picture had inspired in her. She had imagined a rather stout and rubicund woman, with laughing, flashing eyes, and full of vulgar merriment. Instead, here was the picture of a young girl whose features expressed a deep and melancholy soul. A different woman from herself, it is true, but not in the worst sense, as she had previously imagined. On the contrary, this melancholy mouth looked as if it had never smiled, whereas her own had smiled so often and so happily. Certainly, as appeared from the photograph, she was a brunette, and lacked her own blonde, rosy, smiling face.

But why, why, was she so sad?

A horrible thought suddenly struck her mind and took her thoughts away from this woman. Unexpectedly she had stumbled upon a threat, not only to her peace, to her love, which had already been deeply wounded, but also to her pride as an honest woman, who had never entertained the remotest doubt concerning her husband. This other woman had had a lover, and it was because of her lover, and not because of her husband, that she was so sad!

She threw the photograph on to the night table and turned out the light, hoping to fall asleep this time without thinking of this woman, with whom she now had nothing in common. But, when she closed her eyes, she could not help seeing the eyes of the dead woman, and it was in vain that she tried to drive away the vision.

"It was not for his sake, not for him!" she murmured obstinately, as if she could get rid of this woman by insulting her.

She tried hard to recall whatever she had heard of that other man, the lover, in an effort to direct that glance and the sadness of those eyes toward the lover, and not toward herself, the lover of whom she knew nothing but the name, Arthur Valli. She knew that he had married a few years later, as if to prove that he was innocent of the crime of which Brivio accused him. He had refused emphatically to fight a duel with the latter, on the ground that he did not fight with homicidal maniacs. After that, Victor had threatened to kill him wherever he might meet him, even if in church. Then he had left the country with his wife and did not return until Victor went abroad after his second marriage.

Suddenly, Anna was completely filled with the sadness of the events she had recalled: the vileness of Valli and, after so many years, her husband's indifference, which had enabled him to remarry and start life again, as if nothing had happened; the happiness which she herself had experienced on becoming his wife, the three years which she had spent without ever thinking of that other woman. The picture came vividly before her, but as if from a great distance, and it seemed as if those eyes, full of such intense unhappiness, were saying, with a shake of the head: "All of you people are alive, but I alone am dead!"

She felt terribly alone in the house, and she was afraid. It is true, she was alive, but for three years, ever since the day of her marriage, she had never even once seen her parents and her sister. She, who had adored them and had always been obedient and trusting, she had risen in revolt against their wishes and against their advice, because of her love for this man. For love of him she had fallen mortally ill, and she would have died, if the doctors had not induced her father to consent to the marriage. Her father did not consent, but he surrendered, swearing that, as far as he and the family were concerned, she would be as if she had never existed. There was not only the difference of age, her husband being eighteen years older than she, but the even more serious obstacle, from her father's point of view, of his financial position, which was subject to rapid ups and downs, by reason of the risky undertakings in which he became involved, because of his rash faith in himself and in his luck.

In her three years of marriage, surrounded by comforts, Anna had concluded that her father's views were injust or dictated by prejudice, so far as her husband's fortune was concerned, about which in her ignorance she entertained the same faith as he had in himself. As for the difference in their ages, there had been no disillusionment for her, so far, and no subject of surprise for other people. Victor Brivio did not feel the damage of time in his vivacious and nervous body, and even less in his mind, which was filled with indefatigable energy and eager restlessness.

Now that she was considering her life for the first time, without suspecting it, with the eyes of the dead woman, she found reason to complain of her husband. It is true that she had been wounded on several occasions by his almost contemptuous indifference toward her, but never so deeply as today. Now, for the first time, she felt desperately alone, separated from her parents, who seemed at this moment to have abandoned her, as if, by marrying Victor, she had something in common with his dead wife and was not worthy of other companionship. Her husband, who ought to have consoled her, appeared unwilling to give her any credit for the sacrifice she had made to him of her filial and family affection, as if that had cost her nothing, as if he had a right to this sacrifice, and therefore no duty on his part could compensate her for it. Perhaps he had a right, but then why did she so hopelessly fall in love with him? Surely it was then his duty to compensate her? Instead of which . . . .

"That is always the way!" It seemed to Anna that these words came to her from the sad lips of the dead woman.

She turned on the light again and, as she looked at the photograph, she was struck by the expression in the eyes. So you, too, have really suffered through him? You, too, have felt that heartbreaking emptiness, when you saw that you were no longer loved?

"Really? Really?" Anna asked the picture, choked with tears.

Then it seemed to her that those kindly eyes, filled with passion, were pitying her in their turn, sympathizing with her in her abandonment, sympathizing with her unrewarded sacrifice, with the love which remained locked up in her breast, like a treasure, locked in a coffer, to which he had the keys, which he never used, like a miser. ⧛

Heard Melodies Are Sweeter

Art or kitsch: only a wink could tell

The scene: An office, thirty flights up, somewhere in Rockefeller Center. The only noise is the angry *whoomp* of cordovan smacking against Bigelow carpet; a new TV show for singer Timmy Thrush is being conceived. The writers, Manny, Moe, and Jack, pace the room. Leo Gawl, fourth member of the team, has just stomped out; he is having a tantrum, the first of which was thrown in the Winter of 1955, when Omnibus turned down his idea for an all-Negro musical comedy adapted from Henry James's Preface to *What Maisie Knew*. . . . Manny mumbles toward the door.

MANNY: He's *nuts*. How the hell can we give away awards on a first show? Everybody tunes in to see Timmy and there's a guy from Peek-a-boo Magazine giving away awards for *camera* work—

MOE: It's educational, he says.

MANNY: Educational? What are we running, a nursery school? The hell with Gawl! (*He picks up the sponsor's memo from the conference table and reads it in a serious voice, as though he were narrating a documentary about The Rise of Fascism.*) "Remember, you're not writing for Professor Zulli. You're writing a musical-variety show. Timmy is a singer. Goo-goo is a singer. Avoid language." (*He looks to Moe and Jack.*) Now you guys have seen Sinatra, you've seen Como, you know Timmy can't just come out there and *say* something.

MOE: Of course we know. But what is there left for him to do? I mean can a guy pick his ear anymore? No, that's Perry's. Can he just come out and snap his fingers? No, that's Sinatra's. What's left? A guy almost has to say something.

JACK: How about he winks. He just comes out there and winks.

MOE: He just winks. Hey, that's good. A real personal-type-of-thing. A wink. Great. Then what does he do?

MANNY: How about he sings? After he winks he sings.

MOE: I don't know about all those words so soon in the show. . . . How you going to tie the song in with the wink? I mean you sort of want to build the show *around* the wink, don't you?

MANNY: Sure, he could sing something about winking. A ballad. We could work something up. Wink at Me. Wink at My Heart.

JACK: Wink, Wink, Went My Heart.

MANNY (*humming*): Wink at My Heart with Your Eyes.

MOE: All right, the song is over. Then what?

JACK: Then we bring out Goo-goo St. John in a kind of tight gold lamé thing, and *she* winks. . . . And wait. After she winks, old Timmy, he laughs. Kind of casual. Like her wink just knocks him out. And then Goo-goo says . . . she says. . . .

MANNY: How about just a few syllables? Let's hold the words—

JACK: . . . She says, "How goes it, Timmy?" But like she just made it up then. Sort of a low mumble.

MOE: That's it. And then Timmy, he says, "It goes." She says, "How goes it?" and he says, "It goes." But like you said, like it's all made up then. Casual. A no-rehearsal bit.

JACK: Sure. And then *she* laughs.

MOE: And then . . . they sort of stroll around the stage, kind of laughing at all that's happened. And, get this, you can *see* some of the cameras and stuff. Like we come right out and admit it's being televised. Kind of a Dave Garroway-type of thing.

JACK: A visual-type of thing.

MANNY: Then they sing again?

JACK: No, no, catch this—they don't sing—they *dance*!

MOE: Oh, man, you *crush* me. Everybody thinks Timmy and Goo-goo are going to sing, and they *dance*. Oh, man . . . and wait. He says to her in this kind of fake English accent, a stuffy kind of George Sanders thing, he says, "Can I have this dance?"

JACK: And they start to dance, and she says,

Philip Roth began publishing in Esquire *in 1957, two years previous to the publication of his award-winning* Goodbye, Columbus. *His work has continued to appear in* Esquire *through the startling turns his imagination has taken—most recently in* The Great American Novel, *a part of which* Esquire *presented in May, 1973.*

"You've had it."

MANNY: And then *she* laughs.

JACK: No, *he* laughs.

(*There is an impasse. Jack and Manny exchange hostile glances.*)

MOE (*finally*): Look, fellas, how about they both laugh. Like it's a happy-type-of-thing. Then he says, "Not only can you sing, Goo-goo, but you can dance." And she says, "You flatter me," and then he looks down at her what-a-ya-callums and he says, "Flattery will get me *somewhere!*"

MANNY: You mean *nowhere*.

MOE: No, no, that's what everybody expects, see. But we switch.

MANNY: I don't know. This ain't The Seven Lively Arts. You can't—

JACK (*breaking in*): Have I got an idea! Listen. They're dancing, see, and she asks Timmy how his family is, and he says, "Take a look." He sort of grunts it, you know. . . . And there right behind him is his eight-year-old son, his real son, live. I mean it's a television first. And then Timmy says to Goo-goo, "How's your family?" and what comes out on the stage but *her* little girl. And then the kids get introduced, all cute and all, and then the little girl— catch this—she turns to the camera and *she* winks.

MANNY: You mean like—

JACK: That's it! The kids play the whole bit over again.

MOE (*thinking*): A kind of parenty-child thing.

JACK: Sure, the whole thing, dancing and all. And all the time it's cracking Timmy and Goo-goo up, but tender like.

MOE: It's a whole repetition idea. The different generations. The sun also rises. History repeats itself. Do you think maybe it's a little too (*he points to the door and whispers*) Omnibusy? You know, kind of Sunday afternoonish? (*Jack gives him an ugly look.*) I mean—maybe that's what you want. I mean we could play the whole *thing* that way, if you want to. Bring in somebody like Ed Murrow to *analyze* it, sort of gloom it up—

JACK: What are you a wise guy? The finale can be terrific! The kids are holding hands and Timmy and Goo-goo, they can't hold hands, but they sort of beam at each other from behind their respective kids. And then in the end we have all these stars rush out— Sinatra, Crosby, Dinah, Perry—they all rush out onto the stage with *their* respective kids. And they sing this medley. Kind of P.T.A. songs. And then—catch this—they all *wink*. Together.

MOE (*coming around*): Oh, man, all those eyes at once!

JACK: And then next week we give away the awards. And at the end somebody comes out—maybe Murrow—and gives Timmy the award for the best first show on TV in the musical-variety division.

MOE: Terrific. As long as he doesn't gloom it up.

JACK: No, no, serious kind of, but no gloom. And when Murrow gives it to him, what do you think Timmy does? He winks!

André Maurois:

An Idea for a Story

The re-allocation of the center of modesty,
a very fetching idea for a novel never to be written

The other day I was thinking of the general laws governing a type of writing which I have always liked, while trying to make a story out of a subject which had amused me. This is the subject: Sexual pleasure has been the basis of an entire civilization, which began about the twelfth century and now seems on the decline. It is possible to argue indefinitely about these two dates, but not, I think, about the phenomenon itself, the birth of romantic love and its astounding influence on the art and morals of Europe. It is rather extraordinary, I said to myself, that a simple physical need should have given rise to such complex emotions and should be the subject of almost every artistic masterpiece, whereas other needs, equally urgent, like hunger and thirst, have remained rather primitive with most people.

A moment's reflection showed me that the difference is easily explained by the completely egotistic satisfaction of hunger and thirst. The civilizing and aesthetic value of love lies in the fact that it presupposes the harmony of two human beings, and that, from the time when both were free, owing to the relative emancipation of women, every kind of harmony and discord entered into their agreement. If human beings had been so constructed, I thought, that the satisfaction of thirst was only possible or agreeable between two people, then thirst would have been the cause of devastating passion and the subject of sublime masterpieces.

Why, I thought, should it not be possible to imagine a race so formed and governed by such desires, and to endow another form of desire with all the passion of love? Then I saw an island on which people like ourselves were living, but they had on their right arm a growth like a breast, only smaller, culminating in a nipple. I could see that this growth enabled them to satisfy each other's thirst, and the picture was somewhat revolting.

I was immediately confronted by a physiological difficulty. Was it not an unlikely supposition that food which was assimilable could come from a creature of the same species?

If these people could live only on the food which they gave each other, where did the liquid they secreted originally come from? Suppose that they secreted this liquid as plants produce sap. But plants draw their sustenance from the earth and from the heat of the sun. Should I endow the inhabitants of my island with green hair and vegetal functions? The more I thought of it the more I could see that the difficulty was not so great as I had imagined. These creatures could feed through the mouth and the digestive tract as we do, but they would require as some sort of supplementary nourishment this juice produced by the human body, just as children need animal milk, and ants need the liquid secreted by plant-lice.

The idea of the island suggested two characters which I had already invented for "The Voyage to the Island of the Articoles," a young French sailor, whom I called Pierre Chambrelan, and his wife, whose name, I believe, was Anne. It was easy to imagine, as Swift did for Gulliver, that these two people, having left the island of the Articoles, had visited other unknown countries, and that one of these was the island on which my monsters lived with breasts on their arms. It was necessary to give these people a name, so I thought it would be natural and euphonic to call them the Erophagi. Erotophagi was a more correct derivation, but pleased me less. I decided that Pierre Chambrelan and his wife, on leaving the Articoles, should arrive at the island of the Erophagi.

At the beginning of the story it would have been clumsy to reveal to the hero and to the reader the key of the narrative and the symbols on which the fiction was based. In the earlier chapters the secret of the intimate life of the Erophagi must not be apparent to the travellers. They must be impressed by the astounding immodesty of this race. The Erophagi would be nudists, a fact explicable by the warmth of the climate, but they would wear on their shoulders

André Maurois contributed to Esquire in the magazine's earliest days, this story in 1934. His last appearance was in 1960, an essay on the behavior of American tourists in France.

an armlet embroidered with lovely ornaments. They would attach no importance to the gestures of physical love, which took place in public amidst general indifference. It would be the custom of the island for people to ask their friends to come and make love, just as we invite people to come to dinner. The Erophagi would be surprised and shocked by the repugnance of Pierre and Anne towards these collective amusements. They would accuse the travellers of not understanding the most innocent joys of humanity.

Gradually the travellers would discover that young Erophagi couples met several times a day and hid themselves in their rooms, and that it was forbidden, in fact inconceivable, to disturb them. "With such freedom, what on earth can they find to do in secret?" Anne and Pierre Chambrelan asked in astonishment. Another phenomenon which seemed curious to them was that these immodest people have a curiously localized form of modesty, which is in their right shoulder. Everybody, both men and women, always keep the top of their right arm covered up. This is all the more extraordinary because these people spend most of their time in the sea. But then both sexes wear bathing armlets, which are swollen out by a curious protuberance. On the beach strict notices declare that bathing with bare shoulders is prohibited.

It is easy to imagine the episodes which would lead the travellers to discover the truth. Suddenly the secret life of the Erophagi would be revealed. They would discover that every Erophagus, man or woman, secretes in the arm a liquid which another person can absorb by suction. This liquid, whose taste is delicious, and which is not otherwise obtainable in nature, is essential to the life of the Erophagi. If they are deprived of it, they do not die, but become prematurely old and are afflicted by slow and deadly diseases.

Obviously the problem is more complicated than would appear from this first outline. If each of these creatures could derive the necessary liquid from any other, then no deep feelings would be aroused by this simple physiological need, but the drama of their lives consists in the fact that, although the chemical composition of the individual liquids is very similar, and an unaccustomed palate could not distinguish one from the other, they are not interchangeable to a sensitive Erophagus, and most of them are highly sensitive. It is probable that the decided taste which each individual shows for the liquid secreted by a given person could be explained by an analysis of the liquid itself, if our knowledge of chemistry were more exact. It is reasonable to suppose that every organism requires certain juices to complete and maintain itself. The person who can supply those juices becomes indispensable. It is not surprising that an Erophagus should become desperately attached to that person and establish relationships as lasting and as tender as our love. These relationships are based, not on sexual pleasure, but on the exchange of perfectly assorted liquids.

It is easy to understand that such powerful sentiments should produce modesty. Hence the armlets. When two Erophagi withdraw to a room, as the travellers observe, it is always for one of these brachial feasts, which they call unions, and which are, as a matter of fact, a kind of union in normal cases, because the position of these breasts enable the Erophagi to enjoy their pleasures simultaneously. The great Erophagi novelists have no objection to describing sexual relations, and these books are permitted to children, but the description of a brachial feast is considered obscene, and the best authors avoid it.

It is not difficult to imagine the dramas which our travellers would witness, and which would permit them to study the sentimental life of a people so different from ourselves. The fundamental reason for amorous complications with the Erophagi, as with ourselves, is unshared feeling. Sometimes an Erophagus will have a great desire for the liquid of another, but the latter would have no feeling for the liquid secreted by the former. Then there would be the spectacle of an unfortunate human being, hungry and thirsty, importuning a reluctant Erophagus who would find the scene of an unshared brachial feast boring and ridiculous. In certain cases sickness and age would bring about profound changes in the composition of the liquids and destroy relations which had hitherto seemed solid. In other cases a relationship which had begun by an intense mutual delight in this exchange of liquids would become difficult and painful, because one of the lovers, tired of a too familiar savour, would look elsewhere for new sensations, whereas the other, endowed with a more constant taste, would ask nothing better than that their relationship should continue.

Pierre Chambrelan would notice with interest that the usual duration of a passion among the Erophagi is about the same as with ourselves. It varies considerably, and oscillates between a week and ten years. Certain Erophagi who are restless or blasé need a new liquid almost every day. But Anne would discover old couples still thirsting for each other after fifty years of happiness. What are fundamentally relationships of nourishment become the basis of spiritual unions, of tender affections and friendships. Marriage among the Erophagi, whose legal forms resemble our own, is always based on such feelings and never on sexual relations, which are entirely free. Nevertheless, jealousy, among them as among ourselves, often assumes extreme forms and concentrates upon actions which are regarded with indifference by normal people. For example, some Erophagi would prevent their wives from making love with a stranger, just as certain husbands in our countries prevent their wives from dining alone with a man friend. But legal adultery does not exist, unless there has been an exchange of liquids and the parties have been caught in the act of having a brachial feast.

The consequences, so far as the education of children is concerned, are curious, since the children are in the charge of the state, and married life rests upon an entirely different basis. Differences of sex play no part in the marriages of the Erophagi. A man may marry a man, or a woman a woman. In many cases however, when a marriage takes place between people of different sex, sexual relations may complete those of nourishment, perhaps thereby rendering the union more perfect. But this is always a secondary matter, just as a common liking for certain foods may be an additional bond between two lovers among us.

To sum up: the ideas which give its value to love, that is to say, the idea of sin and the idea that only a given individual can satisfy us, though associated with a different desire in the minds of the Erophagi, produce the same results as with us. The romantic story of nutrition follows with them practically the same course as the romantic story of reproduction does with us. Their art, which is very remarkable, has been entirely inspired by the need to sublimate impossible thirsts.

The religion of the Erophagi is also a sublimation of this instinct, a phenomenon which Paul Valéry divined, without knowing the Erophagi, when he said: "Hunger and thirst have not degenerated into sentiment and idolatry. Why? But sex has become a demigod, perhaps even God."

Having reached this point in my reflections on the Erophagi, I decided not to write their story.

Albert Camus:

The Growing Stone

A long story

The automobile swung clumsily around the curve in the red sandstone trail, now a mass of mud. The headlights suddenly picked out in the night—first on one side of the road, then on the other—two wooden huts with sheet-metal roofs. On the right near the second one, a tower made of coarse beams could be made out in the light fog. From the top of the tower a metal cable, invisible at its starting point, shone as it sloped down into the light from the car before disappearing behind the embankment that blocked the road. The car slowed down and stopped a few yards from the huts.

The man who emerged from the seat to the right of the driver labored to extricate himself from the car. Once outside, his huge, broad frame lurched a little. In the shadow beside the car, solidly planted on the ground and weighed down by fatigue, he seemed to be listening to the idling motor. Then he walked in the direction of the embankment and entered the cone of light from the headlights. He stopped at the top of the slope, his huge back outlined against the darkness. After a moment, he turned around. The chauffeur's black face, lighted up by the dash light, was smiling. The man signaled and the chauffeur turned off the motor. At once, a vast, cool silence fell over the trail and the forest. Then the sound of the water could be heard.

The man looked at the river below him, visible solely as a broad, dark motion, flecked with occasional shimmers. A denser, motionless darkness, far beyond, must be the other bank. By looking fixedly, however, one could see in the distance on that still bank a yellowish light like an oil lamp. The big man turned back toward the car and nodded. The chauffeur switched off the lights, turned them on again, then blinked them regu-

larly. On the embankment the man appeared and disappeared, taller and more massive each time he came back to life. Suddenly on the other bank of the river, a lantern held up by an invisible arm swung back and forth several times. At a final signal from the lookout, the chauffeur turned off his lights once and for all. The car and the man disappeared into the night. With the lights out, the river was almost visible, or at least a few of its long liquid muscles shone intermittently. On each side of the road, the dark masses of forest foliage stood out against the sky and seemed very near. The fine rain that had soaked the trail an hour earlier was still hovering in the warm air, intensifying the silence and immobility of this broad clearing in the virgin forest. In the black sky misty stars flickered.

But from the other bank rose sounds of chains and muffled plashings. Above the hut on the right of the waiting man, the cable stretched taut. A dull creaking began to run along it, just as there rose from the river a faint yet quite audible sound of stirred-up water. The creaking became more regular, the sound of water spread further and then became localized as the lantern grew larger. Now the yellowish halo surrounding it could be clearly seen. The halo gradually expanded and again contracted while the lantern shone through the mist and began to light up above it a sort of square roof of dried palms supported by thick bamboos. That crude shelter, around which vague shadows were moving, was slowly approaching the bank. When it was about in the middle of the river, three little men, almost black, naked from the waist up and wearing conical hats, were distinctly outlined in the yellow light. They stood still with feet apart, leaning somewhat to offset the strong drift of the river, which was pressing with all its invisible water against the side of a big crude raft that eventually emerged from the darkness. When the ferry came still closer, the man could see behind the shelter on the downstream side two tall Negroes likewise wearing nothing but broad straw hats and cotton trousers. Side by side they weighed with all their might on long poles that sank slowly into the river toward the stern while the

Shortly after selling this story to Esquire, Albert Camus won the Nobel Prize in Literature. Commenting on the award, Arnold Gingrich remarked that the Prize had then fallen for the tenth time to an Esquire author, and that these artists were little known when their work first appeared in our pages. He added—and we wish to restate—the following: "It's hitting the ball on the up-bounce that's exciting, in magazine-making as in tennis, and that's the way we like to think we'll be playing it, in the future as in the past."

Negroes, with the same slow motion, bent over the water as far as their balance would allow. In the bow the three mulattoes, still and silent, watched the bank approach without raising their eyes toward the waiting man.

The ferry suddenly bumped against a pier jutting into the water, which was now lighted up by the lantern swaying from the shock. The tall Negroes stood still with hands above their heads gripping the ends of the poles which were barely stuck in the bottom, but their taut muscles rippled constantly with a motion that seemed to come from the very thrust of the water. The other ferrymen looped chains over the dock's posts, leaped onto the boards and lowered a sort of gangplank that covered the bow of the raft with its inclined plane.

The man came back to the car and slid into it while the chauffeur stepped on the starter. The car slowly climbed the embankment, pointed its hood toward the sky and then lowered it toward the river as it tackled the downward slope. With brakes on, it rolled forward, slipped somewhat on the mud, stopped, started up again. It rolled onto the pier with a noise of bouncing planks, reached the end where the mulattoes, still silent, were standing on either side, and plunged slowly toward the raft. The raft ducked its nose in the water as soon as the front wheels struck it and almost immediately bobbed back to receive the car's full weight. Then the chauffeur ran the vehicle to the stern in front of the square roof where the lantern was hanging. At once the mulattoes swung the inclined plane back onto the pier and jumped simultaneously onto the ferry, pushing it off from the muddy bank. The river strained under the raft and raised it on the surface of the water, where it drifted slowly at the end of the long drawbar running along the cable overhead. The tall Negroes relaxed their effort and drew in their poles. The man and the chauffeur got out of the car and came over to stand on the edge of the raft facing upstream. No one had spoken during the maneuver and even now each remained in his place, motionless and quiet except for one of the tall Negroes who was rolling a cigarette in coarse paper.

The man was looking at the gap through which the river sprang from the vast Brazilian forest and swept down toward them. Several hundred yards wide at that point, it pressed its muddy, silky waters against the side of the ferry and then, unimpeded at the two ends of the raft, sheered off and again spread out in a single powerful flood gently flowing through the dark forest toward the sea and the night. A stale smell, coming from the water or the spongy sky, hung in the air.

Now the slapping of the water under the ferry could be heard, and at intervals from the two banks the calls of bullfrogs or the strange cries of birds. The big man approached the small, thin chauffeur who was leaning against one of the bamboos with his hands in the pockets of his dungarees, once blue but now cov-

ered with the same red dust they had had in their faces all day long. His wrinkled young face was wreathed in a smile. Without seeing them, he was staring at the faint stars still swimming in the damp sky.

But the birds' cries became sharper and unfamiliar chatterings mingled with them, and almost at once the cable began to creak. The tall Negroes plunged their poles into the water and groped blindly for the bottom. The man turned around toward the shore they had just left. Now it was its turn to be obscured by the darkness and the water, vast and savage like the continent of trees stretching beyond it for thousands of kilometers. Between the nearby ocean and that sea of vegetation, the handful of men drifting at that moment on a wild river seemed lost. When the raft bumped the new pier it was as if, having cast off all moorings, they were landing on an island in the darkness after days of frightened sailing.

Once on land, the men's voices were at last heard. The chauffeur had just paid them and, with voices that sounded strangely gay in the heavy night, they were saying farewell in Portuguese as the car started up again.

"They said sixty—the kilometers to Iguape. Three hours more and it'll be over. Socrates is happy," the chauffeur announced.

The man laughed with a warm, hearty laugh that resembled him.

"Me too, Socrates; I'm happy too. The trail is hard."

"Too heavy, Mr. D'Arrast, you too heavy." And the chauffeur laughed too as if he would never stop.

The car had taken on a little speed. It was advancing between high walls of trees and inextricable vegetation, amidst a soft, sweetish smell. Fireflies on the wing constantly crisscrossed in the darkness of the forest and every once in a while red-eyed birds would bump against the windshield. At times a strange, savage sound would reach them from the depths of the night and the chauffeur would roll his eyes comically as he looked at his passenger.

The road kept turning and crossing little streams on bridges of wobbly boards. After an hour, the fog began to thicken. A fine drizzle began to fall, dimming the car's lights. Despite the jolts, D'Arrast was half asleep. He was no longer riding in the damp forest, but on the roads of the Serra do Mar that they had taken in the morning as they left São Paulo. From those dirt trails constantly rose the red dust of which they still had the taste in their mouths; on both sides as far as the eye could see it covered the sparse vegetation of the plains. The harsh sun, the pale mountains full of ravines, the starved zebus encountered along the roads, escorted solely by a tired flight of ragged urubus, the long, endless crossing of an endless desert. . . . He gave a start. The car had stopped. Now they were in Japan: fragile houses on both sides of the road and, in the houses, furtive kimonos. The chauffeur was talking to a Japanese wearing soiled dungarees and a Brazilian straw hat. Then the car started up again.

"He said only forty kilometers."

"Where were we? In Tokyo?"

"No. Registro. In Brazil all the Japanese come here."

"Why?"

"Don't know. They're yellow, you know, Mr. D'Arrast."

But the forest was gradually thinning out, and the road was becoming easier, though slippery. The car was skidding on sand. The window let in a warm, damp breeze that was rather sour.

"You smell it?" the chauffeur asked, smacking his lips. "That's the good old sea. Soon, Iguape."

"If we have enough gas," D'Arrast said. And he went back to sleep peacefully.

Sitting up in bed early in the morning, D'Arrast looked in amazement at the huge room in which he had just awakened. The big walls were newly calcimined brown on the lower half. Higher up, they had once been painted white, and patches of yellowish paint covered them up to the ceiling. Two rows of beds faced each other. D'Arrast saw only one bed unmade at the end of his row and that bed was empty. But he heard a noise on his left and turned toward the door where Socrates, a bottle of mineral water in each hand, stood laughing. "Happy memory!" he said. D'Arrast shook himself. Yes, the hospital in which the Mayor had lodged them the night before was named Happy Memory. "Sure memory," Socrates continued. "They told me first build hospital, later build water. Meanwhile, happy memory, take fizz water to wash." He disappeared, laughing and singing, apparently not at all exhausted by the cataclysmic sneezes that had shaken him all night long and kept D'Arrast from closing an eye.

Now D'Arrast was completely awake. Through the iron-latticed window he could see a little red-earth courtyard soaked by the rain that was noiselessly pouring down on a clump of tall aloes. A woman passed holding a yellow scarf over her head. D'Arrast lay back in bed, then sat up at once and got out of the bed, which creaked under his weight. Socrates came in at that moment: "For you Mr. D'Arrast. The Mayor is waiting outside." But seeing the look on D'Arrast's face, he added: "Don't worry; he never in a hurry."

After shaving with the mineral water, D'Arrast went out under the portico of the building. The Mayor —who had the proportions and, under his gold-rimmed glasses, the look of a nice little weasel—seemed lost in dull contemplation of the rain. But a charming smile transfigured him as soon as he saw D'Arrast. Holding his little body erect, he rushed up and tried to stretch his arms around the engineer. At that moment an automobile drove up in front of them, on the other side of the low wall, skidded in the wet clay, and came to a stop on an angle. "The Judge!" said the Mayor. Like the Mayor, the Judge was dressed in navy blue. But he was much younger, or at least seemed so because of his elegant figure and the look of a startled adolescent. Now he was crossing the courtyard in their direction, gracefully avoiding the puddles. A few steps from D'Arrast, he was already holding out his arms and welcoming him. He was proud to greet the noble engineer who was honoring their poor village; he was delighted by the priceless service the noble engineer was going to do Iguape by building that little jetty to prevent the periodic flooding of the lower quarters of town. What a noble profession to command the waters and dominate rivers! Ah, surely the poor people of Iguape would long remember the noble engineer's name and many years from now would still mention it in their prayers. D'Arrast, won over by such charm and eloquence, thanked him and didn't dare wonder what possible connection a judge could have with a jetty. Besides, according to the Mayor, it was time to go to the club, where the leading citizens wanted to receive the noble engineer appropriately before going to inspect the poorer quarters. Who were the leading citizens?

"Well," the Mayor said, "myself as Mayor, Mr. Carvalho here, the Harbor Captain, and a few others less important. Besides, you won't have to pay much attention to them, for they don't speak French."

D'Arrast called Socrates and told him he would meet him when the morning was over.

"All right," Socrates said. "I'll go to the Garden of the Fountain."

"The Garden?"

"Yes, everybody knows. Have no fear, Mr. D'Arrast."

The hospital, as D'Arrast saw upon leaving it, was built on the edge of the forest whose heavy foliage almost hung over the roofs. Over the whole surface of the trees a sheet of fine rain was falling, which the dense forest was noiselessly absorbing like a huge sponge. The town, some hundred houses roofed with faded tiles, extended between the forest and the river, whose distant murmur reached the hospital. The car entered drenched streets and almost at once came out on a rather large rectangular square which showed, among numerous puddles in its red clay, the marks of tires, iron wheels and horseshoes. All around, brightly plastered low houses closed off the square behind which could be seen the two round towers of a blue and white church of colonial style. This bare setting was dominated by a smell of salt water coming from the estuary. In the center of the square a few wet silhouettes were wandering. Along the houses a motley crowd of Gauchos, Japanese, half-breed Indians, and elegant leading citizens, whose dark suits looked exotic here, were sauntering with slow gestures. They stepped aside with dignity to make way for the car, then stopped and watched it. When the car stopped in front of one of the houses on the square, a circle of wet Gauchos silently formed around it.

At the club—a sort of small bar on the second floor provided with a bamboo counter and iron café tables—the leading citizens were numerous. Sugarcane alcohol was drunk in honor of D'Arrast after the Mayor, glass in hand, had wished him welcome and all the happiness in the world. But while D'Arrast was drinking near the window, a huge lout of a fellow in riding breeches and leggings came over and, staggering somewhat, delivered himself of a rapid and obscure speech in which the engineer recognized solely the word "passport." He hesitated and then took out the document which the fellow seized greedily. After having thumbed through the passport, he manifested obvious displeasure. He resumed his speech while shaking the document under the nose of the engineer who, without getting excited, merely looked at the angry man. Whereupon the Judge, with a smile, came over and asked what was the matter. For a moment the drunk scrutinized the frail creature who dared to interrupt him and then, staggering even more dangerously, shook the passport in the face of his new interlocutor. D'Arrast peacefully sat beside a café table and waited. The dialogue became very lively and suddenly the Judge broke out in a deafening voice that would never have been suspected in him. Without any forewarning, the lout suddenly backed down like a child caught in the act. At a final order from the Judge, he went toward the door with the oblique gait of a punished schoolboy and disappeared.

The Judge immediately came over to explain to D'Arrast, in a voice that had become harmonious again, that that coarse individual was the Chief of Police, that he had dared claim the passport was not in order, and that he would be punished for his outburst. Mr. Carvalho next addressed himself to the leading citizens, who stood in a circle around him, and seemed to be questioning them. After a brief discussion, the Judge expressed solemn excuses to D'Arrast, asked him to agree that nothing but drunkenness could explain such forgetfulness of the sentiments of respect and gratitude that the whole town of Iguape owed him and, finally, asked him to decide himself on the punishment to be inflicted on that wretched individual. D'Arrast said that he didn't want any punishment, that it was a trivial incident, and that he was particularly eager to go to the river. Then the Mayor spoke up to assert with much simple good humor that punishment was really indispensable, that the guilty man would remain incarcerated and that they would all wait together until their distinguished visitor decided on his fate. No protest could soften that smiling severity, and D'Arrast had to promise that he would think it over. Then it was decided to visit the poorer quarters of the town.

The river was already spreading its yellowish waters over the low, slippery banks. They had left behind them the last houses of Iguape and stood between the river and a high, steep embankment to which clung huts made of clay and branches. In front of them, at the end of the embankment, the forest began again abruptly, as on the other bank. But the gap made by the water rapidly widened between the trees up to a vague line, a little greyer than it was yellow, that marked the sea. With-

out saying a word, D'Arrast walked toward the slope where the various flood levels had left marks that were still fresh. A muddy path led up toward the huts. In front of them, Negroes stood silently staring at the newcomers. Several couples were holding hands and, on the edge of the mound in front of the adults, a row of black children, with bulging bellies and spindly legs, were gaping with round eyes.

Having arrived in front of the huts, D'Arrast beckoned to the Harbor Captain. He was a fat, laughing Negro wearing a white uniform. D'Arrast asked him in Spanish if it were possible to visit a hut. The Captain was sure it was, he even thought it a good idea, and the noble engineer would see very interesting things. He harangued the Negroes at length, pointing to D'Arrast and to the river. They listened without saying a word. When the Captain had finished, no one stirred. He spoke again in an impatient voice. Then he called upon one of the men, who shook his head. Whereupon the Captain said a few brief words in a tone of command. The man stepped forth from the group, faced D'Arrast, and with a gesture showed him the way. But his look was hostile. He was an elderly man with short, greying hair and a thin, wizened face; yet his body was still young, with hard wiry shoulders and muscles visible through his duck trousers and torn shirt.

They went ahead, followed by the Captain and the crowd of Negroes, and climbed a new, steeper embankment where the huts of clay, tin, and reeds clung to the ground with such difficulty that their bases had had to be strengthened with heavy stones. They encountered a woman going down the path in her bare feet, sometimes slipping, who was carrying on her head an iron drum full of water. Then they reached a sort of small square bordered by three huts. The man walked toward one of them and pushed open a bamboo door on hinges made of tropical liana. He stood aside without saying a word, staring at the engineer with the same impassive look. In the hut, D'Arrast saw nothing at first but a dying fire built right on the ground in the exact center of the room. Then in a back corner he made out a brass bed with a bare, broken mattress, a table in the other corner covered with earthenware dishes and, between the two, a sort of stand supporting a color print representing Saint George. Nothing else but a pile of rags to the right of the entrance and, hanging from the ceiling, a few loincloths of various colors drying over the fire. Standing still, D'Arrast breathed in the smell of smoke and poverty that rose from the ground and choked him. Behind him, the Captain clapped his hands. The engineer turned around and, against the light, saw the graceful silhouette of a black girl approach and hold out something to him. He took a glass and drank the thick sugarcane alcohol it contained. The girl held out her tray to receive the empty glass and went out with such a supple motion that D'Arrast suddenly wanted to hold her back.

But on following her out he didn't recognize her in the crowd of Negroes and leading citizens gathered around the hut. He thanked the old man, who bowed without a word. Then he left. The Captain, behind him, resumed his explanations and asked when the

French company from Rio could begin work and whether or not the jetty could be built before the rainy season. D'Arrast didn't know; to tell the truth, he wasn't thinking of that. He went down toward the cool river under the fine mist. He was still listening to that great pervasive sound he had been hearing continually since his arrival, which might have come equally well from the rustling of the water or of the trees. Having reached the bank, he looked out in the distance at the vague line of the sea, the thousands of kilometers of solitary waters leading to Africa and, beyond them, his native Europe.

"Captain," he asked, "what do these people we have just seen live on?"

"They work when they're needed," the Captain said. "We are poor."

"Are they the poorest?"

"They are the poorest."

The Judge, who arrived at that moment, slipping somewhat in his best shoes, said they already loved the noble engineer who was going to give them work.

"And you know, they dance and sing every day."

Then, without transition, he asked D'Arrast if he had thought of the punishment.

"What punishment?"

"Why, our Chief of Police."

"Let him go."

The Judge said that this was not possible; there had to be a punishment.

D'Arrast was already walking toward Iguape.

In the little Garden of the Fountain, mysterious and pleasant under the fine rain, clusters of exotic flowers hung down along the lianas among the banana trees and pandanus. Piles of wet stones marked the intersection of paths on which a motley crowd was strolling. Half-breeds, mulattoes, a few Gauchos were chatting in low voices or sauntering along the bamboo paths to the point where groves and bush became thicker and more impenetrable. There, the forest began abruptly.

D'Arrast was looking for Socrates in the crowd when Socrates suddenly bumped into his back.

"It's holiday," he said, laughing, and clung to D'Arrast's tall shoulders, jumping up and down.

"What holiday?"

"Why, you not know?" Socrates said in surprise as he faced D'Arrast. "The feast of good Jesus. Each year, they all come to the grotto with a hammer."

Socrates pointed out, not a grotto, but a group that seemed to be waiting in a corner of the garden.

"You see? One day the good statue of Jesus, it came upstream from the sea. Some fishermen found it. How beautiful! How beautiful! Then they washed it here in the grotto. And now a stone grew up in the grotto. Every year, it's the feast. With the hammer you break, you break off pieces for blessed happiness. And then it keeps growing and you keep breaking. It's the miracle!"

They had reached the grotto and could see its low entrance beyond the waiting men. Inside, in the darkness studded with the flickering flames of candles, a squatting figure was pounding with a hammer. The man, a thin Gaucho with a long moustache, got up and came out holding in his open palm, so that all might see, a small piece of moist schist, over which he soon closed his hand carefully before going away. Another man then stooped down and entered the grotto.

D'Arrast turned around. On all sides pilgrims were waiting, not looking at him, motionless under the water dripping from the trees in thin sheets. He too was waiting in front of the grotto under the same film of water, and he didn't know for what. He had been constantly waiting for a month, to tell the truth, since he had arrived in this country. He had been waiting—in the red heat of humid days, under the little stars of night, despite the tasks to be accomplished, the jetties to be built, the roads to be cut through—as if the work he had come to do here were merely a pretext for a surprise or for an encounter he did not even imagine yet which had been waiting patiently for him at the end of the world. He shook himself and without anyone in the little group paying attention to him, he walked toward the exit. He had to go back toward the river and go to work.

But Socrates was waiting for him at the gate, lost in voluble conversation with a short, fat, strapping man whose skin was yellow rather than black. His completely shaved head gave even more sweep to a considerable forehead. On the other hand, his broad, smooth face was adorned with a very black beard, trimmed square.

"He's champion!" Socrates said by way of introduction. "Tomorrow he's in the procession."

The man, wearing a sailor's outfit of heavy serge, a blue and white jersey under the pea jacket, was examining D'Arrast attentively with his calm, black eyes. At the same time he was smiling, showing all his very white teeth between his full, shiny lips.

"He speaks Spanish," Socrates said and, turning toward the stranger, added: "Tell Mr. D'Arrast." Then he danced off toward another group. The man ceased to smile and looked at D'Arrast with outright curiosity.

"You are interested, Captain?"

"I'm not a Captain," D'Arrast said.

"That doesn't matter. But you're a noble. Socrates told me."

"Not I. But my grandfather was. His father too and all those before his father. Now there are no more nobles in our country."

"Ah!" the Negro said laughing. "I understand; everybody is a noble."

"No, that's not it. There are neither nobles nor common people."

The fellow reflected; then he made up his mind: "No one works? No one suffers?"

"Yes, millions of men."

"Then that's the common people."

"In that way, yes, there is a common people. But its masters are policemen or merchants."

The mulatto's kindly face frowned. Then he grumbled: "Humph! Buying and selling, eh! What filth! And with the police, dogs command." Suddenly, he burst out laughing. "You, you don't sell?"

"Hardly at all. I make bridges, roads."

"That's good. Me, I'm a ship's cook. If you wish, I'll make you our dish of black beans."

"I'm willing."

The cook came closer to D'Arrast and took his arm.

"Listen, I like what you tell. I'm going to tell you too. Maybe you will like."

He drew him over near the gate to a damp wooden bench beneath a clump of bamboos.

"I was at sea, off Iguape, on a small coastwise tanker that supplies the harbors along here. It caught fire on board. Not by my fault! I know my job! No, just bad luck. We were able to launch the lifeboats. During the night, the sea got rough; it capsized the boat and I went down. When I came up, I hit the boat with my head. I drifted. The night was dark, the waters are vast, and besides I don't swim well; I was afraid. Just then I saw a light in the distance and recognized the church of the good Jesus in Iguape. So I told the good Jesus that at His procession I would carry a hundred-pound stone on my head if He saved me. You don't have to believe me, but the waters became calm and my heart too. I swam slowly, I was happy, and I reached the shore. Tomorrow I'll keep my promise."

He looked at D'Arrast in a suddenly suspicious manner. "You're not laughing?"

"No, I'm not laughing. A man has to do what he has promised."

The fellow clapped him on the back. "Now, come to my brother's, near the river. I'll cook you some beans."

"No," D'Arrast said, "I have things to do. This evening, if you wish."

"Good. But tonight there's dancing and praying in the big hut. It's the feast for Saint George."

D'Arrast asked him if he danced too. The cook's face hardened suddenly; for the first time his eyes became shifty.

"No, no, I won't dance. Tomorrow I must carry the stone. It is heavy. I'll go this evening to celebrate the saint. And then I'll leave early."

"Does it last long?"

"All night and a little into the morning." He looked at D'Arrast with a vague look of shame. "Come to the dance. You can take me home afterward. Otherwise, I'll stay and dance. I probably won't be able to keep myself from it."

"You like to dance?"

"Oh, yes! I like. Besides, there are cigars, saints, women. You forget everything and you don't obey anymore."

"There are women too? All the women of the town?"

"Not of the town, but of the huts."

The ship's cook resumed his smile. "Come. I'll obey the Captain. And you will help me keep my promise tomorrow."

D'Arrast felt vaguely annoyed. What did that ab- surd promise mean to him? But he looked at the handsome frank face smiling trustingly at him, its dark skin gleaming with health and vitality.

"I'll come," he said. "Now I'll walk along with you a little."

Without knowing why, he simultaneously had a vision of the black girl offering him the drink of welcome.

They went out of the garden, walked along several muddy streets, and reached the bumpy square which looked even larger because of the low structures surrounding it. The humidity was now dripping down the plastered walls, although the rain had not increased. Through the spongy expanse of the sky, the sound of the river and of the trees reached them somewhat muted. They were walking in step, D'Arrast heavily and the cook with elastic tread. From time to time the latter would raise his head and smile at his companion. They went in the direction of the church, which could be seen above the houses, reached the end of the square, walked along other muddy streets now filled with aggressive smells of cooking. From time to time a woman, holding a plate or kitchen utensil, would peer out inquisitively from one of the doors and then disappear at once. They passed in front of the church, plunged into an old section of similar low houses, and suddenly came out on the sound of the invisible river behind the area of the huts that D'Arrast recognized.

"Good. I'll leave you. See you this evening," D'Arrast said.

"Yes, in front of the church."

But the cook did not let go of D'Arrast's hand. He hesitated. Finally he made up his mind.

"And you, have you never called out, made a promise?"

"Yes, once, I believe."

"In a shipwreck?"

"If you wish." And D'Arrast roughly pulled his hand away. But as he was about to turn on his heels, he encountered the cook's eyes. He hesitated, and then smiled. "I can tell you, although it was unimportant. Someone was about to die through my fault. It seems to me that I called out."

"Did you promise?"

"No. I should have liked to promise."

"Long ago?"

"Not long before coming here."

The cook seized his beard with both hands. His eyes were shining.

"You are a Captain," he said. "My house is yours. Besides, you are going to help me keep my promise, and it's as if you had made it yourself. That will help you too."

D'Arrast smiled, saying: "I don't think so."

"You are proud, Captain."

"I used to be proud; now I'm alone. But just tell me: has your good Jesus always answered you?"

"Always . . . no, Captain!"

"Well, then?"

The cook burst out with a gay, childlike laugh. "Well," he said. "He's free, isn't He?"

At the club, where D'Arrast lunched with the leading citizens, the Mayor told him he must sign the town's guest book so that some trace would remain of the great event of his coming to Iguape. The Judge found two or three new expressions to praise, besides their guest's virtues and talents, the simplicity with which he represented among them the great country to which he had the honor to belong. D'Arrast simply said that there was that honor, which certainly was one to him, and that there was also the advantage for his firm to have been awarded the allocation of this long construction job. Whereupon the Judge expressed his admiration for such humility. "By the way," he asked, "have you thought of what should be done to the Chief of Police?" D'Arrast smiled at him and said: "Yes, I have a solution." He would consider it a personal favor and an exceptional grace if the foolish man could be forgiven in his name so that his stay in Iguape, whose beautiful town and generous inhabitants he rejoiced to know, could begin in a climate of peace and friendship. The Judge, attentive and smiling, nodded his head. For a moment he meditated on the expression as an expert, then called on those present to applaud the magnanimous traditions of the great French nation and, turning again toward D'Arrast, declared himself satisfied. "Since that's the way it is," he concluded, "we shall dine this evening with the Chief." But D'Arrast said that he was invited by friends to the ceremony of the dances in the huts. "Ah, yes!" said the Judge. "I am glad you are going. You'll see, one can't resist loving our people."

That evening, D'Arrast, the ship's cook, and his brother were seated around the ashes of a fire in the center of the hut the engineer had already visited in the morning. The brother had not seemed surprised to see him return. He hardly spoke Spanish at all and most of the time merely nodded his head. As for the cook, he had shown interest in cathedrals and then had expatiated at length on the black bean soup. Now night had almost fallen and, although D'Arrast could still see the cook and his brother, he could scarcely make out in the back of the hut the squatting figures of an old woman and of the same girl who had served him. Down below could be heard the monotonous river.

The cook rose, saying: "It's time." They got up, but the women did not stir. The men went out alone. D'Arrast hesitated, then joined the others. Night had now fallen and the rain had stopped. The pale black sky still seemed liquid. In its transparent dark water, stars began to light up, low on the horizon. Almost at once they flickered out, falling one by one into the river as if the sky were dripping with its last lights. The heavy air smelled of water and smoke. Nearby the sound of the huge forest could be heard too, though it was motionless. Suddenly drums and singing broke out in the distance, at first muffled and then distinct, approaching closer and closer and finally stopping. Soon after was seen a procession of black girls wearing low-waisted white dresses of coarse silk. A tall Negro

followed them in a tight-fitting red jacket adorned with a necklace of varicolored teeth, and, behind him, was a disorderly crowd of men in white pajamas and musicians carrying triangles and broad, short drums. The cook said they should follow the men.

The hut they reached by following the river a few hundred yards beyond the last huts was large, empty and relatively comfortable with inside walls plastered. It had a dirt floor, a roof of thatch and reeds supported by a central pole, and bare walls. On a little palm-clad altar at the end, covered with candles that barely lighted half the hall, could be seen a magnificent colored print in which Saint George, with alluring grace, was getting the better of a bewhiskered dragon. Under the altar a sort of niche decorated with rococo paper sheltered, between a candle and a bowl of water, a little statue in red-painted clay representing a horned god. With a fierce look he was brandishing an oversized knife made of silver paper.

The cook led D'Arrast to a corner where they stood against the wall near the door. "This way," he whispered, "we can leave without disturbing." Indeed, the hut was filled with men and women packed in. Already the heat was rising. The musicians took their places on both sides of the little altar. The men and women dancers separated into two concentric circles with the men inside. The black leader in the red jacket took his stand in the very center. D'Arrast, with arms folded, leaned against the wall.

But the leader, elbowing his way through the circle of dancers, came toward them and, in a solemn way, said a few words to the cook. "Unfold your arms, Captain," the cook said. "You are hugging yourself and keeping the saint's spirit from descending." Obediently D'Arrast let his arms fall to his sides. Still leaning against the wall, with his long, heavy limbs and his big face already shiny with sweat, he himself looked like some bestial and kindly god. The tall Negro looked at them and, satisfied, went back to his place. At once, in a resounding voice, he intoned the opening notes of a song that they all picked up in chorus, accompanied by the drums. Then the circles began to turn in opposite directions in a sort of heavy, insistent dance rather like stamping, slightly emphasized by the double swaying of hips.

The heat had increased. Yet the pauses gradually decreased, the stops became less frequent, and the dance speeded up. Without any slowing of the others' rhythm, without ceasing to dance himself, the tall Negro again elbowed his way through the circles to go toward the altar. He came back with a glass of water and a lighted candle that he stuck in the ground in the center of the hut. He poured the water around the candle in two concentric circles, and, again erect, turned maddened eyes toward the roof. He was waiting, his whole body taut and still. "Saint George is coming. Look! Look!" whispered the cook, whose eyes were popping.

Indeed, some dancers now showed signs of trance, but a rigid trance with hands on hips, steps stiff, eyes staring and vacant. Others quickened their rhythm, bent convulsively backward, and began to utter inarticulate cries. The cries gradually rose higher and when they fused in a collective shriek the leader, with eyes still raised, uttered a long, barely phrased outcry at the top of his lungs. In it the same words kept recurring. "You see," said the cook, "he says he is the god's field of battle." Struck by the change in his voice, D'Arrast looked at the cook who, leaning forward with fists clenched and eyes staring, was mimicking the others' measured stamping without moving from his place. Then he noticed that he himself, though without moving his feet, had for some little time been dancing with his whole weight.

But all at once the drums began to beat violently and suddenly the big red fellow broke loose. His eyes flashing, his four limbs whirling around him, he hopped with bent knee on one leg after the other, speeding up his rhythm until it seemed that he must eventually fly to pieces. But abruptly he stopped in mid-spring to stare at those around him with a proud and terrible look while the drums thundered on. Immediately a dancer sprang from a far corner, knelt down and held out a short saber to the man possessed of the spirit. The tall Negro took the saber without ceasing to look around him and then whirled it above his head. At that moment D'Arrast noticed the cook dancing among the others. The engineer had not seen him leave his side.

In the reddish, vague light, a stifling dust rose from the ground, making the air even thicker as it stuck to one's skin. D'Arrast felt gradually overcome by fatigue and breathed with ever greater difficulty. He did not even see how the dancers had got hold of the huge cigars they were now smoking while still dancing; their strange smell filled the hut and rather made his head swim. He merely saw the cook passing near him, still dancing and puffing on a cigar. "Don't smoke," he said. The cook grunted without losing the beat, staring at the central pole with the expression of a boxer about to collapse, his spine constantly twitching in a long shudder. Beside him a heavy Negress, rolling her animal face from side to side, kept barking. But the young Negresses especially went into the most frightful trance, their feet glued to the floor and their bodies shaken from feet to head by convulsive motions that became more violent upon reaching the shoulders. Their heads would wag backward and forward, as though separated from decapitated bodies. At the same time all began to howl incessantly with a long collective and toneless howl, apparently not pausing to breathe or to introduce modulations—as if the bodies were tightly knotted muscles and nerves—in a single exhausting outburst, at last giving voice in each of them to a creature that until then had been absolutely silent. And without the howl's ceasing, the women began to fall one by one. The black leader knelt by each one and quickly and convulsively pressed her temples with his huge, black-muscled hand. Then they would get up, staggering, return to

the dance and resume their howls, at first feebly and then louder and faster, before falling again, and getting up again, and beginning over again, and for a long time more, until the general howl decreased, changed, and degenerated into a sort of coarse barking which shook them with gasps. D'Arrast, exhausted, his muscles taut from his long dance as he stood still, choked by his own silence, felt groggy on his legs. The heat, the dust, the smoke of the cigars, the smell of bodies now made the air almost unbreathable. He looked for the cook, who had disappeared. D'Arrast let himself slide down along the wall and squatted down, holding back his nausea.

When he opened his eyes, the air was still as stifling, but the noise had stopped. The drums alone were beating out a figured bass, and groups in every corner of the hut, covered with whitish cloths, were marking time by stamping. But in the center of the room, from which the glass and candle had now been removed, a group of black girls in a semi-hypnotic state were dancing slowly, always on the point of letting the beat get ahead of them. Their eyes closed and yet erect, they were swaying lightly on their toes, almost in the same spot. Two of them, fat ones, had their faces covered with a curtain of raffia. They surrounded another girl, tall, thin, and wearing a fancy costume, in whom D'Arrast suddenly recognized the daughter of his host. In a green dress and a huntress' hat of blue gauze turned up in front and adorned with plumes, she held in her hand a green and yellow bow and its arrow on the tip of which was spitted a multicolored bird. On her slim body her pretty head swayed slowly, tipped backward a little, and her sleeping face reflected an innocent melancholy. At the pauses in the music she staggered as if half asleep. Yet the intensified beat of the drums provided her with a sort of invisible support around which to entwine her languid arabesques until stopping again, together with the music, and tottering on the edge of equilibrium, she uttered a strange bird cry, shrill and yet melodious.

D'Arrast, bewitched by that slow dance, was watching the black Diana when the cook suddenly loomed up before him, his smooth face now distorted. The kindness had disappeared from his eyes, which revealed nothing but a sort of unsuspected avidity. Coldly, as if speaking to a stranger, he said: "It's late, Captain. They are going to dance all night long, but they don't want you to stay now." With head heavy, D'Arrast got up and followed the cook who went along the wall toward the door. On the threshold the cook stood aside holding the bamboo door, and D'Arrast went out. He turned back and looked at the cook who had not moved. "Come. In a little while you'll have to carry the stone."

"I'm staying," the cook said with a set expression. "And your promise?"

Without replying, the cook gradually pushed the door that D'Arrast was holding with one hand. They remained this way for a second until D'Arrast gave in, shrugging his shoulders. He went away.

The night was full of fresh aromatic scents. Above the forest the few stars in the austral sky, blurred by an invisible haze, were shining dimly. The humid air was heavy. Yet it seemed delightfully cool on coming out of the hut. D'Arrast climbed the slippery slope, staggering like a drunken man in the potholes. The forest, nearby, rumbled slightly. The sound of the river increased. The whole continent was emerging from the night, and loathing overcame D'Arrast. It seemed to him that he would have liked to spew forth this whole country, the melancholy of its vast expanses, the glaucous light of its forests, and the nocturnal lapping of its big, deserted rivers. This land was too vast, blood and seasons mingled here, and time liquefied. Life here was flush with the soil and, to identify oneself with it, one had to lie down and sleep for years on the muddy or dried-up ground itself. Yonder, in Europe, it was shame and wrath; here, exile or solitude, among these listless and convulsive madmen who danced to die. But through the humid night, heavy with vegetable scents, the wounded bird's outlandish cry, uttered by the beautiful sleeping girl, still reached his ears.

When D'Arrast, his head in the vise of a crushing migraine, had awakened after a bad sleep, a humid heat was weighing upon the town and the still forest. He was waiting now under the hospital portico, looking at his stopped watch, uncertain of the time, surprised by the broad daylight and the silence of the town. The almost clear blue sky hung low over the first dull roofs. Yellowish urubus, motionless in the heat, were sleeping on the house opposite the hospital. One of them suddenly fluttered, opened his beak, ostensibly got ready to fly away, flapped his dusty wings twice against his body, rose a few inches above the roof, fell back and went to sleep almost at once.

The engineer went down toward the town. The main square was empty, like the streets he had just walked through. In the distance, and on both sides of the river, a low mist hung over the forest. The heat fell vertically and D'Arrast looked for a shady spot. At that moment, under the overhang on one of the houses, he saw a little man gesturing toward him. As he came closer, he recognized Socrates.

"Well, Mr. D'Arrast, you like the ceremony?"

D'Arrast said it was too hot in the hut and he preferred the sky and night air.

"Yes," Socrates said, "in your country there's only the Mass. No one dances." He rubbed his hands, jumped on one foot, whirled about, laughed uproariously. "Not possible, they're not possible."

Then he looked at D'Arrast inquisitively. "And you, are you going to Mass?"

"No."

"Then, where are you going?"

"Nowhere. I don't know."

Socrates laughed again. "Not possible! A noble without a church, without anything!"

D'Arrast laughed likewise. "Yes, you see, I never found my place. So I left."

"Stay with us, Mr. D'Arrast. I love you."

"I'd like to, Socrates, but I don't know how to dance." Their laughter echoed in the silence of the empty town.

"Ah," Socrates said, "I forget. The Mayor wants to see you. He is lunching at the club." And without a warning he started off in the direction of the hospital. "Where are you going?" D'Arrast shouted. Socrates imitated a snore. "Sleep. Soon the procession." And, half running, he resumed his snores.

The Mayor simply wanted to give D'Arrast a place of honor to see the procession. He explained it to the engineer while sharing with him a dish of meat and rice such as would miraculously cure a paralytic. First they would take their places on a balcony of the Judge's house, opposite the church, to see the procession come out. Then they would go to the town hall in the main street leading to the church, which the penitents would take on their way back. The Judge and the Chief of Police would accompany D'Arrast, the Mayor being obliged to take part in the ceremony. The Chief of Police was in fact in the club room and kept paying court to D'Arrast with an indefatigable smile, lavishing upon him incomprehensible but obviously well-meaning speeches. When D'Arrast left, the Chief of Police hastened to make a way for him, holding all the doors open before him.

Under the burning sun, in the still empty town, the two men walked toward the Judge's house. Their steps were the only sound heard in the silence. But all of a sudden a firecracker exploded in a neighboring street and started up from every roof the heavy, awkward flocks of baldnecked urubus. Almost at once dozens of firecrackers went off in all directions, doors opened, and people began to issue from the houses and fill the narrow streets.

The Judge told D'Arrast how proud he was to receive him in his unworthy house and led him up a handsome baroque staircase calcimined blue. On the landing, as D'Arrast passed, doors opened and children's dark heads popped out and disappeared at once with smothered laughter. The main room, beautiful in architecture, contained nothing but rattan furniture and large cages of birds squawking deafeningly. The balcony on which they settled overlooked the little square in front of the church. The crowd was now beginning to fill it, strangely silent, motionless under the heat that came down from the sky in almost visible waves. Children were running around the square, stopping abruptly to light firecrackers, and sharp reports followed one another in rapid succession. Seen from the balcony, the church

—with its plaster walls, its dozen blue steps, its blue and gold towers—looked smaller.

Suddenly the organ burst out inside the church. The crowd, turned toward the portico, drew over to the sides of the square. The men took off their hats and the women knelt down. The distant organ played at length something like marches. Then an odd sound of wings came from the forest. A tiny airplane with transparent wings and frail fuselage, out of place in this ageless world, came in sight over the trees, swooped a little above the square, and, with the clacking of a big rattle, passed over the heads raised toward it. Then the plane turned and disappeared in the direction of the estuary.

But in the shadow of the church a vague bustle again attracted attention. The organ had stopped, replaced now by brasses and drums, invisible under the portico. Black-surpliced penitents came out of the church one by one, formed groups outside the doors, and began to descend the steps. Behind them came white penitents bearing red and blue banners, then a little group of boys dressed up as angels, sodalities of Children of Mary with little black, serious faces. Finally, on a multicolored shrine borne by leading citizens sweating in their dark suits, the effigy of the good Jesus Himself, a reed in His hand and His head crowned with thorns, bleeding and tottering above the crowd that lined the steps.

When the shrine reached the bottom of the steps, there was a pause during which the penitents tried to line up in a semblance of order. Then it was that D'Arrast saw the ship's cook. Bare from the waist up, he had just come out under the portico carrying on his bearded head an enormous rectangular block set on a cork mat. With steady tread he came down the church steps, the stone perfectly balanced in the arch formed by his short, muscular arms. As soon as he fell in behind the shrine, the procession moved. From the portico burst the musicians, wearing bright colored coats and blowing into beribboned brasses. To the beat of a quick march, the penitents hastened their step and reached one of the streets opening off the square. When the shrine had disappeared behind them, nothing could be seen but the cook and the last musicians. Behind them, the crowd got in motion amidst firecrackers, while the plane, with a great rattle of its engine, flew back over the last groups. D'Arrast was looking exclusively at the cook, who was disappearing in the street now and whose shoulders he thought he saw sag. But at that distance he couldn't see well.

Through the empty streets, between closed shops and bolted doors, the Judge, the Chief of Police, and D'Arrast reached the town hall. As they got away from the band and the firecrackers, silence again enveloped the town and already a few urubus re-

turned to the places on the roofs that they seemed to have occupied for all time. The town hall stood in a long, narrow street leading from one of the outlying sections to the church square. For the moment, it was empty. From its balcony could be seen, as far as the eye could reach, nothing but a pavement full of potholes in which the recent rain had left puddles. The sun, now slightly lower, was still nibbling at the windowless facades of the houses across the street.

They waited a long time, so long that D'Arrast, from staring at the reverberation of the sun on the opposite wall, felt his fatigue and dizziness returning. The empty street with its deserted houses attracted and repelled him at one and the same time. Once again, he wanted to get away from this country; at the same time he thought of that huge stone; he would have liked that trial to be over. He was about to suggest going down to find out something when the church bells began to peal forth loudly. Simultaneously, from the other end of the street to their left, a clamor burst out and a seething crowd appeared. From a distance it could be seen swarming around the shrine, pilgrims and penitents mingled and advanced, amidst firecrackers and shouts of joy, along the narrow street. In a few seconds they filled it to the edges, advancing toward the town hall in an indescribable disorder—ages, races, and costumes fused in a motley mass full of gaping eyes and yelling mouths. From it emerged like lances an army of tapers, their flames fading into the burning sunlight. But when they were close and the crowd was so thick under the balcony that it seemed to rise up along the walls, D'Arrast saw that the ship's cook was not there.

Quick as lightning, without excusing himself, he left the balcony and the room, dashed down the staircase and stood in the street under the deafening sound of the bells and firecrackers. There he had to struggle against the crowd of merrymakers, the taper bearers, the shocked penitents. But bucking the human tide with all his weight, he irresistibly cut a path in such an impetuous way that he staggered and almost fell when he was eventually free, beyond the crowd, at the end of the street. Leaning against the burning hot wall, he waited until he had caught his breath. Then he resumed his way. At that moment a group of men emerged into the street. The first of them were walking backward, and D'Arrast saw that they surrounded the cook.

He was obviously dead tired. He would stop, then, bent under the huge stone, run a little with the hasty step of stevedores and coolies—the rapid, flat-footed trot of drudgery. Gathered about him, penitents in surplices soiled with dust and candle drippings encouraged him when he stopped. On his left his brother was walking or running in silence. It seemed to D'Arrast that they took an interminable time to cover the space separating them from him. Having almost reached him, the cook stopped again and glanced around with dull eyes. When he saw D'Arrast —yet without appearing to recognize him—he stood still, turned toward him. An oily, dirty sweat covered his face that had gone grey; his beard was full of threads of saliva; and a brown, dry froth glued his lips together. He tried to smile. But motionless under his load, his whole body was trembling except for the shoulders, where the muscles were obviously caught in a sort of cramp. The brother, who had recognized D'Arrast, said to him simply: "He already fell." And Socrates, popping up from nowhere, whispered in his ear: "Dance too much, Mr. D'Arrast, all night long. He's tired."

The cook advanced again with his jerky trot, not like a man who wants to progress but as if he were fleeing the crushing load, as if he hoped to lighten it through motion. Without knowing how, D'Arrast found himself at his right. He laid his hand lightly on the cook's back and walked beside him with hasty, heavy steps. At the other end of the street the shrine had disappeared, and the crowd, which probably now filled the square, did not seem to advance any more. For several seconds the cook, between his brother and D'Arrast, made progress. Soon a mere space of some twenty yards separated him from the group gathered in front of the town hall to see him pass. Again, however, he stopped. D'Arrast's hand became heavier. "Come on, cook, just a little more," he said. The man trembled; the saliva began to trickle from his mouth again, while the sweat literally spurted from all over his body. He tried to breathe deeply and stopped short. He started off again, took three steps, and tottered. And suddenly the stone slipped onto his shoulder, gashing it, and then forward onto the ground, while the cook, having lost his balance, toppled over on his side. Those who were preceding him and urging him on jumped back with loud shouts. One of them seized the cork mat while the others took hold of the stone to load it on him again.

Leaning over him, D'Arrast with his bare hand wiped the blood and dust from his shoulder, while the little man, his face against the ground, panted. He heard nothing and did not stir. His mouth opened avidly with each breath as if it were his last. D'Arrast grasped him around the waist and raised him up as easily as if he had been a child. Holding him upright in a tight grasp with his whole height leaning over him, D'Arrast spoke into his face as if to breathe his own strength into him. After a moment, the cook, bloody and caked with earth, detached himself with a haggard expression on his face. He staggered toward the stone, which the others were raising a little. But he stopped, looked at the stone with a vacant stare, and shook his head. Then he let his arms fall at his sides and turned toward D'Arrast.

Huge tears flowed silently down his ravaged face. He wanted to speak, he was speaking, but his mouth hardly formed the syllables. "I promised," he was saying. And then, "Oh, Captain! Oh, Captain!" and the tears drowned his voice. His brother suddenly appeared behind him, threw his arms around him, and the cook, weeping, collapsed against him, defeated, his head thrown back.

D'Arrast looked at him, not knowing what to say. He turned toward the crowd in the distance, now shouting again. Suddenly he tore the cork mat from the hands holding it and walked toward the stone. He gestured to the others to hold it up and loaded it al-most effortlessly. His head pressed down under the weight of the stone, his shoulders hunched, and breathing rather hard, he looked down at his feet as he listened to the cook's sobs. Then with vigorous tread he started off on his own, covered without flagging the space separating him from the crowd at the end of the street, and energetically forced his way through the first rows, which stood aside as he approached. In the hubbub of bells and firecrackers he entered the square between two solid masses of onlookers, suddenly silent and gaping at him in amazement. He advanced with the same impetuous pace and the crowd opened a path for him to the church. Despite the weight, which was beginning to crush his head and neck, he saw the church and the shrine which seemed to be waiting for him at the door. He had already gone beyond the center of the square in that direction when brutally, without knowing why, he veered off to the left and turned away from the church, forcing the pilgrims to face him. Behind him, he heard someone running. In front of him mouths opened on all sides. He didn't understand what they were shouting although he seemed to recognize the Portuguese word that was being constantly hurled at him. Suddenly Socrates appeared before him, rolling startled eyes, speaking incoherently and pointing out the way to the church behind him. "To the church! To the church!" was what Socrates and the crowd were shouting at him. Yet D'Arrast continued in the direction he was launched. And Socrates stood aside, his arms raised in the air comically, while the crowd fell silent. When D'Arrast entered the first street, which he had already taken with the cook and therefore knew it led to the river section, the square had become but a vague murmur behind him.

The stone weighed painfully on his head now and he needed all the strength of his long arms to lighten it. His shoulders were already stiffening when he reached the first streets on the slippery slope. He stopped and listened. He was alone. He settled the stone firmly on its cork base and went down with a cautious but still steady tread toward the huts. When he reached them, his breath was beginning to fail, his arms were trembling under the stone. He hastened his pace, finally reaching the little square where the cook's hut stood, ran to it, kicked the door open, and brusquely hurled the stone onto the still glowing fire in the center of the room. And there, straightening up until he was suddenly enormous, drinking in with desperate gulps the familiar smell of poverty and ashes, he felt rising within him a surge of vague and panting joy that he was powerless to name.

When the inhabitants of the hut arrived, they found D'Arrast standing with his shoulders against the back wall and eyes closed. In the center of the room, in the place of the hearth, the stone was half buried in ashes and earth. They stood in the doorway without advancing and looked at D'Arrast in silence as if questioning him. But he didn't speak. Whereupon the brother led the cook up to the stone, where he dropped on the ground. The brother sat down too, beckoning to the others. The old woman joined him, then the girl of the night before, but no one looked at

D'Arrast. They were squatting in a silent circle around the stone. No sound but the murmur of the river reached them through the heavy air. Standing in the darkness. D'Arrast listened without seeing anything, and the sound of the waters filled him with a riotous happiness. With eyes closed, he joyfully acclaimed his own strength; he acclaimed, once again, a fresh beginning in life. At that moment, a firecracker went off that seemed very close. The brother moved a little away from the cook and, half turning toward D'Arrast but without looking at him, pointed to the empty place and said: "Sit down with us."

Georges Simenon:

The Case of Dr. Ceccioni

A new solution for the classic murder puzzle
where the victim dies alone in a guarded house

I had never seen Joseph Leborgne at work and I was shocked by his appearance. His blond hair, usually brushed smooth, was in disorder. His face was pale and drawn, and he looked so ill-natured that my first thought was to apologize for interrupting him and leave.

"You came at a very bad time," he grumbled, his words bearing out his manner.

From the time he had accepted me as a friend, discussed with me his criminal investigations, he had always been most cordial. I was on the point of leaving when I noticed upon the table a plan that Leborgne evidently had been studying. During the moment that curiosity held me, his attitude changed.

"Do you know the quarter of the Red Cross in Lyon?" he began.

"I've passed through it."

"It's not the sort of place to linger long. The cottage shown in this plan is in one of the most deserted corners—where no part is touched by the illumination of the streets."

"What do those black crosses in the garden and upon the road mean?" I asked.

"Agents of police."

"Killed—all of them!"

He laughed harshly: "No, indeed. They were on watch during the night of the eighth and ninth of April. The cross that is heavier than the others represents Sergeant Manchard."

He stared at the plan with the same furious regard that he had previously turned on me.

"So you don't ask me why the agents were there to the number of six on that night?" he suggested.

"I'm hoping you'll tell me."

"The day before, the police received this note." He opened a folder and handed me the paper, which read:

Dr. Luigi Ceccioni will be assassinated in his

When Georges Simenon published this short mystery with us in 1935, and for many years to come, whodunits showed up with some regularity in Esquire. But it's been some while since we have published mysteries as such—perhaps because in drawing from the best of contemporary fiction we are confronting the reader with mystery enough.

domicile on the night of April 8th and 9th. (*signed*) *A Friend.*

"Was the doctor warned?"

"No. He was an Italian exile. It seemed probable it was a political affair. The police preferred to take precaution without informing him.

"He was a man of fifty, lived alone in this lamentable cottage, did his own housework, went out for his dinner every evening to a little restaurant in the quarter. On the eighth at seven o'clock he left his domicile as was his custom. Sergeant Manchard then searched the cottage, entering with a passkey the cellar, attic, closets, every conceivable place where an assassin might hide. Convinced that it was impossible to enter other than by the door, dismissing the fantastic theory of a hidden door or subterranean passage, Manchard posted his men, five of them, at each issue.

"At nine o'clock the silhouette of the doctor was profiled against the wall. He went into his house absolutely alone, did not appear to see the agents of police hidden in the shadows.

"Soon after a lamp on the second floor in his bedroom was lighted. Then the police watched. No one slept. No one left his post. No one lost view of the precise point that he was charged to watch. Sergeant Manchard made his rounds quietly and regularly every quarter of an hour.

"Toward three o'clock the lamp on the second floor commenced to go out slowly, as if it lacked oil. The sergeant hesitated. He decided to ring the bell. He did so. There was no answer. Then he entered with the passkey.

"He found the doctor slumped on the side of the bed, hands clutched over his chest, dead. He was completely dressed, still wore his overcoat. His hat had rolled to the floor. His shirt and clothes were soaked with blood and his hands were buried in it. There was a bullet hole about a centimeter above the heart."

I stared at Leborgne stupefied: "No one entered? No one came out?"

"No one. I speak as if I had mounted guard myself

because I know what a fine officer Sergeant Manchard is.

"Manchard found no revolver in the house, in the fireplace or sewer, in the garden or anywhere on the premises. In other words a shot had been fired in a place where there was no one but the dead man and no weapon was found. The windows were closed and had they been open the shot could not have been fired from the outside because of the limited range and the agents who were on watch."

"What is known of Ceccioni?" I asked.

"He was a rich man until he meddled in politics. He lived on vague subsidies that he received from political sympathizers. He has been trying to support a son who is in school in the Argentine."

"Was there anything stolen from the cottage?"

"No sign of theft."

I felt a sudden desire to laugh. It seemed as if some grim joker had prepared an unsolvable case to teach Joseph Leborgne modesty.

He must have seen my lips relax. He flung himself into his chair, angrily.

"When you've got the answer please tell me!"

"How can I if you can't?"

"Thanks," he said drily. "All I ask of you is to stay quiet and not breathe so heavily. I'm on track of something."

Ten minutes passed. I could think of nothing but the black crosses that marked the positions of the agents.

"Is there proof that his son is in the Argentine?" I asked timidly.

Leborgne shrugged, put down his cigarette and spat in the fireplace.

"It's utterly impossible!" I concluded, after a moment.

Leborgne left his chair, paced back and forth, stopped in front of the mirror and seemed shocked at the unkempt appearance of his hair.

He brushed it back with his palms and adjusted his tie.

"The truth is easy to find when preconceived ideas do not warp the judgment," he said. "You say it is impossible, and you are right. Let's admit there was no assassin in the cottage, no revolver."

"How, then—?"

"When Dr. Luigi Ceccioni entered the house alone the ball was already in his breast. No one has thought to search for the revolver hidden in some dark alley in the quarter.

"He was a physician, he knew anatomy, knew where to place the ball so that he could walk back to his house, mount the stairs, reach the bed. Once there he massaged around his heart to make the ball penetrate. I have here a report:

"*Autopsy reveals ecchymoses around the wound and traces of pressure of fingers.*

"We will find that he had taken out a life insurance for the benefit of his son, and he wished to die without suspicion of suicide."

A few days later Joseph Leborgne showed me a telegram that confirmed his theory.

"If someone else wants to reach the same conclusion that's all right," he said. "As for me I think it would be a shame for a man to suffer so much pain for nothing. The insurance company has a capital of four hundred millions!"

Vladimir Nabokov:

The Potato Elf

Others were allowed to use that sunny day but God gave it especially to Fred Dobson, a dwarf in mouse-colored spats

Actually his name was Frederic Dobson. To his friend the conjurer, he talked about himself thus:

"There was no one in Bristol who didn't know Dobson the tailor for children's clothes. I am his son—and am proud of it out of sheer stubbornness. You should know that he drank like an old whale. Sometime around 1900, a few months before I was born, my gin-soaked dad rigged up one of those waxwork cherubs, you know—sailor suit, with a lad's first long trousers—and put it in my mother's bed. It's a wonder the poor thing did not have a miscarriage. As you can well understand, I know all this only by hearsay—yet, if my kind informers were not liars, this is, apparently, the secret reason I am—"

And Fred Dobson, in a sad and good-natured gesture, would spread out his little hands. The conjurer, with his usual dreamy smile, would bend down, pick up Fred like a baby, and, sighing, place him on the top of a wardrobe, where the Potato Elf would meekly roll up and start to sneeze softly and whimper.

He was twenty, and weighed less than fifty pounds, being only a couple of inches taller than the famous Swiss dwarf, Zimmermann (dubbed "Prince Balthazar"). Like friend Zimmermann, Fred was extremely well built, and had there not been those wrinkles on his round forehead and at the corners of his narrowed eyes, as well as a rather eerie air of tension (as if he were resisting growth), our dwarf would have easily passed for a gentle eight-year-old boy. His hair, the hue of damp straw, was sleeked down and evenly parted by a line which ran up the exact middle of his head to conclude a cunning agreement with its crown. Fred walked lightly, had an easy demeanor, and danced rather well, but his very first manager deemed it wise to weight the notion of "elf" with a comic epi-

When Vladimir Nabokov first published this story in Esquire the year was 1939 and his signature read "Vladimir Sirin." The story has since been retranslated for this 1973 reprinting, and the by-line corresponds with that which is found on some of the most distinguished novels of the century.

thet upon noticing the fat nose inherited by the dwarf from his plethoric and naughty father.

The Potato Elf, by his sole aspect, aroused a storm of applause and laughter throughout England, and then in the main cities of the Continent. He differed from most dwarfs in being of a mild and friendly nature. He became greatly attached to the miniature pony Snowdrop on which he trotted diligently around the arena of a Dutch circus; and, in Vienna, he conquered the heart of a stupid and glum giant hailing from Omsk by stretching up to him the first time he saw him and pleading like an infant to be taken up in Nurse's arms.

He usually performed not alone. In Vienna, for example, he appeared with the Russian giant and minced around him, neatly attired in striped trousers and a smart jacket, with a voluminous roll of music under his arm. He brought the giant's guitar. The giant stood like a tremendous statue and took the instrument with the motions of an automaton. A long frock coat that looked carved out of ebony, elevated heels, and a top hat with a sheen of columnar reflections increased the height of the stately three hundred and fifty pound Siberian. Thrusting out his powerful jaw, he beat the strings with one finger. Backstage, in womanish tones, he complained of giddiness. Fred grew very fond of him and even shed a few tears at the moment of separation, for he rapidly became accustomed to people. His life, like a circus horse's, went round and round with smooth monotony. One day in the dark of the wings he tripped over a bucket of house paint and mellowly plopped into it— an occurrence he kept recalling for quite a long while as something out of the ordinary.

In this way the dwarf traveled around most of Europe, and saved money, and sang with a *castrato*-like silvery voice, and in German variety theatres the audience ate thick sandwiches and candied nuts on sticks, and in Spanish ones, sugared violets and also nuts on sticks. The world was invisible to him. There remained in his memory the same faceless abyss laughing at him, and afterward, when the performance was over, the soft, dreamy echo of a cool night that seems of such a deep blue when you leave the theatre.

Upon returning to London he found a new partner in the person of Shock, the conjurer. Shock had a tuneful delivery, slender, pale, virtually ethereal hands, and a lick of chestnut-brown hair that came down on one eyebrow. He resembled a poet more than a stage magician, and demonstrated his skill with a sort of tender and graceful melancholy, without the fussy patter characteristic of his profession. The Potato Elf assisted him amusingly, and, at the end of the act, would turn up in the gallery with a cooing exclamation of joy, although a minute before everyone had seen Shock lock him up in a black box right in the middle of the stage.

All this happened in one of those London theatres where there are acrobats soaring in the tinkle and shiver of the trapezes, and a foreign tenor (a failure in his own country) singing barcaroles, and a ventriloquist in naval uniform, and bicyclists, and the inevitable clown-eccentric shuffling about in a minuscule hat and a waistcoat coming down to his knees.

2

Latterly Fred had been growing gloomy, and sneezing a lot, soundlessly and sadly, like a little Japanese spaniel. While not experiencing for months any hankering after a woman, the virginal dwarf would be beset now and then by sharp pangs of lone amorous anguish which went as suddenly as they came, and again, for a while, he would ignore the bare shoulders showing white beyond the velvet boundary of loges, as well as the little girl acrobats, or the Spanish dancer whose sleek thighs were revealed for a moment when the orange-red curly fluff of her nether flounces would whip up in the course of a rapid swirl.

"What you need is a female dwarf," said pensively Shock, producing with a familiar flick of finger and thumb a silver coin from the ear of the dwarf whose little arm went up in a brushing-away curve as if chasing a fly.

That same night, as Fred, after his number, snuffling and grumbling in bowler and tiny topcoat, was toddling along a dim backstage passage, a door came ajar with a sudden splash of gay light and two voices called him in. It was Zita and Arabella, sister acrobats, both half-undressed, sun-tanned, black-haired, with elongated blue eyes. A shimmer of theatrical disorder and the fragrance of lotions filled the room. The dressing table was littered with powder puffs, combs, cut-glass atomizers, hairpins in an ex-chocolate box, and rouge sticks.

The two girls instantly deafened Fred with their chatter. They tickled and squeezed the dwarf, who, glowering, and empurpled with lust, rolled like a ball in the embrace of the bare-armed teases. Finally, when frolicsome Arabella drew him to her and fell backward upon the couch, Fred lost his head and began to wriggle against her, snorting and clasping her neck. In attempting to push him away, she raised her arm and, slipping under it, he lunged and glued his lips to the hot pricklish hollow of her shaven axilla. The

other girl, weak with laughter, tried in vain to drag him off by his legs. At that moment the door banged open, and the French partner of the two aerialists came into the room wearing marble-white tights. Silently, without any resentment, he grabbed the dwarf by the scruff of the neck (all you heard was the snap of Fred's wing collar as one side broke loose from the stud), lifted him in the air and threw him out like a monkey. The door slammed. Shock, who happened to be wandering past, managed to catch a glimpse of the marble-bright arm and of a black little figure with feet retracted in flight.

Fred hurt himself in falling and now lay motionless in the corridor. He was not really stunned, but had gone all limp with eyes fixed on one point, and fast chattering teeth.

"Bad luck, old boy," sighed the conjurer, picking him up from the floor. He palpated with translucent fingers the dwarf's round forehead and added, "I told you not to butt in. Now you got it. A dwarf woman is what you need."

Fred, his eyes bulging, said nothing.

"You'll sleep at my place tonight," decided Shock and carried the Potato Elf toward the exit.

3

There existed also a Mrs. Shock.

She was a lady of uncertain age, with dark eyes which had a yellowish tinge around the iris. Her skinny frame, parchment complexion, lifeless black hair, a habit of strongly exhaling tobacco smoke through her nostrils, the studied untidiness of her attire and hairdo —all this could hardly attract many men, but, no doubt, was to Mr. Shock's liking, though actually he never seemed to notice his wife, as he was always engaged in imagining secret devices for his show, always appeared unreal and shifty, thinking of something else when talking about trivialities, but keenly observing everything around him when immersed in astral fancies. Nora had to be constantly on the lookout since he never missed the occasion to contrive some small, inutile, yet subtly artful deception. There had been, for instance, that time when he amazed her by his unusual gluttony: he smacked his lips juicily, sucked chicken bones clean, again and again heaped up food on his plate; then he departed after giving his wife a sorrowful glance; and a little later the maid, giggling into her apron, informed Nora that Mr. Shock had not touched one scrap of his dinner, and had left all of it in three brand-new pans under the table.

She was the daughter of a respectable artist who painted only horses, spotty hounds, and huntsmen in pink coats. She had lived in Chelsea before her marriage, had admired the hazy Thames sunsets, taken drawing lessons, gone to ridiculous meetings attended by the local Bohemian crowd—and it was there that the ghost-grey eyes of a quiet slim man had singled her out. He talked little about himself, and was still unknown. Some people believed him to be a composer of lyrical poems. She fell headlong in love with him. The poet absentmindedly became engaged to her, and on the very first day of matrimony explained, with a sad smile, that he did not know how to write poetry, and there and then, in the middle of the conversation, he transformed an old alarm clock into a nickel-plated chronometer, and the chronometer into a miniature gold watch, which Nora had worn ever since on her wrist. She understood that nevertheless conjurer Shock was, in his own way, a poet; only she could not get used to his demonstrating his art every minute, in all circumstances. It is hard to be happy when one's husband is a mirage, a peripatetic leger-demain of a man, a deception of all five senses.

4

She was idly tapping a fingernail against the glass of a bowl in which several goldfish that looked cut out of orange peel breathed and fin-flashed when the door opened noiselessly, and Shock appeared (silk hat askew, strand of brown hair on his brow) with a little creature all screwed up in his arms.

"Brought him," said the conjurer with a sigh.

Nora thought fleetingly: Child. Lost. Found. Her dark eyes grew moist.

"Must be adopted," softly added Shock, lingering in the doorway.

The small thing suddenly came alive, mumbled something and started to scrabble shyly against the conjurer's starched shirtfront. Nora glanced at the tiny boots in chamois spats, at the little bowler.

"I'm not so easy to fool," she sneered.

The conjurer looked at her reproachfully. Then he laid Fred on a plush couch and covered him with a lap robe.

"Blondinet roughed him up," explained Shock, and could not help adding, "bashed him with a dumbbell. Right in the tummy."

And Nora, kindhearted as childless women frequently are, felt such an especial pity that she almost broke into tears. She proceeded to mother the dwarf, she fed him, gave him a glass of port, rubbed his forehead with eau de cologne, moistened with it his temples and the infantine hollows behind his ears.

Next morning Fred woke up early, inspected the unfamiliar room, talked to the goldfish, and after a quiet sneeze or two, settled on the ledge of the bay window like a little boy.

A melting, enchanting mist washed London's grey roofs. Somewhere in the distance an attic window was thrown open, and its pane caught a glint of sunshine. The horn of an automobile sang out in the freshness and tenderness of dawn.

Fred's thoughts dwelt on the previous day. The laughing accents of the girl tumblers got oddly mixed up with the touch of Mrs. Shock's cold fragrant hands. At first he had been ill-treated, then he had been caressed; and, mind you, he was a very affectionate, very ardent dwarf. He dwelt in fancy on the possibility of his rescuing Nora someday from a strong, brutal man resembling that Frenchman in white tights. Incongruously, there floated up the memory of a fifteen-year-old female dwarf with whom he appeared together at one time. She was a bad-tempered, sick, sharp-nosed little thing. The two were presented to the spectators as an engaged couple, and, shivering with disgust, he had to dance an intimate tango with her.

Again a lone klaxon sang out and swept by. Sunlight was beginning to infuse the mist over London's soft wilderness.

Around half-past seven the flat came to life. With an abstract smile Mr. Shock left for an unknown destination. From the dining room came the delicious smell of bacon and eggs. With her hair done anyhow, wearing a kimono embroidered with sunflowers, appeared Mrs. Shock.

After breakfast she offered Fred a perfumed cigarette with a red-petaled tip and half-closing her eyes had him tell her about his existence. At such narrative moments Fred's little voice deepened slightly: he spoke slowly, choosing his words, and, strange to say, that unforeseen dignity of diction became him. Bent-headed, solemn, and elastically tense, he sat sideways at Nora's feet. She reclined on the plush divan, her arms thrown back, revealing her sharp bare elbows. The dwarf, having finished his tale, lapsed into silence but still kept turning this way and that the palm of his tiny hand, as if softly continuing to speak. His black jacket, inclined face, fleshy little nose, tawny hair, and that middle parting reaching the back of his head vaguely moved Nora's heart. As she looked at him through her lashes she tried to imagine that it was not an adult dwarf sitting there, but her *non-existing* little son in the act of telling her how his schoolmates bullied him. Nora stretched her hand and stroked his head lightly—and, at that moment, by an enigmatic association of thought, she called forth something else, a curious, vindictive vision.

Upon feeling those light fingers in his hair, Fred at first sat motionless, then began to lick his lips in feverish silence. His eyes, turned askance, could not detach their gaze from the green pompon on Mrs. Shock's slipper. And all at once, in some absurd and intoxicating way, everything came into motion.

5

On that smoke-blue day, in the August sun, London was particularly lovely. The tender and festive sky was reflected in the smooth spread of the asphalt, the glossy pillar-boxes glowed crimson at the street corners, through the Gobelin green of the park cars flashed and rolled with a low hum—the entire city shimmered and breathed in the mellow warmth, and only underground, on the platforms of the Tube, could one find a region of coolness.

Every separate day in the year is a gift presented to only one man—the happiest one; all other people use his day, to enjoy the sunshine or berate the rain, never knowing, however, to whom that day really belongs; and its fortunate owner is pleased and amused by their ignorance. A person cannot foreknow which day exactly will fall to his lot, what trifle he will remember forever: the ripple of reflected sunlight on a wall bordering water or the revolving fall of a maple leaf; and it often happens that he recognizes *his* day only in retrospection, long after he has plucked, and crumpled, and chucked under his desk the calendar leaf with the forgotten figure.

Providence granted Fred Dobson, a dwarf in mouse-grey spats, the merry August day in 1920 which began with the melodious hoot of a motor horn and the flash of a casement swung open in the distance. Children coming back from a walk told their parents, with gasps of wonder, that they had met a dwarf in a bowler hat and striped trousers, with a cane in one hand and a pair of tan gloves in the other.

After ardently kissing Nora good-bye (she was expecting visitors), the Potato Elf came out on the broad smooth street, flooded with sunlight, and instantly knew that the whole city had been created for him and only for him. A cheerful taxi driver turned down with a resounding blow the iron flag of his meter; the street started to flow past, and Fred kept slipping off the leathern seat, while chuckling and cooing under his breath.

He got out at the Hyde Park entrance, and without noticing the looks of curiosity, minced along, by the green folding chairs, by the pond, by the great rhododendron bushes, darkling under the shelter of elms and lindens, above a turf as bright and bland as billiard cloth. Riders sped past, lightly going up and down on their saddles, the yellow leather of their leggings creaking, the slender faces of their steeds springing up, their bits clinking; and expensive black motorcars, with a dazzling glitter of wheel spokes, progressed sedately over the ample lacework of violet shade.

The dwarf walked, inhaling the warm whiffs of benzine, the smell of foliage that seemed to rot with the overabundance of green sap, and twirled his cane, and pursed his lips as if about to whistle, so great was the sense of liberation and lightness overwhelming him. His mistress had seen him off with such hurried tenderness, had laughed so nervously, that he realized how much she feared that her old father, who always came to lunch, would begin to suspect something if he found a strange gentleman in the house.

That day he was seen everywhere: in the park where a rosy nurse in a starched bonnet offered him for some reason a ride in the pram she was pushing; and in the halls of a great museum; and on the escalator that slowly crept out of rumbling depths where electric winds blew among brilliant posters; and in an elegant shop where only men's handkerchiefs were sold; and on the crest of a bus where he was hoisted by someone's kind hands.

And after a while he became tired—all that motion and glitter dazed him, the laughing eyes staring at him got on his nerves, and he felt he must ponder carefully the ample sensation of freedom, pride, and happiness which kept accompanying him.

When finally a hungry Fred entered the familiar restaurant where all kinds of performers gathered and where his presence could not surprise anyone, and when he looked around at those people, at the old dull clown who was already drunk, at the Frenchman, a former enemy, who now gave him a friendly nod, Mr. Dobson realized with perfect clarity that never again would he appear on the stage.

The place was darkish, with not enough lamps lit inside and not enough outside day filtering in. The dull clown resembling a ruined banker and the acrobat who looked oddly uncouth in mufti were playing a silent game of dominoes. The Spanish dancing girl,

wearing a cartwheel hat that cast a blue shadow on her eyes, sat with crossed legs all alone at a corner table. There were half a dozen people whom Fred did not know; he examined their features which years of makeup had bleached; meanwhile the waiter brought a cushion to prop him up, changed the tablecloth, nimbly laid the cover.

All at once, in the dim depths of the restaurant, Fred distinguished the delicate profile of the conjurer, who was talking in undertone to an obese old man of an American type. Fred had not expected to run here into Shock—who never frequented taverns—and in point of fact had totally forgotten about his existence. He now felt so sorry for the poor magician that, at first, he decided to conceal everything; but then it occurred to him that Nora could not cheat anyway and would probably tell her husband that very evening ("I've fallen in love with Mr. Dobson. . . . I'm leaving you")—and that she should be spared a difficult, disagreeable confession, for was he not her knight, did he not feel proud of her love, should he not, therefore, be justified in causing her husband pain, no matter the pity?

The waiter brought him a piece of kidney pie and a bottle of ginger beer. He also switched on more light. Here and there, above the dusty plush, crystal flowers glowed forth, and the dwarf saw from afar a golden gleam bring out the conjurer's chestnut forelock and the light and shade shuttle over his tender transparent fingers. His interlocutor rose, clawing at the belt of his pants and obsequiously grinning, and Shock accompanied him to the cloakroom. The fat American donned a wide-brimmed hat, shook Shock's ethereal hand, and, still hitching up his pants, made for the exit. Momentarily one discerned a chink of lingering daylight, while the restaurant lamps glowed yellower. The door closed with a thud.

"Shock!" called the Potato Elf, wiggling his short feet under the table.

Shock came over. On his way, he pensively took a lighted cigar out of his breast pocket, inhaled, let out a puff of smoke, and put the cigar back. Nobody knew how he did it.

"Shock," said the dwarf, whose nose had reddened from the ginger beer, "I must speak to you. It is most important."

The conjurer sat down at Fred's table and leaned his elbow upon it.

"How's your head—doesn't hurt?" he inquired indifferently.

Fred wiped his lips with the napkin; he did not know how to start, still fearing to cause his friend too much anguish.

"By the way," said Shock, "tonight I appear together with you for the last time. That chap is taking me to America. Things look pretty good."

"I say, Shock—" said the dwarf, crumbling bread, groped for adequate words. "The fact is. . . . Be brave, Shock. I love your wife. This morning, after you left, she and I, we two, I mean, she—"

"Only I'm a bad sailor," mused the conjurer, "and it's a week to Boston. I once sailed to India. Afterward I felt as a leg does when it goes to sleep."

Fred, flushing purple, rubbed the tablecloth with his tiny fist. The conjurer chuckled softly at his own thoughts, and then asked, "You were about to tell me something, my little friend?"

The dwarf looked into his ghostly eyes and shook his head in confusion.

"No, no, nothing. . . . One can't talk to you."

Shock's hand stretched out—no doubt he intended to snip out a coin from Fred's ear—but for the first time in years of masterly magic, the coin, not grasped by the palm muscles firmly enough, fell out the wrong way. He caught it up and rose.

"I'm not going to eat here," said he, examining curiously the crown of the dwarf's head. "I don't care for this place."

Sulky and silent, Fred was eating a baked apple.

The conjurer quietly left. The restaurant emptied. The languorous Spanish dancer in the large hat was led off by a shy, exquisitely dressed young man with blue eyes.

"Well, if he doesn't want to listen, that settles it," reflected the dwarf; he sighed with relief and decided that after all Nora would explain things better. Then he asked for notepaper and proceeded to write her a letter. It closed as follows:

Now you understand why I cannot continue to live as before. What feelings would you experience knowing that every evening the common herd rocks with laughter at the sight of your chosen one? I am breaking my contract, and tomorrow I shall be leaving. You will receive another letter from me as soon as I find a peaceful nook where after your divorce we shall be able to love one another, my Nora.

Thus ended the swift day given to a dwarf in mouse-colored spats.

6

London was cautiously darkling. Street sounds blended in a soft hollow note, as if someone had stopped playing but still kept his foot on the piano pedal. The black leaves of the limes in the park were patterned against the transparent sky like aces of spades. At this or that turning, or between the funereal silhouettes of twin towers, a burning sunset was revealed like a vision.

It was Shock's custom to go home for dinner and change into professional tails so as to drive afterward straight to the theatre. That evening Nora awaited him most impatiently, quivering with evil glee. How glad she was to have now her own private secret! The image of the dwarf himself she dismissed. The dwarf was a nasty little worm.

She heard the lock of the entrance door emit its delicate click. As so often happens when one has betrayed a person, Shock's face struck her as new, as almost that of a stranger. He gave her a nod, and shamefully, sadly lowered his long-lashed eyes. He took his place opposite her at the table without a word. Nora considered his light grey suit that made him seem still more slender, still more elusive. Her eyes lit up with warm triumph; one corner of her mouth twitched malevolently.

"How's your dwarf?" she inquired, relishing the casualness of her question. "I thought you'd bring him along."

"Haven't seen him today," answered Shock, beginning to eat. All at once he thought better of it—took out a vial, uncorked it with a careful squeak, and tipped it over a glassful of wine.

Nora expected with irritation that the wine would turn a bright blue, or become as translucent as water, but the claret did not change its hue. Shock caught his wife's glance and smiled dimly.

"For the digestion—just drops," he murmured. A shadow rippled across his face.

"Lying as usual," said Nora. "You've got an excellent stomach."

The conjurer laughed softly. Then he cleared his throat in a businesslike way, and drained his glass in one gulp.

"Get on with your food," said Nora. "It will be cold."

With grim pleasure she thought, "Ah, if you only knew. You'll never find out. That's my power!"

The conjurer ate in silence. Suddenly he made a grimace, pushed his plate away, and started to speak. As usual, he kept looking not directly at her, but a little above her, and his voice was melodious and soft. He described his day, telling her he had visited the King at Windsor where he had been invited to amuse the little dukes who wore velvet jackets and lace collars. He related all this with light vivid touches, mimicking the people he had seen, twinkling, cocking his head slightly.

"I produced a whole flock of white doves from my gibus," said Shock.

"And the dwarf's little palms were clammy, and you're making it all up," reflected Nora in brackets.

"Those pigeons, you know, went flying around the Queen. She shoo-flied them but kept smiling out of politeness."

Shock got up, swayed, lightly leaned on the table edge with two fingers, and said, as if completing his story:

"I'm not feeling well, Nora. That was poison I drank. You shouldn't have been unfaithful to me."

His throat swelled convulsively, and, pressing a handkerchief to his lips, he left the dining room. Nora sprang up; the amber beads of her long necklace caught at the fruit knife upon her plate and brushed it off.

"It's all an act," she thought bitterly. "Wants to scare me, to torment me. No, my good man, it's no use. You shall see!"

How vexing that Shock had somehow discovered her secret! But at least she would now have the opportunity to reveal all her feelings to him, to shout that she hated him, that she despised him furiously, that he was not a person, but a phantom of rubber, that she could not bear to live with him any longer, that—

The conjurer sat on the bed, all huddled up and gritting his teeth in anguish, but he managed a faint smile when Nora stormed into the bedroom.

"So you thought I'd believe you," she said, gasping. "Oh no, that's the end! I, too, know how to cheat. You repel me, oh, you're a laughingstock with your unsuccessful tricks—"

Shock, still smiling helplessly, attempted to get off the bed. His foot scraped against the carpet. Nora paused in an effort to think what else she could yell in the way of insult.

"Don't," uttered Shock with difficulty. "If there was something that I . . . please, forgive. . . ."

The vein in his forehead was tensed. He hunched up still more, his throat rattled, the moist lock on his brow shook, and the handkerchief at his mouth got all soaked with bile and blood.

"Stop playing the fool!" cried Nora and stamped her foot.

He managed to straighten up. His face was wax pale. He threw the balled rag into a corner.

"Wait, Nora. . . . You don't understand. . . . This is my very last trick. . . . I won't do any other. . . ."

Again a spasm distorted his terrible, shiny face. He staggered, fell on the bed, threw back his head on the pillow.

She came near, she looked, knitting her brows. Shock lay with closed eyes and his clenched teeth creaked. When she bent over him, his eyelids quivered, he glanced at her vaguely, not recognizing his wife, but suddenly he did recognize her and his eyes flickered with a humid light of tenderness and pain.

At that instant Nora knew that she loved him more than anything in the world. Horror and pity overwhelmed her. She whirled about the room, poured out some water, left the glass on the washstand, dashed back to her husband, who had raised his head and was pressing the edge of the sheet to his lips, his whole body shuddering as he retched heavily, staring with unseeing eyes which Death had already veiled. Then Nora with a wild gesture dashed into the next room, where there was a telephone, and there, for a long time, she joggled the holder, repeated the wrong number, rang again, sobbing for breath and hammering the telephone table with her fist; and finally when the doctor's voice responded, Nora cried that her husband had poisoned himself, that he was dying; upon which she flooded the receiver with a storm of tears, and cradling it crookedly, ran back into the bedroom.

The conjurer, bright-faced and sleek, in white waistcoat and impeccably pressed black trousers, stood before the pier glass and, elbows parted, was meticulously working upon his tie. He saw Nora in the mirror, and without turning gave her an absent-minded twinkle while whistling softly and continuing to knead with transparent fingertips the black ends of his silk bow.

7

Drowse, a tiny town in the north of England, looked, indeed, so somnolent that one suspected it might have been somehow mislaid among those misty, gentle-sloped fields where it had fallen asleep forever. It had a post office, a bicycle shop, two or three tobacconists with red and blue signs, an ancient grey church surrounded by tombstones over which stretched sleepily the shade of an enormous chestnut tree. The main street was lined with hedges, small gardens, and brick cottages diagonally girt with ivy. One of these had been rented to a certain F. R. Dobson whom nobody knew except his housekeeper and the local doctor, and he was no gossiper. Mr. Dobson, apparently, never went out. The housekeeper, a large stern woman who had formerly been employed in an insane asylum, would answer the casual questions of neighbors by explaining that Mr. Dobson was an aged paralytic, doomed to vegetate in curtained silence. No wonder the inhabitants forgot him the same year that he arrived in Drowse: he became an unnoticeable presence whom people took for granted as they did the unknown bishop whose stone effigy had been standing so long in its niche above the church portal. The mysterious old man was thought to have a grandchild—a quiet fair-haired little boy who sometimes, at dusk, used to come out of the Dobson cottage with small, timid steps. This happened, however, so seldom that nobody could say for sure that it was always the same child, and, of course, twilight at Drowse was particularly blurry and blue, softening every outline. Thus the uncurious and sluggish Drowsians missed the fact that the supposed grandson of the supposed paralytic did not grow as the years went by and that his flaxen hair was nothing but an admirably made wig; for the Potato Elf started to go bald at the very beginning of his new existence, and his head was soon so smooth and glossy that Ann, his housekeeper, thought at times what fun it would be to fit one's palm over that globe. Otherwise, he had not much changed: his tummy, perhaps, had grown plumper, and purple veins showed through on his dingier, fleshier nose which he powdered when dressed up as a little boy. Furthermore, Ann and his doctor knew that the heart attacks besetting the dwarf would come to no good.

He lived peacefully and inconspicuously in his three rooms, subscribed to a circulating library at the rate of three or four books (mostly novels) per week, acquired a black yellow-eyed cat because he mortally feared mice (which bumped about somewhere behind the wardrobe as if rolling minute bits of wood), ate a lot, especially sweetmeats (sometimes jumping up in the middle of the night and pattering along the chilly floor, eerily small and shivery in his long nightshirt, to get, like a little boy, at the chocolate-coated biscuits in the pantry), and recalled less and less frequently his love affair and the first dreadful days he had spent in Drowse.

Nevertheless, in his desk, among wispy, neatly folded playbills, he still preserved a sheet of peach-colored notepaper with a dragon-shaped watermark, scribbled over in an angular, barely legible hand. Here is what it said:

Dear Mr. Dobson

I received your first letter, as well as your second one, in which you ask me to come to D. All this, I am afraid, is an awful misunderstanding. Please try to forget and forgive me. Tomorrow my husband and I are leaving for the States and shall probably not be back for quite some time. I simply do not know what more I can write you, my poor Fred.

It was then that the first attack of angina pectoris occurred. A meek look of astonishment remained since then in his eyes. And during a number of days afterward he would walk from room to room, swallowing his tears and gesturing in front of his face with one trembling tiny hand.

Presently, though, Fred began to forget. He grew fond of the cosiness he had never known before—of the blue film of flame over the coals in the fireplace, of the dusty small vases on their own rounded small shelves, of the print between two casements: a St. Bernard dog, complete with barrelet, reviving a mountaineer on his bleak rock. Rarely did he recollect his past life. Only in dream did he sometimes see a starry sky come alive with the tremor of many trapezes while he was being clapped into a black trunk: through its walls he distinguished Shock's bland singsong voice but could not find the trap in the floor of the stage and suffocated in sticky darkness, while the conjurer's voice grew sadder and more remote and melted away, and Fred would wake up with a groan on his spacious bed, in his snug, dark room, with its faint fragrance of lavender, and would stare for a long time, gasping for breath and pressing his child's fist to his stumbling heart, at the pale blur of the window blind.

As the years passed, the yearning for a woman's love sighed in him fainter and fainter, as if Nora had drained him of all the ardor that had tormented him once. True, there were certain times, certain vague spring evenings, when the dwarf, having shyly put on short pants and the blond wig, left the house to plunge into crepuscular dimness, and there, stealing along some path in the fields, would suddenly stop as he looked with anguish at a dim pair of lovers locked in each other's arms near a hedge, under the protection of brambles in blossom. Presently that too passed, and he ceased seeing the world altogether. Only once in a while the doctor, a white-haired man with piercing black eyes, would come for a game of chess and, across the board, would consider with scientific delight those tiny soft hands, that little bulldoggish face, whose prominent brow would wrinkle as the dwarf pondered a move.

8

Eight years elapsed. It was Sunday morning. A jug of cocoa under a cosy in the guise of a parrot's head was awaiting Fred on the breakfast table. The sunny greenery of apple trees streamed through the window. Stout Ann was in the act of dusting the little pianola on which the dwarf occasionally played wobbly waltzes. Flies settled on the jar of orange marmalade and rubbed their front feet.

Fred came in, slightly sleep-rumpled, wearing carpet slippers and a little black dressing gown with yellow frogs. He sat down slitting his eyes and stroking his bald head. Ann left for church. Fred pulled open the illustrated section of a Sunday paper and, alternately drawing in and pouting his lips, examined at length prize pups, a Russian ballerina folding up in a swan's languishing agony, the top hat and mug of a financier who had bamboozled everyone.

. . . Under the table the cat, curving her back, rubbed herself against his bare ankle. He finished his breakfast; rose, yawning: he had had a very bad night, never yet had his heart caused him such pain, and now he felt too lazy to dress, although his feet were freezing. He transferred himself to the window-nook armchair and curled up in it. He sat there without a thought in his head, and near him the black cat stretched, opening tiny pink jaws.

The doorbell tinkled.

"Doctor Knight," reflected Fred indifferently, and remembering that Ann was out, went to open the door himself.

Sunlight poured in. A tall lady all in black stood on the threshold. Fred recoiled, muttering and fumbling at his dressing gown. He dashed back into the inner rooms, losing one slipper on the way but ignoring it, his only concern being that whoever had come must not notice he was a dwarf. He stopped, panting, in the middle of the parlor. Oh, why hadn't he simply slammed shut the entrance door! And who on earth could be calling on him? A mistake, no doubt.

And then he heard distinctly the sound of approaching steps. He retreated to the bedroom; wanted to lock himself up, but there was no key. The second slipper remained on the rug in the parlor.

"This is dreadful," said Fred under his breath and listened.

The steps had entered the parlor. The dwarf emitted a little moan and made for the wardrobe, looking for a hiding place.

A voice that he certainly knew pronounced his name, and the door of the room opened:

"Fred, why are you afraid of me?"

The dwarf, barefooted, black-robed, his pate beaded with sweat, stood by the wardrobe, still holding on to the ring of its lock. He recalled with the utmost clarity the orange-gold fish in their glass bowl.

She had aged unhealthily. There were olive-brown shadows under her eyes. The little dark hairs above her upper lip had become more distinct than before; and from her black hat, from the severe folds of her black dress, there wafted something dusty and woeful.

"I never expected—" Fred slowly began, looking up at her warily.

Nora took him by the shoulders, turned him to the light, and with eager, sad eyes examined his features. The embarrassed dwarf blinked, deploring his wiglessness and marveling at Nora's excitement. He had ceased thinking of her so long ago that now he felt nothing except sadness and surprise. Nora, still holding him, shut her eyes, and then, lightly pushing the dwarf away, turned toward the window.

Fred cleared his throat and said:

"I lost sight of you entirely. Tell me, how's Shock?"

"Still performing his tricks," replied Nora absently. "We returned to England only a short while ago."

Without removing her hat she sat down near the window and kept staring at him with odd intensity.

"It means that Shock—" hastily resumed the dwarf, feeling uneasy under her gaze.

"—Is the same as ever," said Nora, and, still not taking her glistening eyes from the dwarf, quickly peeled off and crumpled her glossy black gloves which were white inside.

"Can it be that she again—?" abruptly wondered the dwarf. There rushed through his mind the fish bowl, the smell of eau de cologne, the green pompons on her slippers.

Nora got up. The black balls of her gloves rolled on the floor.

"It's not a big garden but it has apple trees," said Fred, and continued to wonder inwardly: had there really been a moment when I—? Her skin is quite sallow. She has a moustache. And why is she so silent?

"I seldom go out, though," said he, rocking slightly back and forth in his seat and massaging his knees.

"Fred, do you know why I'm here?" asked Nora.

She rose and came up to him quite close. Fred with an apologetic grin tried to escape by slipping off his chair.

It was then that she told him in a very soft voice: "The fact is I had a son from you."

The dwarf froze, his gaze fixing a minuscule casement burning on the side of a dark blue cup. A timid smile of amazement flashed at the corners of his lips, then it spread, and lit up his cheeks with a purplish flush.

"My . . . son. . . ."

And all at once he understood everything, all the meaning of life, of his long anguish, of the little bright window upon the cup.

He slowly raised his eyes. Nora sat sideways on a chair and was shaking with violent sobs. The glass head of her hatpin glittered like a teardrop. The cat, purring tenderly, rubbed itself against her legs.

He dashed up to her, he remembered a novel read a short while ago: "You have no cause," said Mr. Dobson, "no cause whatever for fearing that I may take him away from you. I am so happy!"

She glanced at him through a mist of tears. She was about to explain something, but gulped—saw the tender and joyful radiance with which the dwarf's countenance breathed—and explained nothing.

She hastened to pick up her crumpled gloves.

"Well, now you know. Nothing more is necessary. I must be going."

A sudden thought stabbed Fred. Acute shame joined the quivering joy. He inquired, fingering the tassel of his dressing gown.

"And . . . and what is he like? He is not—"

"Oh, on the contrary," replied Nora rapidly. "A big boy, like all boys." And again she burst into tears.

Fred lowered his eyes.

"I would like to see him."

Joyously he corrected himself: "Oh, I understand! He must not know that I am like this. But perhaps you might arrange—"

"Yes, by all means," said Nora, hurriedly, and almost sharply, as she stepped through the hall. "Yes, we'll arrange something. I must be on my way. It's a twenty-minute walk to the station."

She turned her head in the doorway and for the last time, avidly and mournfully, she examined Fred's features. Sunlight trembled on his bald head, his ears were of a translucent pink. He understood nothing in his amazement and bliss. And after she had gone, Fred remained standing for a long time in the hallway, as if afraid to spill his full heart with an imprudent movement. He kept trying to imagine his son, and all he could do was to imagine his own self dressed as a schoolboy and wearing a little blond wig. And by the act of transferring his own aspect onto his boy, he ceased to feel that he was a dwarf.

He saw himself entering a house, a hotel, a restaurant, to meet his son. In fancy, he stroked the boy's fair hair with poignant parental pride. . . . And then, with his son and Nora (silly goose—to fear he would snatch him away!) he saw himself walking down a street, and there—

Fred clapped his thighs. He had forgotten to ask Nora where and how he could reach her!

Here commenced a crazy, absurd sort of phase. He rushed to his bedroom, began to dress in a wild hurry. He put on the best things he had, an expensive starched shirt, practically new, striped trousers, a jacket made by Resartre of Paris years ago—and as he dressed, he kept chuckling, and breaking his fingernails in the chinks of tight commode drawers, and had to sit down once or twice to let his swelling and knocking heart rest; and again he went skipping about the room looking for the bowler he had not worn for years, and at last, on consulting a mirror in passing, he glimpsed the image of a stately elderly gentleman, in smart formal dress, and ran down the steps of the porch, dazzled by a new idea: to travel back with Nora—whom he would certainly manage to overtake—and to see his son that very evening!

A broad dusty road led straight to the station. It was more or less deserted on Sundays—but unexpectedly a boy with a cricket bat appeared at a corner. He was the first to notice the dwarf. In gleeful surprise he slapped himself on the top of his bright-colored cap as he watched Fred's receding back and the flicking of his mouse-grey spats.

And instantly, from God knows where, more boys appeared, and with gaping stealthiness started to follow the dwarf. He walked faster and faster, now and then looking at his watch, and chuckling excitedly. The sun made him feel a little queasy. Meanwhile, the number of boys increased, and chance passersby stopped to look in wonder. Somewhere afar church chimes rang forth: the drowsy town was coming to life—and all of a sudden it burst into uncontrollable, long-restrained laughter.

The Potato Elf, unable to master his eagerness, switched to a jog. One of the lads darted in front of him to have a look at his face; another yelled something in a rude hoarse voice. Fred, grimacing because of the dust, ran on, and abruptly it seemed to him that all those boys crowding in his wake were his sons, merry, rosy, well-built sons—and he smiled a bewildered smile as he trotted along, puffing and trying to forget the heart breaking his chest with a burning ram.

A cyclist, riding beside the dwarf on glittering

wheels, pressed his fist to his mouth like a megaphone and urged the sprinter along as they do at a race. Women came out on their porches and, shading their eyes and laughing loudly, pointed out the running dwarf to one another. All the dogs of the town woke up. The parishioners in the stuffy church could not help listening to the barking, to the inciting halloos. And the crowd that kept up with the dwarf continued to grow around him. People thought it was all a capital stunt, circus publicity, or the shooting of a picture.

Fred was beginning to stumble, there was a singing in his ears, the front stud of his collar dug into his throat, he could not breathe. Moans of mirth, shouts, the tramping of feet deafened him. Then through the fog of sweat he saw at last her black dress. She was slowly walking along a brick wall in a torrent of sun. She looked back, she stopped. The dwarf reached her and clutched at the folds of her skirt.

With a smile of happiness he glanced up at her, attempted to speak, but instead raised his eyebrows in surprise and collapsed in slow motion on the sidewalk. All around people noisily swarmed. Someone, realizing that this was no joke, bent over the dwarf, then whistled softly and bared his head. Nora looked listlessly at Fred's tiny body resembling a crumpled black glove. She was jostled. A hand grasped her elbow.

"Leave me alone," said Nora in a toneless voice. "I don't know anything. My son died a few days ago."

Translated by Dmitri Nabokov in collaboration with the author.

Truman Capote:

Breakfast at Tiffany's

Whenever Holly Golightly left a man—as she did often—
she left him bewildered;
for although she was a girl of small character
she had a lot of personality

I am always drawn back to places where I have lived, the houses and their neighborhoods. For instance, there is a brownstone in the East Seventies where, during the early years of the war, I had my first New York apartment. It was one room crowded with attic furniture, a sofa and fat chairs upholstered in that itchy, particular red velvet that one associates with hot days on a train. The walls were stucco, and a color rather like tobacco spit. Everywhere, in the bathroom too, there were prints of Roman ruins freckled brown with age. The single window looked out on a fire escape. Even so, my spirits heightened whenever I felt in my pocket the key to this apartment; with all its gloom, it still was a place of my own, the first, and my books were there, and jars of pencils to sharpen, everything I needed, so I felt, to become the writer I wanted to be.

It never occurred to me in those days to write about Holly Golightly, and probably it would not now except for a conversation I had with Joe Bell that set the whole memory of her in motion again.

Holly Golightly had been a tenant in the old brownstone; she'd occupied the apartment below mine. As for Joe Bell, he ran a bar around the corner on Lexington Avenue; he still does. Both Holly and I used to go there six, seven times a day, not for a drink, not always, but to make telephone calls: during the war a private telephone was hard to come by. Moreover, Joe Bell was good about taking messages, which in Holly's case was no small favor for she had a tremendous many.

Of course this was a long time ago, and until last week I hadn't seen Joe Bell in several years. Off and on we'd kept in touch, and occasionally I'd stopped

When Breakfast at Tiffany's *showed up in the November, 1958, issue, it achieved the record for long-distance fiction in* Esquire, *and may still hold it though we have long since stopped counting, for record length, anyhow. Meanwhile, Truman Capote has gone on to extend other possibilities: notably, the novel as journalism and the social event as art.*

by his bar when passing through the neighborhood; but actually we'd never been strong friends except inasmuch as we were both friends of Holly Golightly. Joe Bell hasn't an easy nature, he admits it himself; he says it's because he's a bachelor and has a sour stomach. Anyone who knows him will tell him he's a hard man to talk to; impossible if you don't share his fixations, of which Holly is one. Some others are: ice hockey, Weimaraner dogs, Our Gal Sunday (a soap serial he has listened to for fifteen years), and Gilbert and Sullivan—he claims to be related to one or the other, I can't remember which.

And so when, late last Tuesday afternoon, the telephone rang and I heard, "Joe Bell here," I knew it must be about Holly. He didn't say so, just: "Can you rattle right over here? It's important." And there was a croak of excitement in his froggy voice.

I took a taxi in a downpour of October rain, and on my way I even thought she might be there, that I would see Holly again.

But there was no one on the premises except the proprietor. Joe Bell's is a quiet place compared to most Lexington Avenue bars. It boasts neither neon nor television. Two old mirrors reflect the weather from the streets; and behind the bar is a niche surrounded by photographs of ice-hockey stars; there is always a large bowl of fresh flowers that Joe Bell himself arranges with matronly care. That is what he was doing when I came in.

"Naturally," he said, rooting a gladiola deep into the bowl, "naturally I wouldn't have got you over here if it wasn't I wanted your opinion. It's peculiar. A very peculiar thing has happened."

"You heard from Holly?"

He fingered a leaf, as though uncertain of how to answer. A small man with a fine head of coarse white hair, he has a bony, sloping face better suited to someone far taller; his complexion seems permanently sunburned: now it grew even redder. "I can't say exactly

I heard from her. I mean, I don't know. That's why I want your opinion. Let me build you a drink. Something new. They call it a White Angel," he said, mixing one-half vodka, one-half gin, no vermouth. While I drank the result, Joe Bell stood sucking on a Tums and turning over in his mind what he had to tell me. Then: "You recall a certain Mr. I. Y. Yunioshi? A gentleman from Japan." "From California," I said, recalling Mr. Yunioshi perfectly. He's a photographer on one of the picture magazines, and when I knew him he lived in the studio apartment on the top floor of the brownstone.

"Don't go mixing me up. All I'm asking, you know who I mean? Okay. So last night who comes waltzing in here but this selfsame Mr. I. Y. Yunioshi. I haven't seen him, I guess it's over two years. And where do you think he's been those two years?"

"Africa."

Joe Bell stopped crunching on his Tums; his eyes narrowed. "Yeah? So how did you know?"

"Read it in the Winchell." Which I had, as a matter of fact.

He rang open his cash register, and produced a manila envelope. "Well, see did you read this in Winchell."

In the envelope were three photographs, more or less the same, though taken from different angles: a tall delicate Negro man wearing a calico shirt and with a shy, yet vain smile, displaying in his hands an odd wood sculpture, an elongated carving of a head, a girl's, her hair sleek and short as a young man's, her smooth wood eyes too large and tilted in the tapering face, her mouth wide, overdrawn, not unlike clown lips. On a glance it resembled most primitive carving; and then it didn't, for here was the spit-image of Holly Golightly, at least as much of a likeness as a dark still thing could be.

"Now what do you make of that?" said Joe Bell, satisfied with my puzzlement.

"It looks like her."

"Listen, boy," and he slapped his hand on the bar, "it *is* her. Sure as I'm a man fit to wear britches. The little Jap knew it was her the minute he saw her."

"He saw her? In Africa?"

"Well. Just the statue there. But it comes to the same thing. Read the facts for yourself," he said, turning over one of the photographs. On the reverse was written: Wood Carving, S Tribe, Tococul, East Anglia, Christmas Day, 1956.

He said, "Here's what the Jap says," and the story was this: on Christmas day Mr. Yunioshi had passed with his camera through Tococul, a village in the tangles of nowhere and of no interest, merely a congregation of mud huts with monkeys in the yards and buzzards on the roofs.

He'd decided to move on when he saw suddenly a Negro squatting in a doorway carving monkeys on a walking stick. Mr. Yunioshi was impressed and asked to see more of his work. Whereupon he was shown the carving of the girl's head: and felt, so he told Joe Bell, as if he were falling in a dream. But when he offered to buy it the Negro cupped his private parts in his hand (apparently a tender gesture, comparable to tapping one's heart) and said no. A pound of salt and ten dollars, a wrist watch and two pounds of salt and twenty dollars, nothing swayed him. Mr. Yunioshi was in all events determined to learn how the carving came to be made. It cost him his salt and his watch, and the incident was conveyed in African and pidgin-English and finger talk. But it would seem that in the spring of that year a party of three white persons had appeared out of the brush riding horseback. A young woman and two men. The men, both red-eyed with fever, were forced for several weeks to stay shut and shivering in an isolated hut, while the young woman, having presently taken a fancy to the wood-carver, shared the wood-carver's mat.

"I don't credit that part," Joe Bell said squeamishly. "I know she had her ways, but I don't think she'd be up to anything as much as that."

"And then?"

"Then nothing." He shrugged. "Bye and bye she went like she come, rode away on a horse."

"Alone, or with the two men?"

Joe Bell blinked. "With the two men, I guess. Now the Jap, he asked about her up and down the country. But nobody else had ever seen her." Then it was as if he could feel my own sense of letdown transmitting itself to him, and he wanted no part of it. "One thing you got to admit, it's the only *definite* news in I don't know how many (he counted on his fingers: there weren't enough) years. All I hope, I hope she's rich. She must be rich. You got to be rich to go mucking around in Africa."

"She's probably never set foot in Africa," I said, believing it; yet I could see her there, it was somewhere she would have gone. And the carved head: I looked at the photographs again.

"You know so much, where is she?"

"Dead. Or in a crazy house. Or married. I think she's married and quieted down and maybe right in this very city."

He considered a moment. "No," he said, and shook his head. "I'll tell you why. If she was in this city I'd have seen her. You take a man that likes to walk, a man like me, a man's been walking in the streets going on ten or twelve years, and all those years he's got his eye out for one person, and nobody's ever her, don't it stand to reason she's not there? I see pieces of her all the time, a flat little bottom, any skinny girl that walks fast and straight—" He paused, as though too aware of how intently I was looking at him: "You think I'm round the bend?"

"It's just that I didn't know you'd been in love with her. Not like that."

I was sorry I'd said it; it disconcerted him. He scooped up the photographs and put them back in their envelope. I looked at my watch. I hadn't any place to go, but I thought it was better to leave.

"Hold on," he said, gripping my wrist. "Sure I loved her. But it wasn't that I wanted to touch her." And he added, without smiling: "Not that I don't think about that side of things. Even at my age, and I'll be sixty-seven January ten. It's a peculiar fact—but, the older I grow, that side of things seems to be on my mind more and more. I don't remember think-

ing about it so much even when I was a youngster and it's every other minute. Maybe the older you grow and the less easy it is to put thought into action, maybe that's why it gets all locked up in your head and becomes a burden. Whenever I read in the paper about an old man disgracing himself, I know it's because of this burden. But," he poured himself a jigger of whiskey neat, "I'll never disgrace myself. And I swear, it never crossed my mind about Holly. You can love somebody without it being like that. You keep them a stranger, a stranger who's a friend."

Two men came into the bar, and it seemed the moment to leave. Joe Bell followed me to the door. He caught my wrist again. "Do you believe it?"

"That you didn't want to touch her?"

"I mean about Africa."

At that moment I couldn't seem to remember the story, only the image of her riding away on a horse. "Anyway, she's gone."

"Yeah," he said, opening the door. "Just gone."

Outside the rain had stopped, there was only a mist of it in the air, so I turned the corner and walked along the street where the brownstone stands. It is a street with trees that in the summer make cool patterns on the pavement; but now the leaves are yellowed and mostly down, and the rain had made them slippery, they skidded underfoot. The brownstone is midway in the block, next to a church where a blue tower-clock tolls the hours. It has been sleeked up since my day; a smart black door has replaced the old frosted glass, and grey elegant shutters frame the windows. No one I remember still lives there except Madame Sapphia Spanella, a husky coloratura who every afternoon went roller-skating in Central Park. I know she's still there because I went up the steps and looked at the mailboxes. It was one of these mailboxes that had first made me aware of Holly Golightly.

I'd been living in the house about a week when I noticed that the mailbox belonging to Apt. 2 had a name-slot fitted with a curious card. Printed rather Cartier-formal, it read: *Miss Holiday Golightly*; and, underneath, in the corner, *Traveling*. It nagged me like a tune: *Miss Holiday Golightly, Traveling*.

One night, it was long past twelve, I woke up at the sound of Mr. Yunioshi calling down the stairs. Since he lived on the top floor, his voice fell through the whole house, exasperated and stern. "Miss Golightly! I must protest!"

The voice that came back, welling up from the bottom of the stairs, was silly-young and self-amused. "Oh, darling, I *am* sorry. I lost the goddam key."

"You cannot go on ringing my bell. You must, please, please, have yourself a key made."

"But I lose them all."

"I work, I have to sleep," Mr. Yunioshi shouted. "But always you are ringing my bell. . . ."

"Oh *don't* be angry, you *dear* little man: I *won't*

do it again. And if you promise not to be angry," her voice was coming nearer, she was climbing the stairs, "I might let you take those pictures we mentioned."

By now I'd left my bed and opened the door an inch. I could hear Mr. Yunioshi's silence: hear, because it was accompanied by an audible change of breath.

"When?" he said.

The girl laughed. "Sometime," she said, slurring the word.

"Any time," he said, and closed his door.

I went out into the hall and leaned over the banister, just enough to see without being seen. She was still on the stairs, now she reached the landing, and the ragbag colors of her boy's hair, tawny streaks, strands of albino blonde and yellow, caught the hall light. It was a warm evening, nearly summer, and she wore a slim, cool, black dress, black sandals, a pearl choker. For all her chic thinness, she had an almost breakfast-cereal air of health, a soap-and-lemon cleanness, a rough pink darkening in the cheeks. Her mouth was large, her nose upturned. A pair of dark glasses blotted out her eyes. It was a face beyond childhood, yet this side of belonging to a woman. I thought her anywhere between sixteen and thirty; as it turned out, she was shy two months of her nineteenth birthday.

She was not alone. There was a man following behind her. The way his plump hand clutched at her hip seemed somehow improper; not morally, aesthetically. He was short and vast, sun-lamped and pomaded, a man in a buttressed pin-stripe suit with a red carnation withering in the lapel.

When they reached her door she rummaged her purse in search of a key, and took no notice of the fact that his thick lips were nuzzling the nape of her neck. At last, though, finding the key and opening her door, she turned to him cordially: "Bless you, darling—you were sweet to see me home."

"Hey, baby!" he said, for the door was closing in his face.

"Yes, Harry?"

"Harry was the other guy. I'm Sid. Sid Arbuck. You like me."

"I worship you, Mr. Arbuck. But good night, Mr. Arbuck."

Mr. Arbuck stared with disbelief as the door shut firmly. "Hey, baby, let me in, baby. You like me, baby. I'm a liked guy. Didn't I pick up the check, five people, *your* friends, I never seen them before? Don't that give me the right you should like me? You like me, baby."

He tapped on the door gently, then louder; finally he took several steps back, his body hunching and lowering, as though he meant to charge it, crash it down. Instead, he plunged down the stairs, slamming a fist against the wall. Just as he reached the bottom, the door of the girl's apartment opened and she poked out her head.

"Oh, Mr. Arbuck. . . ."

He turned back, a smile of relief oiling his face: she'd only been teasing.

"The next time a girl wants a little powder-room change," she called, not teasing at all, "take my advice, darling: *don't* give her twenty cents!"

She kept her promise to Mr. Yunioshi; or I assume she did not ring his bell again, for in the next days she started ringing mine, sometimes at two in the morning, three and four: she had no qualms at what hour she got me out of bed to push the buzzer that released the downstairs door. As I had few friends, and none who would come around so late, I always knew that it was she. But on the first occasion of its happening, I went to my door, half-expecting bad news, a telegram; and Miss Golightly called up: "Sorry, darling—I forgot my key."

Of course we'd never met. Though actually, on the stairs, in the street, we often came face-to-face; but she seemed not quite to see me. She was never without dark glasses, she was always well-groomed, there was a consequential good taste in the plainness of her clothes, the blues and greys and lack of luster that made her, herself, shine so. One might have thought her a photographer's model, perhaps a young actress, except that it was obvious, judging from her hours, she hadn't time to be either.

Now and then I ran across her outside our neighborhood. Once a visiting relative took me to "21," and there, at a superior table, surrounded by four men, none of them Mr. Arbuck, yet all of them interchangeable with him, was Miss Golightly, idly, publicly combing her hair; and her expression, an unrealized yawn, put, by example, a dampener on the excitement I felt over dining at so swanky a place. Another night, deep in the summer, the heat of my room sent me out into the streets. I walked down Third Avenue to Fifty-first Street where there was an antique store with an object in its window I admired: a palace of a bird cage, a mosque of minarets and bamboo rooms yearning to be filled with talkative parrots. But the price was three hundred and fifty dollars. On the way home I noticed a cab-driver crowd gathered in front of P. J. Clarke's saloon, apparently attracted there by a happy group of whiskey-eyed Australian army officers baritoning *Waltzing Matilda*. As they sang they took turns spin-dancing a girl over the cobbles under the El; and the girl, Miss Golightly, to be sure, floated round in their arms light as a scarf.

But if Miss Golightly remained unconscious of my existence, except as a doorbell convenience, I became, through the summer, rather an authority on hers. I discovered, from observing the trash basket outside her door, that her regular reading consisted of tabloids and travel folders and astrological charts; that she smoked an esoteric cigarette called Picayunes; survived on cottage cheese and melba toast; that her varicolored hair was somewhat self-induced. The same source made it evident that she received V-letters by the bale. They were always torn into strips like bookmarks. I used occasionally to pluck myself a bookmark in passing. *Remember* and *miss you* and *rain* and *please write* and *damn* and *goddam* were the words that recurred most often on these slips; those, and *lonesome* and *love*.

Also, she had a cat and she played the guitar. On days when the sun was strong, she would wash her hair and, together with the cat, a red tiger-striped tom, sit on the fire escape thumbing a guitar while her hair dried. Whenever I heard the music, I would go stand quietly by my window. She played very well, and sometimes sang too. Sang in the hoarse breaking tones of a boy's adolescent voice. She knew all the show hits, Cole Porter and Kurt Weill; especially she liked the songs from *Oklahoma!* which were new that summer, and everywhere. But there were moments when she played songs that made you wonder where she learned them, where indeed she came from. Harsh-tender wandering tunes with words that smacked of piny woods or prairie. One went: *Don't wanna sleep, Don't wanna die, Just wanna go a-travelin' through the pastures of the sky*; and this one seemed to gratify her the most, for often she continued it long after her hair had dried, after the sun had gone and there were lighted windows in the dusk.

But our acquaintance did not make headway until September, an evening with the first ripple-chills of autumn running through it. I'd been to a movie, come home and gone to bed with a bourbon nightcap and the newest Simenon: so much my idea of comfort that I couldn't understand a sense of unease that multiplied until I could hear my heart beating. It was a feeling I'd read about, written about, but never before experienced. The feeling of being watched. Of someone in the room. Then: an abrupt rapping at the window, a glimpse of ghostly grey. I spilled the bourbon. It was some little while before I could bring myself to open the window, and ask Miss Golightly what she wanted.

"I've got the most terrifying man downstairs," she said, stepping off the fire escape into the room. "I mean he's sweet when he isn't drunk, but let him start lapping up the *vino* and oh God *quel* beast! If there's one thing I loathe, it's men who bite." She loosened a grey flannel robe off her shoulder to show me evidence of what happens if a man bites. The robe was all she was wearing. "I'm sorry if I frightened you. But when the beast got so tiresome I just went out the window. I think he thinks I'm in the bathroom, not that I give a damn what he thinks, the hell with him, he'll get tired, he'll go to sleep, my God, he should, eight Martinis before dinner and enough wine to wash an elephant. Listen, you can throw me out if you want to. I've got a gall barging in on you like this. But that fire escape was damned icy. And you looked so cozy. Like my brother Fred. We used to sleep four in a bed, and he was the only one that ever let me hug him on a cold night. By the way, do you mind if I call you Fred?" She'd come completely into the room now, and she paused there, staring at me. I'd never seen her before not wearing dark glasses, and it was obvious now that they were prescription lenses, for without them her eyes had an assessing squint, like a jeweler's. They were large eyes, a little blue, a little green, dotted with bits of brown: varicolored, like her hair; and, like her hair, they gave out a lively warm light. "I suppose you think I'm very brazen. Or *très fou*. Or something."

"Not at all."

She seemed disappointed. "Yes, you do. Everybody does. I don't mind. It's useful."

She sat down on one of the rickety red-velvet chairs, curved her legs underneath her and glanced round the room, her eyes puckering more pronouncedly. "How can you bear it? It's a chamber of horrors."

"Oh, you get used to anything," I said, annoyed with myself, for actually I was proud of the place.

"I don't. I'll never get used to anything. Anybody that does, they might as well be dead." Her dispraising eyes surveyed the room again. "What do you *do* here all day?"

I motioned toward a table tall with books and papers. "Write things."

"I thought writers were quite old. Of course Saroyan isn't old. I met him at a party, and really he isn't old at all. In fact," she mused, "if he'd give himself a closer shave . . . by the way, is Hemingway old?"

"In his forties, I should think."

"That's not bad. I can't get excited by a man until he's forty-two. I know this idiot girl who keeps telling me I ought to go to a headshrinker; she says I have a father complex. Which is so much *merde*. I simply *trained* myself to like older men, and it was the smartest thing I ever did. How old is W. Somerset Maugham?"

"I'm not sure. Sixty-something."

"That's not bad. I've never been to bed with a writer. No, wait: do you know Benny Shacklett?" She frowned when I shook my head. "That's funny. He's written an awful lot of radio stuff. But *quel* rat. Tell me, are you a real writer?"

"It depends on what you mean by real."

"Well, darling, does anyone *buy* what you write?"

"Not yet."

"I'm going to help you," she said. "I can, too. Think of all the people I know who know people. I'm going to help you because you look like my brother Fred. Only smaller. I haven't seen him since I was fourteen, that's when I left home, and he was already six-feet-two. My other brothers were more your size, runts. It was the peanut butter that made Fred so tall. Everybody thought it was dotty, the way he gorged himself on peanut butter; he didn't care about anything in this world except horses and peanut butter. But he wasn't dotty, just sweet and vague and terribly slow; he'd been in the eighth grade three years when I ran away. Poor Fred. I wonder if the Army's generous with their peanut butter. Which reminds me, I'm starving."

I pointed to a bowl of apples, at the same time asked her how and why she'd left home so young. She looked at me blankly, and rubbed her nose, as though it tickled: a gesture, seeing it often repeated, I came to recognize as a signal that one was trespassing. Like many people with a bold fondness for volunteering intimate information, anything that suggested a direct question, a pinning-down, put her on guard. She took a bite of apple, and said: "Tell me something you've written. The story part."

"That's one of the troubles. They're not the kind of stories you *can* tell."

"Too dirty?"

"Maybe I'll let you read one sometime."

"Whiskey and apples go together. Fix me a drink,

darling. Then you can read me a story yourself."

Very few authors, especially the unpublished, can resist an invitation to read aloud. I made us both a drink and, settling in a chair opposite, began to read to her, my voice a little shaky with a combination of stage fright and enthusiasm: it was a new story, I'd finished it the day before, and that inevitable sense of shortcoming had not had time to develop. It was about two women who share a house, schoolteachers, one of whom, when the other becomes engaged, spreads with anonymous notes a scandal that prevents the marriage. As I read, each glimpse I stole of Holly made my heart contract. She fidgeted. She picked apart the butts in an ash tray, she mooned over her fingernails, as though longing for a file; worse, when I did seem to have her interest, there was actually a telltale frost over her eyes, as if she were wondering whether to buy a pair of shoes she'd seen in some window.

"Is that the *end*?" she asked, waking up. She floundered for something more to say. "Of course I like dykes themselves. They don't scare me a bit. But stories about dykes bore the bejesus out of me. I just can't put myself in their shoes. Well, really, darling," she said, because I was clearly puzzled, "if it's not about a couple of old bull-dykes, what the hell *is* it about?"

But I was in no mood to compound the mistake of having read the story with the further embarrassment of explaining it. The same vanity that had led to such exposure, now forced me to mark her down as an insensitive, mindless show-off.

"Incidentally," she said, "do you happen to *know* any nice Lesbians? I'm looking for a roommate. Well, don't laugh. I'm so disorganized, I simply can't afford a maid; and really, dykes are wonderful homemakers. They love to do all the work; you never have to bother about brooms and defrosting and sending out the laundry. I had a roommate in Hollywood, she played in Westerns, they called her the Lone Ranger; but I'll say this for her, she was better than a man around the house. Of course, people couldn't help but think I must be a bit of a dyke myself. And of course I am. Everyone is: a bit. So what? That never discouraged a man yet; in fact it seems to goad them on. Look at the Lone Ranger, married twice. Usually dykes only get married once, just for the name. It seems to carry such cachet later on to be called Mrs. Something Another. That's not true!" She was staring at an alarm clock on the table. "It can't be four-thirty!"

The window was turning blue. A sunrise breeze bandied the curtains.

"What is today?"

"Thursday."

"*Thursday*." She stood up. "My God," she said, and sat down again with a moan. "It's too gruesome."

I was tired enough not to be curious. I lay down on the bed and closed my eyes. Still it was irresistible: "What's gruesome about Thursday?"

"Nothing. Except that I can never remember when it's coming. You see, on Thursdays I have to catch the eight forty-five. They're so particular about visiting hours, so if you're there by ten that gives you an hour before the poor men eat lunch. Think of it, lunch at eleven. You *can* go at two, and I'd so much rather, but he likes me to come in the morning, he says it sets him up for the rest of the day. I've *got* to stay awake," she said, pinching her cheeks until the roses came; "there isn't time to sleep. I'd look consumptive, I'd sag like a tenement, and that wouldn't be fair; a girl can't go to Sing Sing with a green face."

"I suppose not." The anger I felt at her over my story was ebbing; she absorbed me again.

"All the visitors *do* make an effort to look their best, and it's very tender, it's sweet as hell, the way the women wear their prettiest everything. I mean the old ones and the really poor ones too, they make the dearest effort to look nice and smell nice, too, and I love them for it. I love the kids too, especially the colored ones. I mean the kids the wives bring. It should be sad, seeing the kids there, but it isn't, they have ribbons in their hair and lots of shine on their shoes, you'd think there was going to be ice cream; and sometimes that's what it's like in the visitors' room, a party. Anyway it's not like the movies: you know, grim whisperings through a grill. There isn't any grill, just a counter between you and them, and the kids can stand on it to be hugged; all you have to do to kiss somebody is lean across. What I like most, they're so happy to see each other, they've saved up so much to talk about, it isn't possible to be dull; they keep laughing and holding hands. It's different afterwards," she said; "I see them on the train. They sit so quiet watching the river go by." She stretched a strand of hair to the corner of her mouth and nibbled it thoughtfully. "I'm keeping you awake. Go to sleep."

"Please. I'm interested."

"I know you are. That's why I want you to go to sleep. Because if I keep on, I'll tell you about Sally. I'm not sure that would be quite cricket." She chewed her hair silently. "They never *told* me not to tell anyone. In so many words. And it *is* funny. Maybe you could put it in a story with different names and whatnot. Listen, Fred," she said, reaching for another apple, "you've got to cross your heart and kiss your elbow—"

Perhaps contortionists can kiss their elbows; she had to accept an approximation.

"Well," she said, with a mouthful of apple, "you may have read about him in the papers. His name is Sally Tomato, and I speak Yiddish better than he speaks English; but he's a darling old man, terribly pious. He'd look like a monk if it weren't for the gold teeth; he says he prays for me every night. Of course he was never my lover; as far as that goes, I never knew him until he was already in jail. But I adore him now; after all, I've been going to see him every Thursday for seven months, and I think I'd go even if he didn't pay me. This one's a mushy," she said, and aimed the rest of the apple out the window. "By the way, I *did* know Sally by sight. He used to come to Joe Bell's bar, the one around the corner: never talked to anybody, just stand there, like the kind of man who lives in hotel rooms. But it's funny to remember back and realize how closely he must have been watching me, because right after they sent him up (Joe Bell showed me his picture in the paper. Black-

hand. Mafia. All that mumbo jumbo: but they gave him five years) along came this telegram from a lawyer. It said to contact him immediately for information to my advantage."

"You thought somebody had left you a million?"

"Not at all. I figured Bergdorf was trying to collect. But I took the gamble and went to see this lawyer (if he *is* a lawyer, which I doubt, since he doesn't seem to have an office, just an answering service, and he always wants to meet you in Hamburg Heaven: that's because he's fat, he can eat ten hamburgers and two bowls of relish and a whole lemon meringue pie). He asked me how I'd like to cheer up a lonely old man, at the same time pick up a hundred a week. I told him look, darling, you've got the wrong Miss Golightly, I'm not a nurse that does tricks on the side. I wasn't impressed by the honorarium either: you can do as well as that on trips to the powder room: any gent with the slightest chic will give you fifty for the girl's john, and I always ask for cab fare too, that's another fifty. But then he told me his client was Sally Tomato; he said dear old Sally had long admired me à la distance, so wouldn't it be a good deed if I went to visit him once a week. Well, I couldn't say no: it was too romantic."

"I don't know. It doesn't sound right."

She smiled. "You think I'm lying?"

"For one thing, they can't simply let *any*one visit a prisoner."

"Oh, they don't. In fact they make quite a boring fuss. I'm supposed to be his niece."

"And it's as simple as that? For an hour's conversation he gives you a hundred dollars?"

"He doesn't, the lawyer does. Mr. O'Shaughnessy mails it to me in cash as soon as I leave the weather report."

"I think you could get into a lot of trouble," I said, and switched off a lamp; there was no need of it now, morning was in the room and pigeons were gargling on the fire escape.

"How?" she said seriously.

"There must be something in the lawbooks about false identity. After all, you're *not* his niece. And what about this weather report?"

She patted a yawn. "But it's nothing. Just messages I leave with the answering service so Mr. O'Shaughnessy will know for sure that I've been up there. Sally tells me what to say, things like, oh, 'There's a hurricane in Cuba' and 'It's snowing in Palermo.' Don't worry, darling," she said, moving to the bed, "I've taken care of myself a long time." The morning light seemed refracted through her: as she pulled the bedcovers up to my chin she gleamed like a transparent child; then she lay down beside me. "Do you mind? I only want to rest a moment. So let's don't say another word. Go to sleep."

I pretended to, I made my breathing heavy and regular. Bells in the tower of the next-door church rang the half-hour, the hour. It was six when she put her hand on my arm, a fragile touch careful not to waken. "Poor Fred," she whispered, and it seemed she was speaking to me, but she was not. "Where are you, Fred? Because it's cold. There's snow in the wind." Her cheek came to rest against my shoulder, a warm, damp weight.

"Why are you crying?"

She sprang back, sat up. "Oh, for God's sake," she said, starting for the window and the fire escape, "I *hate* snoops."

T he next day, Friday, I came home to find outside my door a grand-luxe Chârles & Co. basket with her card: *Holiday Golightly, Traveling*; and scribbled on the back in a freakishly awkward, kindergarten hand: *Bless you darling, Fred. Please forgive the other night. You were an angel about the whole thing. Mille tendresse—Holly. P.S. I won't bother you again.* I replied, *Please do*, and left this note at her door with what I could afford, a bunch of street-vendor violets. But apparently she'd meant what she said; I neither saw nor heard from her, and I gathered she'd gone so far as to obtain a downstairs key. At any rate she no longer rang my bell. I missed that; and as the days merged I began to feel toward her certain far-fetched resentments, as if I were being neglected by my closest friend. A disquieting loneliness came into my life, but it induced no hunger for friends of longer acquaintance: they seemed now like a salt-free, sugar-less diet. By Wednesday thoughts of Holly, of Sing Sing and Sally Tomato, of worlds where men forked over fifty dollars for the powder room, were so constant that I couldn't work. That night I left a message in her mailbox: *Tomorrow is Thursday.* The next morning rewarded me with a second note in the playpen script: *Bless you for reminding me. Can you stop for a drink tonight 6-ish?*

I waited until ten past six, then made myself delay five minutes more.

A creature answered the door. He smelled of cigars and Knize cologne. His shoes sported elevated heels; without these added inches, one might have taken him for a Little Person. His bald, freckled head was dwarf-big: attached to it were a pair of pointed, truly elfin ears. He had Pekingese eyes, unpitying and slightly bulged. Tufts of hair sprouted from his ears, from his nose; his jowls were grey with afternoon beard, and his handshake almost furry.

"Kid's in the shower," he said, motioning a cigar toward a sound of water hissing in another room. The room in which we stood (we were standing be-cause there was nothing to sit on) seemed as though it were being just moved into; you expected to smell wet paint. Suitcases and unpacked crates were the only furniture. The crates served as tables. One sup-ported the mixings of a Martini; another a lamp, a Libertyphone, Holly's red cat and a bowl of yellow roses. Bookcases, covering one wall, boasted a half-shelf of literature. I warmed to the room at once; I liked its fly-by-night look.

The man cleared his throat. "You expected?"

He found my nod uncertain. His cold eyes operated on me, made neat, exploratory incisions. "A lot of characters come here, they're not expected. You know the kid long?"

"I live upstairs."

The answer seemed to explain enough to relax him. "You got the same layout?"

"Much smaller."

He tapped ash on the floor. "This is a dump. This is unbelievable. But the kid don't know how to live even when she's got the dough." His speech had a jerky metallic rhythm, like a teletype. "So," he said, "what do you think, is she ain't she?"

"Ain't she what?"

"A phony."

"I wouldn't have thought so."

"You're wrong. She is a phony. But on the other hand you're right. She isn't a phony because she's a real phony. She believes all this crap she believes. You can't talk her out of it. I've tried with tears run-ning down my cheeks. Benny Polan, respected every-where, Benny Polan tried. Benny had it on his mind to marry her, she don't go for it, Benny spent maybe thousands sending her to headshrinkers. Even the famous one, the one can speak only German, boy did he throw in the towel. You can't talk her out of these—" he made a fist, as though to crush an in-tangible— "ideas. Try it sometime. Get her to tell you some of the stuff she believes. Mind you," he said, "I like the kid. Everybody does, but there's lots that don't. I do. I sincerely like the kid. I'm sensitive, that's why. You've got to be sensitive to appreciate her: a streak of the poet. But I'll tell you the truth. You can beat your brains out for her, and she'll hand you the stuff on a platter. To give an example—who is she like you see her today? She's strictly a girl you'll read where she ends up at the bottom of a bottle of Seconals. I've seen it happen more times than you've got toes: and those kids, they weren't even nuts. She's nuts."

"But young. And with a great deal of youth ahead of her."

"If you mean future, you're wrong again. Now a couple of years back, out on the coast, there was a time it could've been different. She had something working for her, she had them interested, she could've really rolled. But when you walk out on a thing like that, you don't walk back. Ask Luise Rainer. And Rainer was a star. Sure, Holly was no star; she never got out of the still-department. But that was before *The Story of Dr. Wassell*. Then she could've really rolled. I know, see, 'cause I'm the guy was giving her the push." He pointed his cigar at himself. "O. J. Berman."

He expected recognition, and I didn't mind obliging him, it was all right by me, except I'd never heard of O. J. Berman. It developed that he was a Hollywood actor's agent.

"I'm the first one saw her. Out at Santa Anita. She's hanging around the track every day. I'm interested professionally. I find out she's some jock's regular, she's living with the shrimp. I get the jock told Drop It if he don't want conversation with the vice-boys: see, the kid's fifteen. But stylish: she's okay, she comes across. Even when she's wearing glasses *this* thick; even when she opens her mouth and you don't know if she's a hillbilly or an Okie or what. I still don't. My guess, nobody'll ever know where she came from. She's such a goddam liar, maybe she don't know herself any more. But it took us a year to smooth out that accent. How we did it finally, we gave her French lessons: after she could imitate French, it wasn't so long she could imitate English. We modeled her along the Margaret Sullavan type, but she could pitch some curves of her own, people were interested, big ones, and to top it all Benny Polan, a respected guy, Benny wants to marry her. An agent could ask for more? Then wham! *The Story of Dr. Wassell.* You see that picture? Cecil B. De Mille. Gary Cooper. Jesus. I kill myself, it's all set: they're going to test her for the part of Dr. Wassell's nurse. One of his nurses, anyway. Then wham! The phone rings." He picked a telephone out of the air and held it to his ear. "She says, this is Holly, I say honey you sound far away, she says I'm in New York, I say what the hell are you doing in New York when it's Sunday and you got the test tomorrow? She says I'm in New York 'cause I've never been to New York. I say get your ass on a plane and get back here, she says, I don't want it, I say what's your angle, doll? She says you got to want it to be good and I don't want it, I say well what the hell do you want, and she says when I find out you'll be the first to know. See what I mean: the stuff on a platter."

The red cat jumped off its crate and rubbed against his leg. He lifted the cat on the toe of his shoe and gave him a toss, which was hateful of him except he seemed not aware of the cat but merely his own irritableness.

"*This* is what she wants?" he said, flinging out his arms. "A lot of characters they aren't expected? Living off tips. Running around with bums. So maybe she could marry Rusty Trawler? You should pin a medal on her for that?"

He waited, glaring.

"Sorry, I don't know him."

"You don't know Rusty Trawler, you can't know much about the kid. Bad deal," he said, his tongue clucking in his huge head. "I was hoping you maybe had influence. Could level with the kid before it's too late."

"But according to you, it already is."

He blew a smoke ring, let it fade before he smiled; the smile altered his face, made something gentle happen. "I could get it rolling again. Like I told you," he said, and now it sounded true, "I sincerely like the kid."

"What scandals are you spreading, O.J.?" Holly splashed into the room, a towel more or less wrapped round her and her wet feet dripping footmarks on the floor.

"Just the usual. That you're nuts."

"Fred knows that already."

"But you don't."

"Light me a cigarette, darling," she said, snatching off a bathing cap and shaking her hair. "I don't mean you, O.J. You're such a slob. You always lip."

She scooped up the cat and swung him onto her

shoulder. He perched there with the balance of a bird, his paws tangled in her hair as if it were knitting yarn; and yet, despite these amiable antics, it was a grim cat with a pirate's cutthroat face; one eye was gluey-blind, the other sparkled with dark-deeds.

"O.J. is a slob," she told me, taking the cigarette I'd lighted. "But he does know a terrific lot of phone numbers. What's David O. Selznick's number, O.J.?"

"Lay off."

"It's not a joke, darling. I want you to call him up and tell him what a genius Fred is. He's written barrels of the most marvelous stories. Well, don't blush, Fred: you didn't say you were a genius, I did. Come on, O.J. What are you going to do to make Fred rich?"

"Suppose you let me settle that with Fred."

"Remember," she said, leaving us, "I'm his agent. Another thing: if I holler, come zipper me up. And if anybody knocks, let them in."

A multitude did. Within the next quarter-hour a stag party had taken over the apartment, several of them in uniform. I counted two Naval officers and an Air Force colonel; but they were outnumbered by greying arrivals beyond draft status. Except for a lack of youth, the guests had no common theme, they seemed strangers among strangers; indeed each face on entering had struggled to conceal dismay at seeing others there. It was as if the hostess had distributed her invitations while zigzagging through various bars, which was probably the case. After the initial frowns, however, they mixed without grumbling, especially O. J. Berman, who avidly exploited the new company to avoid discussing my Hollywood future. I was left abandoned by the bookshelves; of the books there, more than half were about horses, the rest baseball. Pretending an interest in *Horseflesh and How to Tell It* gave me sufficiently private opportunity for sizing Holly's friends.

Presently one of these became prominent. He was a middle-aged child who had never shed its baby fat, though some gifted tailor had almost succeeded in camouflaging his plump and spankable bottom. There wasn't a suspicion of bone in his body; his face, a zero filled in with pretty miniature features, had an unused, a virginal quality: it was as if he'd been born, then expanded, his skin remaining unlined as a blown-up balloon, and his mouth, though ready for squalls and tantrums, a spoiled sweet puckering. But it was not appearance that singled him out: preserved infants aren't all that rare. It was, rather, his conduct; for he was behaving as though the party were his: like an energetic octopus, he was shaking Martinis, making introductions, manipulating the phonograph. In fairness, most of his activities were dictated by the hostess herself: *Rusty, would you mind; Rusty, would you please.* If he was in love with her, then clearly he had his jealousy in check. A jealous man might have lost control, watching her as she skimmed around the room, carrying her cat in one hand but leaving the other free to straighten a tie or remove lapel lint; the Air Force colonel wore a medal that came in for quite a polish.

The man's name was Rutherford ("Rusty") Trawler. In 1908 he'd lost both his parents, his father the victim of an anarchist and his mother of shock, which double misfortune had made Rusty an orphan, a millionaire and a celebrity, all at the age of five. He'd been a stand-by of the Sunday supplements ever since, a consequence that had gathered hurricane momentum when, still a schoolboy, he had caused his godfather-custodian to be arrested on charges of sodomy. After that, marriage and divorce sustained his place in the tabloid-sun. His first wife had taken herself, and her alimony, to a rival of Father Divine's. The second wife seems unaccounted for, but the third had sued him in New York State with a full satchel of the kind of testimony that entails. He himself divorced the last Mrs. Trawler, his principal complaint stating that she'd started a mutiny aboard his yacht, said mutiny resulting in his being deposited on the Dry Tortugas. Though he'd been a bachelor since, apparently before the war he'd proposed to that famous British lady Fascist, at least he was supposed to have sent her a cable offering to marry her if Hitler didn't. This was said to be the reason Winchell always referred to him as a Nazi; that, and the fact that he attended rallies in Yorkville.

I was not told these things. I read them in *The Baseball Guide*, another selection off Holly's shelf which she seemed to use for a scrapbook. Tucked between the pages were Sunday features, together with scissored snippings from gossip columns: *Rusty Trawler and Holly Golightly two-on-the-aisle at One Touch of Venus preem*. Holly came up from behind, and caught me reading: *Miss Holiday Golightly of the Boston Golightlys making every day a holiday for 24-carat Rusty Trawler.*

"Admiring my publicity, or are you just a baseball fan?" she said, adjusting her dark glasses as she glanced over my shoulder.

I said, "What was this week's weather report?"

She winked at me, but it was humorless: a wink of warning. "I'm all for horses, but I loathe baseball," she said, and the sub-message in her voice was saying she wished me to forget she'd ever mentioned Sally Tomato. "I hate the sound of it on a radio, but I have to listen, it's part of my research. There're so few things men can talk about. If a man doesn't like baseball, then he must like horses, and if he doesn't like either of them, well I'm in trouble anyway: he don't like girls. And how are you making out with O.J.?"

"We've separated by mutual agreement."

"He's an opportunity, believe me."

"I do believe you. But what have I to offer that would strike him as an opportunity?"

She persisted. "Go over there and make him think he isn't funny-looking. He really can help you, Fred."

"I understand you weren't too appreciative." She seemed puzzled until I said: *"The Story of Dr. Wassell."*

"He's still harping?" she said, and cast an affectionate look across the room at Berman. "But he's got a point, I *should* feel guilty. Not because they would have given me the part or because I would have been good: they wouldn't and I wouldn't. If I do feel guilty, I guess it's because I let him go on dreaming when I wasn't dreaming a bit. I was just vamping for time to make a few self-improvements: I knew damn well I'd never be a movie star. It's too hard; and if you're intelligent, it's too embarrassing. My complexes aren't inferior enough: being a movie star and having a big fat ego are supposed to go hand-in-hand; actually, it's essential not to have any ego at all. I don't mean I'd mind being rich and famous. That's very much on my schedule, and someday I'll try to get around to it; but if it happens, I'd like to have my ego tagging along. I want to still be me when I wake up one fine morning and have breakfast at Tiffany's. You need a glass," she said, noticing my empty hands. "Rusty! will you bring my friend a drink?"

She was still hugging the cat. "Poor slob," she said, tickling his head, "poor slob without a name. It's a little inconvenient, his not having a name. But I haven't any right to give him one: he'll have to wait until he *belongs* to somebody. We just sort of took up by the river one day, we don't belong to each other: he's an independent, and so am I. I don't want to own anything until I know I've found the place where me and things belong together. I'm not quite sure where that is just yet. But I know what it's like." She smiled, and let the cat drop to the floor. "It's like Tiffany's," she said. "Not that I give a hoot about jewelry. Diamonds, yes. But it's tacky to wear diamonds before you're forty; and even that's risky. They only look right on the really old girls. Maria Ouspenskaya. Wrinkles and bones, white hair and diamonds: I can't wait. But that's not why I'm mad about Tiffany's. Listen. You know those days when you've got the mean reds?"

"Same as the blues?"

"No," she said slowly. "No, the blues are because you're getting fat or maybe it's been raining too long. You're sad, that's all. But the mean reds are horrible. You're afraid and you sweat like hell, but you don't know what you're afraid of. Except something bad is going to happen only you don't know what it is. You've had that feeling?"

"Quite often. Some people call it angst."

"All right. Angst. But what do you do about it?"

"Well, a drink helps."

"I've tried that. I've tried aspirin, too. Rusty thinks I should smoke marijuana, and I did for a while, but it only makes me giggle. What I've found does the most good is just to get into a taxi and go to Tiffany's. It calms me down right away, the quietness and the proud look of it; nothing very bad could happen to you there, not with those kind men in their nice suits, and that lovely smell of silver and alligator wallets. If I could find a real-life place that made me feel like Tiffany's then I'd buy some furniture and give the cat a name. I've thought maybe after the war, Fred and I—" She pushed up her dark glasses, and her eyes, the differing colors of them, the greys and wisps of blue and green, had taken on a far-seeing sharpness. "I went to Mexico once. It's wonderful country for raising horses. I saw one place near the sea. Fred's good with horses."

Rusty Trawler came carrying a Martini; he handed it over without looking at me. "I'm hungry," he announced, and his voice, retarded as the rest of him, produced an unnerving bratwhine that seemed to blame Holly. "It's seven-thirty, and I'm hungry. You know what the doctor said."

"Yes, Rusty. I know what the doctor said."

"Well, then break it up. Let's go."

"I want you to behave, Rusty." She spoke softly, but there was a governess threat of punishment in her tone that caused an odd flush of pleasure, of gratitude, to pink his face.

"You don't love me," he complained, as though they were alone.

"Nobody loves naughtiness."

Obviously she'd said what he wanted to hear; it appeared to both excite and relax him. Still he continued, as though it were a ritual: "Do you love me?"

She patted him. "Tend to your chores, Rusty. And when I'm ready, we'll go eat wherever you want."

"Chinatown?"

"But that doesn't mean sweet-and-sour spareribs. You know what the doctor said."

As he returned to his duties with a satisfied waddle, I couldn't resist reminding her that she hadn't answered his question. "*Do* you love him?"

"I told you: you can make yourself love anybody. Besides, he had a stinking childhood."

"If it was so stinking, why does he cling to it?"

"Use your head. Can't you see it's just that Rusty feels safer in diapers than he would in a skirt? Which is really the choice, only he's awfully touchy about it. He tried to stab me with a butter knife because I told him to grow up and face the issue, settle down and play house with a nice fatherly truck driver. Meantime, I've got him on my hands; which is okay, he's harmless, he thinks girls are dolls literally."

"Thank God."

"Well, if it were true of most men, I'd hardly be thanking God."

"I meant thank God you're not going to marry Mr. Trawler."

She lifted an eyebrow. "By the way, I'm not pretending I don't know he's rich. Even land in Mexico costs something. Now," she said motioning me forward, "let's get hold of O.J."

I held back while my mind worked to win a postponement. Then I remembered: "Why *Traveling*?"

"On my card?" she said, disconcerted. "You think it's funny?"

"Not funny. Just provocative."

She shrugged. "After all, how do I know where I'll be living tomorrow? So I told them to put *Traveling*. Anyway, it was a waste of money, ordering those cards. Except I felt I owed it to them to buy some little *something*. They're from Tiffany's." She reached for my Martini, I hadn't touched it; she drained it in two swallows, and took my hand. "Quit stalling. You're going to make friends with O.J."

An occurrence at the door intervened. It was a young woman, and she entered like a wind rush, a squall of scarves and jangling gold. "H-H-Holly," she said, wagging a finger as she advanced, "you miserable h-h-hoarder. Hogging all these simply r-r-riveting m-m-men!"

She was well over six feet, taller than most men there. They straightened their spines, sucked in their stomachs; there was a general contest to match her swaying height.

Holly said, "What are you doing here?" and her lips were taut as drawn string.

"Why n-n-nothing, sugar. I've been upstairs working with Yunioshi. Christmas stuff for the *Ba-bazaar*. But you sound vexed, sugar?" She scattered a roundabout smile. "You b-b-boys not vexed at me for butting in on your p-p-party?"

Rusty Trawler tittered. He squeezed her arm, as though to admire her muscle, and asked her if she could use a drink.

"I surely could," she said. "Make mine b-b-bourbon."

Holly told her, "There *isn't* any." Whereupon the Air Force colonel suggested he run out for a bottle.

"Oh, I declare, don't let's have a f-f-fuss. I'm happy with ammonia. Holly, honey," she said, slightly shoving her, "don't you bother about me. I can introduce myself." She stooped toward O.J. Berman who, like many short men in the presence of tall women, had an aspiring mist in his eye. "I'm Mag W-W-Wildwood, from Wild-w-w-wood, Arkansas. That's hill country."

It seemed a dance, Berman performing some fancy footwork to prevent his rivals cutting in. He lost her to a quadrille of partners who gobbled up her stammered jokes like popcorn tossed to pigeons. It was a comprehensible success. She was a triumph over ugliness, so often more beguiling than real beauty, if only because it contains paradox. In this case, as opposed to the scrupulous method of plain good taste and scientific grooming, the trick had been worked by exaggerating defects: she'd made them ornamental by admitting them boldly. Heels that emphasized her height, so steep her ankles trembled; a flat tight bodice that indicated she could go to a beach in bathing trunks; hair that was pulled straight back, accentuating the spareness, the starvation of her fashion-model face. Even the stutter, certainly genuine but still a bit laid on, had been turned to advantage. It was the master stroke, that stutter; for it contrived to make her banalities sound somehow original, and secondly, despite her tallness, her assurance, it served to inspire in male listeners a protective feeling. To illustrate: Berman had to be pounded on the back because she said, "Who can tell me w-w-where is the j-j-john?"; then, completing the cycle, he offered an arm to guide her himself.

"That," said Holly, "won't be necessary. She's been here before. She knows where it is." She was emptying ashtrays, and after Mag Wildwood had left the room, she emptied another, then said, sighed rather: "It's really very sad." She paused long enough to calculate the number of inquiring expressions; it was sufficient. "And so mysterious. You'd think it would show more. But heaven knows, she *looks* healthy. So, well, clean. That's the extraordinary part. Wouldn't you," she asked with concern, but of no one in particular, "wouldn't you say she *looked* clean?"

Someone coughed, several swallowed. A Naval officer, who had been holding Mag Wildwood's drink, put it down.

"But then," said Holly, "I hear so many of these Southern girls have the same trouble." She shuddered delicately, and went to the kitchen for more ice.

Mag Wildwood couldn't understand it, the abrupt absence of warmth on her return; the conversations she began behaved like green logs, they fumed but would not fire. More unforgivably, people were leaving without taking her telephone number. The Air Force colonel decamped while her back was turned, and this was the straw too much: he'd asked her to dinner. Suddenly, she was blind. And since gin to artifice bears the same relation as tears to mascara, her attractions at once dissembled. She took it out on everyone. She called her hostess a Hollywood degenerate. She invited a man in his fifties to fight. She told Berman Hitler was right. She exhilarated Rusty Trawler by stiff-arming him into a corner: "You know what's going to happen to you?" she said, with no hint of a stutter, "I'm going to march you over to the zoo and feed you to the yak." He looked altogether willing, but she disappointed him by sliding to the floor where she sat picking her nose and humming.

"You're a bore. Get up from there," Holly said, stretching on a pair of gloves. The remnants of the party were waiting at the door, and when the bore didn't budge Holly cast me an apologetic glance. "Be an angel, would you? Put her in a taxi. You *are* an angel, Fred."

They were gone. The prospect of steering an Amazon into a taxi obliterated whatever resentment I felt. But she solved the problem herself. Rising on her own steam, she stared down at me with a lurching loftiness. She said, "Let's go Stork. Catch lucky balloon," and fell full-length, like an axed oak. My first thought was to run for a doctor. But examination proved her pulse fine and her breathing regular. She was simply asleep. After finding a pillow for her head, I left her to enjoy it.

The following afternoon I collided with Holly on the stairs. "*You*," she said, hurrying past with a package from the druggist. "There she is, on the verge of pneumonia. A hangover out to here. And the mean reds on top of it." I gathered from this that Mag Wildwood was still in the apartment, but Holly gave me no chance to explore her surprising sympathy.

Over the weekend, mystery deepened. First, there was the Latin who came to my door: mistakenly, for he was inquiring after Miss Wildwood. It took a while to correct his error, our accents seemed mutually incoherent, but by the time we had I was charmed. He'd

been put together with care, his brown head and bull-fighter's figure had an exactness, a perfection, like an apple, an orange, something nature has made just right. Added to this, as decoration, were an English suit and a brisk cologne and, what is still more un-Latin, a bashful manner. The second event of the day involved him again. It was toward evening, and I saw him on my way out to dinner. He was arriving in a taxi; the driver helped him totter into the house with a load of suitcases. That gave me something to chew on: by Sunday my jaws were quite tired.

Then the picture became both darker and clearer.

Sunday was an Indian-summer day, the sun was strong, my window was open, and I heard voices on the fire escape. Holly and Mag were sprawled there on a blanket, the cat between them. Their hair, newly washed, hung lankly. They were busy, Holly varnishing her toenails, Mag knitting on a sweater. Mag was speaking.

"If you ask me, I think you're l-l-lucky. At least there's one thing you can say for Rusty. He's an American."

"Bully for him."

"*Sugar.* There's a war on."

"And when it's over, you've seen the last of me, boy."

"I don't feel that way. I'm p-p-proud of my country. The men in my family were great soldiers. There's a statue of Papadaddy Wildwood smack in the center of Wildwood."

"Fred's a soldier," said Holly. "But I doubt if he'll ever be a statue. Could be. They say the more stupid you are the braver. He's pretty stupid."

"Fred's that boy upstairs? I didn't realize he was a soldier. But he *does* look stupid."

"Yearning. Not stupid. He wants awfully to be on the inside staring out: anybody with their nose pressed against a glass is liable to look stupid. Anyhow, he's a different Fred. Fred's my brother."

"You call your own f-f-flesh and b-b-blood stupid?"

"If he is he is."

"Well, it's poor taste to say so. A boy that's fighting for you and me and all of us."

"What is this: a bond rally?"

"I just want you to know where I stand. I appreciate a joke, but underneath I'm a s-s-serious person. Proud to be an American. That's why I'm sorry about José." She put down her knitting needles. "You *do* think he's terribly good-looking, don't you?" Holly said *Hmn*, and swiped the cat's whiskers with her lacquer brush. "If only I could get used to the idea of m-m-marrying a Brazilian. And *being* a B-B-Brazilian myself. It's such a canyon to cross. Six thousand miles, and not knowing the language—"

"Go to Berlitz."

"Why on earth would they be teaching P-P-Portuguese? It isn't as though anyone spoke it. No, my only chance is to try and make José forget politics and become an American. It's such a useless thing for a man to want to be: p-p-president of *Brazil*." She sighed and picked up her knitting. "I must be madly in love. You saw us together. Do you think I'm madly in love?"

"Well. Does he bite?"

Mag dropped a stitch. "Bite?"

"You. In bed."

"Why, no. *Should* he?" Then she added, censoriously: "But he does laugh."

"Good. That's the right spirit. I like a man who sees the humor. Most of them, they're all pant and puff."

Mag withdrew her complaint; she accepted the comment as flattery reflecting on herself. "Yes. I suppose."

"Okay. He doesn't bite. He laughs. What else?"

Mag counted up her dropped stitch and began again, knit, purl, purl.

"I said—"

"I heard you. And it isn't that I don't want to tell you. But it's so difficult to remember. I don't d-d-dwell on these things. The way you seem to. They go out of my head like a dream. I'm sure that's the n-n-normal attitude."

"It may be normal, darling; but I'd rather be natural." Holly paused in the process of reddening the rest of the cat's whiskers. "Listen. If you can't remember, try leaving the lights on."

"Please understand me, Holly. I'm a very-very-very-*conventional* person."

"Oh, balls. What's wrong with a decent look at a guy you like? Men are beautiful, a lot of them are, José is, and if you don't even want to *look* at him, well I'd say he's getting a pretty cold plate of macaroni."

"L-l-lower your voice."

"You can't possibly be in love with him. Now. Does that answer your question?"

"No. Because I'm not a cold plate of m-m-macaroni. I'm a warm-hearted person. It's the basis of my character."

"Okay. You've got a warm heart. But if I were a man on my way to bed, I'd rather take along a hot-water bottle. It's more tangible."

"You won't hear any squawk out of José," she said compacently, her needles flashing in the sunlight. "What's more, I *am* in love with him. Do you realize I've knitted ten pairs of Argyles in less than three months? And this is the second sweater." She stretched the sweater and tossed it aside. "What's the point, though? Sweaters in Brazil. I ought to be making s-s-sun helmets."

Holly lay back and yawned. "It must be winter sometime."

"It *rains*, that I know. Heat. Rain. J-j-jungles."

"Heat. Jungles. Actually, I'd like that."

"Better you than me."

"Yes," said Holly, with a sleepiness that was not sleepy. "Better me than you."

On Monday, when I went down for the morning mail, the card on Holly's box had been altered, a name added: Miss Golightly and Miss Wildwood were now traveling together. This might have held my interest longer except for a letter in my own mailbox. It was from a small university review to whom I sent a story. They

liked it; and, though I must understand they could not afford to pay, they intended to publish. Publish: that meant *print*. Dizzy with excitement is no mere phrase. I had to tell someone; and, taking the stairs two at a time, I pounded on Holly's door.

I didn't trust my voice to tell the news; as soon as she came to the door, her eyes squinty with sleep, I thrust the letter at her. It seemed as though she'd had time to read sixty pages before she handed it back. "I wouldn't let them do it, not if they don't pay you," she said, yawning. Perhaps my face explained she'd misconstrued, that I'd not wanted advice but congratulations; her mouth shifted from a yawn into a smile. "Oh, I see. It's wonderful. Well, come in," she said. "We'll make a pot of coffee and celebrate. No. I'll get dressed and take you to lunch."

Her bedroom was consistent with her parlor: it perpetuated the same camping-out atmosphere; crates and suitcases, everything packed and ready to go, like the belongings of a criminal who feels the law not far behind. In the parlor there was no conventional furniture, but the bedroom had the bed itself, a double one at that, and quite flashy: blond wood, tufted satin.

She left the door of the bathroom open, and conversed from there; between the flushing and the brushing most of what she said was unintelligible, but the gist of it was: she *supposed* I knew Mag Wildwood had moved in, and wasn't that *convenient*? Because if you're going to *have* a roommate, and she *isn't* a dyke, then the next best thing is a perfect fool, which Mag *was*, because then you can dump the lease on them *and* send them out for the laundry.

One could see that Holly had a laundry problem; the room was strewn, like a girl's gymnasium.

"—and you know, she's quite a successful model: isn't that *fan*tastic? But a good thing," she said, hobbling out of the bathroom as she adjusted a garter. "It ought to keep her out of my hair most of the day. And there shouldn't be too much trouble on the man front. She's engaged. Nice guy, too. Though there's a tiny difference in height: I'd say a foot, her favor. Where the hell—" She was on her knees poking under the bed. After she'd found what she was looking for, a pair of lizard shoes, she had to search for a blouse, a belt, and it was a subject to ponder, how, from such wreckage, she evolved the eventual effect: pampered, calmly immaculate, as though she'd been attended by Cleopatra's maids. She said, "Listen," and cupped her hand under my chin, "I'm glad about the story. Really I am."

That Monday in October, 1943: a beautiful day with the buoyancy of a bird. To start, we had Manhattans at Joe Bell's and, when he heard of my good luck, champagne cocktails on the house. Later, we wandered toward Fifth Avenue, where there was a parade. The flags in the wind, the thump of military bands and military feet, seemed to have nothing to do with war, but to be, rather, a fanfare arranged in my personal honor.

We ate lunch at the cafeteria in the park. Afterward, avoiding the zoo (Holly said she couldn't bear to see anything in a cage), we giggled, ran, sang along the paths toward the old wooden boathouse, now gone. Leaves floated on the lake; on the shore, a parkman was fanning a bonfire of them, and the smoke, rising like Indian signals, was the only smudge on the quivering air. Aprils have never meant much to me, autumns seem that season of beginning, spring; which is how I felt sitting with Holly on the railings of the boathouse porch. I thought of the future, and spoke of the past, because Holly wanted to know about my childhood. She talked of her own, too; but it was elusive, nameless, placeless, an impressionistic recital, though the impression was contrary to what one expected, for she gave an almost voluptuous account of swimming and summer, Christmas trees, pretty cousins and parties: in short, happy in a way that she was not, and never, certainly, the background of a child who had run away.

Or, I asked, wasn't it true she'd been out on her own since she was fourteen? She rubbed her nose. "That's true. The other isn't. But really, darling, you made such a tragedy out of *your* childhood I didn't feel I should compete."

She hopped off the railing. "Anyway, it reminds me: I ought to send Fred some peanut butter." The rest of the afternoon we were east and west worming out of reluctant grocers cans of peanut butter, a wartime scarcity; dark came before we'd rounded up a half-dozen tins, the last at a delicatessen on Third Avenue. It was near the antique shop with the palace of a bird cage in its window, so I took her there to see it, and she enjoyed the point, its fantasy: "But still, it's a cage."

Passing a Woolworth's, she gripped my arm: "Let's steal something," she said, pulling me into the store, where at once there seemed a pressure of eyes, as though we were already under suspicion. "Come on. Don't be chicken." She scouted a counter piled with paper pumpkins and Halloween masks. The saleslady was occupied with a group of nuns who were trying on masks. Holly picked up a mask and slipped it over her face; she chose another and put it on mine; then she took my hand and we walked away. It was as simple as that. Outside, we ran a few blocks, I think to make it more dramatic; but also because, as I'd just discovered, successful theft exhilarates. I wondered if she'd often stolen. "I used to," she said. "I mean I had to. If I wanted anything. But I still do it every now and then, sort of to keep my hand in." We wore the masks all the way home.

I have a memory of spending many hither and yonning days with Holly; and it's true, we did at odd moments see a great deal of each other; but on the whole, the memory is false. Because toward the end of the month I found a job. What is there to add? The less the better, except to say it was necessary and lasted from nine to five. Which made our hours, Holly's and mine, extremely different.

Unless it was Thursday, her Sing Sing day, or unless she'd gone horseback riding in the park, as she did occasionally, Holly was hardly up when I came home.

Sometimes, stopping there, I shared her wake-up coffee while she dressed for the evening. She was forever on her way out, not always with Rusty Trawler, but usually; and usually, too, they were joined by Mag Wildwood and the handsome Brazilian, whose name was José Ybarra-Jaeger: his mother was German. As a quartet, they struck an unmusical note, primarily the fault of Ybarra-Jaeger, who seemed as out of place in their company as a violin in a jazz band. He was intelligent, he was presentable, he appeared to have a serious link with his work, which was obscurely governmental, vaguely important, and which took him to Washington several days a week. How, then, could he survive night after night in La Rue, El Morocco, listening to the Wildwood ch-ch-chatter and staring into Rusty's raw baby-buttocks face? Perhaps, like most of us in a foreign country, he was incapable of placing people, selecting a frame for their picture, as he would at home; therefore all Americans had to be judged in a pretty equal light, and on this basis his companions appeared to be tolerable examples of local color and national character. That would explain much; Holly's determination explains the rest.

Late one afternoon, while waiting for a Fifth Avenue bus, I noticed a taxi stop across the street to let out a girl who ran up the steps of the 42nd Street public library. She was through the doors before I recognized her, which was pardonable, for Holly and libraries were not an easy association to make. I let curiosity guide me between the lions, debating on the way whether I should admit following her or pretend coincidence. In the end I did neither, but concealed myself some tables away from her in the general reading room, where she sat behind her dark glasses and a fortress of literature she'd gathered at the desk. She sped from one book to the next, intermittently lingering on a page, always with a frown, as if it were printed upside down. She had a pencil poised above paper—nothing seemed to catch her fancy; still, now and then, for the hell of it, she made laborious scribblings.

Watching her, I remembered a girl I'd known in school, a grind, Mildred Grossman. Mildred: with her moist hair and greasy spectacles, her stained fingers that dissected frogs and carried coffee to picket lines, her flat eyes that only turned toward the stars to estimate their chemical tonnage. Earth and air could not be more opposite than Mildred and Holly, yet in my head they acquired a Siamese twinship, and the thread of thought that had sewn them together ran like this: the average personality reshapes frequently, every few years even our bodies undergo a complete overhaul—desirable or not, it is a natural thing that we should change.

All right; here were two people who never would change. This is what Mildred Grossman had in common with Holly Golightly. They would never change because they'd been given their character too soon; which, like sudden riches, leads to a lack of proportion: the one had splurged herself into a topheavy realist, the other a lopsided romantic. I imagined them in a restaurant of the future, Mildred still studying the menu for its nutritional values, Holly still gluttonous for everything on it. It would never be different. They

347

would walk through life and out of it with the same determined step that took no notice of those cliffs at the left.

Such profound observations made me forget where I was; I came to, startled to find myself in the gloom of the library, and surprised all over again to see Holly there. It was after seven, she was freshening her lipstick and perking up her appearance from what she deemed correct for a library to what, by adding a bit of scarf, some earrings, she considered suitable for the Colony. When she'd left, I wandered over to the table where her books remained; they were what I had wanted to see. *South by Thunderbird. Byways of Brazil. The Political Mind of Latin America.* And so forth.

On Christmas Eve she and Mag gave a party. Holly asked me to come early and help trim the tree. I'm still not sure how they maneuvered that tree into the apartment. The top branches were crushed against the ceiling, the lower ones spread wall to wall; altogether it was not unlike the yuletide giant we see in Rockefeller Plaza. Moreover, it would have taken a Rockefeller to decorate it, for it soaked up baubles and tinsel like melting snow. Holly suggested she run out to Woolworth's and steal some balloons; she did, and they turned the tree into a fairly good show. We made a toast to our work, and Holly said: "Look in the bedroom. There's a present for you."

I had one for her, too: a small package in my pocket that felt even smaller when I saw, square on the bed and wrapped with a red ribbon, the beautiful bird cage.

"But Holly! It's dreadful!"

"I couldn't agree more; but I thought you wanted it."

"The money! Three hundred and fifty dollars!"

She shrugged. "A few extra trips to the powder room. Promise me, though. Promise you'll never put a living thing in it."

I started to kiss her, but she held out her hand. "Gimme," she said, tapping the bulge in my pocket.

"I'm afraid it isn't much." And it wasn't: A St. Christopher's medal. But it came from Tiffany's.

Holly was not a girl who could keep anything, and surely by now she has lost that medal, left it in a suitcase or some hotel drawer. But the bird cage is still mine. I've lugged it to New Orleans, Nantucket, all over Europe, Morocco, the West Indies. Yet I seldom remember that it was Holly who gave it to me, because at one point I chose to forget: we had a big falling-out, and among the objects rotating in the eye of our hurricane were the bird cage and O. J. Berman and my story, a copy of which I'd given Holly when it appeared in the university review.

Sometime in February Holly had gone on a winter trip with Rusty, Mag and José Ybarra-Jaeger. Our altercation happened soon after she returned. She was brown as iodine, her hair was sun-bleached to a ghost color, she'd had a wonderful time: "Well, first of all we were in Key West, and Rusty got mad at some sailors, or vice versa, *any*way he'll have to wear a spine brace the rest of his life. Dearest Mag ended up in the hospital, too. First-degree sunburn. Disgusting: all blisters and citronella. We couldn't stand the smell of her. So José and I left them in the hospital and went to Havana. He says wait till I see Rio, but as far as I'm concerned Havana can take my money right now. We had an irresistible guide, most of him Negro and the rest of him Chinese, and while I don't go much for one or the other, the combination was fairly riveting; so I let him play kneesie under the table, because frankly I didn't find him at all banal; but then one night he took us to a blue movie, and what do you suppose? There *he* was *on* the screen. Of course when we got back to Key West, Mag was positive I'd spent the whole time sleeping with José. So was Rusty: but he doesn't care about that, he simply wants to hear the details. Actually, things were pretty tense until I had a heart-to-heart with Mag."

We were in the front room where, though it was now nearly March, the enormous Christmas tree, turned brown and scentless, its balloons shriveled as an old cow's dugs, still occupied most of the space. A recognizable piece of furniture had been added to the room: an army cot; and Holly, trying to preserve her tropic look, was sprawled on it under a sun lamp.

"And you convinced her?"

"That I hadn't slept with José? God, yes. I simply told—but you know: made it sound like an agonized confession—simply told her I was a dyke."

"She couldn't have believed that."

"The hell she didn't. Why do you think she went out and bought the army cot? Leave it to me: I'm always top banana in the shock department. Be a darling, darling, rub some oil on my back." While I was performing this service, she said: "O. J. Berman's in town, and listen, I gave him your story in the magazine. He was quite impressed. He thinks maybe you're worth helping. But he says you're on the wrong track. Negroes are children: who cares?"

"Not Mr. Berman, I gather."

"Well, I agree with him. I read that story twice. Brats and Negroes. Trembling leaves. *Description*. It doesn't *mean* anything."

My hand, smoothing oil on her skin, seemed to have a temper of its own: it yearned to raise itself and come down on her buttocks. "Give me an example," I said, "of something that means something. In your opinion."

"*Wuthering Heights*," she said, without hesitation.

The urge in my hand was growing beyond control. "But that's unreasonable. You're talking about a work of genius."

"It was, wasn't it? *My wild sweet Cathy*. God, I cried buckets. I saw it ten times."

I said, "Oh," with recognizable relief, with a shameful, rising inflection, "the *movie*."

Her muscles hardened; the touch of her was like stone warmed by the sun. "Everybody has to feel superior to somebody," she said. "But it's customary to present a little proof before you take the privilege."

"I don't compare myself to you. Or Berman. Therefore I can't feel superior. We want different things."

"Don't you want to make money?"

"I haven't planned that far."

"That's how your stories sound. As though you'd written them without knowing the end. Well, I'll tell you: you'd better make money. You have an expensive imagination. Not many people are going to buy you bird cages."

"Sorry."

"You will be if you hit me. You wanted to a minute ago; I could feel it in your hand; and you want to now."

I did, terribly; my hand, my heart was shaking as I recapped the bottle of oil. "Oh, no, I wouldn't regret that. I'm only sorry you wasted your money on me: Rusty Trawler is too hard a way of earning it."

She sat up on the army cot, her face, her naked breasts coldly blue in the sun-lamp light. "It should take you about four seconds to walk from here to the door. I'll give you two."

I went straight upstairs, got the bird cage, took it down and left it in front of her door. That settled that. Or so I imagined until the next morning when, as I was leaving for work, I saw the cage perched on a sidewalk ash can waiting for the garbage collector. Rather sheepishly, I rescued it and carried it back to my room, a capitulation that did not lessen my resolve to put Holly Golightly absolutely out of my life. She was, I decided, a crude exhibitionist, a time-waster, an utter fake; someone never to be spoken to again.

And I didn't. Not for a long while. We passed each other on the stairs with lowered eyes. If she walked into Joe Bell's, I walked out. At one point, Madame Sapphia Spanella, the coloratura and roller-skating enthusiast who lived on the first floor, circulated a petition among the brownstone's other tenants asking them to join her in having Miss Golightly evicted: she was, said Madame Spanella, "morally objectionable" and the "perpetrator of all-night gatherings that endanger the safety and sanity of her neighbors." Though I refused to sign, secretly I felt Madame Spanella had cause to complain. But her petition failed, and as April approached May, the open-windowed, warm spring nights were lurid with the party sounds, the loud-playing phonograph and Martini laughter that emanated from Apt. 2.

It was no novelty to encounter suspicious specimens among Holly's callers, quite the contrary; but one day late that spring, while passing through the brownstone's vestibule, I noticed a *very* provocative man examining her mailbox: a person in his early fifties with a hard, weathered face, grey forlorn eyes. He wore an old sweat-stained grey hat, and his cheap summer suit, a pale blue, hung too loosely on his lanky frame; his shoes were brown and brand-new. He seemed to have no intention of ringing Holly's bell. Slowly, as though he were reading Braille, he kept rubbing a finger across the embossed lettering of her name.

That evening, on my way to supper, I saw the man again. He was standing across the street, leaning against a tree and staring up at Holly's windows. Sinister speculations rushed through my head. Was he a detective? Or some underworld agent connected with her Sing Sing friend, Sally Tomato? The situation revived my tenderer feelings for Holly; it was only fair to interrupt our feud long enough to warn her that she was being watched.

As I walked to the corner, heading east toward the Hamburg Heaven at 79th and Madison, I could feel the man's attention focused on me. Presently, without turning my head, I knew that he was following me. Because I could hear him whistling. Not any ordinary tune, but the plaintive, prairie melody Holly sometimes played on her guitar: *Don't wanna sleep, don't wanna die, just wanna go a-travelin' through the pastures of the sky*. The whistling continued across Park Avenue and up Madison. Once, while waiting for a traffic light to change, I watched him out of the corner of my eye as he stooped to pet a sleazy Pomeranian. "That's a fine animal you got there," he told the owner in a hoarse, countrified drawl.

Hamburg Heaven was empty. Nevertheless, he took a seat right beside me at the long counter. He smelled of tobacco and sweat. He ordered a cup of coffee, but when it came he didn't touch it. Instead, he chewed on a toothpick and studied me in the wall mirror facing us.

"Excuse me," I said, speaking to him via the mirror, "but what do you want?"

The question didn't embarrass him; he seemed relieved to have had it asked. "Son," he said, "I need a friend."

He brought out a wallet. It was as worn as his leathery hands, almost falling to pieces; and so was the brittle, cracked, blurred snapshot he handed me. There were seven people in the picture, all grouped together on the sagging porch of a stark wooden house, and all children, except for the man himself, who had his arm around the waist of a plump, blonde little girl with a hand shading her eyes against the sun.

"That's me," he said, pointing at himself. "That's her. . . ." he tapped the plump girl. "And this one over here," he added, indicating a towheaded bean pole, "that's her brother, Fred."

I looked at "her" again: and yes, now I could see it, an embryonic resemblance to Holly in the squinting, fat-cheeked child. At the same moment, I realized who the man must be.

"You're Holly's *father*."

He blinked, he frowned. "Her name's not Holly. She was a Lulamae Barnes. Was," he said, shifting the toothpick in his mouth, "till she married me. I'm her husband. Doc Golightly. I'm a horse doctor, animal man. Do some farming, too. Near Tulip, Texas. Son, why are you laughing?"

It wasn't real laughter: it was nerves. I took a swallow of water and choked; he pounded me on the back. "This here's no humorous matter, son. I'm a tired man. I've been five years looking for my woman. Soon as I got that letter from Fred, saying where she was, I bought myself a ticket on the Greyhound. Lulamae belongs home with her husband and her churren."

"Children?"

"*Them's her churren,*" he said, almost shouting. He meant the four other young faces in the picture, two barefoot girls and a pair of overalled boys. Well, of course, the man was deranged.

"But Holly can't be the mother of those children. They're older than she is. Bigger."

"Now, son," he said in a reasoning voice, "I didn't claim they was her natural-born churren. Their own precious mother, precious woman, Jesus rest her soul, she passed away July 4th, Independence Day, 1936. The year of the drought. When I married Lulamae, that was in December, 1938, she was going on fourteen. Maybe an ordinary person, being only fourteen, wouldn't know their right mind. But you take Lulamae, she was an exceptional woman. She knew good and well what she was doing when she promised to be my wife and the mother of my churren. She plain broke our hearts when she ran off like she done." He sipped his cold coffee, and glanced at me with a searching earnestness. "Now, son, do you doubt me? Do you believe what I'm saying is so?"

I did. It was too implausible not to be fact; moreover, it dovetailed with O. J. Berman's description of the Holly he'd first encountered in California: *You don't know whether she's a hillbilly or an Okie or what.* Berman couldn't be blamed for not guessing that she was a child-wife from Tulip, Texas.

"Plain broke our hearts when she ran off like she done," the horse doctor repeated. "She had no cause. All the housework was done by her daughters. Lulamae could just take it easy: fuss in front of mirrors and wash her hair. Our own cows, our own garden, chickens, pigs: son, that woman got positively fat. While her brother growed into a giant. Which is a sight different from how they came to us. 'Twas Nellie, my oldest girl, 'twas Nellie brought 'em into the house. She came to me one morning, and said: 'Papa, I got two wild younguns locked in the kitchen. I caught 'em outside stealing milk and turkey eggs.' That was Lulamae and Fred. Well, you never saw a more pitiful something. Ribs sticking out everywhere, legs so puny they can't hardly stand, teeth wobbling so bad they can't chew mush. Story was: their mother died of the TB, and their papa done the same—and all the churren, a whole raft of 'em, they been sent off to live with different mean people. Now Lulamae and her brother, them two been living with some mean, no-count people a hundred miles east of Tulip. She had good cause to run off from that house. She didn't have none to leave mine. 'Twas her home."

He leaned his elbows on the counter and, pressing his closed eyes with his finger tips, sighed. "She plumped out to be a real pretty woman. Lively, too. Talky as a jaybird. With something smart to say on every subject: better than the radio. First thing you know I'm out picking flowers. I tamed her a crow and taught it to say her name. I showed her how to play the guitar. Just to look at her made the tears spring to my eyes. The night I proposed, I cried like a baby. She said: 'What you want to cry for, Doc? 'Course we'll be married. I've never been married before.' Well, I had to laugh, hug and squeeze her: *never been married before!*" He chuckled, chewed on his toothpick a moment.

"Don't tell me that woman wasn't happy!" he said, challengingly. "We all doted on her. She didn't have to lift a finger, 'cept to eat a piece of pie. 'Cept to comb her hair and send away for all the magazines. We must've had a hundred dollars' worth of magazines come into that house. Ask me, that's what done it. Looking at show-off pictures. Reading dreams. That's what started her walking down the road. Every day she'd walk a little further: a mile, and come home. Two miles, and come home. One day she just kept on." He put his hands over his eyes again; his breathing made a ragged noise. "The crow I give her went wild and flew away. All summer you could hear him. In the yard. In the garden. In the woods. All summer that damned bird was calling: Lulamae, Lulamae."

He stayed hunched over and silent, as though listening to the long-ago summer sound. I carried our checks to the cashier. While I was paying, he joined me. We left together and walked over to Park Avenue. It was a cool, blowy evening; swanky awnings flapped in the breeze. The quietness between us continued until I said: "But what about her brother? He didn't leave?"

"No, sir," he said, clearing his throat. "Fred was with us all right till they took him in the Army. A fine boy. Fine with horses. He didn't know what got into Lulamae, how come she left her brother and husband and churren. After he was in the Army, though, Fred started hearing from her. The other day he wrote me her address. So I come to get her. I know she's sorry for what she done. I know she wants to go home."

He seemed to be asking me to agree with him. I told him that I thought he'd find Holly, or Lulamae, somewhat changed.

"Listen, son," he said, as we reached the steps of the brownstone, "I advised you I need a friend. Because I don't want to surprise her. Scare her none. That's why I've held off. Be my friend: let her know I'm here."

The notion of introducing Mrs. Golightly to her husband had its satisfying aspects; and, glancing up at her lighted windows, I hoped her friends were there, for the prospect of watching the Texan shake hands with Mag and Rusty and José was more satisfying still. But Doc Golightly's proud earnest eyes and sweat-stained hat made me ashamed of such anticipations. He followed me into the house and prepared to wait at the bottom of the stairs. "Do I look nice?" he whispered, brushing his sleeves, tightening the knot of his tie.

Holly was alone. She answered the door at once; in

fact, she was on her way out: white satin dancing pumps and quantities of perfume announced gala intentions.

"Well, idiot," she said, and playfully slapped me with her purse, "I'm in too much of a hurry to make up now. We'll smoke the pipe tomorrow, okay?"

"Sure, Lulamae. If you're still around tomorrow."

She took off her dark glasses and squinted at me. It was as though her eyes were shattered prisms, the dots of blue and grey and green like broken bits of sparkle. "*He* told you that," she said in a small, shivering voice. "Oh, please. *Where* is he?" She ran past me into the hall. "Fred!" she called down the stairs. "Fred! Where are you, darling?"

I could hear Doc Golightly's footsteps climbing the stairs. His head appeared above the banisters, and Holly backed away from him, not as though she were frightened, but as though she were retreating into a shell of disappointment. Then he was standing in front of her, hangdog and shy. "Gosh, Lulamae," he began, and hesitated, for Holly was gazing at him vacantly, as though she couldn't place him. "Gee, honey, don't they feed you up here? You're so skinny. Like when I first saw you. All wild around the eye."

Holly touched his face; her fingers tested the reality of his chin, his beard stubble. "Hello, Doc," she said gently, and kissed him on the cheek. "Hello, Doc," she repeated happily, as he lifted her off her feet in a rib-crushing grip. Whoops of relieved laughter shook him. "Gosh, Lulamae. Kingdom come."

Neither of them noticed me when I squeezed past them and went up to my room. Nor did they seem aware of Madame Sapphia Spanella, who opened her door and yelled: "Shut up! It's a disgrace. Do your whoring elsewhere."

Divorce him? Of course I never divorced him. I was only fourteen, for God's sake. It couldn't have been *legal*." Holly tapped an empty Martini glass. "Two more, my darling Mr. Bell."

Joe Bell, in whose bar we were sitting, accepted the order reluctantly. "You're rocking the boat kinda early," he complained, crunching on a Tums. It was not yet noon, according to the mahogany clock behind the bar, and he'd already served us three rounds.

"But it's Sunday, Mr. Bell. Clocks are slow on Sundays. Besides, I haven't been to bed yet," she told him, and confided to me: "Not to sleep." She blushed, and glanced away guiltily. For the first time since I'd known her, she seemed to feel a need to justify herself: "Well, I had to. Doc really loves me, you know. And I love him. He may have looked old and tacky to *you*. But you don't know the sweetness of him, the confidence he can give to birds and brats and fragile things like that. Anyone who ever gave you confidence, you owe them a lot. I've always remembered Doc in my prayers. Please stop smirking!" she demanded, stabbing out a cigarette. "I *do* say my prayers."

"I'm not smirking. I'm smiling. You're the most amazing person."

"I suppose I am," she said, and her face, wan, rather bruised-looking in the morning light, brightened; she smoothed her tousled hair, and the colors of it glimmered like a shampoo advertisement.

"I must look fierce. But who wouldn't? We spent the rest of the night roaming around in a bus station. Right up till the last minute Doc thought I was going to go with him. Even though I kept telling him: But, Doc, I'm not fourteen any more, and I'm not Lulamae. But the terrible part is (and I realized it while we were standing there) I am. I'm still stealing turkey eggs and running through a brier patch. Only now I call it having the mean reds."

Joe Bell disdainfully settled the fresh Martinis in front of us.

"Never love a wild thing, Mr. Bell," Holly advised him. "That was Doc's mistake. He was always lugging home wild things: a hawk with a hurt wing; one time it was a full-grown bobcat with a broken leg. But you can't give your heart to a wild thing: the more you do, the stronger they get. Until they're strong enough to run into the woods. Or fly into a taller tree. Then the sky. That's how you'll end up, Mr. Bell. If you let yourself love a wild thing. You'll end up looking at the sky."

"She's drunk," Joe Bell informed me.

"Moderately," Holly confessed. "But Doc knew what I meant. I explained it to him very carefully, and it was something he could understand. We shook hands and held on to each other and he wished me luck." She glanced at the clock. "He must be in the Blue Mountains by now."

"What's she talking about?" Joe Bell asked me.

Holly lifted her Martini. "Let's wish the Doc luck, too," she said, touching her glass against mine. "Good luck: and believe me, dearest Doc—it's better to look at the sky than live there. Such an empty place; so vague. Just a country where the thunder goes and things disappear."

TRAWLER MARRIES FOURTH. I was on a subway somewhere in Brooklyn when I saw that headline. The paper that bannered it belonged to another passenger. The only part of the text that I could see read: *Rutherford "Rusty" Trawler, the millionaire playboy often accused of pro-Nazi sympathies, eloped to Greenwich yesterday with a beautiful. . . .* Not that I wanted to read any more. Holly had married him: well, I wished I were under the wheels of the train. But I'd been wishing that before I spotted the headline. For a headful of reasons. I hadn't seen Holly, not really, since our drunken Sunday at Joe Bell's bar. The intervening weeks had given me my own case of the mean reds. First off, I'd been fired from my job: deservedly, and for an amusing misdemeanor too complicated to recount here. Also, my draft board was displaying an uncomfortable interest; and, having so recently escaped the regimentation of a small town, the idea of entering another form of disciplined life made me desperate. Between the uncertainty of my draft status and a lack of specific experience, I couldn't seem to find another job. That was what I was doing on a subway in Brooklyn: returning from a discouraging interview with an editor of the now defunct newspaper, *PM*.

All this, combined with the city heat of the summer, had reduced me to a state of nervous inertia. So I more than half meant it when I wished I were under the wheels of the train. The headline made the desire quite positive. If Holly could marry that "absurd fetus," then the army of wrongness rampant in the world might as well march over me. Or, and the question is apparent, was my outrage a little the result of being in love with Holly myself? A little. For I *was* in love with her. Just as I'd once been in love with my mother's elderly colored cook and a postman who let me follow him on his rounds and a whole family named McKendrick. That category of love generates jealousy, too.

When I reached my station I bought a paper and, reading the tail end of that sentence, discovered that Rusty's bride was a beautiful cover girl from the Arkansas hills, Miss Margaret Thatcher Fitzhue Wildwood. Mag! My legs went so limp with relief I took a taxi the rest of the way home.

Madame Sapphia Spanella met me in the hall, wild-eyed and wringing her hands. "Run," she said. "Bring the police. She is killing somebody! Somebody is killing her!"

It sounded like it. As though tigers were loose in Holly's apartment. A riot of crashing glass, of rippings and fallings and overturned furniture. But there were no quarreling voices inside the uproar, which made it seem unnatural. "Run," shrieked Madame Spanella, pushing me. "Tell the police murder!"

I ran, but only upstairs to Holly's door. Pounding on it had one result: the racket subsided. Stopped altogether. But pleadings to let me in went unanswered, and my efforts to break down the door merely culminated in a bruised shoulder. Then below I heard Madame Spanella commanding some newcomer to go for the police. "Shut up," she was told, "and get out of my way."

It was José Ybarra-Jaeger. Looking not at all the smart Brazilian diplomat, but sweaty and frightened. He ordered me out of his way, too. And, using his own key, opened the door. "In here, Doctor Goldman," he said, beckoning to a man accompanying him.

Since no one prevented me, I followed them into the apartment, which was tremendously wrecked. At last the Christmas tree had been dismantled, very literally: its brown dry branches sprawled in a welter of torn-up books, broken lamps and phonograph records. Even the icebox had been emptied, its contents tossed around the room: raw eggs were sliding down the walls and, in the midst of the debris, Holly's no-name cat was calmly licking a puddle of milk.

In the bedroom, the smell of smashed perfume bottles made me gag. I stepped on Holly's dark glasses;

they were lying on the floor, the lenses already shattered, the frames cracked in half.

Perhaps that is why Holly, a rigid figure on the bed, stared at José so blindly, seemed not to see the doctor who, testing her pulse, crooned: "You're a tired young lady. Very tired. You want to go to sleep, don't you? Sleep."

Holly rubbed her forehead, leaving a smear of blood from a cut finger. "Sleep," she said, and whimpered like an exhausted, fretful child. "He's the only one would ever let me. Let me hug him on cold nights. I saw a place in Mexico. With horses. By the sea."

"With horses by the sea," lullabyed the doctor, selecting a hypodermic from his black case.

José averted his face, queasy at the sight of a needle. "Her sickness is only grief?" he asked, his difficult English lending the question an unintended irony. "She is grieving only?"

"Didn't hurt a bit, now did it?" inquired the doctor, smugly dabbing Holly's arm with a scrap of cotton.

She came to sufficiently to focus the doctor. "*Everything* hurts. Where are my glasses?" But she didn't need them. Her eyes were closing of their own accord.

"She is only grieving?" insisted José.

"Please, sir!" The doctor was quite short with him. "If you will leave me alone with the patient."

José withdrew to the front room, where he released his temper on the snooping, tiptoeing presence of Madame Spanella. "Don't touch me! I'll call the police," she threatened as he whipped her to the door with Portuguese oaths.

He considered throwing me out, too, or so I surmised from his expression. Instead, he invited me to have a drink. The only unbroken bottle we could find contained dry vermouth. "I have a worry," he confided. "I have a worry that this should cause scandal. It is too delicate: my name, my work."

He seemed cheered to learn that I saw no reason for a "scandal"; demolishing one's own possessions was, presumably, a private affair.

"It is only a question of grieving," he firmly declared. "When the sadness came, first she throws the drink she is drinking. The bottle. Those books. A lamp. Then I am scared. I hurry to bring a doctor."

"But why?" I wanted to know. "Why should she have a fit over Rusty? If I were Holly, I'd celebrate."

"Rusty?"

I was still carrying my newspaper, and showed him the headline.

"Oh, that." He grinned rather scornfully. "They do us a grand favor, Rusty and Mag. We laugh over it: how they think they break our hearts when all the time we *want* them to run away. I assure you, we were laughing when the sadness came." From the litter on the floor, he picked up a ball of yellow paper. "This," he said.

It was a telegram from Tulip, Texas: *Received notice young Fred killed in action overseas stop your husband and children join in the sorrow of our mutual loss stop letter follows love Doc.*

Holly never mentioned her brother again: except once. Moreover, she stopped calling me Fred. June, July, all through the warm months she hibernated like a winter animal who did not know spring had come and gone. Her hair darkened, she put on weight. She became rather careless about her clothes: used to rush round to the delicatessen wearing a rain slicker and nothing underneath. José moved into the apartment, his name replacing Mag Wildwood's on the mailbox. Still, Holly was a good deal alone, for José stayed in Washington three days a week. During his absences she entertained no one and seldom left the apartment—except on Thursdays, when she made her weekly trip to Ossining.

Which is not to imply that she had lost interest in life; far from it, she seemed more content, altogether happier than I'd ever seen her. A keen sudden un-Hollylike enthusiasm for homemaking resulted in several unHollylike purchases: at a Parke-Bernet auction she acquired a stag-at-bay hunting tapestry and, from the William Randolph Hearst estate, a gloomy pair of Gothic "easy" chairs; she bought the complete Modern Library, shelves of classical records, innumerable Metropolitan Museum reproductions (including a statue of a Chinese cat that her own cat hated and hissed and ultimately broke), a Waring mixer and a pressure cooker and a library of cookbooks.

She spent whole *hausfrau* afternoons slopping about in the sweatbox of her midget kitchen: "José says I'm better than the Colony. Really, who would have dreamed I had such a great natural talent? A month ago I couldn't scramble eggs." And still couldn't, for that matter. Simple dishes, steak, a proper salad, were beyond her. Instead, she fed José, and occasionally myself, *outré* soups (brandied black terrapin poured into avocado shells), Nero-ish novelties (roasted pheasant stuffed with pomegranates and persimmons) and other dubious innovations (chicken and saffron rice with a chocolate sauce: "An East Indian classic, *my* dear"). Wartime sugar and cream rationing restricted her imagination when it came to sweets: nevertheless, she once managed something called Tobacco Tapioca; best not describe it.

Nor describe her attempts to master Portuguese, an ordeal as tedious to me as it was to her, for whenever I visited her an album of Linguaphone records never ceased rotating on the phonograph. Now, too, she rarely spoke a sentence that did not begin, "After we're married—" or, "When we move to Rio—" Yet José had never suggested marriage. She admitted it. "But, after all, he *knows* I'm preggers. Well, I am, darling. Six weeks gone. I don't see why that should surprise you. It didn't me. Not *un peu* bit. I'm delighted. I want to have at least nine. I'm sure some of them will be rather dark—José has a touch of *le nègre*. I suppose you guessed that? Which is fine by me: what could be prettier than a quite coony baby with bright green beautiful eyes? I wish, please don't laugh—but I wish I'd been a virgin for him, for José. Not that I've warmed the multitudes some people say: I don't blame the bastards for *saying* it, I've always thrown out such a jazzy line.

Really, though, I toted up the other night, and I've only had eleven lovers—not counting anything that happened before I was thirteen because, after all, that just doesn't count. Eleven. Does that make me a whore? Look at Mag Wildwood. Or Honey Tucker. Or Rose Ellen Ward. They've had the old clap-yo'-hands so many times it amounts to applause. Of course I haven't anything *against* whores. Except this: some of them may have an honest tongue but they all have dishonest hearts. I mean, you can't bang the guy and cash his checks and at least not *try* to believe you love him. I never have. Even Benny Shacklett and all those rodents. I sort of hypnotized myself into thinking their sheer rattiness had a certain allure. Actually, except for Doc, if you want to count Doc, José is my first non-rat romance. Oh, he's not my idea of the absolute *finito*. He tells little lies and he worries what people *think* and he takes about fifty baths a day: men ought to smell somewhat. He's too prim, too cautious to be my guy ideal; he always turns his back to get undressed and he makes too much noise when he eats and I don't like to see him run because there's something funny-looking about him then. If I were free to choose from everybody alive, just snap my fingers and say come here you, I wouldn't pick José. Nehru, he's nearer the mark. Wendell Willkie. I'd settle for somebody like Carole Landis any day. Why not? A person ought to be able to marry men or women or—listen, if you came to me and said you wanted to hitch up with Man o' War, I'd respect your feeling. No, I'm serious. Love should be allowed. I'm all for it. Now that I've got a pretty good idea what it is. Because I *do* love José—I'd stop smoking if he asked me to. He's *friendly*, he can laugh me out of the mean reds, only I don't have them much any more, except sometimes, and even then they're not so hideola that I gulp Seconal or have to haul myself to Tiffany's: I take his suit to the cleaner, or stuff some mushrooms, and I feel fine, just great. Another thing, I've thrown away my horoscopes. I must have spent a dollar on every goddam star in the goddam planetarium. It's a bore, but the answer is good things only happen to you if you're good. Good? Honest is more what I mean. Not law-type honest—I'd rob a grave, I'd steal two bits off a dead man's eyes if I thought it would contribute to the day's enjoyment—but unto-thyself-type honest. Be anything but a coward, a pretender, an emotional crook, a whore: I'd rather have cancer than a dishonest heart. Which isn't being pious. Just practical. Cancer *may* cool you, but the other's sure to. O screw it, cookie—hand me my guitar and I'll sing you a *fada* in *the* most perfect Portuguese."

Those final weeks, spanning the end of summer and the beginning of another autumn, are blurred in memory, perhaps because our understanding of each other had reached that sweet depth where two people communicate more often in silence than in words; an affectionate quietness replaces the tensions, the un-relaxed chatter and chasing about that produce a friendship's more showy, more, in the surface sense, dramatic moments.

Frequently, when *he* was out of town (I'd developed hostile attitudes toward *him*, and seldom used his name) we spent entire evenings together during which we exchanged less than a hundred words; once, we walked all the way to Chinatown, ate a chow mein supper, bought some paper lanterns and stole a box of joss sticks, then moseyed across the Brooklyn Bridge, and on the bridge, as we watched seaward-moving ships pass between the cliffs of burning skyline, she said: "Years from now, years and years, one of those ships will bring me back, me and my nine Brazilian brats. Because yes, they must see this, these lights, the river—I love New York, even though it isn't mine, the way something has to be, a tree or a street or a house, something, anyway, that belongs to me because I belong to it."

And I said, "Do shut up," for I felt infuriatingly left out—a tugboat in dry dock while she, glittery voyager of secure destination, steamed down the harbor with whistles whistling and confetti in the air.

So the days, the last days, blow about in memory, hazy, autumnal, all alike as leaves: until a day unlike any other I've lived.

It happened to fall on the 30th of September, my birthday, a fact which had no effect on events, except that, expecting some form of monetary remembrance from my family, I was eager for the postman's morning visit. Indeed, I went downstairs and waited for him. If I had not been loitering in the vestibule, then Holly would not have asked me to go horseback riding; and would not, consequently, have had the opportunity to save my life.

"Come on," she said, when she found me awaiting the postman, "let's walk a couple of horses around the park." She was wearing a windbreaker and a pair of blue jeans and tennis shoes; she slapped her stomach, drawing attention to its flatness: "Don't think I'm out to lose the heir. But there's a horse, my darling old Mabel Minerva—I can't go without saying good-by to Mabel Minerva."

"Good-by?"

"A week from Saturday. José bought the tickets." In rather a trance, I let her lead me down to the street. "We change planes in Miami. Then over the sea. Over the Andes. Taxi!"

Over the Andes. As we rode in a cab across Central Park it seemed to me as though I, too, were flying, desolately floating over snow-peaked and perilous territory.

"But you can't. After all, what about? Well, what about. Well, you can't really run off and leave everybody."

"I don't think anyone will miss me. I have no friends."

"I will. Miss you. So will Joe Bell, and oh—millions. Like Sally. Poor Mr. Tomato."

"I loved old Sally," she said, and sighed. "You know I haven't been to see him in a month? When I told him I was going away, he was an angel. *Actually*—" she frowned—"he seemed *delighted* that I was leaving the country. He said it was all for the best. Because sooner or later there might be trouble. If they found out I wasn't his real niece. That fat lawyer O'Shaughnessy sent me five hundred dollars. In cash. A wedding present from Sally."

I wanted to be unkind. "You can expect a present from me, too. When, and if, the wedding happens."

She laughed. "He'll marry me, all right. In church. And with his family there. That's why we're waiting till we get to Rio."

"Does he know you're married already?"

"What's the matter with you? Are you trying to ruin the day? It's a beautiful day: leave it alone!"

"But it's perfectly possible—"

"It *isn't* possible. I've told you, that wasn't legal. It *couldn't be.*" She rubbed her nose, and glanced at me sideways. "Mention that to a soul, darling. I'll hang you by your toes and dress you for a hog."

The stables, I believe they have been replaced by television studios, were on West 65th Street. Holly selected for me an old swayback black-and-white mare: "Don't worry, she's safer than a cradle." Which, in my case, was a necessary guarantee, for ten-cent pony rides at childhood carnivals were the limit of my equestrian experience. Holly helped hoist me into the saddle, then mounted her own horse, a silvery animal that took the lead as we jogged across the traffic of Central Park West and entered a riding path dappled with leaves that denuding breezes danced about.

"See?" she shouted. "It's great!"

And suddenly it was. Suddenly, watching the tangled colors of Holly's hair flash in the red-yellow leaf light, I loved her enough to forget myself, my self-pitying despairs, and be content that something she thought happy was going to happen. Very gently the horses began to trot, waves of wind splashed us, spanked our faces, we plunged in and out of sun and shadow pools, and joy, a glad-to-be-alive exhilaration jolted through me like a jigger of nitrogen. That was one minute; the next introduced farce in grim disguise.

For all at once, like savage members of a jungle ambush, a band of Negro boys leapt out of the shrubbery along the path. Hooting, cursing, they launched rocks and thrashed at the horses' rumps with switches.

Mine, the black-and-white mare, rose on her hind legs, whinnied, teetered like a tightrope artist, then blue-streaked down the path, bouncing my feet out of the stirrups and leaving me scarcely attached. Her hoofs made the gravel stones spit sparks. The sky careened. Trees, a lake with little-boy sailboats, statues went by lickety-split. Nursemaids rushed to rescue their charges from our awesome approach; men, bums and others, yelled, "Pull in the reins!" and, "Whoa, boy, whoa!" and "Jump!" It was only later that I remembered these voices; at the time I was simply conscious of Holly, the cowboy sound of her racing behind me, never quite catching up and over and over calling encouragements. Onward, across the park and out into Fifth Avenue: stampeding against the noon-day traffic, taxis, buses that screechingly swerved. Past the Duke mansion, the Frick museum, past the Pierre and the Plaza. But Holly gained ground; moreover, a mounted policeman had joined the chase: flanking my runaway mare, one on either side, their horses performed a pincer movement that brought her to a steamy halt. It was then, at last, that I fell off her back. Fell off and picked myself up and stood there, not altogether certain where I was. A crowd gathered. The policeman huffed and wrote in a book: presently he was most sympathetic, grinned and said he would arrange for our horses to be returned to their stable.

Holly put us in a taxi. "Darling. How do you feel?"

"Fine."

"But you haven't *any* pulse," she said, feeling my wrist.

"Then I must be dead."

"No, idiot. This is serious. Look at me."

The trouble was, I couldn't see her; rather, I saw several Hollys, a trio of sweaty faces so white with concern I was touched and embarrassed. "Honestly. I don't feel anything. Except ashamed."

"Please. Are you sure? Tell me the truth. You might have been killed."

"But I wasn't. And thank you. For saving my life. You're wonderful. Unique. I love you."

"Damn fool." She kissed me on the cheek. Then there were four of her, and I fainted dead away.

That evening, photographs of Holly were front-paged by the late edition of the *Journal-American* and by the early editions of both the *Daily News* and the *Daily Mirror*. The publicity had nothing to do with runaway horses. It concerned quite another matter, as the headlines revealed: PLAYGIRL ARRESTED IN NARCOTICS SCANDAL (*Journal-American*); ARREST DOPE SMUGGLING ACTRESS (*Daily News*); DRUG RING EXPOSED, GLAMOUR GIRL HELD (*Daily Mirror*).

Of the lot, the *News* printed the most striking picture: Holly, entering police headquarters, wedged between two muscular detectives, one male, one female. In this squalid context even her clothes (she was still wearing her riding costume, windbreaker and blue jeans) suggested a gang-moll hooligan, an impression the dark glasses, disarrayed coiffure and a Picayune cigarette dangling from sullen lips did not diminish. The caption read: *Twenty-year-old Holly Golightly, beautiful movie starlet and Café Society celebrity D.A. alleges to be key-figure in international drug-smuggling racket linked to racketeer Salvatore "Sally" Tomato. Dets. Patrick Connor and Sheilah Fezzonetti (L. and R.) are shown escorting her into 67th St. Precinct. See story on Pg. 3.*

The story, featuring a photograph of a man identified as Oliver "Father" O'Shaughnessy (shielding his face with a fedora), ran three full columns. Here, somewhat condensed, are the pertinent paragraphs: *Members of Café Society were stunned today by the arrest of gorgeous Holly Golightly, twenty-year-old Hollywood starlet and highly publicized girl-about-New York. At the same time, 2 p.m., police nabbed Oliver O'Shaughnessy, 52, of the Hotel Seabord, W. 49th St., as he exited from a Hamburg Heaven on Madison Ave. Both are alleged by District Attorney Frank L. Donovan to be important figures in an international drug ring dominated by the notorious Mafia-fuhrer Salvatore "Sally" Tomato, currently in Sing Sing serving a five-year rap for political bribery. * * * O'Shaughnessy, a defrocked priest variously known in crimeland circles as "Father" and "The Padre," has a history of arrests dating back to 1934, when he served two years for operating a phony Rhode Island mental institution, The Monastery. Miss Golightly, who has no previous criminal record, was arrested in her luxurious apartment at a swank East side address. * * * Although the D.A.'s office has issued no formal statement, responsible sources insist the blonde and beautiful actress, not long ago the constant companion of multimillionaire Rutherford Trawler, has been acting as "liaison" between the imprisoned Tomato and his chief-lieutenant, O'Shaughnessy. * * * Posing as a relative of Tomato's Miss Golightly is said to have paid weekly visits to Sing Sing, and on these occasions Tomato supplied her with verbally coded messages which she then transmitted to O'Shaughnessy. Via this link, Tomato, believed to have been born in Cefalù, Sicily, in 1874, was able to keep first-hand control of a world-wide narcotics syndicate with outposts in Mexico, Cuba, Sicily, Tangier, Teheran and Dakar. But the D.A.'s office refused to offer any detail on these allegations or even verify them. * * * Tipped-off, a large number of reporters were on hand at the E. 67th St. Precinct station when the accused pair arrived for booking. O'Shaughnessy, a burly red-haired man, refused comment and kicked one cameraman in the groin. But Miss Golightly, a fragile eyeful, even though attired like a tomboy in slacks and leather jacket, appeared relatively unconcerned. "Don't ask me what the hell this is about," she told reporters. "Parce que je ne sais pas, mes chères. (Because I do not know, my dears.) Yes—I have visited Sally Tomato. I used to go to see him every week. What's wrong with that? He believes in God, and so do I." * * * Then, under the subheading ADMITS OWN DRUG ADDICTION: Miss Golightly smiled when a reporter asked whether or not she herself is a narcotics user. "I've had a little go at marijuana. It's not half so destructive as brandy. Cheaper, too. Unfortunately, I prefer brandy. No, Mr. Tomato never mentioned drugs to me. It makes me furious, the way these wretched people keep persecuting him. He's a sensitive, a religious person. A darling old man."*

There is one especially gross error in this report: she was not arrested in her "luxurious apartment." It took place in my own bathroom. I was soaking away my horse-ride pains in a tub of scalding water laced with Epsom salts; Holly, an attentive nurse, was sitting on the edge of the tub waiting to rub me with Sloan's liniment and tuck me into bed. There was a knock at the front door. As the door was unlocked, Holly called, "Come in." In came Madame Sapphia Spanella, trailed by a pair of civilian-clothed detectives, one of them a lady with thick yellow braids roped around her head.

"*Here* she is: the wanted woman!" boomed Madame Spanella, invading the bathroom and leveling a finger, first at Holly, then at my nakedness. "Look. What a whore she is." The male detective seemed embarrassed by Madame Spanella and by the situation; but a harsh enjoyment tensed the face of his companion—she plumped a hand on Holly's shoulder and, in a surprising baby-child voice, said: "Come along, sister. You're going places." Whereupon Holly coolly told her: "Get them cotton-pickin' hands off of me, you dreary driveling old bull-dyke." Which rather enraged the lady: she slapped Holly damned hard. So hard her head twisted on her neck, and the bottle of liniment, flung from her hand, smithereened on the tile floor—where I, scampering out of the tub to enrich the fray, stepped on it and all but severed both big toes. Nude and bleeding a path of bloody footprints, I followed the action as far as the hall. "Don't forget," Holly managed to instruct me as the detectives propelled her down the stairs, "please feed the cat."

Of course I believed Madame Spanella was to blame: she'd several times called the authorities to complain about Holly. It didn't occur to me the affair could have dire dimensions until that evening when Joe Bell showed up flourishing the newspapers. He was too agitated to speak sensibly; he caroused the room hitting his fists together while I read the accounts.

Then he said, "You think it's so? She was mixed up in this lousy business?"

"Well, yes."

He popped a Tums in his mouth and, glaring at me, chewed it as though he were crunching my bones. "Boy, that's rotten. And you meant to be her friend. What a bastard!"

"Just a minute. I didn't say she was involved *knowingly*. She wasn't. But there, she did do it. Carry messages and whatnot—"

He said, "Take it pretty calm, don't you? Jesus, she could get ten years. More." He yanked the papers away from me. "You know her friends. These rich fellows. Come down to the bar, we'll start phoning. Our girl's going to need fancier shysters than I can afford."

I was too sore and shaky to dress myself; Joe Bell had to help. Back at his bar he propped me in the telephone booth with a triple Martini and a brandy tumbler full of coins. But I couldn't think who to contact. José was in Washington, and I had no notion where to reach him there. Rusty Trawler? Not that rat! Only: what other friends of hers did I know? Perhaps she'd been right when she'd said she had none, not really.

I put through a call to Crestview 5-6958 in Beverly Hills, the number long-distance information gave me for O. J. Berman. The person who answered said Mr. Berman was having a massage and couldn't be disturbed: sorry, try later. Joe Bell was incensed—told me I should have said it was a life and death matter; and he insisted on my trying Rusty. First, I spoke to Mr. Trawler's butler—Mr. and Mrs. Trawler, he announced, were at dinner and might he take a message? Joe Bell shouted into the receiver: "This is urgent, mister. Life and death." The outcome was that I found myself talking—listening, rather—to the former Mag Wildwood: "Are you starkers?" she demanded. "My husband and I will positively sue anyone who attempts to connect our names with that re-re-revolting and de-de-degenerate girl. I always *knew* she was a hop-hop-head, with no more morals than a hound-bitch in heat. Prison is where she belongs. And my husband agrees one thousand per cent. We will positively *sue* anyone who—"

Hanging up, I remembered old Doc down in Tulip, Texas; but no, Holly wouldn't like it if I called him, she'd kill me good. I rang California again; the circuits were busy, stayed busy, and by the time O. J. Berman was on the line I'd emptied so many Martinis he had to tell me why I was phoning him: "About the kid, is it? I know already. I spoke to Iggy Fitelstein. Iggy's the best shingle in New York. I said Iggy you take care of it, send me the bill, only keep my name anonymous, see. Well, I owe the kid something. Not that I owe her *any*thing, you want to come down to it. She's crazy. A phony. But a *real* phony, you know? Anyway, they only got her in ten thousand bail. Don't worry, Iggy'll spring her tonight—it wouldn't surprise me she's home already."

But she wasn't; nor had she returned the next morning when I went down to feed her cat. Having no key to the apartment, I used the fire escape and gained entrance through a window. The cat was in the bedroom, and he was not alone: a man was there, crouching over a suitcase. The two of us, each thinking the other a burglar, exchanged uncomfortable stares as I stepped through the window. He had a pretty face, lacquered hair, he resembled José; moreover, the suitcase he'd been packing contained the wardrobe José kept at Holly's, the shoes and suits she fussed over, was always carting to menders and cleaners. And I said, certain it was so: "Did Mr. Ybarra-Jaeger send you?"

"I am the cousin," he said with a wary grin and just-penetrable accent.

"Where is José?"

He repeated the question, as though translating it into another language. "Ah, *where* she is! She is waiting," he said and, seeming to dismiss me, resumed his valet activities.

So: the diplomat was planning a powder. Well, I

wasn't amazed; or in the slightest sorry. Still, what a heartbreaking stunt: "He ought to be horse-whipped."

The cousin giggled, I'm sure he understood me. He shut the suitcase and produced a letter. "My cousin, she ask me leave that for his chum. You will oblige?"

On the envelope was scribbled: *For Miss H. Golightly—Courtesy Bearer.*

I sat down on Holly's bed, and hugged Holly's cat to me, and felt as badly for Holly, every iota, as she could feel for herself.

"Yes, I will oblige."

And I did: without the least wanting to. But I hadn't the courage to destroy the letter; or the will power to keep it in my pocket when Holly very tentatively inquired if, if by any chance, I'd had news of José. It was two mornings later; I was sitting by her bedside in a room that reeked of iodine and bedpans, a hospital room. She had been there since the night of her arrest. "Well, darling," she'd greeted me, as I tiptoed toward her carrying a carton of Picayune cigarettes and a wheel of new-autumn violets, "I lost the heir." She looked not quite twelve years: her pale vanilla hair brushed back, her eyes, for once minus their dark glasses, clear as rain water; one couldn't believe how ill she'd been.

Yet it was true: "Christ, I nearly cooled. No fooling, the fat woman almost had me. She was yakking up a storm. I guess I couldn't have told you about the fat woman. Since I didn't know about her myself until my brother died. Right away I was wondering where he'd gone, what it meant, Fred's dying; and then I saw her, she was there in the room with me, and she had Fred cradled in her arms, a fat mean red bitch rocking in a rocking chair with Fred on her lap and laughing like a brass band. The mockery of it! But it's all that's ahead of us, my friend: this comedienne waiting to give you the old razz. Now do you see why I went crazy and broke everything?"

Except for the lawyer O. J. Berman had hired, I was the only visitor she had been allowed. Her room was shared by other patients, a trio of triplet-like ladies who, examining me with an interest not unkind but total, speculated in whispered Italian. Holly explained that: "They think you're my downfall darling. The fellow what done me wrong"; and, to a suggestion that she set them straight, replied: "I can't. They don't speak English. Anyway, I wouldn't dream of spoiling their fun." It was then that she asked about José.

The instant she saw the letter she squinted her eyes and bent her lips in a tough tiny smile that advanced her age immeasurably. "Darling," she instructed me, "would you reach in the drawer there and give me my purse. A girl doesn't read this sort of thing without her lipstick."

Guided by a compact mirror, she powdered, painted every vestige of twelve-year-old out of her face. She shaped her lips with one tube, colored her cheeks from another. She penciled the rims of her eyes, blued the lids, sprinkled her neck with 4711; attached pearls to her ears and donned her dark glasses; thus armored, and after a displeased appraisal of her manicure's shabby condition, she ripped open the letter and let her eyes race through it while her stony small smile grew smaller and harder. Eventually she asked for a Picayune. Took a puff: "Tastes bum. But divine," she said and, tossing me the letter: "Maybe this will come in handy—if you ever write a rat-romance. Don't be hoggy: read it aloud. I'd like to hear it myself."

It began, "My dearest little girl—"

Holly at once interrupted. She wanted to know what I thought of the handwriting. I thought nothing: a tight, highly legible, uneccentric script. "It's him to a T. Buttoned-up and constipated," she declared. "Go on."

"My dearest little girl, I have loved you knowing you were not as others. But conceive of my despair upon discovering in such a brutal and public style how very different you are from the manner of woman a man of my faith and career could hope to make his wife. Verily I grieve for the disgrace of your present circumstance, and do not find it in my heart to add my condemn to the condemn that surrounds you. So I hope you will find it in your heart not to condemn me. I have my family to protect, and my name, and I am a coward where those institutions enter. Forget me, beautiful child. I am no longer here. I am gone home. But may God always be with you and your child. May God be not the same as—José."

"Well?"

"In a way it seems quite honest. And even touching."

"*Touching?* That square-ball jazz!"

"But after all, he *says* he's a coward; and from his point of view, you must see—"

Holly, however, did not want to admit that she saw; yet her face, despite its cosmetic disguise, confessed it. "All right, he's not a rat without reason. A super-sized, King Kong-type rat like Rusty. Benny Shacklett. But oh, gee, golly goddam," she said, jamming a fist into her mouth like a bawling baby, "I *did* love him. The rat."

The Italian trio imagined a lover's crisis and, placing the blame for Holly's groaning where they felt it belonged, tut-tutted their tongues at me. She quieted when I offered her another cigarette. She swallowed and said, "Bless you, Buster. And bless you for being such a bad jockey. If I hadn't had to play Calamity Jane I'd still be looking forward to the grub in an unwed mama's home. Strenuous exercise, that's what did the trick. But I've scared *la merde* out of the whole badge-department by saying it was because Miss Dykeroo slapped me. Yessir, I can sue them on several counts, including false arrest."

Until then, we'd skirted mention of her more sinister tribulations, and this jesting reference to them seemed appalling, pathetic, so definitely did it reveal how incapable she was of recognizing the bleak realities before her. "Now, Holly," I said, thinking: be strong, mature, an uncle, "now Holly. We can't treat it as a joke. We have to make plans."

"You're too young to be stuffy. Too small. By the way, what business is it of yours?"

"None. Except you're my friend, and I'm worried. I mean to know what you intend doing?"

She rubbed her nose, and concentrated on the ceiling. "Today's Wednesday, isn't it? So I suppose I'll sleep until Saturday, really get a good *schlafen*. Saturday morning I'll skip out to the bank. Then I'll stop by the apartment and pick up a nightgown or two and my Mainbocher. Following which, I'll report to Idlewild. Where, as you damn well know, I have a perfectly fine reservation on a perfectly fine plane. And since you're such a friend I'll let you wave me off. *Please* stop shaking your head."

"Holly, Holly. You can't do that."

"*Et pourquoi pas?* I'm not hotfooting after José, if that's what you suppose. According to my census, he's strictly a citizen of Limboville. It's only: why should I waste a perfectly fine ticket? Already paid for? Besides, I've never been to Brazil."

"Just what kind of pills have they been feeding you here? Can't you realize, you're under a criminal indictment? If they catch you jumping bail, they'll throw away the key. Even if you get away with it, you'll never be able to come home."

"Well, so, tough. Anyway, home is where you feel at home. I'm still looking."

"No, Holly, it's stupid. You're innocent. You've got to stick it out."

She said, "Rah, team, rah," and blew smoke in my face. She was impressed, however; her eyes were dilated by unhappy visions, as were mine: iron rooms, steel corridors of gradually closing doors. "Oh, screw it," she said, and stabbed out her cigarette. "I have a fair chance they *won't* catch me. Provided *you* keep your *bouche fermez*. Look. Don't despise me, darling." She put her hand over mine and pressed it with sudden immense sincerity. "I haven't much. choice. I talked it over with the lawyer: oh, I didn't tell *him* anything *re* Rio—he'd tip the badgers himself, rather than lose his fee, to say nothing of the nickels O. J. put up for bail. Bless O. J.'s heart; but once on the coast I helped him win more than ten thou in a single poker hand: we're square. No, here's the real shake: all the badgers want from me is a couple of free grabs and my services as a state's witness against Sally—nobody has any intention of prosecuting me, they haven't a ghost of a case. Well, I may be rotten to the core, Maude, *but*: testify against a friend I will not. Not if they can prove he doped Sister Kenny. My yardstick is how somebody treats me, and Old Sally, all right he wasn't absolutely white with me, say he took a slight advantage, just the same Sally's an okay shooter, and I'd let the fat woman snatch me sooner than help the law-boys pin him down." Tilting her compact mirror above her face, smoothing her lipstick with a crooked pinky, she said: "And to be honest, that isn't all. Certain shades of limelight wreck a girl's complexion. Even if a jury gave me the Purple Heart, this neighborhood

holds no future: they'd still have up every rope from LaRue to Perona's Bar and Grill—take my word, I'd be about as welcome as Mr. Frank E. Campbell. And if you lived off my particular talents, cookie, you'd understand the kind of bankruptcy I'm describing. Uh, uh, I don't just fancy a fade-out that finds me bellybumping around Roseland with a pack of West Side hillbillies. While the excellent Madame Trawler sashays her ass in and out of Tiffany's. I couldn't take it. Give me the fat woman any day."

A nurse, soft-shoeing into the room, advised that visiting hours were over. Holly started to complain, and was curtailed by having a thermometer popped in her mouth. But as I took leave, she unstoppered herself to say: "Do me a favor, darling. Call up the *Times*, or whatever you call, and get a list of the fifty richest men in Brazil. I'm *not* kidding. The fifty richest: regardless of race or color. Another favor—poke around my apartment till you find that medal you gave me. The St. Christopher. I'll need it for the trip."

T he sky was red Friday night, it thundered, and Saturday, departing day, the city swayed in a squall-like downpour. Sharks might have swum through the air, though it seemed improbable a plane could penetrate it.

But Holly, ignoring my cheerful conviction that her flight would not go, continued her preparations—placing, I must say, the chief burden of them on me. For she had decided it would be unwise of her to come near the brownstone. Quite rightly, too: it was under surveillance, whether by police or reporters or other interested parties one couldn't tell—simply a man, sometimes men, who hung around the stoop. So she'd gone from the hospital to a bank and then straight to Joe Bell's bar. "She don't figure she was followed," Joe Bell told me when he came with a message that Holly wanted me to meet her there as soon as possible, a half hour at most, bringing: "Her jewelry. Her guitar. Toothbrushes and stuff. And a bottle of hundred-year-old brandy; she says you'll find it hid down in the bottom of the dirty clothes basket. Yeah, oh, and the cat. She wants the cat. But hell," he said, "I don't know we should help her at all. She ought to be protected against herself. Me, I feel like telling the cops. Maybe if I go back and build her some drinks, maybe I can get her drunk enough to call it off."

Stumbling, skidding up and down the fire escape between Holly's apartment and mine, wind-blown and winded and wet to the bone (clawed to the bone as well, for the cat had not looked favorably upon evacuation, especially in such inclement weather) I managed a fast, first-rate job of assembling her going-away belongings. I even found the St. Christopher's medal. Everything was piled on the floor of my room, a poignant pyramid of brassieres and dancing slippers and pretty things I packed in Holly's only suitcase. There was a mass left over that I had to put in paper grocery bags. I couldn't think how to carry the cat; until I thought of stuffing him in a pillowcase.

Never mind why, but once I walked from New Orleans to Nancy's Landing, Mississippi, just under five hundred miles. It was a lighthearted lark compared to the journey to Joe Bell's bar. The guitar filled with rain, rain softened the paper sacks, the sacks split and perfume spilled on the pavement, pearls rolled in the gutter; while the wind pushed and the cat scratched, the cat screamed—but worse, I was frightened, a coward to equal José: these storming streets seemed as warm with unseen presences waiting to trap, imprison me for aiding an outlaw.

The outlaw said: "You're late, Buster. Did you bring the brandy?"

And the cat, released, leapt and perched on her shoulder: his tail swung like a baton conducting rhapsodic music. Holly, too, seemed inhabited by melody, some bouncy *bon voyage* oompahpah. Uncorking the brandy, she said: "This was meant to be part of my hope chest. The idea was, every anniversary we'd have a swig. Thank Jesus I never bought the chest. Mr. Bell, sir, three glasses."

"You'll only need two. I won't drink to your foolishness."

The more she cajoled him ("Ah, Mr. Bell. The lady doesn't vanish every day. Won't you toast her?"), the gruffer he was: "I'll have no part of it. If you're going to hell, you'll go on your own. With no further help from me." An inaccurate statement: because seconds after he'd made it a chauffeured limousine drew up outside the bar, and Holly, the first to notice it, put down her brandy, arched her eyebrows, as though she expected to see the district attorney himself alight. So did I. And when I saw Joe Bell blush, I had to think: by God, he *did* call the police. But then, with burning ears, he announced, "It's nothing. One of them Carey-Cadillacs. I hired it. To take you to the airport."

He turned his back on us to fiddle with one of his flower arrangements. Holly said, "Kind, dear Mr. Bell. Look at me, sir."

He wouldn't. He wrenched the flowers from the vase and thrust them at her; they missed their mark, scattered on the floor. "Good-by," he said; and, as though he were going to vomit, scurried to the men's room. We heard the door lock.

The Carey chauffeur was a worldly specimen who accepted our slapdash luggage most civilly and remained rock-faced when, as the limousine swished uptown through a lessening rain, Holly stripped off her clothes, the riding costume she'd never had a chance to substitute, and struggled into a slim black dress. We didn't talk: talk could have only led to argument; and also, Holly seemed too preoccupied for conversation. She hummed to herself, swigged brandy, she leaned constantly forward to peer out the windows, as if she were hunting an address—or, I decided, taking a last impression of a scene she wanted to remember. It was neither of these. But this: "Stop here," she ordered the

driver, and we pulled to the curb of a street in Spanish Harlem. A savage, a garish, moody neighborhood garlanded with poster-portraits of movie stars and madonnas. Sidewalk litterings of fruit rind and rotted newspapers were hurled about by the wind, for the wind still boomed, though the rain had hushed and there were bursts of blue in the sky.

Holly stepped out of the car; she took the cat with her. Cradling him, she scratched his head and asked: "What do you think? This ought to be the right kind of place for a tough guy like you. Garbage cans. Rats galore. Plenty of cat-bums to gang around with. So scram," she said, dropping him; and when he did not move away, instead raised his thug face and questioned her with yellow pirate eyes, she stamped her foot: "I said scram!" He rubbed against her leg. "I said, beat it!" she shouted, then jumped back in the car, slammed the door, and: "Go," she told the driver. "Go. Go."

I was stunned. "Well, you *are*. You *are* a bitch."

We'd traveled a block before she replied "I told you. We just met by the river one day: that's all. Independents, both of us. We never made each other any promises. We never—" she said, and her voice collapsed, a tic, an invalid whiteness seized her face. The car had paused for a traffic light. Then she had the door open, she was running down the street; and I ran after her.

But the cat was not at the corner where he'd been left. There was no one, nothing on the street except a urinating drunk and two Negro nuns herding a file of sweet-singing children. Other children emerged from doorways and ladies leaned over their window sills to watch as Holly darted up and down the block, ran back and forth chanting: "You. Cat. Where are you? Here, cat." She kept it up until a bumpy-skinned boy came forward dangling an old tom by the scruff of its neck: "You wants a nice kitty, Miss? Gimme a dollar."

The limousine had followed us. Now Holly let me steer her toward it. At the door, she hesitated; she looked past me, past the boy still offering his cat ("Halfa dollar. Two bits, maybe? Two bits, it ain't much"), and she shuddered, she had to grip my arm to stand up; "Oh, Jesus God. We did belong to each other. He was mine."

Then I made her a promise. I said I'd come back and find her cat: "I'll take care of him, too. I promise."

She smiled: that cheerless new pinch of a smile. "But what about me?" she said, whispered, and shivered again. "I'm very scared, Buster. Yes, at last. Because it could go on forever. Not knowing what's yours until you've thrown it away. The mean reds, they're nothing. The fat woman, she's nothing. This, though: my mouth's so dry, if my life depended on it I couldn't spit." She stepped in the car. "Sorry, driver. Let's go."

Tomato's tomato missing. And: Drug-case actress believed gangland victim. In due time, however, the press reported: Fleeing playgirl traced to Rio. Apparently no attempt was made by American authorities to recover her, and soon the matter diminished to an occasional gossip-column mention; as a news story it was revived only once: on Christmas day, when Sally Tomato died of a heart attack at Sing Sing.

Months went by, a winter of them, and not a word from Holly. The owner of the brownstone sold her abandoned possessions: the white-satin bed, the tapestry, her precious Gothic chairs; a new tenant acquired the apartment, his name was Quaintance Smith, and he entertained as many gentleman callers of a noisy nature as Holly ever had—though now Madame Spanella did not object.

But in the spring a postcard came: it was scribbled in pencil and signed with a lipstick kiss: *Brazil was beastly but Buenos Aires the best. Not Tiffany's, but almost. Am joined at the hip with duhvine $senor. Love? Think so. Anyhoo am looking for somewhere to live ($senor has wife, 7 brats) and will let you know address when I know it myself. Mille tendresse.*

But the address, if it ever existed, never was sent, which made me sad, there was so much I wanted to write her: that I'd sold two stories, had read where the Trawlers were countersuing for divorce, was moving out of the brownstone because it was haunted.

But mostly, I wanted to tell about her cat. I had kept my promise; I had found him. It took weeks of after-work roaming through those Spanish Harlem streets, and there were many false alarms—flashes of tiger-striped fur that, upon inspection, were not he. But one day, one cold sunshiny Sunday winter afternoon, it was. Flanked by potted plants and framed by clean lace curtains, he was seated in the window of a warm-looking room: I wondered what his name was, for I am certain he had one now, certain he'd arrived somewhere he belonged. African hut or whatever, I hope Holly has too.

FORTY YEARS

OF

ESQUIRE FASHIONS

The Double-Breasted Suit
1933

Reversibles
1934

Mixed Suiting
1934

The First White Dinner Jacket
1934

The White Suit
1934

The Prince of Wales Look
1934

Four-Pleat Pants
1935

Knickers
1936

The Covert Coaching Coat
1937

The Thirties

**The Plaid Ulster
1934**

**The First Dungarees
1935**

**Walk Shorts
1938**

An editorial in the first issue of this magazine stated, "Esquire aims to be, among other things, a fashion guide for men. . . . We feel that men have long since ceased to believe that there is anything effeminate or essentially un-businesslike about devoting a little care and thought and study to the selection of clothes." Since that first issue, which contained fourteen pages of men's fashions ranging from campus wear to dinner clothes, Esquire has not only reported the sartorial scene but has also played a considerable role in the development of men's fashions. For this compendium of four fashion decades, the accompanying illustrations from past issues represent the most notable looks of the period.

When Esquire began publishing in the Autumn of 1933, the nation was in the midst of the Depression. It is paradoxical that despite economic conditions the Thirties was an era of enormous fashion development with the specific styles and fabrics reflecting the opulent life of the rich, idle or otherwise. In Thirties fashions, prodigality was paramount. Thus, the popularity of the double-breasted suit, extravagant of material to begin with and made even more expansive with wide-lapel jackets and full-cut trousers. Thus, the influx of resort wear from Antibes and St. Tropez, with full-cut pleated walk shorts striking the proper affluent note. Thus, the appearance of the mixed suit, the odd jacket and contrasting slacks permitting the display of two rich materials rather than one. Thus, too, the huge Ulster coat; the covert coaching coat with its English gentry snob overtones; the white suit and innovative white dinner jacket for summer swank at the country club; and the wastefully baggy and heavily tweedy golf knickers. Even the first dungarees emerged as a fashion force not on the basis of economy but as a trendy item adopted by the rich vacationing on dude ranches. Perhaps the most extreme example of Thirties prodigality was the British Blade suit, cut with such fullness that vertical wrinkles were actually tailored into the shoulders for maximum comfort.

The fashion pacemaker was Edward, Prince of Wales as the Thirties began, Duke of Windsor as they ended. It is impossible to overstate this single man's influence on fashion, an influence which remains almost as strong today as when he was alive. Whatever Edward wore immediately became fashionable, particularly the white chalk-stripe grey flannel double-breasted suit. Most notably, he gave us the Windsor knot. One of the greatest reader responses Esquire has ever received occurred in the Thirties when the magazine carried a diagram on how to tie the Windsor knot. The mail room was flooded with requests for reprints.

Three other permanent fashions stem from the Thirties. From Norway came "weejuns," slip-on moccasin-tipped shoes that were the forerunner of the loafer. In hats, the first porkpie. And, finally, the Thirties brought that radical shift from buttons to the zipper fly.

The Cutaway
1941

Beach Coordinates
1941

The British Warm
1941

The War Production Board Suit
1942

The Military Look
1942

Officer's Shorts
1944

The Collarless Blazer,
1945

The Cord Suit
1948

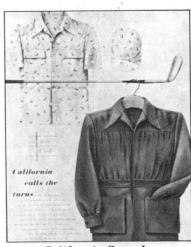

California Casuals
1948

The Forties

**Downhill Skier
1942**

**The Eisenhower Jacket
1945**

**The Bold Look
1948**

The decade of the Forties divides into three enormously different fashion periods. During the prewar days, there was a continuation of the rich look of the Thirties. On Fifth Avenue, gentlemen wore cutaway coats in the Easter Parade—the last cutaways, since they were soon to be banned under wartime regulations. In Florida and Nassau, vacationers made coordinated beach wear the new vogue and the precursor of cabana outfits. And in North Conway, Lake Placid and Sun Valley, winter-sports enthusiasts took to the slopes in the new tapered downhill skier look, and ski clothes emerged as an entirely new fashion category. Yet, even in this period, events in Europe were bringing military overtones to American fashions. The favorite coat of the day was the British Warm, a civilian adaptation of the short-length, fleece officer's coat.

Suddenly, it was all over, replaced by wartime austerity. The War Production Board set stringent restrictions to conserve the use of wool. Tailcoats and cutaways? Out. Dinner jackets? Single-breasted only. Jackets? Shorter, and no patch pockets, belt, vent, pleats, tucks or yokes. Vests? Only with single-breasted suits, and no collar, lapels or patch pockets. Trousers? Narrower, and no cuffs, pleats, tucks or overlapping waistband. Overcoats? Knee-length and less width at the bottom. So it went, and nobody cared. There was only one meaningful fashion: military uniforms. While Esquire continued to show civilian attire throughout the war years, it also saluted the military by pictorially presenting the uniforms of every service arm. Even the civilian fashions bore a marked wartime influence: summer shorts, for instance, being an adaptation of the tan cotton shorts worn by the Army in the tropics; striped cotton shirts inspired by the colors of American campaign area service ribbons; and, of course, a new jacket style called the Eisenhower.

Immediately after the war, clothing materials were in extremely short supply and manufacturers were forced to scrimp, as evidenced in the collarless blazer of the period. To fill up the slack in dress-shirting materials, manufacturers turned to sport patterns such as tattersalls and checks. As a result, not only did the white shirt finally become less than sacrosanct, but the entire sportswear field was launched and there was no stopping it. Cool, comfortable cords made their first appearance, and California casual wear came into its own.

As supplies became more abundant, a fashion splurge began that Esquire dubbed *The Bold Look*, an assertive, masculine styling that first coordinated the entire wardrobe. All men's wearables took on the new big, bold feeling. Big suit lapels. Massive tie clips and cuff links. Broad suspenders. Thick belts. Wide-rib socks. Spread-collar shirts. The Windsor knot. Broad bindings on hat brims and accented stitching on suits and shirts.

At the end of the Forties, fashion was flourishing. Much would remain and evolve. But *The Bold Look* was about to go the way of the cutaway coat.

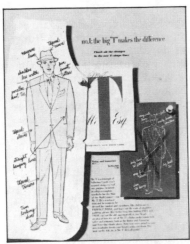

The First Ivy League Look
1950

The Tartan Dinner Jacket
1950

Stadium Coats
1950

The Fancy Vest
1953

The First Men's Shoulder Bag
1954

Clam Diggers
1956

Shearlings
1957

The Evening Cape
1957

The Continental Look
1958

The Fifties

The Hawaiian Shirt
1950

Roman Stripes
1957

The London Line
1959

The Fifties represents the most eclectic of the fashion decades. There was a diversity of new styles, but none had sufficient fashion impact to shape a definitive Fifties look. From the vantage point of today, it would seem that the advent of the Ivy League suit should rank as a fashion landmark. At the time, however, it caused a surprisingly mild reaction, although its influence was to grow steadily throughout the Fifties. It first appeared in 1950 to counteract the excesses of *The Bold Look*. Although men were tiring of *The Bold Look*, the memories of wartime austerity were still too strong for a majority of men to embrace a suit so trimmed and narrowed and tapered. Only in the East did it meet with wholehearted acceptance; the rest of the country settled for a neutral suiting somewhere between the two looks. The little belt in the back of the trousers was the most widespread Ivy idea. With suit styling unresolved, the fashion focus shifted to other areas—fabrics, textures, accessory items. In the early Fifties, nubby Italian silks came into prominence. Tartans became extremely popular, in shirting, blazers and, ultimately, the first tartan dinner jacket. On the campuses, the return to normality meant the return to Saturday football games, and stadium coats were of major importance in outerwear. On the beach, a lot of men turned up in splashy Hawaiian shirts, looking just like their favorite ex-haberdasher, Harry Truman. In the mid-Fifties, parfait-colored dinner jackets supplanted white. Fancy vests in paisleys, stripes and checks had their day, as did three-quarter-length clam-digger beach pants, colorful Roman stripes in beach wear, the cowboy shearling coat and, for a daring few, full-length evening opera capes. In 1953, the perfection of polyester fibers brought in wash 'n wear suits. From Australia came the side-zippered bush boot; from Russia, the Persian-lamb fur hat. Esquire contributed its own idea to the fashion mélange with what it called the sidekick: "a saddlebag, practically, without the horse, is this rugged, masculine leather sidekick shaped like a trout fisherman's creel." In other words, it was the first men's bag, and it proved to be too far ahead of its time to meet with acceptance.

Toward the end of the Fifties, fashion finally got back on the suiting track with two distinctive and significant looks. *The Continental Look* arrived from Rome and Paris, a slim-line profile with a very short jacket, extremely tapered sleeves and pants. And *The London Line* was imported from Great Britain, suits cut along more traditional, conservative lines and tailored with English perfection by manufacturers of the British Menswear Guild. Esquire was not only instrumental in the founding of the Guild but introduced its first collection at Esquire's 1959 International Fashion Forum. Since at last the Ivy League suit had permeated the country, *The London Line* continued strong as a British-cousin version. *The Continental Look*, however, based on a more radical cut, proved ephemeral.

The Ivy League Years
1962

The Mod Look
1966

Youth Quake Vinyls
1967

The Boot Boom
1968

The Maxi Coat
1968

Ethnic Clothes
1969

Patterned Knits
1970

Gadgetry
1972

The Newport Look
1972

The Sixties and Seventies

**Evening Turtlenecks
1967**

**The Peacock Revolution
1969**

**The Return to Elegance
1972**

As with the Forties, the period from 1960 to the present divides into three distinct fashion eras. The first half of the Sixties was dominated by *The Ivy League Look*—sedate, businesslike and, viewed from today, a bit uptight. Then, with two words, all hell broke loose: Carnaby Street. Quicker than you can say electric guitar, *The London Mod Look* was everywhere, with department stores rapidly installing Carnaby Street boutiques. Flamboyance sprouted and so did hair. "Do your own thing" was the motto, and Turnbull and Asser did theirs by revolutionizing the neckwear business with ties as wide as an Ivy League muffler. With the wide ties came a shirt shift to new, long-point collars. From *The Mod Look*'s declaration of fashion independence, the last of the Sixties became a period of fashion by whim. Wet-look vinyls. Bell-bottoms. Ranch leathers. Boots of every style. Jump suits. Wide butterfly ties. The big hat. Safari outfits. The Nehru jacket. Paper clothes. The maxi coat. Caftans. Ruffled evening shirts. You paid your money and you took your choice. Lord Snowdon chose a turtleneck to wear with his dinner jacket; for a while, so did everyone else. But as the decade ended, the peacock revolution was just about over as well.

Throughout the volatile period of the late Sixties, a less trendy movement had begun which was to have a more lasting impact on fashion. The designer collection was born. In 1966, Pierre Cardin introduced his first men's collection in the United States. Esquire, recognizing the importance of this new development in menswear, held two International Designers' Conferences featuring collections of such luminaries as Cardin, Hardy Amies, Bill Blass and John Weitz. By 1970, it was an established fact that menswear was worthy of the same talent and taste expended on women's fashions.

Technology produced the first fashion news of the Seventies as wrinkle-resistant double knits came on the scene. They enabled designers to introduce new patterns to suiting, patterns that went particularly well with the wide lapel while the shaped jacket supplied the necessary restraint. New knit dress shirts also came into being. As for more frivolous matters, accessories took on a look of gadgetry with clunky belts and chunky bracelets being the fancy of the more casual, or the less fastidious, depending on the point of view.

In the last year, fashion has once more shifted abruptly. The tricks and the kicks have had it. In a reversal that seems almost too pat an ending to this forty-year overview, fashion is back to where Esquire first found it in 1933. Today, the look is one of elegance, a return to the grandeur of the Thirties. The illustration at bottom left, which sums up the look of today, represents the current homage to classic Windsorian elegance.

Whatever tomorrow brings, Esquire will continue to fulfill the promise it made its readers in the first issue: to be, among other things, a fashion guide for men.